D1297541

STAGE LIGHTING

STAGE LIGHTING

THEODORE FUCHS
CONSULTING ILLUMINATING ENGINEER

WITH ILLUSTRATIONS

BENJAMIN BLOM New York/London

Reprinted 1963 by Benjamin Blom, Inc. NY 10452 and
56 Doughty Street, London W.C. 1,
by arrangement with the Author

Library of Congress Catalog Card No. 63-23184

Printed in U.S.A. by
NOBLE OFFSET PRINTERS, INC.
NEW YORK 3, N. Y.

PUBLISHER'S STATEMENT

Since its first publication in 1929, Theodore Fuchs' STAGE LIGHTING has remained a classic in its field. It seems almost inconceivable—a third of a century after its first appearance—to think of any serious study of lighting as an art from without reference to his book.

Yet its author had many doubts about granting permission to reprint his book. And understandably so: There have been major, almost revolutionary, changes in the instrumentation and techniques of stage lighting since the book was first published, and to represent this unaltered reprint as an unqualified guide for today's needs would be an injustice to the buyer, and to the author.

By no means, however, need all the technical data in STAGE LIGHTING be discarded, but this phase of the book must be studied in relation to later treaties. Used intelligently, Fuchs' book yields much that is still valid and useful.

But lighting is more than technique; it is part of the *art* of the theatre. And, just as earlier classics on the art of acting can help us to determine the essential nature of the actor's art, so Fuchs' book will continue to guide and challenge those interested in elevating stage lighting to an art form.

The Publisher

New York,
February, 1964

ACKNOWLEDGMENTS

THE writer wishes to acknowledge his indebtedness to the many individuals and organizations for the courtesies and assistance of many kinds which he received, both directly and indirectly, in connection with this work. Particularly is he indebted to Mr. A. L. Powell, for much valuable experience gained under his direction; to Mr. Louis Hartmann, for important practical suggestions and advice; to Mr. S. R. McCandless, for many helpful suggestions and for details of the equipment at the Yale University Theatre; to Mr. William J. Pape, for access to an excellent short history of stage lighting, in manuscript form; to Mr. F. A. Benford, for specific suggestions regarding the calculation of spotlight projection data; to Mr. A. W. Kakilty, for revision of certain technical data; to Mr. W. J. Canada, for revision of several paragraphs dealing with electrical circuit protective systems; and to Mr. Montrose J. Moses, for valuable advice in regard to planning the volume as well as for many other courtesies. The writer appreciates the coöperation of the following companies in supplying descriptive and illustrative matter, not only in relation to their own products but also in relation to general stage-lighting topics: Ward Leonard Electric Company; Trumbull Electric Manufacturing Company; Kliegl Brothers Universal Electric Stage Lighting Company; Pevear Color Specialty Company; General Electric Company, and two of its constituent organizations, the Edison Lamp Works and the National Lamp Works; Display Stage Lighting Company; Bull Dog Electric Products Company; and Frank Adam Electric Company. To the Theatre Guild and to the Charles Frohman Company, and to several of the outstanding nonprofessional producing organizations in America, he is indebted for production pictures that are especially valuable for the noteworthy stage-lighting effects they depict. For permission to reprint material controlled by them, the writer is indebted to the Illuminating Engineering Society; Dodd, Mead and Company; and Harcourt, Brace and Company. To his publishers, Little, Brown and Company, he is indebted for their extraordinary patience and for the courtesy and consideration that have marked his relations with them. But most of all he wishes to express his appreciation of the aid so generously extended by his friend, Doctor S. Marion Tucker, whose expert knowledge and wide experience in the field of the theatre were always at the service of the writer, and who in many other significant ways facilitated the work on this volume.

CONTENTS

TABLES

CURVES

STAGE LIGHTING

CHAPTER I · INTRODUCTION

Functions of stage lighting – illumination, realism, composition and design, plastic expression, psychological expression; survey of stage-lighting conditions – equipment, practice :: professional, amateur; synopsis of volume.

UP to a comparatively recent period virtually the sole medium available for the expression of a play on the stage was the actor. Illusion scenery, without which few present-day playgoers would be content, was generally unknown before the seventeenth century. The use of light was also generally unknown, except, of course, for the purely utilitarian purpose of illumination. In fact, before the theatre moved indoors (which took place, in England, in the late sixteenth century), even the problem of illumination solved itself, since plays were presented out of doors and in daylight.

However, with the introduction and rapid development of the incandescent electric lamp as a light source that lends itself more readily to control and color modification, and with notable contributions from the fields of optics and color, there has been placed at the disposal of the producer the new art of stage lighting as a means of visual expression on the stage. The art of stage lighting, and the art of stage design, which has happily been lately revolutionized and revitalized, should complement each other, and together should complement the more transitory art of the actor, and thus elevate the all-inclusive art of the theatre to planes that it has never before attained.

As the mechanical methods of producing and controlling light have become more refined and more adaptable to the needs of the theatre, its use on the stage has gradually evolved from its primary function of mere illumination by which the spectators were enabled to view the action, to a state where it is now considered one of the most important factors in the interpretation of a play. In this present state, in spite of many all too obvious shortcomings, light is the one artistic medium that can effectively exert its own subtle, subconscious influence, serving not only as a vibrant background, but also, and at the same time, working in conjunction with all the other expressive media of the theatre, and acting as a flux, fusing them all together — accentuating some, subduing others, as necessary — itself filling the sometimes open gaps between them, and rounding them all out into a harmonious, clarified, unified medium of complete expression — the art of the theatre.

I. Functions of Stage Lighting

Light, as used on the stage, has five separate and distinct functions: (*a*) illumination; (*b*) the production of realistic effects — "realism"; (*c*) as a means of producing the stage "picture" — as an aid in composition and design; (*d*) as an aid to plastic expression; and (*e*) as a means of psychological expression. Each of these functions requires brief discussion.

A. ILLUMINATION

As soon as the theatre moved under a roof — or, rather, when the playhouse itself became a completely enclosed building — it faced the problem of *visibility*. Obviously, the very walls and roof which sheltered the players and spectators also excluded the natural light and rendered artificial light necessary. It is reasonable to suppose that at first no effort was made to differentiate between the lighting of the stage and the lighting of the auditorium; both were lighted alike, by the means then in common use. Then it was discovered that the players could be much more easily discerned if the light was restricted to the stage, and the auditorium was darkened. This might well represent the first definite step in the evolution of stage lighting: the use of light for the same purpose for which it was used in the outside world — for illumination — for rendering clearly visible to the spectators the players and their action. The nature of light sources was for many years such that the attention of the producers, in regard to light, was wholly occupied with the problem of visibility. At the present time the pendulum seems to have swung to the other extreme: some producers are willing to sacrifice visibility to effect. This tendency is deplored, perhaps not unreasonably, by the conservative body of playgoers, who, while they readily admit the potent possibilities of light as an element of stagecraft, believe that the art of the actor is supreme in the theatre, and that under no circumstances should it be subordinated to, or even submerged with, any other factor of stage production. Hence they insist upon having the features of their actors so lighted that every emotional and expressive detail be clearly perceptible. The choice between these two uses of light is a perplexing problem, and is one for each individual director to solve for himself according to his own

Photograph by Francis Bruguiere.

A scene from the second act of *Goat Song*, a Theatre Guild production designed by Lee Simonson, showing the unity of effect made possible by the use of light that is predominantly undirectional in character.

dictates. The future will undoubtedly see an appreciable part of the actor's burden assumed by the lighting. Far from this condition restricting his field of usefulness, it should be instrumental in affording him the opportunity to pursue his art to heights that lie open to the actor only — the one living, organic factor among all those that contribute to the complete ensemble, the finished production, in which all the arts of the theatre combine.

B. REALISM

The problem of mere illumination having been solved, there came the desire to reproduce on the stage the simulation of lighting conditions as they existed in real life. For example, night scenes were not lighted so brightly as were day scenes, and to simulate stormy weather the light was considerably reduced. The advent of gas lighting made it practicable to control the intensity of the light from a point remote from its source, and it was then possible to "bring up" the dawn, and "bring down" the dusk. This was the inception of the wave of realism which swept the theatre, and from which the theatre has just begun to free itself. This attempt at realism was by no means confined to lighting; in fact, it was probably more pronounced in the realm of scenic design, on account of the greater facilities and experience that existed in that art. As an ultimate indication of it to-day we find, listed in the catalogues of scenic studios, carefully classified, stock-in-trade settings, such as "log-cabin interior", "ballroom of palace", and "exterior drop with lake and mountains", "olio drop: street scene", and in the catalogues of stage-lighting firms special lighting "effects" that range from the modest and more excusable "moving clouds", through "rain", "snow", and "lighting" to the more pretentious "desert sandstorm" and "volcano eruption." The already discarded Fortuny system of lighting, by means of which is obtained the closest approach to diffused, natural daylight, and the intricate and ponderous *Grossewolkenapparat* (large cloud machine), weighing several tons and requiring a crane to move it, represent the extent to which this movement of realism has been carried in the European theatre. Electric light made possible not only the more careful and accurate control of light intensity by means of the variable-resistance dimmer, but also the easy production of colored light by means of conveniently applied color media, which opened new fields for the realistically-inclined stage worker. It became possible to heighten the realistic effect by using amber light for a sunny midday scene, red for a sunset, and blue-green for moonlight. The extensiveness of this phase of realism may be indicated by the fifty-odd

Photograph by Francis Bruguiere.

A scene from the fourth act of *Goat Song*, a Theatre Guild production designed by Lee Simonson, showing how effective is a well-balanced contrast between luminous highlights and shadowy silhouettes.

colors and tints in which gelatin color media are commercially available. As a result of all this effort to achieve realism, the stage worker of the future will at least have at his disposal two exceptionally valuable mechanical heritages developed by his fellow worker of the past, and these are the dimmer and color-producing equipment. The very nature of light will render these two devices extremely useful, whatever trend the application of stage lighting may take.

With the advent of all this elaborate mechanism, the stage worker had not only solved the problem of illumination, but was also able to simulate natural conditions by indicating the season, the weather, the very hour of the day; in other words, he had achieved "realism." The next, or, perhaps, rather the coincident step was the use of light as a means in helping to create the stage picture — as a portion of the stage setting.

C. COMPOSITION AND DESIGN

The stage designer was slow to realize the potential value of light as an important contributing factor to his stage design — the extent of his responsibility for the stage "picture." In the method of building up a stage picture by means of areas of light and shade — in several colors, perhaps, in varying degrees of brightness and depth, some carefully and skillfully blended, others deliberately harsh and contrasting, some of definite shape, others fleeting and formless — lie unfathomed possibilities in technique of design and composition.

And only recently has light been used as a component of the "paint" with which scenery is decorated. The vibrant, living quality and texture with which carefully applied lighting endows what would otherwise be a dull, lifeless, flat piece of canvas is now constantly being achieved. Probably the most notable general advance in this direction is the abolition of the painted sky drop, and the substitution, in its place, of the faintly tinted cyclorama. This serves as an actual canvas upon which is painted, by means of light alone, the wonderful skies that defy reproduction by unassisted paint. A visit backstage during the inactive hours of some production noted for the effective beauty or realism of its settings will, under the strong, merciless glare of the stage work lights, most likely reveal the drab, crude, almost ugly appearance of these same settings that looked so lovely from the front of the house. By means of the transformation possible only with the magic aid of light, they are made to realize the conception of the designing artist by assuming the lifelike quality, the texture, the vibrancy, the rich coloring upon which their effectiveness depends.

D. PLASTIC EXPRESSION

The use of light for plastic expression on the stage, while less general than its use as a factor in stage design, is yet of vast possibilities. The painted shadow is gradually disappearing from the stage as the value and use of light for formative or plasmic purposes — for revealing the plastic nature of three-dimensional or solid objects — is becoming more generally comprehended. Painted shadows included not only those executed by the scene painter in his feeble effort to simulate form and perspective on two-dimensional plane surfaces (such as canvas flats or borders and drops that swayed and flapped in every stage-door draft); but also those applied by the actor, as part of his make-up, particularly to the under side of his eye sockets, in his effort to supply that deficiency, namely, the formative or statuesque quality, in the generally unintelligent application of light in the past. The scene painter was forced to rely on painted shadows not only because he worked on plane surfaces, on which shadows were obviously impossible, but also because the lighting applied to his work lacked the correct directional component so necessary to formative effect even had his work been carried out in three-dimensional form. The actor was forced to rely on painted shadows for much the same reason, the principal factor in his case being the strong, unnatural, unbalanced glare from the footlights. The stage designer now avails himself of this important function of stage lighting and uses it to lend relief to the plastic, the architectural, the sculptural elements of his setting. This he accomplishes by means of high lights and shadows, the arrangement and composition of which convey to the mind of the spectator, because of long association, a definite impression of form and shape. This same principle he also applies to costume design and to stage properties, and, in fact, to every solid or three-dimensional component of the stage picture that he creates. One of the most difficult problems of stage lighting is the application of this principle to the actor. It is difficult because of the almost innumerable changes, in both expression and position, on the part of each actor, during the course of a single act or scene. However, the effectiveness of the solution to this problem is directly proportional to the difficulty encountered, since the human figure is concededly the richest of all in possibilities for plastic effects. This fourth function of stage lighting is, then, to reveal, by means of the relief provided by high lights and shadows, the plastic elements of the stage picture — the setting, the properties, the costumes, and, most important of all, the actors.

E. PSYCHOLOGICAL EXPRESSION

Still another function of stage lighting, probably the one latest to be realized and the one in which the more significant future developments will most likely take place, is to symbolize the meanings of the play, where symbolism is at all necessary or desirable, and to accompany the action of the play, providing the background, the "atmosphere", for it, and reinforcing its psychology. As with the other functions of stage lighting, control of light (that is, of its brightness or intensity) and color modification are the two most important faculties of present-day lighting equipment which contribute to the successful fulfillment of this subtle but potent purpose. This function of stage lighting, which is only now beginning to be used in its finer applications, was recognized, in its crude, elemental form, many years ago. The rule of thumb seems to have been: bright light in full blast for comedy and farce, a dim light for deep tragedy, and all the proportional gradations of lighting for the intervening range of emotions.[1] But a far more subtle art of the adaptation of light, shade, and color is now being developed in which the intensity of light is but one of many factors — direction, form, quality, movement, and color — particularly color — all contributing in harmonious unison to achieve the desired psychological and, indeed, physiological, effect on the mind of the spectator, which will be synchronous with, and which will fortify, the same effect produced by other means, through other physical and mental channels. As further experiments determine the more subtle emotional value of the various forms of light, and of the methods of their application, it will become more and more possible to express exactly the mood and feeling of a play, and hence to recognize and utilize light as an actual motive force of the drama, — in short, to help act the play.

Irving Pichel, in his "Modern Theatres", summarizes most concisely the five functions of stage lighting which have just been discussed, and gives a very apt example to show how one single shaft

[1] It has been frequently pointed out that, in the outdoor theatres of the Greeks and of the Elizabethan period, the light of the sun, far from accentuating the mood of a play, actually detracted from it. The baleful, gloomy tragedies of the Greeks, the bloody tragedies of the Elizabethans, must have seemed far less terrible with the actors bathed in bright sunlight, than they do to-day, when virtually every change in mood is a cue for the electrician to play upon the emotional sensibilities of the audience by means of subtle, skillfully applied lighting. It is therefore not unreasonable to suppose that, were the Greek and Elizabethan dramatists writing for the stage of to-day, they would place upon light much of the burden of mood creation, or reinforcement, which they formerly had to assume themselves when the human personality of the actor was the sole medium of expression available to them.

Photograph by White.

The forest scene of *Chantecler*, a Charles Frohman production designed by the late John W. Alexander. The illusion of distance is gained by the use of several separately-lighted zones between gauze drops and a black velvet backdrop. This method was perfected by J. Monroe Hewlett and Bassett Jones.

of light may simultaneously achieve the purposes of these several functions. He says [1]:

Light, in the theatre, then: (1) illuminates the stage and actors; (2) states hour, season, and weather, through suggestion of the light effects in nature; (3) helps paint the scene (stage picture) by manipulation of masses of light and shadow and by heightening color values; (4) lends relief to the actors and to the plastic elements of the scene; and (5) helps act the play, by symbolizing its meanings and reinforcing its psychology.

To achieve these five functions of stage light, five different kinds or sources of light are not, of course, needed. One light may combine several, or all, of these functions. In Joseph Urban's lighting and setting of the last act of "Tristan and Isolde" some years ago at the Boston Opera House, a beam of late afternoon sunlight struck across the stage to the figure of Tristan lying beneath a great oak tree. Slowly, as the day waned, the sun patch crept from the figure, until, at his death, it had left him in cool shadow. Thus, a light that illuminated, that told the time of day, that gave the figure of the singer and the bole of the great tree high relief by striking from only one side, also aided symbolically and psychologically in the interpretation of the drama. Thus to make light function in many ways is to use it with a sense of its ductility and subtlety as a medium of theatre art. In it we have the only single agency in the theatre that can work with all the other agencies, binding them together — that can reveal with the dramatist, paint with the designer, and act with the actors.

II. Survey of Stage Lighting Conditions

The actual *equipment*, the machinery, the physical means by which the several functions of stage lighting are carried out in the desired method of treatment, is divided into two classes. First, the individual pieces of stage-lighting equipment — the actual sources of light and the apparatus for projecting and coloring it; and second, the mechanism for centrally controlling this apparatus — the wiring and switchboard. The former is often compared to the pipes of an organ, the latter to the console.

Most of this equipment has been brought to its present state of development by the worker in the illusion theatre, in his effort to achieve realistic effects. Even for this purpose of achieving realism, the equipment has been, for the most part, crude, unwieldy, inefficient, and consequently unsatisfactory. The only improvements, if such they may be called, were the successive adaptations and conversions of original types of equipment to the increasingly efficient,

[1] "Modern Theatres," by Irving Pichel, published by Harcourt, Brace and Company.

flexible, and useful luminants which were used as the light sources. Only recently has level-headed scientific knowledge, even ordinary common sense, been brought to bear on the problems of stage lighting; the result has been a general improvement in equipment.

The equipment found in the regular professional theatres in America is of many types and covers a wide range of convenience, usefulness, and effectiveness. It may be divided roughly into four classes, depending upon the year in which it was installed, the ability and intention of the builder or architect, and the progressiveness of the present operators or management. First, there is the equipment of the type found in theatres such as small town "opera houses", which is, in general, obsolete, antiquated, and practically worthless, as those who are forced to use it — usually local societies and amateur groups in occasional productions — soon realize to their dismay. Second, there is the equipment of the type found in the more modern theatres in the smaller cities, which, although comparatively out of date, still possesses some degree of usefulness, and which is ordinarily utilized by the local stock company or by an occasional traveling road company which does not carry its own lighting effects. Third, there is the equipment of the type found in the average theatres used for regular "legitimate" productions in the metropolitan centers and larger cities, and in the vaudeville and motion-picture theatres generally throughout the country. Such equipment represents the usual present-day commercial practice and serves well enough the purposes of the not too discriminating producers, but, also, often falls far short of being able to provide satisfactorily the effects desired. The constant building of costly new motion-picture and vaudeville houses has resulted in the installation of a very large quantity of the most modern stage-lighting equipment, and to this volume of lucrative business may be traced, in a measure, the opportunities for the recent development of equipment to its present status. Fourth, there is the equipment of the type found in a very few of the most recently equipped theatres, of which the Guild Theatre and Hampden's Theatre in New York, and the Yale University Theatre in New Haven, are outstanding examples. Such equipment not only embodies the latest developments, but also has been laid out and installed in a manner most practical and flexible — and hence also most useful and satisfactory.

The generally unsatisfactory nature of stage-lighting equipment in the average theatre, and, incidentally, an ever-increasing desire for better and more distinctive stage lighting, is indicated by the fact that many productions, especially those of a more elaborate kind, are outfitted completely with their own equipment, both apparatus and switchboard — special set-ups that are designed for the individual needs of each production. Even a large proportion of the productions in Broadway theatres place no dependence upon regular "house" installations, and virtually every production that is sent upon a "road tour" is forced to rely upon its own equipment, which it carries with it, because of the poor conditions that prevail in the few and rather neglected theatres throughout the country that are still available for road companies. Such equipment is entirely independent of the standard house equipment, and uses nothing but the electric current, which it taps off from a "company switch."

Stage-lighting equipment in the realm of the amateur theatre (an all-embracing term which may be taken to include community theatres, little theatres, and amateur producing organizations affiliated with universities, colleges, schools, churches, settlements, clubs, and so forth), compared with that in the professional theatre, is of an even wider variety, for here the element of "home-built" devices enters in. And this general characteristic — its freedom from the hampering restrictions imposed by tradition and usage — constitutes one of the chief advantages of the amateur theatre over the professional. Many amateur workers, however, sell this precious birthright for the questionable privilege of imitating the professional theatre in its methods, if not even in its results. For instance, the amateur theatre worker who spends the sum of money at his disposal for lighting equipment, however small that sum may be, either for basic materials from which good, simple, effective home-built devices can be constructed (if the necessity for a rather complete equipment is immediate), or for fewer pieces of much more expensive though more convenient and finished standard modern equipment, the characteristics, usefulness, and desirability of which have been carefully investigated, and which can be added to from time to time, as finances allow and conditions dictate, until a complete, flexible set has been built up — is far better off than the one who is so short-sighted that he borrows the troubles of the professional theatre by buying second-hand lighting equipment that has been virtually rescued from the scrap heap, repainted, and sold at a somewhat reduced though still highly profitable figure by the electrician of the local vaudeville or stock theatre. And this homemade equipment, or this equipment bought piecemeal, forces upon the amateur worker a flexibility of arrangement and control which is conducive to far better results than a set, permanent, ill-selected, expensive outfit. This principle of flexibility is now beginning to

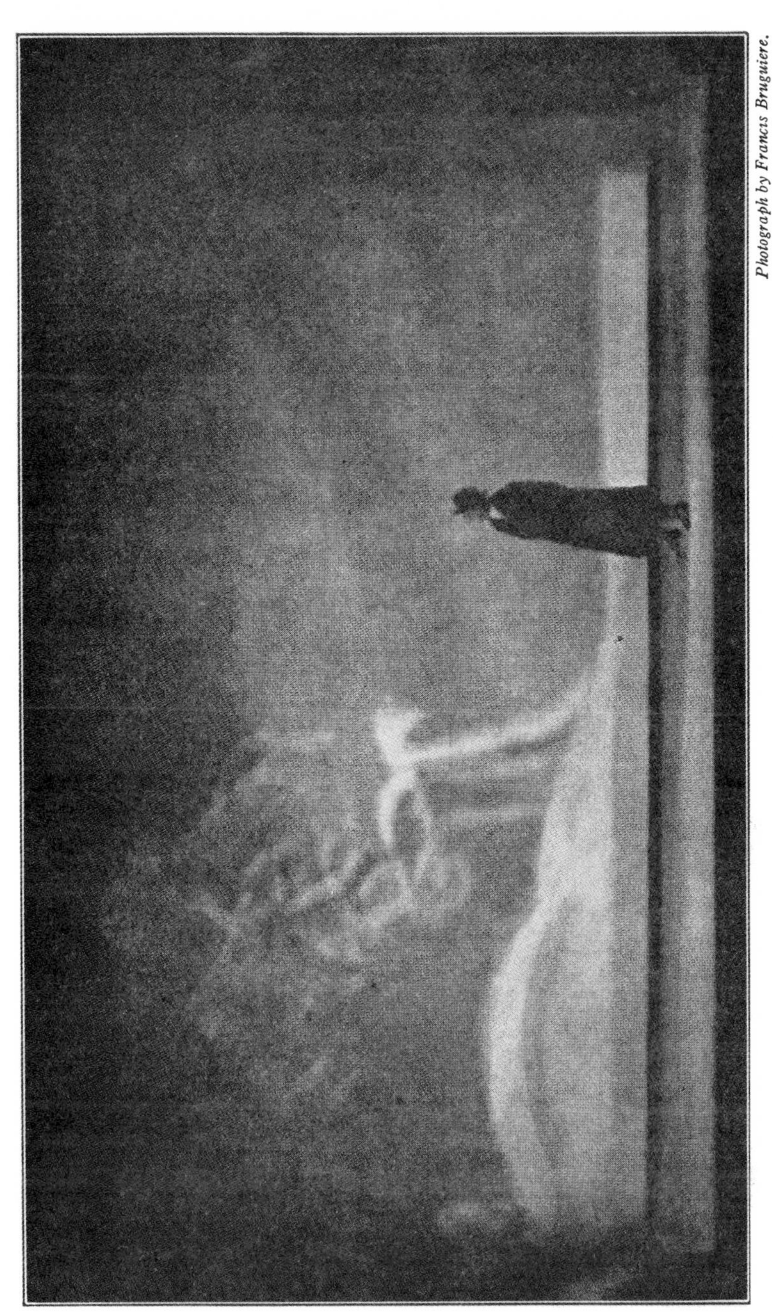

Photograph by Francis Bruguiere.

The third scene of *From Morn to Midnight*, a Theatre Guild production designed by Lee Simonson. The bare, snow-incrusted branches of a weirdly-shaped tree dissolve gradually into the form of a crouching, menacing skeleton — "one of Fate's policemen" — that confronts a fugitive embezzler who is crossing a desolate, snow-covered field. This highly effective and dramatic transformation was achieved by the use of two Linnebach lanterns that provided "projected scenery" on the translucent drop.

be understood and adopted by the more thoughtful and progressive professional producers.

Fortunate, indeed, is the amateur producing organization that has built or remodeled its own playhouse, and has provided the stage equipment best suited to its purposes and finances, no matter how inexpensive, simple, or crude it may be from the professional point of view, and has properly provided for future additions and expansion. Less fortunate, and to be sincerely sympathized with, is the organization that must cope with the many and diverse problems of play production on a stage designed by some architect who, though prompted undoubtedly by the best of intentions, succeeded only in providing an expensive but useless outfit that is the cause of much unnecessary hardship and discouragement. The average architect, knowing but little about stage equipment, and still less of the demands made upon it by active and serious play production, follows the path of least resistance and turns over to his stenographer a set of sample, stereotyped specifications (such as is written and furnished by every manufacturer, featuring his individual products and having their sale as its primary purpose) to be written into the general building specifications without further thought or effort on his part. This is evidenced not only by the great number of impossible stages in existence, mainly in church halls, high schools, Y. M. C. A.'s, and such, but also by inconvenient features on many professional theatre stages. One of the fundamental faults of many amateur-theatre stage-lighting installations is the lack of sufficient electrical capacity, that is, an inadequate supply of electric current for the complete set of apparatus. This is a serious, severe, and absolute limitation that would restrict the proper functioning of even the best and most complete equipment.

Future developments in the field of stage-lighting equipment should be fundamental in nature. The light source should receive particular attention. As excellent as the modern incandescent lamp is, in comparison with previous luminants, it still is far from being the ideal light source. It is highly inefficient (in the absolute), converting only several per cent of the electrical energy it consumes into light; the remainder, in the form of heat, being wasted. The proportions of the color constituents of the light it emits are very unbalanced, the red and the yellow components far exceeding the blue and the green. For greater optical efficiency in projection, a nearer approach to the technically desirable "point source" should be achieved. And finally, the light source should be much more powerful, and still be in a convenient form, than those now available. In short, the desirable luminant would be more powerful, be more efficient, be highly concentrated, be capable of being dimmed, contain equal quantities of light of all wave lengths and retain this proportion constant on being dimmed.

The lighting apparatus — the various types of instruments — and the means of control are also open to fundamental improvement, aside from the more obvious superficial faults that should be corrected. Further and deeper study of the sciences of optics and color as applied to stage lighting, such as is being carried on by Munroe R. Pevear of Boston, who was at one time a practicing architect, should accomplish much towards providing the means of producing light and color that will be both efficient and pliable in the hands of the lighting director. Further research into the electrical and mechanical features of light control should render more accurate, more flexible, and more convenient the manipulation of the stage switchboard, the nerve center of the entire lighting system — the intricate keyboard at which will be played the symphonic complement, in light, to the art of the actor and of the stage designer.

More definite information is needed as to the more subtle psychological and, in fact, physiological effects of light and color upon the spectator, for, after all, workers in the theatre arts rely upon the spectators' reactions for the basic effectiveness of their efforts.

Much progress has been made in the theatre of continental Europe in the scientific means of producing and controlling light and color on the stage. So rapid has this progress been, and so far has it been carried, that in some instances the lighting has eclipsed the other theatre arts and detracted from them. From the standpoint of the production of *plays*, this condition is unfortunate. It is hardly likely, however, that such an extreme condition will evolve in America, — at least not from the same cause. Equipment of the type used in playhouses abroad possesses physical characteristics, such as huge size, lack of compactness, and awkwardness of manipulation, that will prevent its general adoption in a country where theatre design is dominated by high real-estate values. Nevertheless, a study of such equipment will furnish many excellent, pertinent suggestions, which, if rationally applied to domestic problems, will materially advance the art of stage lighting.

The *practice*, that is, the art, of stage lighting has, ever since its inception, been governed by several factors, chief among which is the mechanical means, the *equipment*, available for its execution. In even its general applications, light itself, whose nature and propagation, for centuries the subjects of scientific deliberation, have not yet been satisfactorily explained, has always been surrounded by an unpenetrated veil of mystery, in spite of its overwhelming abundance and man's commonplace association with it. Consequently, its use has never become very refined, nor have its possibilities been fully realized. In addition, light came to be produced by electricity, whose nature and behavior, to the layman and to the average stage worker are equally as abstruse as those of light, if not still more mystifying. Stage lighting was thus further removed from the realm of the other factors of play production, which are either human, or artistically or mechanically simple, and therefore easy of comprehension. It then constituted a subject whose depths could be sounded, if at all, only by careful, scientifically directed thought and study. The electrical and mechanical means for producing, projecting, and controlling light for the purposes of dramatic production — the stage lighting equipment — have been discussed in the paragraphs immediately preceding.

Almost equal in importance to the equipment in their influence on the practice of stage lighting are the factors of *experience* — familiarity with equipment and with the principles of its most effective disposition and utilization; *procedure* — the mechanics of play production in general; and *method* — the manner, the style, in which the lighting is applied to the production.

The value of *experience* as an adjunct of the theatre worker who strives to attain the highest possible degree of success in stage lighting can hardly be overestimated. By experience is meant not only that in stage-lighting design, but also that in manipulation of equipment. In every art, design is more or less dependent upon, and restricted by, the available media of expression; in the field of stage lighting perhaps more so than in others. This is due to the fact that, measured in the absolute, the media of expression — the equipment — are still in rather a primitive and undeveloped state. Consequently, a thorough knowledge of the possibilities and limitations of equipment and of how these possibilities may be fully realized is most essential to those stage workers who essay lighting design and application. Such knowledge can be acquired only by active use of equipment and by intelligent experimentation with it. Thorough experience in the manipulation of equipment makes it possible, in many cases, to obtain effective results with mediocre equipment, and lack of such experience will reduce the effectiveness of the best and most modern equipment. No better proof of this statement could be found than the two cases cited below. At the Metropolitan Opera House the lighting equipment is, generally, the most antiquated and obsolete imaginable. Yet, poor as this equipment is, constant association with it on the part of a well-trained and artistically appreciative stage crew and technical department, the per-

A well-lighted night interior: a scene from *John Ferguson*, as produced at Stanford University under the direction of Gordon Davis, with settings by Leslie Kiler.

sonnels of which remain virtually intact from season to season, and repeated performances and rehearsals, which, with some productions, have extended over a range of many years, produce lighting effects (in the realistic method, for the most part) which, as regards their smoothness, beauty, and general effectiveness, are seldom equaled and rarely surpassed. And this in spite of the fact that two performances of the same production are rarely given in succession, and that, in some instances, several different productions, all very elaborate, are presented in the same week. On the other hand, the lighting at the opening performance of the Guild Theatre in New York, which possesses a set of installed lighting equipment that is undoubtedly of the most modern and improved type, was notoriously poor. This was decidedly not the fault either of the equipment or of the stage crew. It was due to the urgent economic necessity of opening a new theatre "cold", that is, before those persons who were to use the stage equipment were able to familiarize themselves thoroughly with their tools. After a week or two of regular performances those difficulties which so marred the performance on the opening night had been smoothed out, and, ever since, the full possibilities of the equipment have been regularly realized. These two contrasting cases prove conclusively the value of experience as a factor in stage-lighting practice.

Workers in the amateur theatre are somewhat at a disadvantage in the matter of experience, because in the majority of cases not more than six or eight productions are done during the year, and only in the few larger organizations are more than three or four performances of each production given. This restricted program of performances, coupled very often with the lack of a suitable permanent playhouse and adequate equipment, naturally can provide only a limited experience. But the time available between productions offers an excellent opportunity to the really interested and serious amateur stage workers to practice and experiment with their equipment, and to acquire a good working knowledge of its capabilities and of its most convenient and effective operation, and, perhaps most important, to prepare, well in advance, for the forthcoming production.

And in this phase of theatre activity — the *procedure*, the mechanics, the "modus operandi", of producing a play, of mounting it and presenting it before an audience — lies another of the inherent advantages of the amateur theatre over the professional. The simpler conditions that control play production, the simpler and more direct environment in which the work of play production is carried out in the amateur theatre, favor the more satisfactory application of the several theatre arts in general, and of stage lighting in particular.

The usual procedure of play production in the professional theatre is, roughly, as follows: the producer appoints a director (who directs only the *actors*), a cast is chosen, and rehearsals begin; a specialist is commissioned to design the settings, which are constructed by one company and painted by another; properties are furnished by a third company, and costumes, when necessary, are often designed by a second specialist and are furnished by still another company. The highly specialized activities of the various stage workers — the director, the scenic designer, the costume designer, and others — being executed each apart from the others, lack a unifying element, and often do not jibe, do not form a harmonious whole. Hence light would be at a disadvantage and its possible effectiveness greatly reduced, even were it planned and carried out with the utmost care. But at this point in the production of a play the lighting has not yet been thought of. In fact, the playhouse has not yet been assigned by the theatre real-estate "interests." The lighting is left until the dress rehearsal, for the stage electrician (who has seen the production for the first time) to work out as best he can. Under this deplorable system, which is the result of economic conditions, good lighting is usually accidental, and in many productions is just what one would expect it to be — utterly inadequate, meaningless, and ugly. Of course, there are exceptions to this vicious system, some of which are notable ones. The attention which David Belasco bestows upon the lighting of his productions has become almost proverbial, especially in the cases of "The Return of Peter Grimm" and "The Darling of the Gods." The extensive light rehearsals (some continuing for many weeks) and the experimental work constantly being carried on in a completely equipped lighting workshop under the direction of Louis Hartman, Mr. Belasco's lighting director for the past quarter-century, are two production expenses that most other producers, not fully sharing Mr. Belasco's deep convictions as to the value of carefully planned and executed stage lighting, refuse to incur. Permanent producing organizations such as the Theatre Guild, and Walter Hampden's and Eva Le Gallienne's permanent repertory companies, employing permanent staffs and controlling their own playhouses, are more in a position to produce better results and to advance the art of stage lighting than are their less fortunate contemporaries who must brave the vicissitudes of the usual channels of professional play production.

The average amateur producing group resembles, in many respects, the organizations just referred to, and, like them, can prepare its productions in a more leisurely, sheltered, and careful fashion, and under a more centralized control, than can the average professional producer. The Little Theatre Tournament, held annually, in New York, affords an excellent opportunity to observe the effect of the rigorous procedure of professional production when it is applied to an amateur production which has been transplanted bodily from the sheltered sanctuary of its own playhouse and the tender care of its own staff. One case is outstanding — that of the Fireside Players, who produced William Manley's "The Crow's Nest", a play that depends in a very large measure upon the lighting for its effectiveness. At their own playhouse in White Plains, N. Y., the Players accorded this imaginative little comedy an excellent production, smooth and finished to the last detail. At the tournament, the labor union rules decreed that the members of the Players' expert technical staff, who had worked out the lighting and who were experienced in carrying it out by virtue of many rehearsals and several performances, should relinquish the direct control of the lighting equipment and place it in the hands of the stage electrician. Unfamiliar with the play, and unappreciative of its demands, he bungled the lighting in so thorough a fashion as to ruin it utterly.

Thus, in the professional theatre, even when conditions are most favorable to good lighting, its possibilities are often not fully realized because of the lack of knowledge and even of intelligent interest on the part of the actual operators of the lighting equipment. The power, that is, the authority, of "playing the light" — of stage lighting control — of actual switchboard manipulation, should be vested in an artist who thoroughly understands his media — light, color, and more fundamentally, electricity — rather than in an electrician who possesses but limited artistic ability, and still less inclination to make use of it. The truly perfunctory attitude of many modern theatre electricians may perhaps be traced to the training which they received in the service of some equally perfunctory and slapdash producers. This attitude on the part of many theatre workers who now have direct and final control of stage equipment in professional theatres, seems to be safeguarded, if not actually encouraged, by the labor union rules, under which, unfortunately, those present-day producers who realize the value of keeping abreast of the trend toward a greater artistry in stage productions are now obliged to chafe.

Because of the complete, self-contained, organizational set-ups in the amateur theatre, stage lighting there can be carried out without the hampering influences discussed above. Lack of unity in direction rarely exists: almost every organization, intelligently realizing the situation, appoints or employs one person to assume full authority for productions, and the workers then place them-

A well-lighted day interior: the final scene of *Paolo and Francesca*, as produced by the Hart House Theatre at Toronto under the direction of Walter Sinclair.

selves under his controlling guidance. That these workers are ever indifferent or perfunctory is not at all likely: the very impulse that prompts them to devote themselves, unremunerated, to the art of the theatre, precludes any such possibility. These amateur theatre workers are not committed to set methods of obtaining results, as are those in the professional theatre. Being unhampered by tradition and usage, they are able to approach each of their problems with freshness and a clearly defined purpose, and to work out these problems in a manner which can but produce more truly original and pleasing results. This advantage applies not only to the field of stage lighting but to all the divisions of theatre activity.

Stage lighting practice is, of course, directly affected by the *method* used in lighting, whether it is realistic, symbolistic, esthetic, or psychological. The method in vogue at some particular period, that is, the general tendency of the theatre arts, will affect practice *generally*, and the method in use for the particular production at hand will affect practice *specifically*. Here the professional and the amateur theatre alike must depend upon their audiences for approval, and hence, for dictation and guidance. In his choice of method the stage worker must depend for his guidance not only upon the type of play to be produced, but also upon the intellectual and esthetic capacities of the audience that will witness the production. The broader the standard of acceptance of the audience, the wider will be his range of choice of method. But, since this standard of acceptance of the audience is usually what he has made it, through careful and subtle training and "education" (although it is, of course, fundamentally controlled by the type of person constituting his audience), the stage worker determines, in a large measure, the method, the style, in which his productions, and consequently also his lighting, shall be done. If he essays to light his play by the psychological method, he must have a working knowledge of psychology in general, and of the psychology of light and color in particular.

The advantages inherent in the amateur theatre in its methods and in its organization have already been pointed out, as well as some drawbacks, such as the somewhat restricted opportunity for acquiring actual production experience, and the lack of adequate playhouses and stages and equipment, or, expressed fundamentally, lack of funds. Because of its ability to help overcome the ill effects of these drawbacks, light is a great boon to the amateur producer. Workers in many organizations, whose playhouses and stages not only are insufficient in size and equipment, but also seem possessed of every possible drawback and fiendish inconvenience, will find in light a compensating medium that will render tolerable, even dis-

A scene from the second act of *Anna Christie*, as produced by the Little Theatre of Dallas under the direction of Oliver Hinsdell, which illustrates how light can be used very simply yet with telling effect. The scene represents the stern deck of a barge. By the skillful, restrained use of a single overhead source of light for the two characters in the scene, the plasmic, statuesque power of light has been very effectively utilized.

tinctive and beautiful, the results of their labor, which might otherwise prove mean and tawdry. Lighting, produced by the simplest means, provided it be applied with intelligence, will transform into things of beauty and richness the commonest and cheapest materials that have been used in creating the stage picture. But, on the other hand, the impossible must not be expected of light. The phrase, "painting scenery with light", has been repeated so often by enthusiastic writers on stage production that it is now often used without a true conception of its real meaning. The impression seems to prevail that a few draperies, a few screens, perhaps, and a few lights are all that is necessary to achieve any effect imaginable. For instance, the staid and reliable *Journal* of the American Institute of Electrical Engineers, commenting editorially, declares that "the proper use of light on the stage may transform a bare set of draperies into almost any scenic illusion desired." This statement is misleading. Although these simple accessories to stage production can accomplish much, they have their clearly defined limitations, beyond which they fail, and fail utterly. Light alone, while it can perhaps provide settings for a limited class of plays, cannot be used to paint scenery — at least, not in the sense in which the term "scenery" is generally accepted. Even "projected scenery", spoken of a great deal but seldom actually used, is not applicable to general purposes but is restricted to the stylized or symbolic method of representation.

In order to derive the greatest benefit from this valuable ally at his disposal — light — the amateur stage worker must school himself in all its phases; he must make himself intelligently familiar with its fundamental characteristics so that he will be enabled to adapt it and apply it to his needs in the most finished and — not less important — the most convenient manner. Perhaps the greatest cause of discouragement to the amateur stage worker is the fact that much of his zeal, his ardor, such a primary and invaluable source of potential success, is often unguided, and, in some instances, even misguided. Much energy is wasted and results are often disappointing because lack of technical knowledge leads to clumsy, roundabout, expensive methods, and to cumbrous equipment that is difficult and awkward to manage.

Technical problems that arise in the course of dramatic production work should be treated as being new and original; that is, they should be dealt with on their own merits. The technical problems met with in everyday life must be viewed from an entirely different angle when their parallels are encountered in connection with stage work, because of the peculiar, widely different conditions that abound on the stage.

This setting, designed by Robert R. Sharpe for the second act of *The Makropoulos Secret*, produced by the Pasadena Community Playhouse Association under the direction of Gilmor Brown, is an excellent example of the symbolic use of light. It represents the bare stage of a theatre, with a throne chair for the heroine, who is a supernatural representation of eternal youth, and "who is clad in a scarlet gown which she flaunts cynically at Time. But behind her rise the spokes of a gigantic wheel, pinning her to the center of Space, to its very vortex."

The amateur producing group that interests and enlists or hires the services of the local electrician or electrical contractor to help carry out its lighting work is fortunate indeed — in so far as it acquires the services of a skilled mechanic. But often this individual is unaware of the demands made by stage work, and he is likely to advise the use of materials and methods with which he comes in contact in the course of his every-day, regular routine of work. Unless he is able and willing to translate his knowledge and ability into terms of stagecraft, the organization would do better if it dispensed with his services and struggled along for a time as best it could and gradually evolved its own processes and instruments, even in spite of some possible deficiencies. This would be much more gratifying in the long run than to endure perhaps equally deficient results obtained by a fundamentally unsympathetic outsider. Furthermore, it is just as hazardous for an amateur group to rely to any great extent upon a local stage electrician, because his point of view will rarely fit in with the purposes and ideals of the organization. The professional theatre in the past has developed certain set methods of accomplishing results that have proved more or less satisfactory. New problems that arise are hardly ever solved; they are usually forced, willy-nilly, into some category for the items of which a stock solution stands ready. If these methods of the professional theatre are applied indiscriminately to the problems of the amateur theatre, the latter is deprived of one of its prime reasons for existence.

Nevertheless, both the local electrical contractor and the local stage electrician are in a position to be of great help to and a source of much useful information for the inexperienced lighting director of an amateur group. He should draw upon the professional theatre and upon ordinary lighting practice for as much knowledge and assistance as is consistent with and applicable to his own methods and problems. Beyond that point, however, his work should be original — creative. He should use the information he obtains from these sources actually to carry out his own work and to advance his own standards; he should subject it to a process of evaluation for his own needs, but never should he feel himself in any way restricted by it.

It is to meet the needs of such theatre workers and of students of dramatic production that this volume is primarily designed. It attempts to present the fundamentals of the arts and sciences and technical processes as they are adapted to stage lighting, rather than to accord the subject a superficial treatment from the standpoint of practice alone. It will be noticed that but little space is devoted to the discussion of individual problems. This would be hardly feasible, since no two problems are at all alike, and since a working knowledge of fundamentals will prove of much greater value: with intelligent development and application to individual needs, it will provide far more satisfactory results.

To this end, material has been prepared and included which makes the nature of the volume essentially that of a handbook — a practical manual of application. The place of light in the theatre — its functions, its methods of application — has been discussed and a general survey of equipment and practice in both the professional and amateur fields has been presented. The chapter immediately following, on the history of stage lighting, possesses but a limited practical value, save perhaps the notes on the more recent developments. It furnishes, nevertheless, a rather interesting historical background that should serve to acquaint the present-day worker with the problems and achievements of his predecessors, and hence help him to carry out his own work with a better perspective of the entire subject and with a deeper insight into it.

The material on electricity, light, color, lighting and control equipment, and color media has been selected and arranged so as to serve not only as a guide for the lighting technician, but also as a means of informing the lighting artist what he has, in general, at his disposal. This takes into consideration the dual approach which is required by every problem of play production — the artist deciding upon what to do, and the technician deciding upon how to do it. The more technical the artist, and the more artistic the technician, the more reasonable will be the demands of the former, and the more satisfactory will be the execution of the latter. The material in this introductory chapter is for artist and technician alike. The material in the chapter on "Electricity" is mainly for the technician. The subjects of "Light" and "Color" have each been divided into two parts: the objective, mainly for the technician, and the subjective, mainly for the artist. Although the titles would seem to indicate that they are meant for the technician alone, the chapters on "Equipment", "Control", and "Color Media" are also of importance to the artist. The chapter on "Methods and Practice" contains general suggestions for planning a complete layout of equipment, as well as general suggestions for planning and executing the lighting for a production. The two papers on stage-lighting topics by Louis Hartmann and Claude Bragdon have been included in order to make more generally accessible to persons interested in stage lighting these two interesting and valuable discussions. The bibliography will be of use to persons who wish to investigate further some special phase of the subject; the list of manufacturers and dealers will be useful to those theatre workers who wish to determine, more in detail, prices and specifications of various items of stage-lighting equipment; and the notes for amateur workers may prove useful to those who are just beginning to interest themselves in the practical phases of stage-lighting work. Thus every division of the subject has been touched upon and has been arranged in what is seemingly a logical and convenient order.

Although stage lighting is still, in the main, a problem that must be solved principally by "cut and try" methods, with little if any previous consideration beyond a general conception of the ultimate results desired, the newer stagecraft gives every indication that, in the future, more and more specific attention will be given to stage lighting design *per se*. This tendency will make it necessary for the stage designer not only to possess a working knowledge of his lighting media, but also to be familiar with the actual units in which they are measured, and with the method in which these units are employed. Just as he now uses lineal measurements in giving the final instructions for his settings, so in the future will he be required, perhaps, to specify his light and color in their respective units of measurement. Although it is hardly probable that stage lighting will be reduced to terms of illuminating engineering, and perhaps not at all desirable that it should be, still, a thorough foundation in the principles and methods that enter into light design can but aid the stage designer to achieve, more conveniently and fully, the realization of his abstract conceptions. Leonardo da Vinci warns that "Those who become enamored of the practice of art without having previously applied themselves to the diligent study of the scientific part of it may be compared to mariners who put to sea in a ship without a rudder or compass and, therefore, cannot be certain of arriving at the wished-for port. Practice must always be founded on good theory."

CHAPTER II · HISTORY OF STAGE LIGHTING

Early development of the theatre – Greek, Roman, miracles and mysteries, moralities; introduction of stage lighting – flares, oil lamps, candles; gas lighting – open jets, glass chimneys, mantles, the limelight, colored lighting; electric lighting – carbon arcs, incandescent lamps, control of lighting; recent advances in stage lighting.

THE theatre, as it is understood to-day, is generally considered to have been instituted in the fifth century B.C., when, with the plays of Aeschylus, dramatic art freed itself of the more obvious forms of Dionysiac worship. But stage lighting (again, as it is understood to-day) received no attention until, in the sixteenth century A.D., late-afternoon performances in the roofed-over winter theatres presented, at least, the problem of adequate artificial illumination. Compared with the twenty-five-century history of the organized theatre, the five-century history of stage lighting is a short and recent one indeed. But what an eventful and crowded one! From its beginning to the present time, the history and development of stage lighting has run a very close parallel to the history and rapid development of artificial illuminants in general, and this promises to continue to be the case in the future. Almost every newly developed light source of the past and every improvement received its first practical use in the service of play production. Theatre managers and stage directors, ever on the alert to improve the quality of their productions, have always availed themselves of new illuminants long before they were placed in common, general use. In addition to new illuminants, the rapid improvement of mechanical and electrical accessory apparatus has also greatly influenced the history of stage lighting.

The *theatron* of the Greeks, that is, what might be called the "playhouse", was built in the open. A hill, with an even, gentle slope, furnished a convenient site. In the more primitive of the Greek theatres the spectators arranged themselves on the face of the hill as best they could, but in later theatres they occupied regular tiers of seats and benches rising one above the other on the slope. At the foot of the hill, almost two thirds surrounded by the curved rows of seats, was a circular space, the *orchestra*, in which the play was enacted by the principal actors and the chorus. The orchestra was not raised, but was on the same level as the lowest tier of seats. Not far behind the orchestra was a two-storied building, the *skene*. The skene was rectangular in plan, several times as long as it was wide, and presented its broad side to the spectators. In the skene were kept the masks, the buskins, the costumes, and the properties for the plays; in it the actors attired themselves for the play and into it they retired when their presence was not required in the orchestra. In front of the skene, between it and the orchestra, was the *proskenion*, usually porticoed, which served really as the more or less decorative façade of the skene. The proskenion was not quite as tall as the skene, and its top formed a sort of balcony or terrace which was occasionally used in the play; it served especially well for the appearance of gods, who played no insignificant rôles in many of the plays.

Dramatic art in Rome first began to flourish in the second century B.C. with the plays of Plautus, followed shortly after by those of Terence. In the main, the plays of both Plautus and Terence were comedies adapted, and even translated, from the work of Greek playwrights. Just as the plays of the early Roman theatre were almost literal translations of those of the Greeks, so were their earlier playhouses almost exact reproductions. Soon, though, the Romans elaborated the design of the theatre. They reduced the size of the orchestra, because, as the importance of the chorus grew less, a smaller space sufficed for the action of the play. After a while, the action of the play was restricted entirely to the space directly in front of the proskenion. The remaining portion of the orchestra was lowered several feet, whereupon the elevated stage came into existence. In this lowered portion of the orchestra were placed seats of honor for senators and other distinguished citizens. In the later Roman theatres the proskenion was made architecturally more elaborate, and became more adapted to use as a scenic background for the play. The *paraskena* (wings jutting forward from each end of the proskenion) were enlarged, and the playing space, which by that time had become quite distinct from the Auditorium, was roofed over. The Romans also used a drop curtain, which, during the course of the play, lay folded in a deep groove that ran the length of the proskenion. This groove separated the proskenion and skene from the mass of spectators, and when the curtain was unfolded by raising its upper edge, the entire "stage" was concealed from view. Thus is apparent the extent to which the early playhouses have influenced not only the design of present-day theatre buildings but also the very terminology used to describe their parts.

Until almost the sixth century after the advent of the Christian era, the theatre flourished. Then, with the fall of the Western empire under the barbarian invasion, it gradually sank into desuetude, and finally the buildings, the playhouses themselves, fell into decay.

During this thousand-year period of the early theatre, plays were produced under the open sky, and only during the daytime. Naturally, then, the problem of artificial illumination was nonexistent. From the standpoint of illumination, the Greek and Roman theatres were dependent only on the weather, which, in their latitudes, was most likely not often unfavorable. Neither was there any problem of realistic scenery. It was unknown. The dignified architecture of the skenion and proskenion served as the background, the scene, of the action. The spectators were usually not so interested in new themes, new plots, as they were in the new treatment of old ones. The play and the actor were accordingly the most important factors in dramatic art. But what to-day are called "stage effects" were then not altogether unknown. Gods would descend from on high by means of cranes located at the top of the skene; there too would stand the impersonator of Zeus, hurling his bolts of lightning — flashes and streaks painted upon wooden slabs — at the players below; then would follow the thunder, which was produced by striking stone-filled hides against metal plates. But there is no record of the use of artificial light. Nevertheless, the beauty of colored light in the theatre, though perhaps not in connection with the play itself, was appreciated at least as a decorative element. In the first century A.D., Valerius Maximus states that yellow, red, and blue awnings were stretched over the large theatres — primarily, of course, for protection from the sun — which, as they fluttered, dyed the spectators and players alike with the color of the transmitted sunlight.

In the dark ages that followed the downfall of Rome, from the sixth century to the eleventh, when civilization hung in the balance, there is virtually no record of any organized form of dramatic art. From this period of chaos, confusion, and struggle, the church emerged triumphant — aggressive rather than defensive. And it was in the service of Christianity that the drama, in a somewhat distorted form, at that time made its reappearance.

The miracle plays and mystery plays fostered (at least, originally) by the Church were used to educate the masses of people in the rudimentary principles of Christianity by presenting crude though apparently entertaining dramatic versions of "key" episodes of Biblical and saintly lore. At first it is very likely that the miracle plays were given within the churches. It is often suggested that under these circumstances the candles in sconces, surrounding the shrines before which these plays were presented, constituted the earliest forms of stage lighting. But such lighting could have been only incidental and unpremeditated, and at best, haphazard. The immense popularity of the miracle plays and mysteries soon made necessary their presentation outdoors, before the churches, on crude platforms. Little is definitely known about these platform stages of the Middle Ages; the existence of the reputed three-storied "heaven, hell, and earth" scaffoldings, not to mention the erroneously reported nine-storied structure at Metz, is now considered doubtful. Portable stages, usually two stories high (the lower story serving as a dressing room) mounted on wheels certainly were used, especially in England, where they were known as *pageants*.

Later, in the fifteenth century, came the Moralities, in which the various vices, virtues, and mental attributes were personified by the characters in the play. These were essentially more dramatic in form than the preceding miracles and mysteries, and required at least more original composition. They led the way to the purely secular plays that soon followed.

The light sources then in use for general purposes were the same that had prevailed centuries before, namely, the blazing pine knots in iron cressets, oil lamps (with open, floating wicks), and also the newer candles. As plays were still given mainly in the daytime, stage lighting, as such, was still unknown. There are, however, definite records of the use of light, in the crude elementary forms of flares and squibs, to lend realism to the appearance of devils, angels, and hell, and to create other impressive effects. From the well-preserved accounts of the passion play at Valenciennes, in 1547, it is apparent that fiery devils and fire-spouting dragons and serpents appeared on the stage, and that the mouth of hell had a background of flames. By ingenious mechanical means angels flew through the air and glowed with magnificent light. In their hands they carried golden staffs, "which at the end had the shape of a lamp, out of which came the said flame, on blowing a little into the said staff." Such spectacular use of fireworks and of open flames was fraught with danger and often resulted in accidents. For example, at a performance of "The Conversion of St. Paul", given at Basle, lightning was supposed to strike Saul: "As a flash of lightning, a rocket of fire was darted, but St. Paul, falling from his horse, had his trousers burned."

Although at this period the theatre was still essentially an outdoor institution, in various parts of Europe, especially in Italy, performances of tableaux, pageants, and other theatrical entertainment were already being given indoors under the patronage of nobles and members of the aristocracy, principally for their own amusement. Serlio, an Italian architect of the sixteenth century, gave much thought and attention to theatre design. In a treatise written in 1566, he discussed the construction of the stage in an Italian theatre,

A fifteenth-century cresset for holding blazing pine knots, which were the earliest sources of artificial light.

Examples of open flame oil lamps with floating wicks, which were used in prehistoric times.

The tallow candle, the successor to the open flame oil lamp.

and, in prescribing for the creation of certain lighting effects, he became the first writer to take up, "with malice aforethought", the subject of stage lighting. For producing colored light upon the stage he recommended the use of lamps or torches before which were placed, to function as color media, bottles containing red wine or white wine (amber), or a solution (blue) of aqua vita, vernis, and sulphuric acid. "The theatre had been brought indoors, its lighting had become a problem, and Serlio was already beginning its solution."

During the later Renaissance, comedies, farces, tragedies (usually based on historical events), romances, and many other types of plays were written for the then completely secularized theatre. This playwriting activity culminated, at the end of the sixteenth century, in the work of Shakespeare. By that time there had been established the Blackfriars' Theatre in London, one of the most important playhouses in the history of early English drama. Shakespeare and Richard Burbage, the great tragedian, had equal shares in the control of this theatre, and alternated their productions between the Blackfriar's and the Globe, the latter an open theatre. The Globe was used for summer performances, and the Blackfriars', a completely enclosed theatre, was used during the winter. The English theatre, by that time, had definitely begun to come indoors.

Several other enclosed theatres were contemporary with the Blackfriars'. It is definitely known that all these indoor theatres resorted to the use of artificial light, mainly that from candles, both in the auditorium and on the stage. That many plays of that period required the use of light of some sort on the stage is indicated by numerous references in their stage directions. That producers were contending with the problem of realistic lighting is indicated by the discussion of the Pyramus and Thisbe players in "A Midsummer Night's Dream."

In the early part of the seventeenth century, in England, the activities of Inigo Jones in staging court masques did much to influence theatre design. Jones had visited the continent and had returned influenced by the Italian theatre, which, in turn, had been influenced by the traditions of the Roman theatre. He introduced the proscenium arch and thereby originated the "picture-frame" type of stage, which is at present still the prevailing type. In stage lighting he was also an innovator, being probably the first to apply to the stage a comparatively high intensity of light by the use of reflectors. He was also the first to make effective the use of color on the stage. Present-day stagecraft can be traced directly to its beginning in Jones' work, which had an enormous influence on the theatre of his day.

In 1628 a German writer, Joseph Fürtenbach, described the size of a stage as well as the means for lighting it in his "Sciena di Comoedia." In this description is found the first definite mention of an arrangement of stage lights which corresponds to present-day footlights and proscenium striplights. Fürtenbach advises the use of a row of oil lamps at the front edge of the stage, out of sight of the audience, and also of vertical rows of lamps just behind each of the wings at the side of the stage.

The common method of lighting the stages of the seventeenth century was by means of chandeliers and bracket lamps, hung above and at the side of the stage, and by shielded lamps placed at the front edge of the stage floor. Candles were usually placed about the circumference of suspended hoops, which were raised above the actors' heads by means of pulley arrangements. The candles were usually of tallow, since wax candles, although they gave a steadier and a whiter light, were much more expensive, and hence were used only on state occasions. These tallow candles "hung in dripping radiance over the stage, whether the scene portrayed a forest, a city square, or a moonlit exterior." With these open flames the possibility of a much dreaded fire was always present. Precautions against it were taken by having quantities of water and large sponges fastened to long sticks readily available. The footlights were then called the "floatlights", since they usually consisted of the old open-flame oil lamps, in which the wick floated in the animal or vegetable oil that was used. Garrick, when he took over the second Drury Lane Theatre, was among the first to introduce the footlights and striplights in the theatres of England. When Sheridan managed the Drury Lane in 1784, the old system of using suspended candle hoops had become obsolete, and all lights used on the stage were out of sight of the spectators, hidden behind the wings and borders which by that time were familiar objects on the stage. Candles of improved quality had superseded the open-flame oil lamps. Late in the eighteenth century, however, with the development of the Argand burner for oil, with its cylindrical wick and glass chimney for improving and steadying the flame, oil lamps of the new type were used, since they provided a much whiter, clearer, and brighter light than had previously been available. Thus the chimneyed oil lamp superseded the candle.

The double-wick open-flame camphine burner, a refinement of the floating-wick oil lamp.

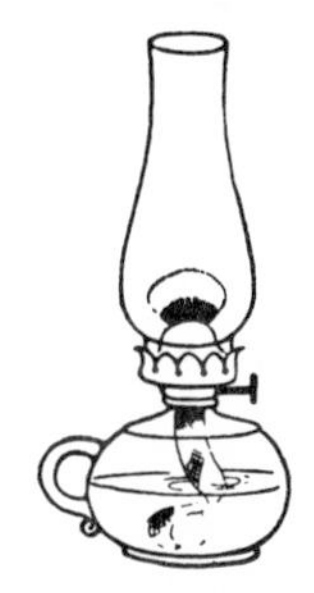

The improved oil lamp with an adjustable wick and glass chimney, a development of the eighteenth century.

The early theatres in America had to use the same methods — more or less crude, from the present-day point of view — of lighting their stages as were in common use in Europe. The familiar historic print of the John Street Theatre, on the walls of which Messrs. E. Bimpey and M. Bennett so naïvely carved their names for all posterity to see in reproduction, shows that playhouse with a rather well-lighted stage on which no light sources are visible. It is apparent that footlights with curved metal shields for the candles were used at that time — the last quarter of the eighteenth century.

At the end of the eighteenth century, then, candles and improved chimneyed oil lamps, principally the latter, were used as stage-lighting illuminants. The conventional forms of footlights, borderlights, and striplights had been established. Stagecraft, and theatre and stage design in general, had developed to what it substantially remains to-day. Stagecraft had advanced as far as it could under the stage lighting existing at that time. It was restricted by the low intensities of light: in spite of the large number of lamps (sometimes hundreds) that were used, theatre managers had to be satisfied if they were able to render their actors and scenery visible. Illuminants were expensive, and they required constant attention; the wicks of candles often had to be trimmed during the action of the play, and it was not uncommon for the snuff-boy to step out before the footlights and, in the midst of an important scene, attend to a smoky candle. Neither was there any convenient means of control, of varying the intensity or color of the light from candles or oil lamps. Candles had to be snuffed out, and "there is record of the amazing rapidity with which candle snuffers made the transformation from light to darkness on the eighteenth-century stage." With oil lamps, ingenious but awkward and cumbersome mechanical systems of placing opaque screens and colored glasses in front of the lights had to be employed. The oil lamps of the Haymarket Theatre in London, for instance, were "furnished with chimneys of white and green glass, which, by an ingenious system of levers, commanded by the prompter, ascend or descend as required and produce moonlight or other optical effects. . . . In some theatres, notably at Birmingham, a series of colored glass screens can be shifted in front by a lever, but with a loud clatter." Such was the status of stage lighting at the beginning of the nineteenth century.

But in the last decade of the previous century, William Murdoch, a Scotch engineer and inventor, had been experimenting with a practical installation of piped gas, distilled from coal, for lighting purposes. This soon proved successful, and the year 1803 witnessed the adaptation of gas lighting for the stage when a German, Frederick A. Winser, installed the first gas-lighting system in the Lyceum Theatre in London. In 1816 a system of gas lighting was installed in the Chestnut Street Opera House in Philadelphia. The advantages of gas lighting in the theatre were quickly realized, and soon it became the standard stage illuminant. In the early days of gas lighting, theatres had to install their own gas-generating equipment, since central gas stations and city mains in all the streets did not come into existence until a demand was created by the general and domestic use of gas as an illuminant to supersede oil lamps.

Even though the gas was burned in open jets, it was capable of providing a much brighter light than the oil lamps and candles which it superseded. No new methods of stage lighting were devised for gas; it simply replaced the old illuminants in the conventional forms of equipment. The footlights, borderlights, and striplights remained essentially the same in form and principle. By far the most important advantage of gas lighting lay in its convenient maintenance and in its comparatively high susceptibility to control. By varying the quantity of gas, by means of suitable

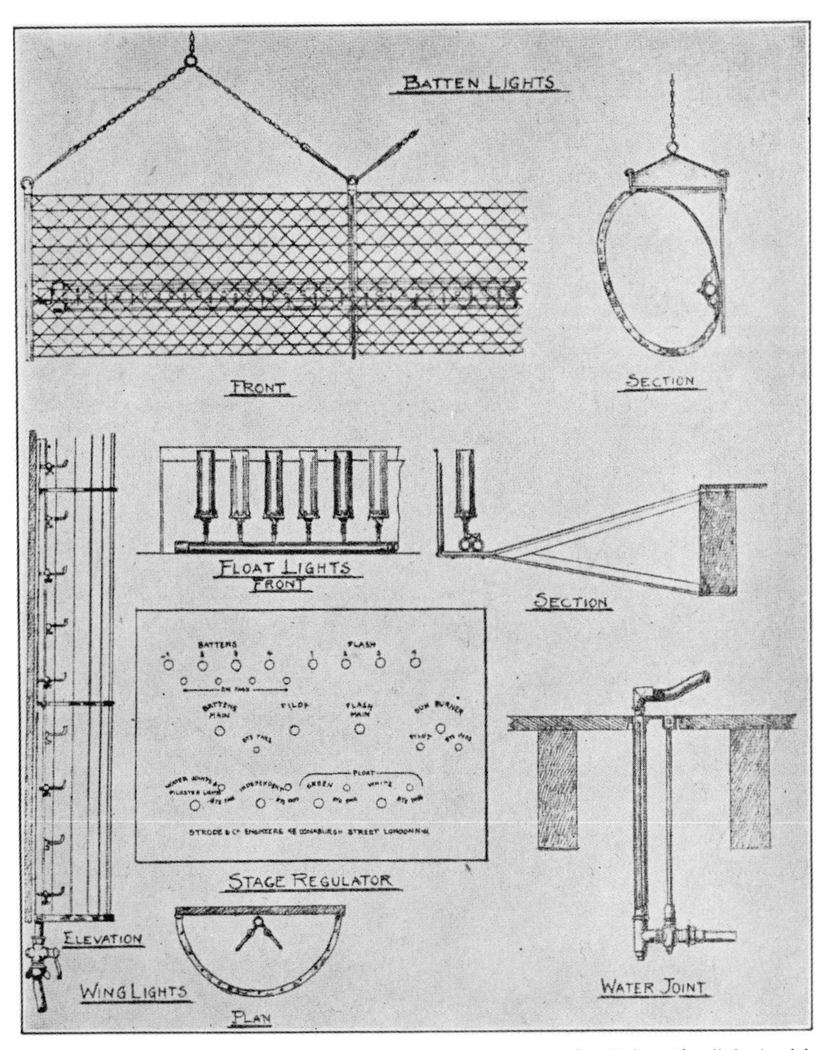

Sketches showing details of gas stage-lighting equipment: floatlights (footlights) with chimneys, batten lights (borderlights), and wing lights (vertical striplights); also a water joint (connection for portable equipment corresponding to present-day stage pocket) and the layout of a stage regulator, or gas table (corresponding to the present-day switchboard).

valves located at some central point of control, flowing to any set of gas jets, a smooth increase or decrease, rapid or slow, in the intensity of light could be easily effected. For the first time in theatre history it became possible to darken the auditorium during the course of the play; a procedure that helped greatly any attempts at realism or illusion on the stage.

The forerunner of the modern switchboard, with its banks of switches and dimmers, was the "gas table", a control table upon which were situated the valves for controlling the various units of lighting equipment. The gas main, oftentimes more than twelve inches in diameter, led up to the regulator, where it was divided into smaller branch mains, each with its valve on the regulator, supplying some unit part of the lighting equipment. Each of the branch mains was brought to a "water joint" (which was analagous to the present-day stage pocket), from which point the gas was conducted by flexible rubber tubing to the individual piece of lighting equipment. The Grand Opéra at Paris was described as having "no less than twenty-eight miles of gas piping, while the controlling *jeu d'orque* comprise eighty-eight 'stops' or cocks, controlling nine hundred and sixty gas jets. . . . A row of jets [borderlights] some thirty or forty feet long, two hundred or three hundred in number, is hoisted aloft, protected from behind by a sort of curved metal screen and in front by a very open wire net." Such lighting equipment was of necessity bulky and cumbersome, especially the lengths of thick rubber tubing, and in an elaborate production the stage was well cluttered up with it.

The chief disadvantages of gas were the great heat and offensive vapors given off by the open flames, and the dangerous fire hazard created by the latter. "The amount of heat and flame may be conceived. The lighting even of these jets, which is done from below with a light rod of enormous length [with a flaming, alcohol-soaked wad of cotton at the upper end], is a matter of danger, as a mere contact with the canvas might set all in a blaze, for the lighter has to carry his rod along every jet. . . . The upper boxes and galleries are oppressively hot, the view of the stage is interfered with, and whatever there is of ventilation is chiefly productive of a current from the stage which carries the sound up to the ventilator instead of allowing it to pass to the audience. As regards the float footlights, the danger for dancers is considerable, as shown by sad accidents. The obstruction not only by the reflectors but also by the visible smoke is great, while the heated air is unfavorable in every respect to the actors and their efforts, and the light dazzles their eyes." While the latter criticisms may appear unduly severe, they indicate that the unsatisfactory features of gas lighting were recognized, even though at the time no better illuminant was available.

Although open-jet gas flames were used at first, these were later surrounded with glass chimneys for protection against currents of air. In 1890 the invention of incandescent gas mantles greatly improved both the quantity and quality of light obtained by the use of gas. The gas mantle was rapidly adopted by all those theatres that had not already installed electric lighting, which was invented a decade before the gas mantle was developed. Gas mantles provided a light much brighter and whiter than the open-jet gas flame.

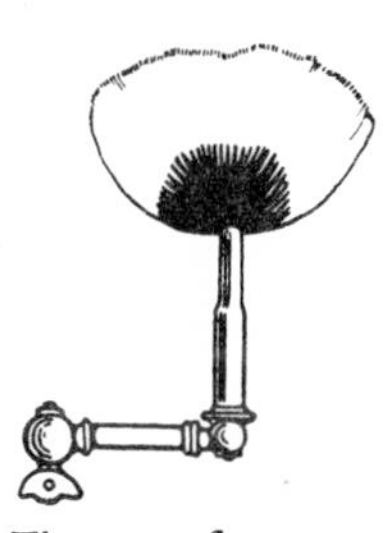

The open-flame gas burner which was introduced almost simultaneously with the chimneyed oil lamp.

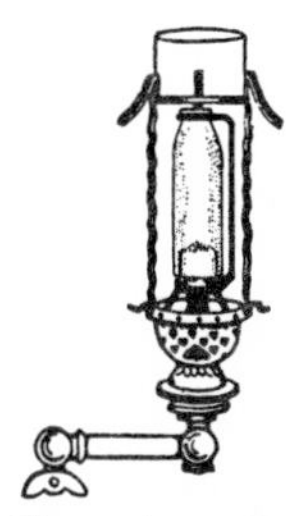

The incandescent gas mantle, which was a development of the late nineteenth century.

Gas lighting, then, made it possible for the stage worker to achieve a fair degree of control over his stage lighting, and to achieve an intrinsically higher brightness. It enabled him to achieve a degree of realism that was not possible with candles and oil lamps, and also it paved the way for rapid advances in the art of scene painting and in other phases of stagecraft, since it was able to provide a little more than mere illumination. Records describe the method of creating various effects. A rising moon, for example, was simulated on the stage by placing a gas light in a round, drum-shaped box, with tissue paper covering the front circular face, and by hauling this apparatus slowly aloft to the accompaniment of squeaking pulleys. The moon wabbled considerably, probably because of the great length of heavy rubber tubing that it had to drag up with it, but it received favorable comment from those of the spectators who appreciated the producer's attempt at realism. For color effects, mechanically shifted color screens were used, as in the days of candles and oil lamps; but later permanent color screens on multiple color "circuits" were installed. To this day, old playgoers who remember the work of Henry Irving insist that he was able with gas to obtain artistic effects that in their opinion have not yet been eclipsed in the present era of electric lighting. While such statements either are gross exaggerations, or indicate unfortunate later playgoing experiences on the part of these critics, they do help to prove that with gas lighting stagecraft had reached a level that was high above that attained during any previous period in theatre history. But with the advantages of gas lighting were coincident also the several serious shortcomings that have been stated. Therefore, when lighting by means of electric incandescent lamps was introduced in 1880, gas lighting on the stage was rapidly

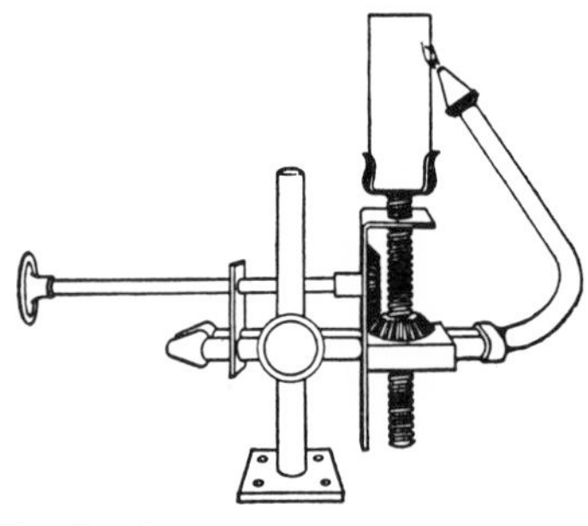

The limelight, which, since its development in 1816, has been intimately associated with the theatre.

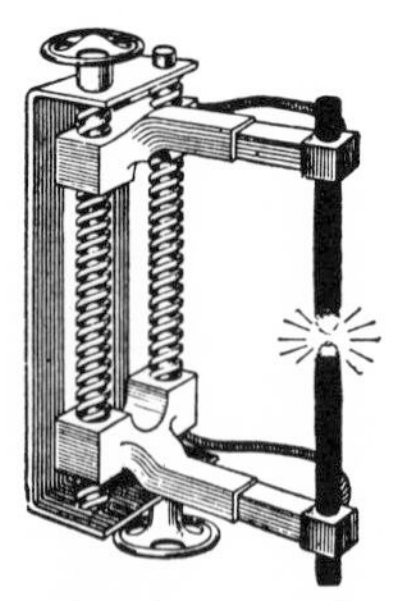

The carbon electric arc, a development of the early nineteenth century which is still used extensively in the theatre.

discarded in favor of the newer, still more convenient, and safer illuminant. Nevertheless, at the close of the nineteenth century, gas was still being used in a number of theatres.

But long before gas lighting had generally disappeared from the theatre, two notable contributions to stage lighting had appeared. One was the limelight; the other was the electric arc. The limelight or calcium light (sometimes also called the Drummond light, after its inventor, Thomas Drummond) was first developed in 1816. It was found that by heating a piece of lime to a high temperature it would become incandescent and would emit a brilliant white light of excellent quality. The limelight, as adapted to the stage, consisted of a cylindrical block of lime, against the side of which was directed the sharp point of an oxyhydrogen flame. The spot upon which the flame impinged glowed to a brilliant incandescence. The fact that the brilliant area of lime was very small made possible the use of a lens for accurately controlling the light. The limelight was placed in a housing with a lens, and thus the first spotlight became a reality. Records indicate that the earliest use of limelight in the theatre took place in 1837, but it was not until some twenty years later that it came into universal use. Although the limelight produced an excellent quality of light — soft, radiant, mellow, yet withal comparatively brilliant, it required almost constant attention. The block of lime had to be constantly shifted so as to expose a fresh surface of lime to the flame as the lime was gradually consumed. As a rule, each limelight required an operator to attend to it.

Because of its intensity, the limelight naturally was soon used for "spotting" individual characters as they moved about the stage. Occasionally, also, batteries of limelights would be directed on to the stage from the auditorium, for general stage lighting. This

The earliest forms of electric stage-lighting projectors: carbon arcs used with parabolic mirrors, that at the left as a sort of floodlight; that at the right, with a thin silk color medium, as a means of simulating sunlight.

innovation in the use of limelight was the forerunner of "front-of-house" or "balcony-face" method of lighting the stage, which to-day is gaining in favor. Even as early as 1847, when the first attack on footlights was recorded, this method of front lighting, at an angle of forty-five degrees downward, was advocated, and the abandonment of footlights was urged: they were severely criticized because of the unnatural and distorting light-and-shade effects they gave rise to. The limelight was also very useful for creating realistic effects, — for simulating lamplight or moonlight or sunlight streaming through a window. Later on, even water ripples and cloud effects were produced with the aid of limelights. Extensive use was made of color media for spectacular and artistic effects. Each limelight required two cylinders of compressed gas — one of oxygen and the other of hydrogen. When the limelight was used for spotlighting work, these cylinders would often be strapped to the back of the operator, and the limelight itself fastened to his chest. He was then free to move about high above the stage, from which position he directed the light upon the scene below.

The other great advance in stage lighting introduced during the first half of the nineteenth century — the electric arc — was first exhibited in experimental form by Sir Humphry Davy before the

Royal Institution in London in 1808. Dynamos and other mechanical means of generating electric current were still to be developed. Davy used a voltaic battery of two thousand cells to provide current for his arc. The arc lamp consisted of two carbon rods, each connected to a terminal of the enormous electric battery. When the tips of the "carbons" were brought together, an electric current was formed and current would flow. When the carbons were separated, the current would "arc" across the gap, heating the tip of the positive carbon to brilliant incandescence. This arcking gradually vaporized the carbons, hence they had continually to be pushed towards each other in order to maintain a constant distance between them. At that time, general practical use of the arc lamp was still more than fifty years in the future. But as early as 1846 there is recorded the use of the electric arc at the Paris Opéra. The arc was used for a special realistic effect—the simulation of a beam of sunlight — rather than for general stage-lighting purposes, for which gas was then being used. For this special purpose a small electric arc was placed at the focus of a parabolic mirror, and the resulting parallel beam of light was passed through a thin silk color screen. This use of this method also indicates that stage workers of that period were beginning to rely more and more upon reflectors for controlling light in the desired manner. For the production of Rossini's "Moses" at the Paris Opéra in 1860 there was prepared a number of spectacular effects which employed the electric arc in some form or other. At this production was used what was probably the first electric spotlight, with enclosing hood, lens, arc unit, shutter, and an adjustable standard. This was used for "spotting" or "following" the principal characters. What might be termed an arc flood, equipped with a parabolic mirror, was permanently placed and was used for lighting a portion of the scene to a higher intensity than the remainder. A rainbow and lightning flashes were also produced with "effect apparatus" that contained electric arc units.

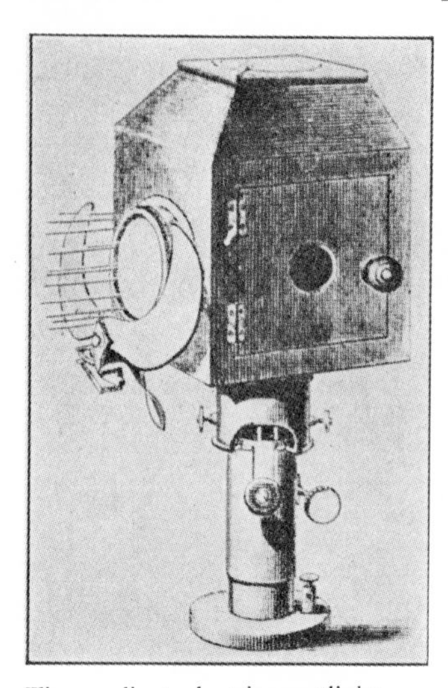

The earliest electric spotlight: a carbon arc spotlight developed at the Paris Opéra in 1860, with enclosed arc mechanism and with focussing, aiming, and shutter adjustments.

Arc lights, like limelights, had the disadvantage of requiring the constant attention of an operator. Unlike gas, they were not susceptible to dimming control; they were noisy in operation; and they produced light that flickered somewhat and that had a rather harsh and unpleasant quality. Later improvements in electric arcs, particularly the more recent ones, such as the flaming arc and the high-intensity arc, have caused arc lights still to be retained, to a limited extent, on the stage. Nevertheless, they have been replaced almost entirely by the concentrated filament incandescent lamp, and are used only when an exceptionally powerful light source is needed, and for long "throws", as for balcony spotlighting in very large theatres. Because of the disadvantages listed above, the arc light was never used exclusively for stage lighting; it was used only as a supplement to gaslight, for helping to achieve special effects. The quality of its light prevented it from immediately supplanting the limelight, which retained its popularity to a very late date.

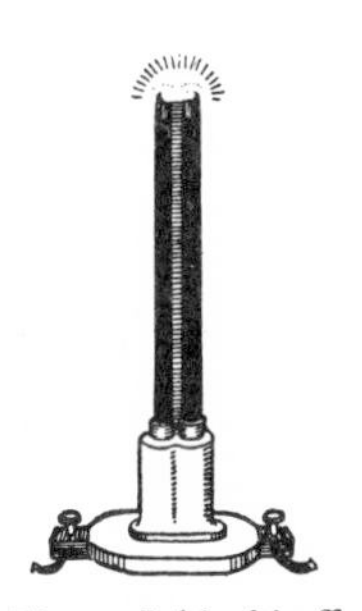

The Jablochkoff candle, an early practical adaptation of the carbon electric arc.

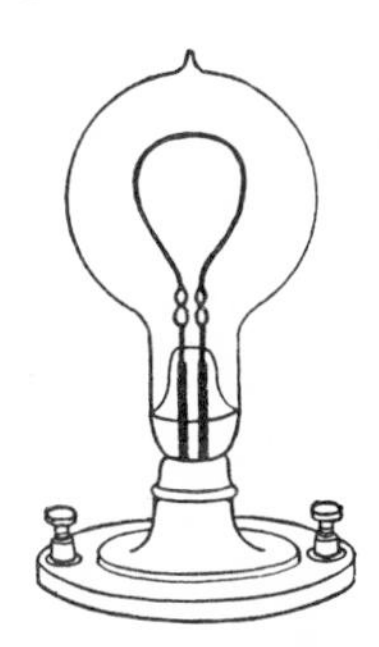

One of Edison's early incandescent electric lamps which inaugurated the latest era of lighting.

In 1876 the Jablochkoff candle made its appearance. This was an arc lamp which consisted of two parallel vertical carbon rods separated by an insulating compound that was vaporized by the heat of the arc and which thus maintained constant the distance between the carbons and permitted continuous burning of the arc without the attention of an operator. In 1879 the Bellecour Theatre at Lyons was equipped with these lamps. But the career of the Jablochkoff candles in the service of the theatre was short-lived, indeed, for in the same year Thomas Edison perfected the first practicable electric incandescent lamp — fundamentally the same type of light source that is in almost universal use to-day.

Edison's invention of the incandescent electric lamp half a century ago ushered in the latest era of stage lighting. Before Sir Humphry Davy had perfected his first electric arc, he had demonstrated the incandescence that resulted when an electric current of sufficient intensity was conducted through a thin strip of platinum. Numerous investigators following Davy attempted to work out a practical application of this phenomenon of electric incandescence, but it remained for Edison in 1879 to achieve a successful device. Instead of platinum he used, for a filament, charred strips of paper, and, later, charred bamboo fibers; instead of heating the filament to incandescence (by means of the electric current flowing through it) in the open air, he enclosed it in a glass bulb from which the air was withdrawn. Thus the first incandescent lamp was a vacuum, carbon lamp. It consumed about 100 watts of electrical energy,

The stage at the Munich Electrotechnical Exposition in 1882: one of the earliest stage-lighting installations employing the then newly-invented incandescent lamp.

and emitted, initially, about 16 candlepower (the average in a horizontal plane) of light, or in units used to-day, about 155 lumens. Thus it provided about 1.55 lumens of light for every watt of electric current that it consumed. Compared with present-day incandescent lamps, many of which have an "efficiency" of over 20 lumens per watt, the early incandescent lamps were not only rather dim, but were expensive to operate.

But even so, the advantages of the incandescent lamp over all previous illuminants were manifest, and one of its earliest uses was in the theatre and on the stage. So quickly was it adopted for stage-lighting purposes that, from existing records, which are frequently contradictory, it is almost impossible to state with certainty which theatre was the first to install a complete system of electric lighting. It is certain, however, that the progressive management of the Paris Opéra caused the new system to be introduced there in 1880 — within a year of its invention in America. In England, the Savoy Theatre in 1881 was the first to install the new lights; in Austria, the Brunn Theatre, in 1882; in New York, the People's Theatre; in Chicago, the Halsted Street Academy of Music; in

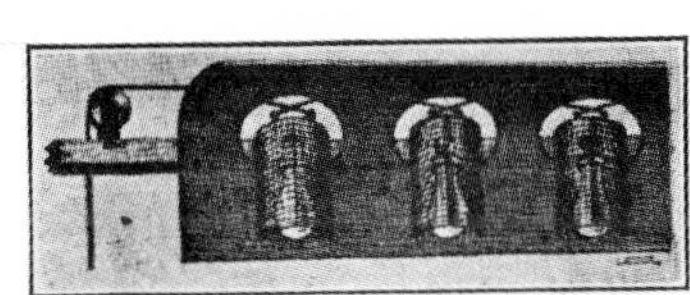

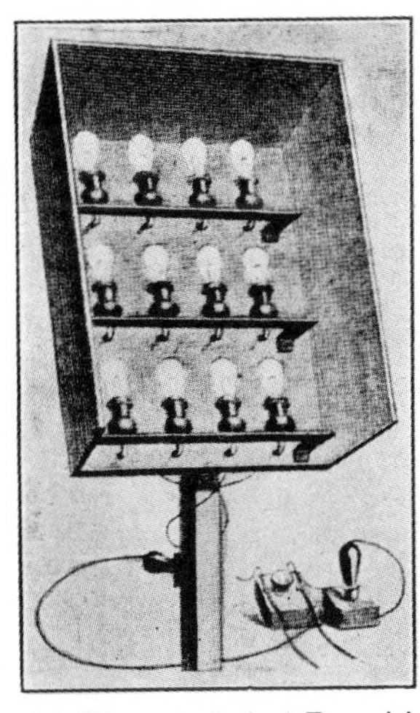

Some units of the stage-lighting equipment used at the Munich Electrotechnical Exposition: footlights, borderlights, and vertical striplights with mechanically-operated color screens, and a bunchlight.

Boston, the Bijou Theatre; and in San Francisco, the Baldwin Theatre. At the Electrotechnical Exposition at Munich in 1882 there was erected a small theatre which employed electric lighting exclusively. This experiment, conducted under scientific auspices, was eminently successful, and attracted world-wide attention. It was undoubtedly a large factor in hastening the adoption of incandescent lamps for theatre and stage-lighting purposes.

The advent of the twentieth century saw incandescent lamps in almost universal use for stage lighting. Theatres were equipped and touring companies often carried their own complete equipment. Carbon incandescent lamps were virtually the same as they were twenty years before, except for certain mechanical improvements. They were used in the footlights, in the borderlights, in striplights, and, in groups of ten or twelve, they were used as "bunchlights" or "floods." For spotlighting, however, their use was limited, since they could not be made powerful enough or concentrated enough for focussing work with lenses. For spotlighting, the limelight and the arc light were still in general use.

In 1905 there was introduced the first of a series of improvements in incandescent lamps that have eventually resulted in their displacing on the stage, to a large extent the electric arc and, almost completely, the limelight. The first improvement was the metallized carbon filament, which provided a brighter light and which was more durable, mechanically, than its predecessor, the untreated carbon filament. A year later, lamps with metallic filaments—of tantalum—made their first appearance in America. In 1907, tungsten in pressed form was used for filaments. These metallic filaments provided light of a much higher intensity than did the carbon filaments. They could also be made in larger sizes. Pressed tungsten filament lamps were made in sizes up to 500 watts. These larger sizes found immediate use on the stage. A powerful, concentrated filament for spotlighting purposes, however, had not yet been obtained. Soon a process of making ductile the brittle tungsten, and of drawing it out in fine wire form, was discovered. This made possible not only a more efficient and rugged lamp, but also the coiled concentrated filament that stage workers had been waiting for. Drawn-tungsten filament lamps appeared in 1911. These tungsten lamps, like the carbon lamps, operated in a vacuum. Soon it was discovered that if the filament operated in an inert gas, such as nitrogen or argon, lamps of higher efficiency and of larger size could be made. Such lamps, in 750 and 1000-watt sizes, first appeared in 1913 and were at once employed on the stage, especially in "olivettes", which then began to replace the bunchlights, and later, concentrated filaments, in incandescent spotlights, which then began to replace the arc spotlights. To-day, most of the incandescent lamps used for stage lighting are gas-filled, with drawn-tungsten filaments.

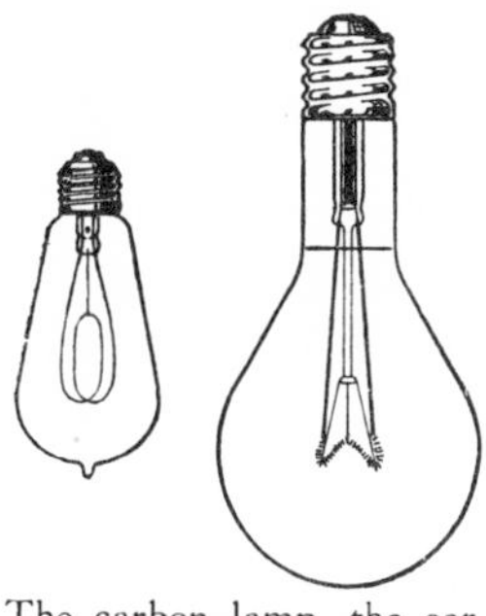

The carbon lamp, the earliest type of incandescent lamp in general use; and the latest type of high-efficiency gas-filled tungsten incandescent lamps.

The major advantages of incandescent lamps that have caused their universal adoption on the stage are the low cost of the light they produce, their cleanliness and comparative lack of heat, the small amount of attention and maintenance they require, the absence of any great fire hazard connected with their use, the higher intensities of illumination they make possible, and, perhaps most important of all, from the standpoint of the stage worker, the high degree of control to which they are so conveniently and readily susceptible. Electric wiring is not nearly so cumbersome as was gas piping and rubber tubing. Hence, though gas lighting lent itself to a fair degree of control, electric lighting offered even greater possibilities principally by means of the dimmer — the device that has contributed so largely to the flexible control of electric lighting on the stage.

Dimmer control equipment used at the Munich Electrotechnical Exposition.

The first dimmers used were the water-barrel resistances, which were used to regulate the amount of current flowing to the incandescent lamps, and hence also their brightness or intensity. Although these water-barrel dimmers were bulky, inconvenient, and in many ways unsatisfactory, and were soon superseded by the coiled-wire dimmers, they are still used to an appreciable extent in theatres in England. The coiled-wire dimmers were more satisfactory than the water-barrel dimmers, but they too were bulky. Their place was later taken by the embedded plate dimmer, which in greatly improved form is standard theatre equipment to-day. The more elaborate reactance type of dimmer is also used in certain installations.

But the most artistic results in stage lighting are not necessarily the result of the most elaborate and modern equipment. The artistry of Henry Irving's work with gas lighting has already been mentioned. Irving might truly be called a pioneer in the art of stage lighting. He was the first to use transparent lacquers (to-day called "colored lamp dips") for color effects; he was the first to break up the footlights into several circuits; and he was the first producer to make organized light rehearsals a regular part of his production activities.

Two pioneers of what is usually termed the "new stagecraft" — Adolphe Appia, a Swiss, and Gordon Craig, an Englishman — were among the first to direct attention to the value and immense possibilities of stage lighting outside its usual functions, which were, principally, to help achieve visibility and realism. Although Appia is essentially a theorist, his influence on stage design has been profound. He has emphasized particularly the plasmic powers of directional light — its sculptural qualities, and has pointed out that darkness and shade are equally as important as light in building up the stage scene. His sound advice has done much to counteract, with the new, powerful illuminants, the popular tendency to over-light the stage with a brilliant glare of light that was not only in-artistic, but was also destructive of all realism. Craig's activities have been directed against the elaborate "staginess" of the theatre. He believes that simplicity and dignity in stage design are essential to proper dramatic effect, and that much depends upon the proper manipulation of light on the stage. The work of both these men has proved very effective, and their ideas are being carried out by the most prominent and active stage designers of the present day.

Soon after 1900, Mariano Fortuny began in Germany an extensive series of investigations and experiments that led to the development of the lighting system that bears his name — the "Fortuny system." Fortuny used high-powered electric arc spotlights. The light from these he projected, not directly upon the stage, but upon colored silk fabrics which, in turn, redirected the light upon the stage. This produced a diffused light of excellent quality whose color could be changed by mechanically varying the areas of colored silk from which the light was reflected. Fortuny devised this indirect system of lighting principally in an attempt faithfully to simulate natural lighting. This simulation of natural lighting he achieved with more than an ordinary degree of success. His system produced truly remarkable results that attracted world-wide attention. But certain inherent disadvantages caused it to be discarded. It was excessively wasteful of electric current; its expensive silk color media faded rapidly and required continual replacement; it required special theatre construction; and it was a bit too intricate, mechanically. In spite of much enthusiastic discussion to the contrary, the "Fortuny system" does not now exist, in fact, never did exist, as a practicality. Nevertheless, in the course of his experiments to reproduce natural atmospheric lighting effects, Fortuny had evolved what the new stagecraft was soon to find indispensable — the cyclorama. Fortuny's original cyclorama, which was dome-shaped and extended partly over the stage (it was virtually a quarter-sphere), occupied much stage space. For this reason it exists in most American theatres only in modified forms. The fundamental principle, however, is the same.

In America, David Belasco has established the reputation of being one of the foremost stage lighting artists. He comprehends perhaps more than any other producer the value of stage lighting in strict coördination with the other elements of play production. For this reason he has always been very painstaking with the lighting of his productions. Weeks are sometimes spent by him in tedious and expensive — but result-producing — light rehearsals. Belasco has established a lighting laboratory (the only one of its kind) in which is planned the lighting of his productions, and in which new developments in stage lighting are constantly being experimented with and perfected, primarily, of course, for Belasco's benefit, but gratuitously available to all who care to use them. Belasco shares his enviable reputation with his chief lighting assistant, Louis Hartmann, who has worked out all his lighting for more than a quarter of a century, and whose experience in stage lighting began many years before he became associated with Belasco. Some of the first incandescent spotlights were developed by Hartmann in Belasco's laboratory, as were also the more recent bowed-silver reflector discs.

Munroe R. Pevear is another outstanding figure in the field of American stage-lighting activity. His investigations in color (1911) have proved especially valuable. These have made possible the manufacture of color media of unusually high spectral purity. He was one of the first to advocate the application of color synthesis to commercial use and stage lighting — the employment of the light primary colors (red, green, and blue), in combination with clear tinting, to obtain any possible color of light. His application of scientific optical principles to special problems in stage lighting has resulted in the development of stage-lighting equipment that is truly unique in general effectiveness, optical efficiency, and mechanical construction combined with convenience of operation. The "soft-edge" spotlight, a footlight unit for indirect as well as direct illumination, the tormentor and teaser lens units, and the special close-operating color-mixing cyclorama lighting units are several of Pevear's comparatively recent developments.

Others who have contributed notable advances to the art and science of stage lighting are J. Monroe Hewlett and Bassett Jones, who together worked out the dioramic use of gauze for special effects (Jones also has designed much special equipment); and Lee Simonson and Claude Bragdon and Robert Edmond Jones and Norman Bel Geddes, who, as stage designers, have made full and effective and intelligent use of light in their productions and have been active in demonstrating its possibilities. And in Europe, besides Craig, Appia, and Fortuny, there are Basil Dean, Max Reinhardt, Adolphe Linnebach, Max Haseit, who are all acknowledged leaders in the field of stagecraft. And not the least important in the general scheme of stage-lighting activities are the several manufacturers of stage lighting and control equipment, whose contributions to the advance of stage lighting are prompted not only by a desire to further theatre art, but also by the keen spur of business competition.

Such, then, in general, is the "history" of stage lighting, "from ancient Greece to contemporary Broadway", here presented, as is evident, in a very short and very scrappy version. What the future holds in store can only be a matter of conjecture, but it is reasonably safe to believe that a new and still better illuminant, most likely being now developed, will soon make its appearance, perhaps even within the next decade, and that the same progressive type of stage workers which has established stage lighting in its present important position in dramatic production will continue to perfect it, in all its phases, with at least equal energy and skill in the future.

CHAPTER III · ELECTRICITY

Units – volts, amperes, watts, ohms; definitions – circuit, Ohm's Law, types of current, three-wire system, series and parallel, fuse; wiring practice – National Electrical Code, subdivision of circuits; wiring devices – wires and cables, wiring, sockets, switches, stage pockets and plugs, cable connectors.

IN order to operate stage-lighting equipment at the maximum degree of usefulness, efficiency, and safety, it is essential that the operator be familiar with the few easily acquired fundamentals of electricity and of standard electrical practice. The possibilities of the most complete and expensive equipment cannot be fully realized if those in charge of it are ignorant of the behavior of electricity and of the methods of distributing and controlling it. On the other hand, such knowledge will enable one, in many cases, to achieve effective results with but a few pieces of comparatively inexpensive, simple, or even crude apparatus.

I. UNITS

The simple units by which electricity is measured are perhaps most easily defined with the help of the familiar analogy of the water-supply system.

Volts are a measure of the voltage, or "potential difference", of an electrical circuit. Voltage is the pressure, or force, that causes the electric current to flow through a circuit (see page 55), that is, through the wiring and apparatus. Voltage is analogous to the pressure that causes the flow of water through a pipe. The voltage of electricity which is supplied by a "central station" — the electric company — for lighting purposes usually ranges between 110 and 120. For convenience in reference, voltages of this range are grouped and are designated as 110 volts. The voltage supplied by a storage battery, such as the type used in motor cars and for radio "A" batteries, is much lower and usually ranges from 6 to 8. The voltage of a dry battery is still lower, approximating $1\frac{1}{2}$. These are cited in order to afford a comparative idea of the voltages ordinarily dealt with.

Amperes are a measure of the amperage, or "current", of an electrical circuit. Amperage is analogous to the "rate of flow" of water through a pipe, which is usually measured in cubic feet per minute. The amperage of an electrical circuit depends altogether upon what apparatus constitutes the circuit. Thus, amperage will increase as the number of lights on any one circuit is increased. The more apparatus on a circuit, the greater the amount of current necessary to supply it.

Watts (the measure of the "rate of flow of electrical energy") are the numerical product of the voltage and amperage of a circuit, that is, the result obtained by multiplying volts by amperes. Thus a 10-ampere fuse, designed to "blow" on a 110-volt circuit when a current of 10 amperes is reached, will "blow" when the wattage on that circuit reaches 110 × 10 or 1100 watts. Conversely, a large 1000-watt lamp, such as is used in an olivette, or floodlight, on the stage, when operated on a 110-volt circuit will require 1000 ÷ 110, or 9.1 amperes of current. A 150-watt lamp such as might be used in the footlights and borderlights would require 150 ÷ 110, or 1.4 amperes.

The *kilowatt* consists of a thousand watts. The *kilowatt hour* is the product of kilowatts and the hours they were used, and is the unit employed for measuring the actual amount of energy consumed by an electrical installation. As indicated directly on an electric meter, the number of kilowatt hours constitutes the basis for payment by the consumer, the usual rate ranging from five to ten cents per kilowatt hour.

Ohms are a measure of electrical resistance. All substances offer some resistance to electric current. Those with very low, almost negligible resistances, such as copper, iron, silver, and carbon, are called *conductors*. Those with very high resistances, such as rubber, porcelain, fiber, and cloth, are called *insulators*. Thus electric current is *conducted* through copper wires and *insulated* from surrounding conducting objects with a layer of rubber and cloth. The greater the diameter of a wire (and hence the greater its cross-sectional area), the less its resistance. Resistance also has its analogy in the water system. It is obvious that a thin pipe with a small hole running through it will offer greater resistance to the flow of water than will a thick pipe with a larger hole.

Metallic conductors such as iron wire and German silver wire can provide an appreciable resistance; that is, if the wire is thin enough and if a sufficient length of it is used. The operation of stage-lighting dimmers is based upon this principle. By means of the dimmer mechanism, short lengths of fine, so-called resistance wire are gradually introduced into a circuit. Each additional length increases the total resistance and hence decreases the current (amperage) supplied to the lighting equipment in that circuit. This gradual decrease of current causes the gradual dimming of the lights until, when sufficient resistance has been introduced into the circuit, no light at all is emitted. The water supply analogy to the dimmer is obviously the tap, or faucet, or valve, which can be so adjusted as to regulate the rate of flow of water through it.

II. Definitions

A *circuit* is the complete path of an electric current. It is formed by a series of two or more electrical devices, including a source of electric current such as the main feed wires brought into a building by the electric light company, so connected as to form a "closed loop" through which the current can flow. The simplest circuit would be a piece of copper wire joining the terminals of a dry battery. No benefit, however, would be derived from such a circuit. In order to utilize electric current it must be conducted through some device which will transform the electrical energy to the particular form of energy desired, be it power, heat, or light. Incandescent electric lamps are the most common medium of transformation used to obtain light by means of electricity. Carbon arc lamps are also used to a limited extent. The operation of both incandescent lamps and arc lamps is discussed in detail in the next chapter.

Ohm's Law expresses the definite and exact relationship that exists, in any circuit, between the three electrical units. This relationship is useful in laying out wiring systems, and is particularly useful in connection with the design of dimmers, which is discussed in Chapter VIII. Letting C represent the current in *amperes*, E the pressure in *volts*, and R the resistance in *ohms*, this relationship may be simply expressed as follows:

$$C = E \div R$$

By means of algebraic transformation, it is possible to evaluate any one member of the equation in terms of the two other members. Thus

$$E = C \times R \quad \text{and} \quad R = E \div C$$

As an example, suppose it is desired to compute the resistance of the lamp load of the blue footlight circuit on a small stage, in order to select the proper size of wire for a dimmer for this circuit. If there are eight 150-watt lamps on this circuit, the total wattage is 1200. The voltage is 110, hence, as explained above, the current used by these lamps equals 1200 ÷ 110, or 10.9 amperes. Having the voltage and the amperage, and using Ohm's Law ($R = E \div C$), the resistance of the lamp equals 110 ÷ 10.9, or 10 ohms. The resistance of the lamp load being known, the size and length of wire necessary for the dimmer may be easily determined. This is discussed in Chapter VIII.

Types of Current. There are two forms of electricity supplied by the lighting companies throughout the country. The first form, the use of which is virtually restricted, by economic considerations, to very large cities, where the consumers are closely grouped, is known as *direct current*, or "D.C." Electricity is a form of flowing energy constantly in circulation, hence two wires are always necessary for any system or piece of equipment — one wire to conduct the *positive* current *to* the equipment, and the other to conduct the *negative* current *away* from the equipment. Direct current flows continuously in a constant direction, one wire being always positive, the other wire being always negative. Current supplied by storage batteries and dry batteries is also D.C. The second form of electricity, which constitutes by far the major portion of that supplied, is known as *alternating current*, or "A.C." Alternating current is intermittent, flowing first in one direction, and then reversing to flow in the opposite direction. Since this reversal of direction takes place so quickly and so often (usually sixty times each second) the flow is virtually continuous. However, neither of the two wires can be termed positive or negative (except for a very brief space of time), because of the continual reversal of direction.

Lamps and dimmers used for stage lighting operate with equal efficiency on either A.C. or D.C. circuits, a limited belief to the contrary notwithstanding. However, arc spotlights and any other equipment employing the carbon arc will work about twice as well on D.C. as they will on A.C. Transformers (devices which raise and lower voltage used to supply small current for signal buzzers, dressing-room call bells, and very small lights on the stage) will operate *only* on A.C. and will be damaged if subjected to D.C.

The "*three-wire system*" combines two circuits, which ordinarily would require four wires, and is used for electric-supply mains because of the consequent economy of copper wire. In the three-wire system, the positive side of the first circuit and the negative side of the second circuit are combined in one wire which is common to both circuits and which is called the "neutral" or "inside" wire. The negative side of the first circuit and the positive side of the second circuit are conducted in the "outside negative" wire and the "outside positive" wire, respectively. The voltage "across" the two outside wires is 220, and across from the neutral wire to each of the outside wires is 110 in each case. This is the form in which the supply main, or "service", is brought inside virtually all but the smallest of buildings. For very large lighting installations, the electric service is often in the form of a high-voltage multi-phase circuit, which requires the use of large transformers before the current can be used for lighting purposes. The following diagram shows the arrangement of a simple three-wire D.C. system, and the method of "tapping off" the regular two-wire "branch circuits"

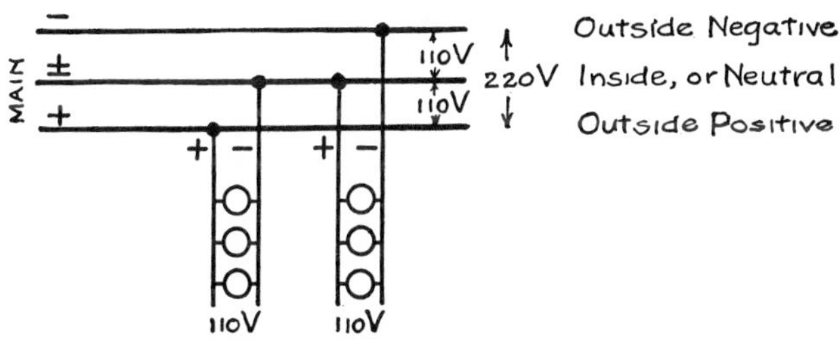

Schematic diagram illustrating the three-wire system of electrical circuits with two-wire branch circuits tapped off each side of a three-wire circuit.

for lighting purposes. This diagram applies also to A.C., except that the polarities of the outside wires and of the branch circuit wires are alternately changing because of the continual reversal of current direction. Nevertheless, at some one instant the polarities would be as indicated.

"Series" and "Parallel." A circuit was defined as the complete path of an electric current. This "complete path", or "closed loop", may be achieved by two fundamental methods of connecting apparatus — either "in series", or "in parallel."

When apparatus is connected in series, the *current* or *amperage* supplied to each piece of apparatus is the same, the voltage varying. When apparatus is connected in parallel, the *pressure*, or *voltage*, supplied to each piece of apparatus is the same, the amperage varying. For stage-lighting purposes *lamps* are always connected, or "wired", *in parallel.* A *switch,* which "opens" the circuit, breaks the flow of current, and hence extinguishes the lamps it controls, is always wired *in series* with those lamps. Similarly a dimmer, which inserts resistance in a circuit, regulates the flow of current — and hence the brightness of the lamps it controls — is also always wired *in series* with those lamps.

The terms "in series" and "in parallel" will be more easily understood with the help of the following diagram, which uses conventional symbols. The source of electricity is always assumed to be the "main", consisting of the heavy wires brought inside the building by the electric light company and connected to their street-distribution system, which is either overhead, on poles, or in conduits underground.

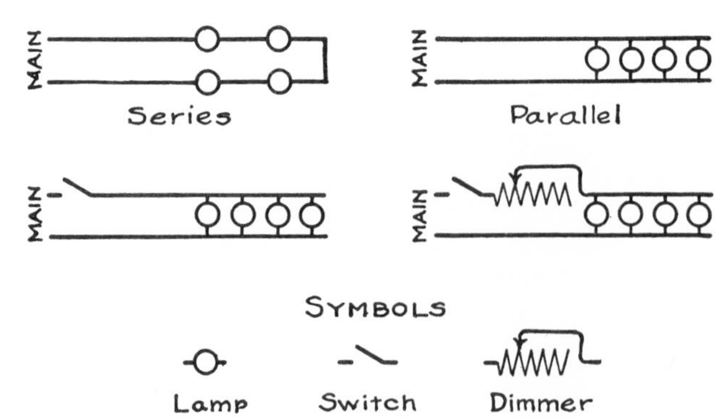

Illustrating series wiring; parallel wiring; a parallel lamp circuit with a switch in series; and a parallel lamp circuit with a switch and dimmer in series, such as comprises the usual stage lighting circuit.

A *fuse* is a protective device, connected in series on each wire, or "side", of an electrical circuit, which "blows", and opens the circuit if for any reason the current flowing through the wires of that circuit becomes too great or too "heavy" for the wires to withstand with safety. A fuse is merely a wire made of lead and other metals having a low melting point, mounted, for convenience in handling,

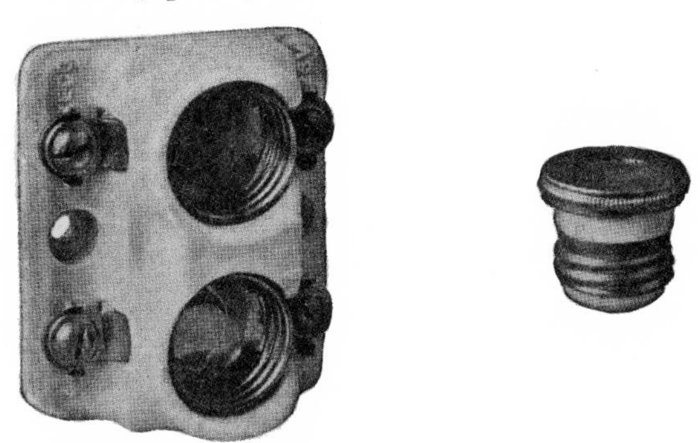

Plug fuse and two-wire cut-out (half size).

in *plug* or *cartridge* form. The size and composition of this wire are so designed as to permit the wire to be melted, or "blown", by the heat generated by the excess current which the fuse guards against. When the fuse blows, it acts as a switch and automatically opens the circuit, thereby disconnecting that condition (a "short circuit", a "ground", a faulty piece of equipment, too great a total wattage, or too heavy a "load", of incandescent lamps) which gave rise to the excess current. Thus a fuse acts as a valuable safeguard against dangerous conditions that might result in fire or in destruction of equipment if they were not immediately suppressed.

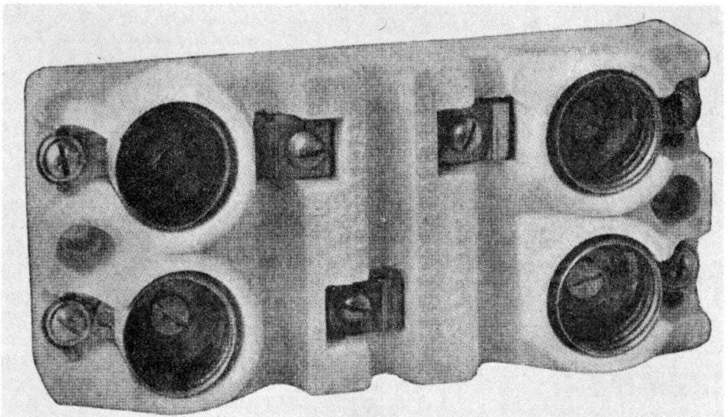

Double-branch plug fuse cut-out for three-wire mains (half size).

Although a fuse is placed on each side of a regular two-wire circuit, the neutral of a three-wire system must never be "fused", because, should the fuse blow on a neutral, a 220-volt current might possibly flow through equipment designed for only 110 volts and damage or destroy it. The following diagram shows just how this would take place.

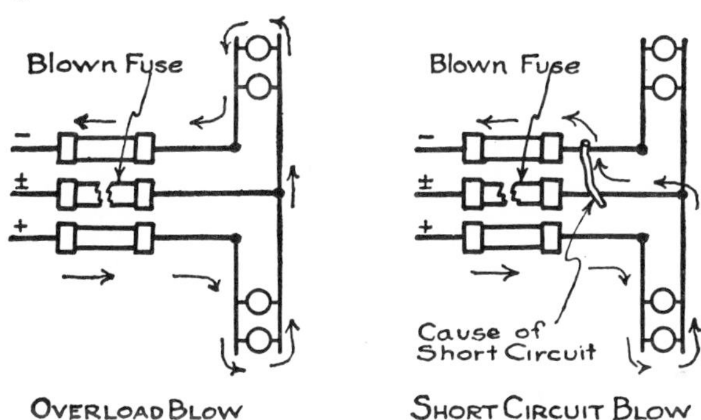

Illustrating reasons why a fuse should never be placed in the neutral wire of a three-wire circuit.

Fuses come in many sizes and are rated in amperes, according to the maximum current they will allow to flow before blowing. A 10-ampere fuse, for instance, will protect a circuit from a current greater than 10 amperes, and will blow when the excess current is reached. As mentioned above, fuses come in two forms, *plug* and *cartridge*. As illustrated, a plug fuse is similar to the base of an incandescent lamp, screwing into its holder, a "plug fuse cut-out." Plug fuses come in the smaller amperage ratings, namely 6, 10, 12, 15, 20, 25, and 30, and all have the same physical dimensions, the wire contained within the fuse alone being different. Plug fuses are provided with a transparent mica cover, through which the fuse wire may be viewed in order to see whether it is intact (and good) or melted (and blown). A cartridge fuse is cylindrical in shape, the fuse wire being surrounded by powdered chalk within a fiber tube which is capped at both ends by the "contacts." As shown in the illustrations, these contacts, by means of which the fuse is held

Cartridge fuse (with ferrule contacts) and cut-out (half size).

securely in place by spring clips on its holder, a "cartridge fuse cut-out", are either of the "ferrule" type, or of the "knife-blade" type. Cartridge fuses with ferrule contacts come in ratings up to 60 amperes, in 5-ampere steps; those with knife-blade contacts come in ratings from 65 to 600 amperes.

A *short circuit*, which is the most dangerous condition that a fuse guards against, is the (usually accidental) connection, by a conductor of very low resistance, of the two sides of an electric circuit. An electric current, like every other natural force, will take the path of least resistance, and the abnormally heavy current that results (since $C = E \div R$, the less the resistance, the greater the current) would burn out the wires of the circuit, unless the circuit were immediately opened by the blowing of one of its protecting fuses. A short circuit is usually caused either by the direct contact of bare (uninsulated) portions of the two wires, or by a loose screw or other metallic component of a socket, switch, plug, cable connector, or other wiring device. A *ground* is a short circuit which is usually caused by each of the two sides of a circuit coming in contact with some metallic object, such as the iron conduit containing the wires, or the sheet-iron trough of the footlights or borderlights, which will act as a conductor of low resistance, even though the actual points of contact are remotely apart.

Should a fuse (of the correct size) blow, the circuit affected should first be opened by its controlling switch. The total lamp load on the circuit should be computed, and if the amperage is *higher* than the fuse rating, this condition should be corrected by placing some of the lamps on another circuit, or by using fewer lamps. If the amperage is lower than the fuse rating, then a short circuit or a ground exists, and the most accessible parts of the circuit — the wires, wiring devices, and equipment — should be carefully inspected and the cause of the trouble located and removed. If, after several attempts, the trouble persists, the services of an expert electrician should be employed.

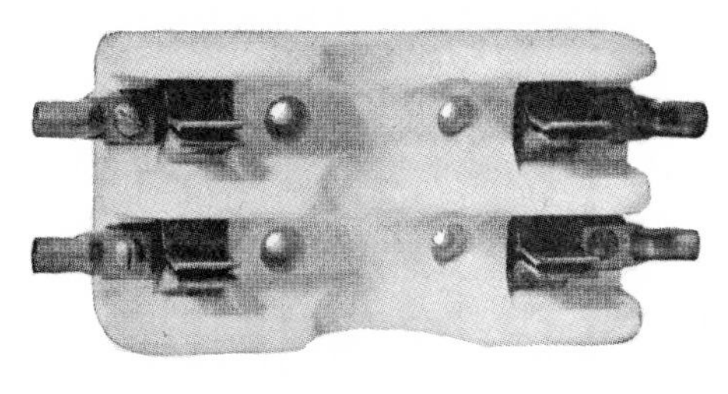

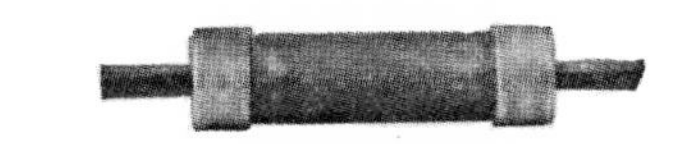

Cartridge fuse (with knife-blade contacts) and cut-out (quarter size).

III. Wiring Practice

The *National Electrical Code* (hereinafter abbreviated to Code) is a set of regulations governing the installation and use of electric systems, drawn up by the National Board of Fire Underwriters. It must be strictly complied with if any building in which an electrical system is installed is to be insured against loss by fire. That this is particularly important in the case of theatre and stage lighting is evidenced by the fact that a special section of the Code applies to this subject with somewhat stricter and more specific rules. In the many cities and towns which have adopted the Code, and have written it into their laws and ordinances, it must be observed, regardless of whether the building is insured or not. *It is of utmost importance, then, that the Code be carefully observed* by all organizations, whether large or small, that own, control, or operate theatres and stages. If a disastrous fire occurs as a result of any Code violation (and electrical fires sometimes have a way of starting that mystify even the most experienced), it will be impossible to collect a cent of insurance. And, in municipalities that have legalized the Code, the organization will also be guilty of a misdemeanor, and even of criminal negligence should personal injury or loss of life result. Copies of the latest edition of the National Electrical Code are

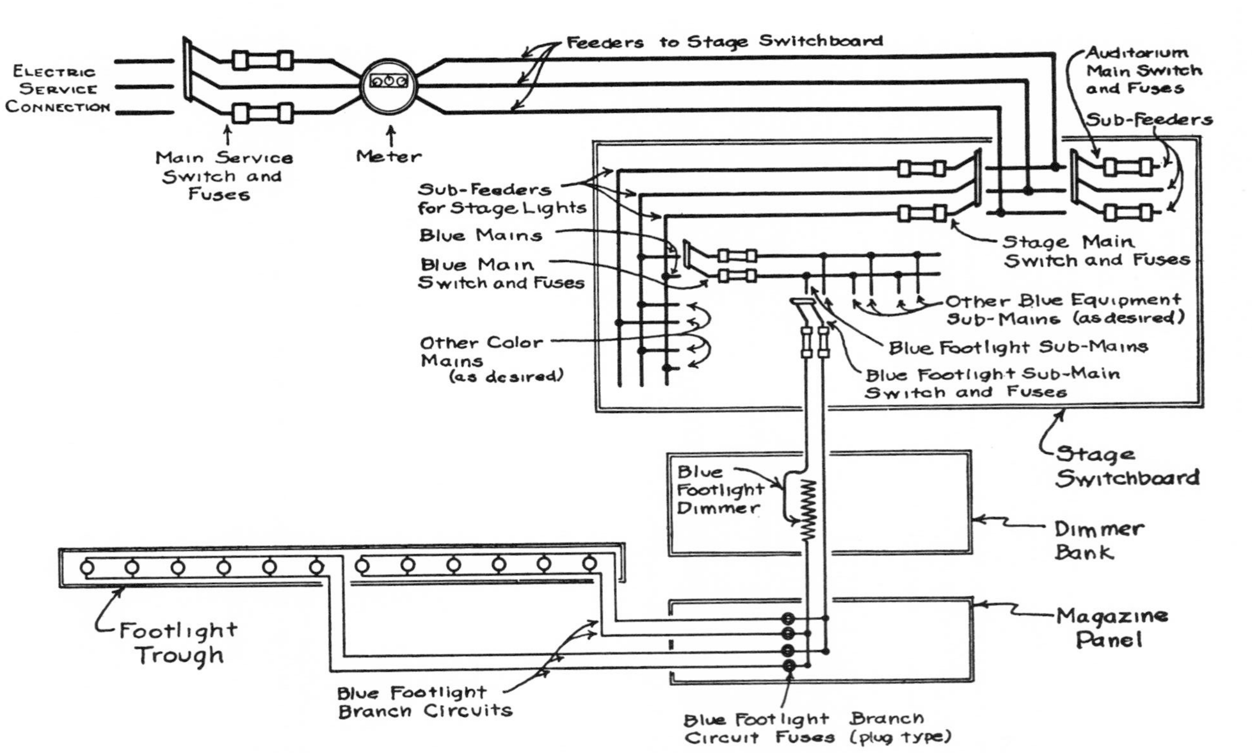

Schematic diagram illustrating the conventional subdivision of circuits as applied to wiring for stage lighting.

always obtainable, free of charge, upon application to the National Board of Fire Underwriters. Thus there is no excuse for any interested organization or individual not being familiar with these regulations, the compliance with which, apart from its more serious aspects, promotes greater efficiency and greater convenience.

Subdivision of Circuits. In a complete wiring installation, all circuits are not so simple as those pictured at the top of page 58. Because of the selective individual control necessary for stage-lighting equipment, the "main" circuit, usually a three-wire supply, must be divided and subdivided several times until the desired refinement and flexibility of control is achieved. This is further complicated by a Code rule which states that not more than 1320 watts must be placed on a "branch circuit." Thus if the blue footlight "switchboard circuit" on a stage consists of twelve 150-watt lamps, the total wattage is 1800. This is too great a load for a single branch circuit, hence it must be divided in the "magazine panel", after passing through its dimmer in the "dimmer bank", preferably by placing the lamps in the right half of the footlights on one branch circuit and those in the left half on a second branch circuit. This will place 900 watts, a safe load, on each of the branch circuits. Both these branch circuits, however, are controlled by a single blue footlight switch on the stage switchboard, which, together with all the other blue circuits on the stage, is controlled by the blue "color main." All the color mains are in turn controlled by the "stage main" switch on the switchboard. The switchboard should also control all the auditorium circuits.

The diagram on page 62 explains such a distribution system, which should be used, and in most cases is used, in the average small theatre. Of course, it is very incomplete, as it shows only a rudimentary visualization of the fundamental principle, instead of all the components of each successive subdivision. In many present stage-lighting installations, one or several of these steps, or subdivisions, are omitted. It is in these instances that the want of adequate facilities, such as a sufficient number of circuits, arranged for flexible control, is most keenly felt.

In the opposite diagram the source of current is the three-wire *service* supplied by the electric light company. From the meter, a three-wire *feeder* runs to the *stage switchboard*, where it is divided into two *sub-feeders*, — one for the auditorium lights, the other for the stage lights. The latter is subdivided into *color mains*, the number depending upon the color circuits, usually clear (white), amber, red, and blue. The blue color main is subdivided (as is each of the other color mains) into *equipment sub-mains* (the number depending upon the equipment circuits), usually footlights, several borderlights, and several stage pockets. The blue footlight submain is connected in series (as is each of the other equipment submains) with the proper size of *dimmer*, in the *dimmer bank*, and is again subdivided, in the *magazine panel*, into *branch circuits*, to which the incandescent lamps are directly connected in parallel. It will be noted that fuses and dimmers are "dead" when the immediate switches controlling the circuits in which they are connected is open.

The wires of the feeder are the largest in the system, because they must conduct the total load of the installation. As the circuits are divided, smaller wires, in conformity with the lighter loads, can be used. The wires on branch circuits are usually size Number 14. Wherever the size of wire is reduced, fuses of lower rating than the previous fuses are interposed to protect the smaller wire. Branch circuits are never fused higher than 15 amperes.

IV. Wiring Devices

Electric wires are rated according to size (and hence according to the maximum current, in amperes, that they can safely carry) and also according to the character and thickness of the insulation that protects them (and hence according to the particular type of service for which they are designed). Wire sizes are designated by gauge numbers, which have been arbitrarily assigned. The actual thicknesses (of the copper only, not including the insulation), the diameter, and the rated maximum current-carrying capacity of the wires most used for stage lighting installations are as follows:

Cross-sectional Area													
B. & S. Gauge No.	0	1	2	3	4	5	6	8	10	12	14	16	18
Diameter: Inches	0.325	0.290	0.258	0.229	.204	.182	.162	.129	.102	.081	.064	.050	.040
Rated Maximum Capacity: Amperes	125	100	90	80	70	55	50	35	25	20	15	6	3

The cross sections and diameters given above apply only to *solid* rubber-covered wires used for rigid permanent wiring. (Incidentally, the use of wire smaller than Number 14 for permanent wiring is forbidden by the Code.) Flexible wires for connecting portable stage-lighting equipment, such as olivettes, spotlights, and striplights to stage pockets, and for connecting suspended borderlights, are not solid but are composed of many very fine wires, or "strands." The total of these cross-sectional areas is equal to the cross-sectional area of the single solid wire of same gauge number. Such wire has particularly heavy and serviceable insulation and covering, and is especially designed for stage work. This is known by the trade and Code designation of *stage cable.*

Single-braid rubber-covered wire (size 14).

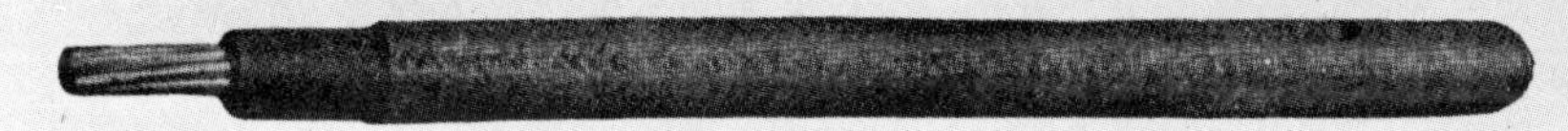

Single-braid rubber-covered wire (size 6).

Two-conductor stage cable (size 14).

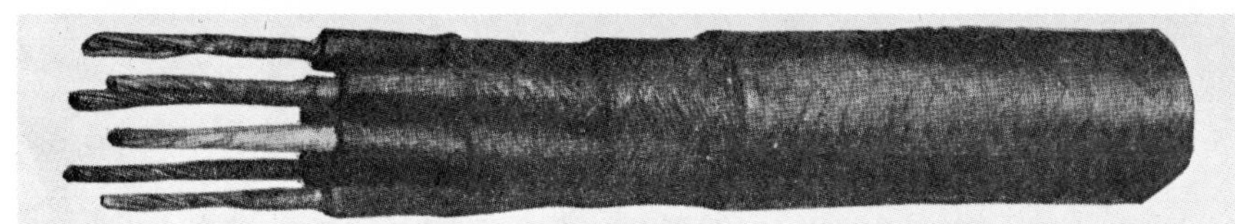

Six-conductor borderlight cable (size 14).

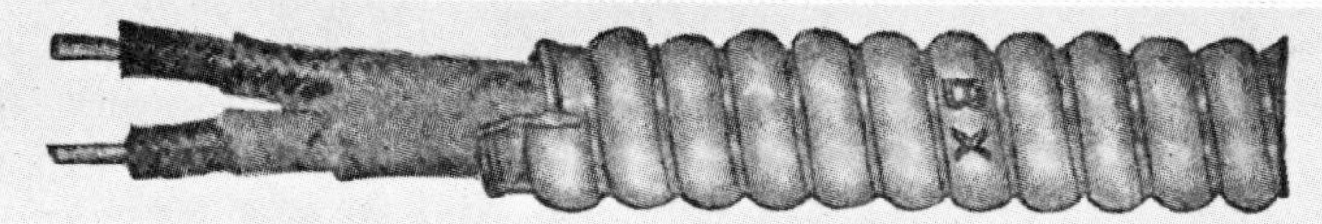

Two-conductor "BX" armored cable (size 14).

A wire, whether solid or flexible, must never be used to conduct a current which is greater than the rated capacity of the wire. To do so is a Code violation, and will cause the wires to become very hot—perhaps hot enough to melt and burn the rubber insulation and start a fire. Wires must always be protected (usually at the switchboard) by fuses whose rated capacity is not greater than the rated capacity of the wire.

Since two wires are necessary to supply any piece of equipment, the term "stage cable" is understood to mean "two-conductor" stage cable; that is, two insulated wires twisted together and again covered, forming a single cable containing two conductors.

Some sizes of stage cable are also available with six and with eight conductors. This is known as *borderlight cable* and is used for connecting 3- and 4-circuit borderlights (the suspended type, which can be raised and lowered, and which requires a flexible connection) with the source of current. "Portable cord", such as is used in the home for connecting table lamps, bridge lamps, vacuum cleaners, and so forth, should not be used on the stage, since the comparatively light

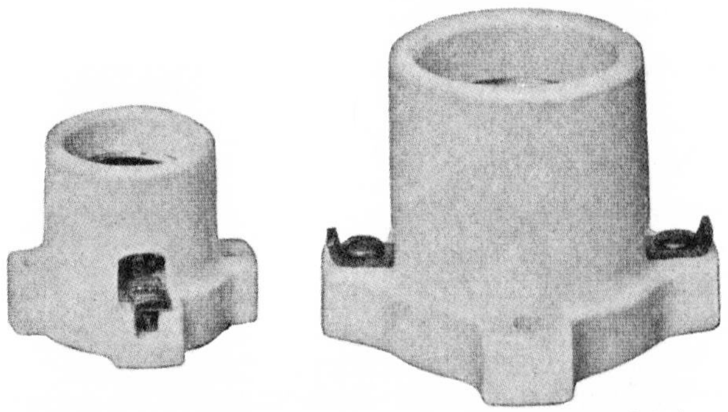

Porcelain cleat sockets: medium and mogul sizes (half size).

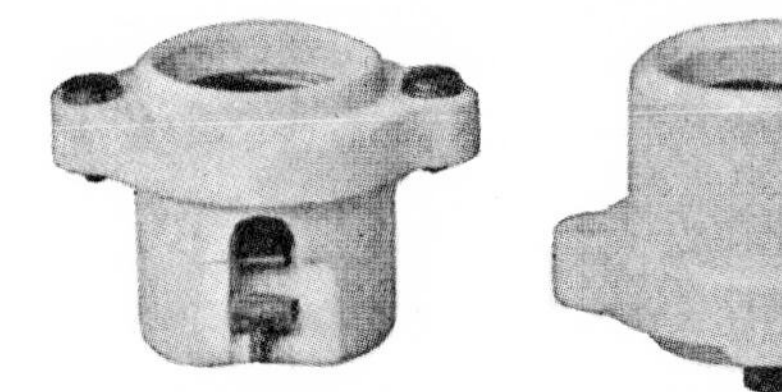

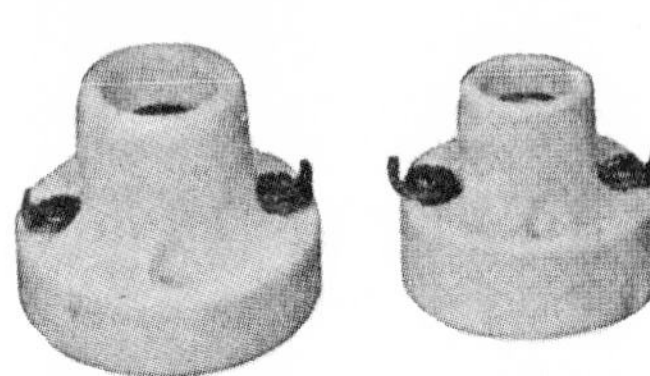

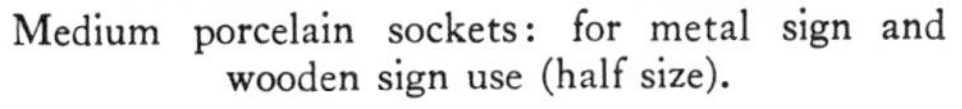

Medium porcelain sockets: for metal sign and wooden sign use (half size).

Porcelain cleat sockets: candelabra and miniature sizes (half size).

TYPES OF SOCKETS.

insulation will not withstand the wear and tear unavoidably entailed by stage use, and will soon be the cause of a short circuit or ground. The Code prohibits the use of wire other than regular stage cable.

Wiring. Permanent stage wiring, which includes all parts of the system except the portable stage cable, should be "run" in rigid electrical conduit (a soft steel pipe specially made for the purpose) of the proper size, with proper accessories, such as pull boxes, couplings, lock nuts, and bushings, in order to afford adequate and permanent protection for the wires. The wires themselves should be of the type known as S.B.R.C. (single braid, rubber covered), or better, and should be of the proper size to carry the circuit load safely, as specified in the table on page 64. Where wire of size Number 12 or 14 must be run (particularly on branch circuits) under conditions where the extreme ruggedness afforded by rigid conduit is not necessary, great economy and convenience can be effected by the use of armored cable (which is generally known among electricians as "BX", although this term is merely the registered trade name of one manufacturer's product) and its appropriate accessories. This consists of two S.B.R.C. solid wires twisted together, covered with an extra layer of insulation and wound about by an interlocking spiral band of soft steel. It is remarkably flexible in the Number 12 and Number 14 sizes, to which its use is virtually restricted, and can therefore be installed much more easily than the rigid conduit.

Single-pole, single-throw. Single-pole, double-throw.

Double-pole, single-throw. Double-pole, double-throw.

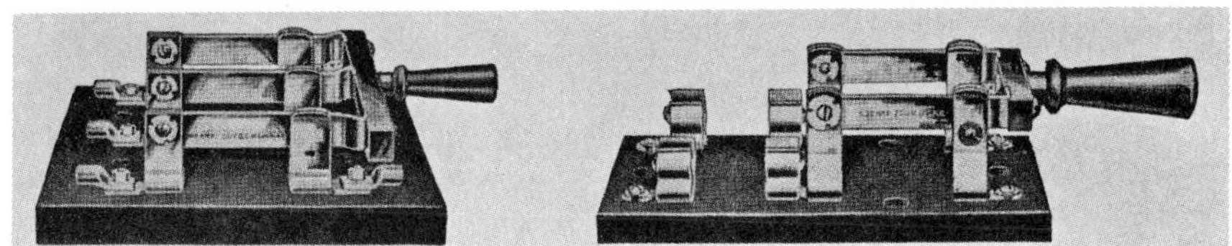

Three-pole, single-throw. Double-pole, single-throw with cartridge ferrule fuse clips.

TYPES OF OPEN KNIFE SWITCHES.

For convenience in making wiring connections, especially with stage cable, "wiring devices" are used, the most common and useful of which are sockets, switches, stage pockets, stage plugs, and cable connectors.

Sockets are universally known as the holders for incandescent lamps. They come in five sizes, according to the lamps they accommodate — the *miniature*, for low-voltage lamps such as those used in flashlights and in Christmas-tree sets; the *candelabra* and *intermediate*, for small, 110-volt lamps of the decorative type; the *medium*, which is by far the most familiar type, for standard lamps up to and including the 200-watt size, such as are used in the footlights, borderlights, striplights, and small spotlights; and the *mogul*, for standard lamps above the 200-watt size, such as are used in olivettes and large spotlights. By means of "terminal screws", the circuit wires are easily fastened to the two sides of the socket, and the current is thus conducted to the lamp screwed in the socket.

A *switch* has been described as a device that is placed in series with a circuit in order to open and close the circuit. In order to disconnect both sides of the circuit, the "knife-blade" type of switch, generally used for stage lighting, is made "double-pole", with two hinged blades. Each blade is on one side of the circuit, and by means of a connecting fiber bar, both blades open and close simultaneously. Thus both sides of the circuit are "dead" when the double-pole switch is open. Three-wire systems are controlled in a similar manner by "three-pole" switches. For convenience, holders for fuses are often mounted on the same base as the controlling switch for the same circuit. Both types of switches are shown in the illustration. Switches are rated according to the maximum capacity, in amperes, that each blade will safely conduct.

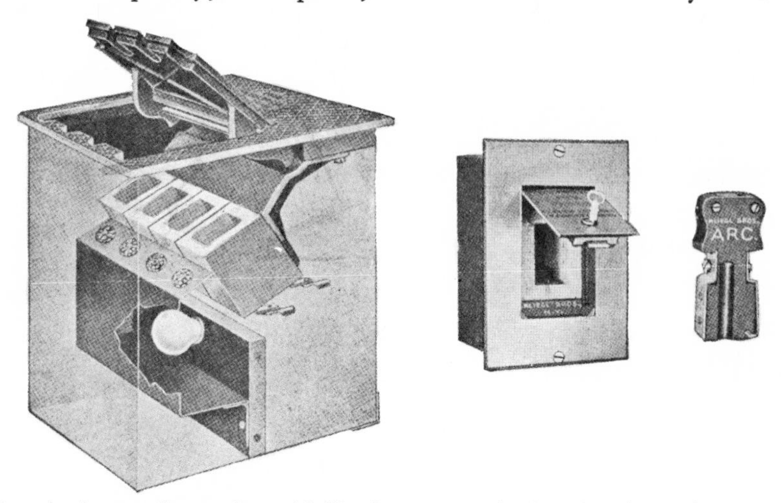

Four-circuit stage floor pocket, with illuminated color-circuit designations; single-circuit stage wall pocket; and stage plug (one-sixth size).

Stage floor pockets are analogous to the "convenience outlets", or "wall plugs", used in the home, being, of necessity, much larger and more heavily constructed in order to carry the greater currents and withstand the rather rough treatment accorded all stage equipment. The circuit wires are fastened by means of terminal screws, and the current is conducted to two flat copper strips on opposite narrow sides of a rectangular porcelain receptacle. From these copper strips the current is transferred to similar spring copper strips on the *stage plug*, the two sets of flat copper strips making contact when the stage plug is inserted in the stage pocket. The stage plug, which is primarily a heavy fiber block, of rectangular cross section (fitting snugly into the porcelain opening in the stage pocket) with copper strips on the narrow sides, is attached to the end of a stage cable, the two conductors being fastened to the strips by terminal screws. Stage pockets and plugs of the same capacity all have the same corresponding physical dimensions, and hence are interchangeable. They are rated according to the maximum loads they can safely carry, these being usually 25, 50, and 100 amperes. Stage floor pockets containing from one to six porcelain plugging receptacles are available. *Plugging boxes* (portable) contain two or more porcelain receptacles, such as are contained in stage pockets, mounted in a heavy wooden box, and may themselves be plugged into stage pockets by means of a length of stage cable to which a stage plug is attached. Thus a plugging box can serve to connect several stage lighting units to a single stage pocket.

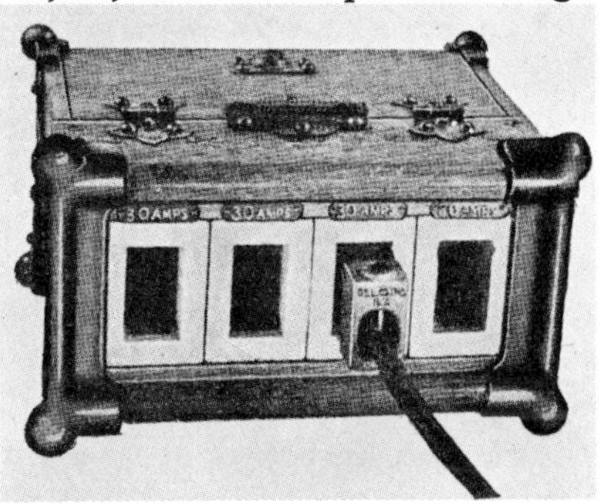

Four-circuit portable plugging box (one-sixth size).

Cable connectors are aptly named, being used for connecting lengths of cable to each other, and also for connecting pieces of portable stage-lighting equipment to lengths of cable. Connectors come in pairs — the *female* connector having two brass-lined cylindrical receptacles into which the two cylindrical brass prongs of the *male* connector fit and make electrical contact between the two conductors of the stage cable to which they are fastened by terminal screws. Cable connectors come in various sizes (non-interchangeable) according to their load ratings, the common sizes being 5, 15, 30, and 60

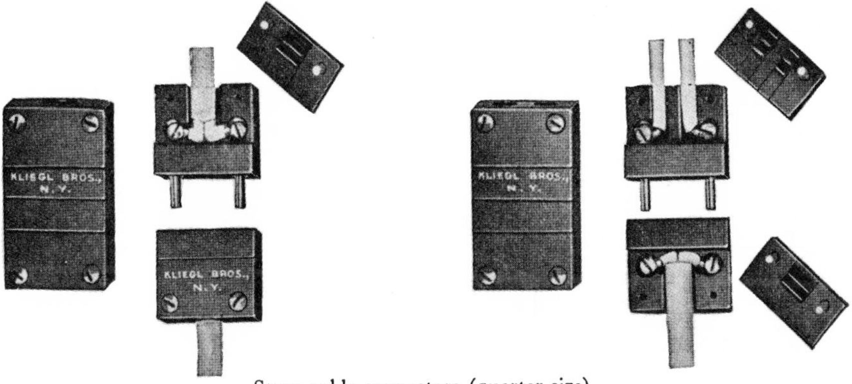

Stage cable connectors (quarter size).

amperes. The rated capacity of a female connector should never exceed the rated capacity of the cable to which it is attached, nor should the rated capacity of a male connector ever be less than that of a female connector attached to the other end of the cable, or less than the total amperage taken by the piece of equipment to which it is attached. Cables will then be protected from overloading by the non-interchangeability of connectors of different ratings.

Every piece of stage-lighting equipment should have a short (two-foot) length of wire to which is attached a male connector. Each length of cable with a stage plug on one end should have a female connector on the other end. Thus a spotlight or an olivette can be supplied with current by inserting the stage plug in the pocket and joining the two cable connectors. Should the single length of cable not be long enough to reach the spotlight or olivette, an additional length of cable (with a male connector on one end and a female connector of the same size on the other end) can be interposed.

Female connectors must always be used on the live ends of stage cable, since the exposed live prongs of a male connector would be dangerous to handle and would cause a short circuit if they rested on a metallic object.

By means of several varieties of multiple-circuit connectors and branch-off connectors, a single circuit can readily be divided into several smaller ones.

CHAPTER IV · LIGHT

Objective light – nature, propagation, illuminants, units, reflection, refraction, reflectors, lenses, light projection; subjective light – colorless visual sensations, light and shade, methods of achieving brightness contrasts, shadows, highlights, visual perception of objects, contribution of subjective light to each of the functions of stage lighting.

A DISCUSSION of light can most logically and conveniently be divided into two parts. The first would consider light *objectively*, as a natural phenomenon, as "visible radiant energy", and would consider only its purely physical characteristics. The second would consider light *subjectively*, as the sense impression formed by the eye and the other components of the human visual system when stimulated by some of this "visible radiant energy", and would consider its more physiological and psychological aspects. The former is the cause; the latter is the effect.

I. Objective Light

A. NATURE

"Light is visible radiant energy." This overworked, sententious definition — often used not without a touch of ostentation — is likely to prove somewhat obscure to many readers unless it is explained in familiar terms. Of course, it cannot be denied that light is *visible* — that is axiomatic; nor that it is *radiant* — it is emitted in all directions from its source; nor that it is *energy* — it energizes and influences living organisms as well as inorganic substances such as the chemicals on photographic plates and films. However, the laconic definition has a deeper significance.

Every natural phenomenon is an outward manifestation of the transfer of energy — either from one place to another, or from one form to another, or both. There is chemical energy, such as is contained in a stick of dynamite; mechanical energy, such as is possessed by a moving object; electrical energy, such as may be obtained from a pair of charged electrical conductors; and other forms of energy. When a transfer of energy takes place, things happen. The forms of energy that have just been mentioned all require material objects for their storage and transfer. But one form of energy, known as radiant energy, utilizes for its transfer a transverse wave motion of the ether, a hypothetical medium (having no relation to the well-known anesthetic) assumed to fill all space and to permeate all bodies.

Radiant energy of this sort embraces several familiar natural phenomena, principal among which are electric waves, or Hertzian waves, such as are used in wireless telegraphy, and, more popularly, for radio broadcasting; heat; light; ultra-violet rays and X-rays. All these forms of radiant energy travel at approximately the same velocity, namely, 186,000 miles per second. The only essential difference between them lies in the length of the waves — the *wave length*. *Electric waves* used for wireless are received by the familiar "receiving sets", and their wave lengths range roughly from one

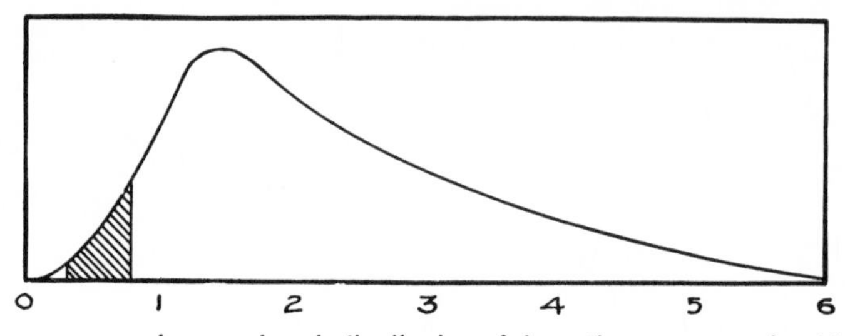

This curve represents the wave-length distribution of the radiant energy emitted by a tungsten-filament incandescent lamp. The values given are expressed in microns. The shaded portion of the curve represents the part of the radiant energy which is visible. Thus it is apparent, by comparing the shaded area with the total area under the curve, that the actual light emitted by a lamp is but a small proportion of the total emitted energy.

meter to 25,000 meters — wave lengths above 600 meters being in general use for commercial work, those from 200 to 600 for popular radio broadcasting, and those below 200 for amateur and experimental work. *Heat waves* are next in order of length, but they are very much shorter than the electric waves. Instead of being measured in meters they are measured in *microns* (a micron is a thousandth part of a millimeter, or a millionth part of a meter). The wave lengths of heat range from about 0.75 microns to 300 microns. Heat is perceptible by its effect on thermometric and calorimetric instruments, and on living organisms and inorganic substances.

Radiant energy ranging in wave length from 0.35 microns to 0.75 microns (the extreme limits), is perceptible by the human visual system, and is known as *light*. Light and heat are really radiant energy of the same sort, differing only in wave length. The wave-length ranges of each are in close proximity — in fact, they border on each other, and, as the dividing line is not a hard and fast one, they may even be said to overlap slightly. This explains why it is extremely difficult, almost impossible, to produce "cold light" — light which is altogether free from heat.

Ultra-violet rays and X-rays are also radiant energy, but of still shorter wave lengths than those of light. They are perceptible only by means of special fluorescent materials.

Just as radio receiving apparatus can be "tuned" to receive only radiant energy whose wave length lies within a limited range, so the human optical system is permanently "tuned" to receive only radiant energy whose wave length lies between the limits of 0.35 microns and 0.75 microns. Light, therefore, may be said to be a transverse ether wave motion of such range as to affect the eye and produce the sensation of vision. This wave motion is caused by a "source of light" — an illuminant — which may be either a burning gas, as in the oil, candle, and gas flames, or an incandescent solid, as in the incandescent electric lamp, the carbon arc, and the limelight.

B. PROPAGATION

Several theories regarding the nature and propagation, or transmission, of light have been formulated, the principal of which are the corpuscular theory of Newton, the undulatory theory of Huygens, the electromagnetic theory of Maxwell, and the quantum emission theory of Planck. The first, that of Newton, has been quite disproved, but scientists are still debating the merits of the three other theories. For the purposes of this discussion, however, it is quite sufficient simply to assume that light travels in *straight lines*, which spread radially in all directions from the source. Light, shade, and shadows, and hence the ability of the human optical system to visualize the size and form of objects, depend upon this rectilinear propagation of light, its rays not being able to bend or turn around corners, or to pierce opaque objects.

A *ray* of light is merely one direction in which the light travels. A collection of rays around an axis constitutes a *beam* of light. If all the rays of a beam of light meet, or pass through one point, they are said to be *focussed* at that point.

C. ILLUMINANTS

The principal illuminant used at the present time for stage lighting is the electric *incandescent lamp*. The incandescent lamp consists essentially of a *filament* made of tungsten, which is able to withstand high temperatures without too rapid volatilization. This filament is mounted (in either a vacuum or in an atmosphere of inert gas, depending upon the size and type of lamp) within a thin, hard, glass *bulb* to which is firmly cemented a screw *base*, which permits of convenient connection, by means of a *socket* (discussed in the chapter immediately preceding), to the electrical system. The filament, heated to incandescence by virtue of the electric current passing through it, is the actual source of the light rays.

The *carbon arc*, which is used on the stage to a limited extent, consists of two sticks of hard carbon, between the tips of which, across a small air gap, arcs an electric current. With direct current, the negative carbon tip is heated to incandescence by the arc, and becomes the source of light. With alternating current, both carbon tips are heated to incandescence by the arc, but each to only half the brightness of the negative carbon tip with direct current. The largest carbon arc is, at the present time, capable of producing a more powerful beam of light than the largest commonly used incandescent lamp, and hence it is used principally for long-throw spotlights.

The *limelight* consists of a stick of lime, a small spot on which is heated to incandescence by the sharp point of an oxyhydrogen flame. This provides a really excellent, intense source of light, but because of the clumsy apparatus needed for its production — gas tanks, tubing, and burners — and the individual, expert attention necessary, the limelight to-day, although it is still used to a very limited extent, lends its name to a figure of speech rather than serves as a practical illuminant.

D. UNITS

The units of electricity have already been taken up in the previous chapter. Although the units of light (even apart from those of color) are many in number, there are but two that have a direct bearing on the subject of stage lighting: the lumen, a measure of quantity of *light*, and the foot candle, a measure of quantity of *illumination*. Light is differentiated from illumination in that the former is the cause; the latter, the effect.

When new illuminants were evolved, it was only natural that they should be compared in strength with the familiar candle, which they superseded. The illuminating power of the new light sources was expressed in terms of that of the candle. Thus the *candle power* as a light unit came into existence. However, since the candle power of a light source expressed only the intensity in one direction, it was of no value at all for expressing the illuminating power of illuminants that emitted more light in some directions than in others. Hence it was analagous to the depth of a pool of water at one point — a measurement that might prove of some use for certain purposes but that gave no indication at all of the quantity of water in the pool.

Nevertheless, the candle power is of value in evolving the *lumen*, a unit used to denote quantity, or amount, of light. Technically a lumen is "the amount of light emitted in a unit solid angle by a unit light source." In other words, a lumen is the amount of light falling upon a surface one square foot in area, every point of which is one foot distant from a light source that emits one candle power of light uniformly in all directions. Although the common rating for incandescent lamps is in watts, an equally important rating is their light output in lumens. For example: a 100-watt lamp gives off about 1300 lumens of light; a 1000-watt lamp gives off about 21,000 lumens of light.

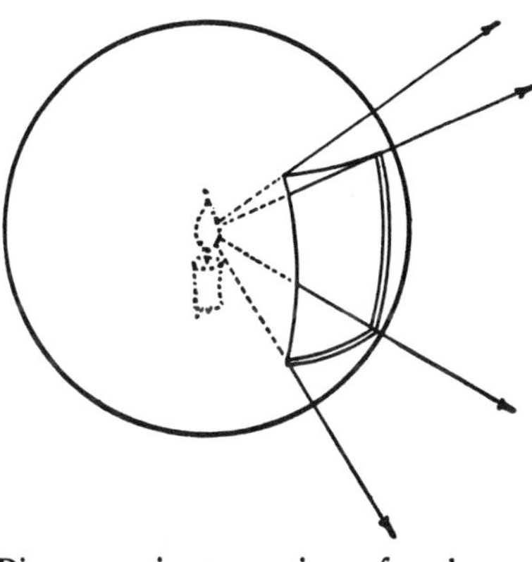

Diagrammatic conception of a lumen. If a light source of one candle power be placed at the center of a hollow sphere of one foot radius, and a hole of one square foot of area be cut in the surface of the sphere, exactly one lumen of light will pass through the opening.

The candle power is also used to evolve the *foot candle*, a unit used to denote quantity, or amount, of illumination. The definition of a foot candle is quite analagous to that of that lumen—a foot candle is the amount, or intensity, of illumination received by a surface one square foot in area, every point of which is one foot distant from a light source that emits one candle power of light uniformly in all directions. Comparing the definition of a foot candle with that of a lumen, it is seen that a definite and very useful relation exists between the two units, namely, a lumen of light, when applied evenly to a square foot of surface, produces one foot candle of illumination. In other words, one lumen per square foot equals one foot candle. Therefore: illumination of any surface (in foot candles) equals the light applied uniformly to the surface (in lumens) divided by the area of the surface (in square feet).

Hence, if it is desired to illuminate a back cloth, or cyclorama, 20 feet high and 40 feet wide (therefore 800 square feet in area) to an intensity of two foot candles, it is necessary to apply, evenly, to its surface, 800 × 2, or 1600, lumens of light by means of available equipment.

It is difficult to convey any impression, to give any idea, of various intensities of illumination. Full strong sunlight, with a bright sky, at noon of a midsummer day, would give an intensity of about 8000 foot candles. In places shaded from the direct rays of the sun, but exposed to the light from the bright sky, the intensity would be in the neighborhood of 500 foot candles. Indoors, on a bright day, within a few feet of a fairly large window, the intensity would be about 100 foot candles. At night, the intensity of illumination in a well-lighted room would probably lie within the range of from 4 to 8 foot candles. The intensity of average street lighting would range, perhaps, from one twentieth (0.05) to one tenth (0.10) of a foot candle, which would also be about the intensity of bright moonlight. The intensities cited are mentioned rather as an indication of the range of intensities encountered, than as specific examples of each case, since these are open to very wide variations.

Lumens and foot candles are measured by optical instruments called photometers. A convenient, inexpensive, portable type of photometer is the *foot-candle meter*, which is more than sufficiently accurate for general use. It is simple to understand and easy to operate. Its range extends from 0 to 100 foot candles. It is a handy little instrument for stage workers who wish to attack the problems of stage lighting from a very sound and practical basis. By its use, the optical characteristics of each piece of stage-lighting apparatus can be exactly determined, and hence taken into careful consideration when stage lighting is being planned. By means of the foot-candle meter, the lighting of any setting, or scene, or special effect may be measured and permanently recorded, and later quickly and faithfully reproduced, as this method measures the results rather than the means of obtaining them.

E. REFLECTION

When a beam of light strikes the surface of an opaque object, a portion of the light is *reflected*, and the remainder is *absorbed*. The actual extent of each portion depends upon the nature of the material that constitutes the reflecting surface. A black, amorphous substance, such as a black drape, or a coat of dense black paint, will *absorb* by far the greater portion of the light falling upon it, and *reflect* but little of it. On the other hand, a highly polished colorless metallic substance, such as a silvered mirror, will *reflect* by far the greater portion of the light falling upon it, and *absorb* but little of it. Between these two extremes, there are, of course, an infinite number of gradations. No existing surface is perfectly reflecting, nor is any perfectly absorbing. Black drapes are used on the stage to feature prominently, by contrast, objects that have a lesser light absorption, such as light-colored screens or properties, or actors, and to give the impression of a limitless void. There are four principal types of reflection: regular, diffused, spread, and mixed.

Regular reflection, such as is provided by mirrors and polished smooth metal surfaces, is carried out in accordance with set laws. If the reflecting surface is flat, the *reflected* ray leaves the surface at the same angle at which the *incident* ray fell upon it. If the reflect-

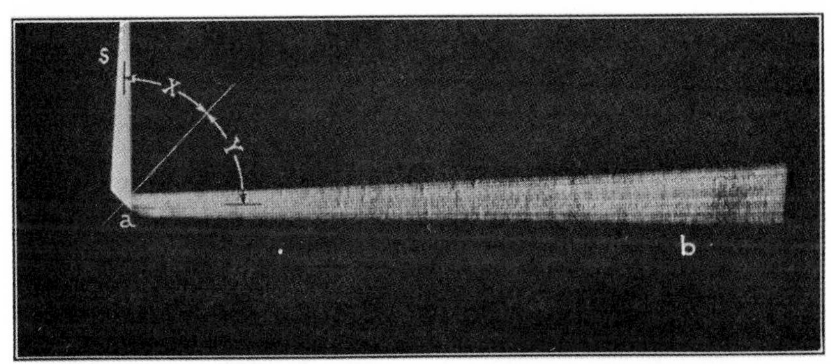

An example of regular reflection: the incident beam of light "sa" reflected from point "a" on a polished metal plane surface in the direction "ab", with the angle of incidence "X" equal to the angle of reflection "Y."

ing surface is curved, as is often the case in stage-lighting equipment, the same relation of equal angles still holds true. However, in this case, the geometrical tangent of the curve, at the point of reflection, forms the basis for the measurement of the angles. By shaping mirrored surfaces according to predetermined optical computations, light may be directed in certain directions, and confined to certain areas, concentrated in some spots, weakened in others—all as desired.

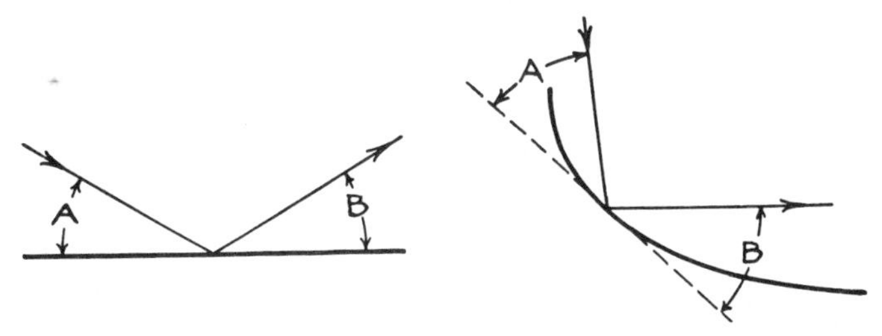

Illustrating the law of regular reflection. The angle, "A", at which the incident ray strikes the reflecting surface is always equal to angle "B", at which the reflected ray leaves the reflected surface. For a curved reflecting surface, these angles are measured from the tangent to the curve at the point of reflection.

Diffuse reflection results when the character of the reflecting surface is such as to break up the incident light and reflect it, scattered, in all directions. *Matte* surfaces, such as a piece of white blotting paper, or a piece of rough white paper, provide almost perfect diffusion. The white paint used in footlight and borderlight troughs and on the inside of olivettes, and also the rough plaster surface of various types of permanent cycloramas, are important applications of diffuse reflection to stage work.

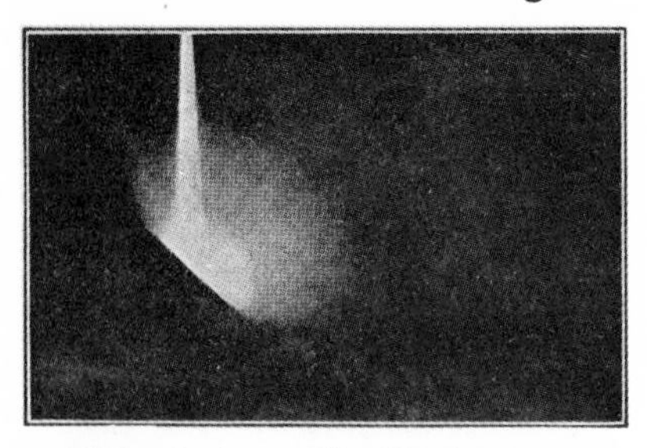

Diffused: from white blotting paper.

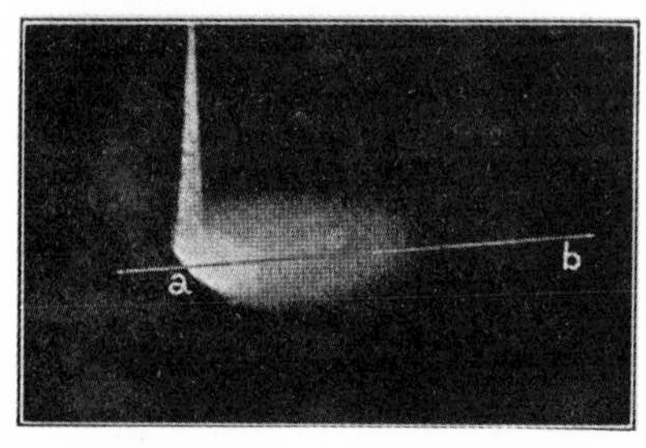

Spread: from aluminum paint.

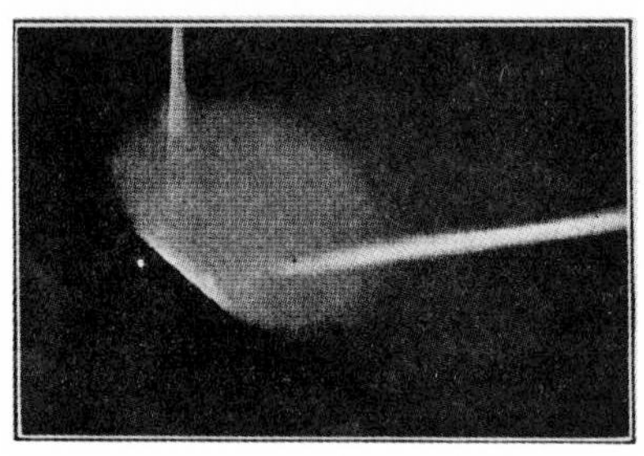

Mixed: from porcelain-enamelled steel.

TYPES OF REFLECTION FROM VARIOUS SURFACES.

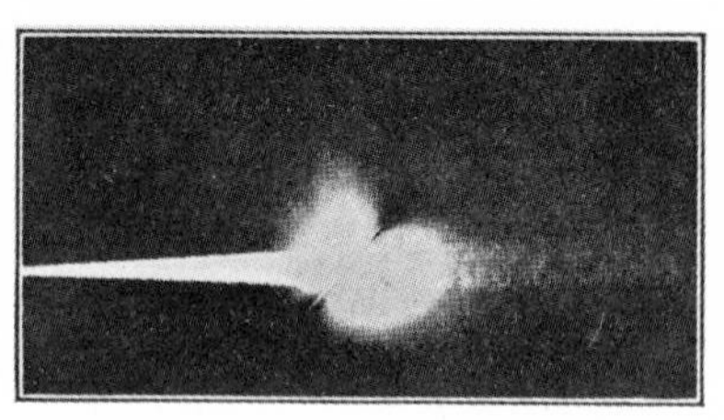

White, or "opal", glass.

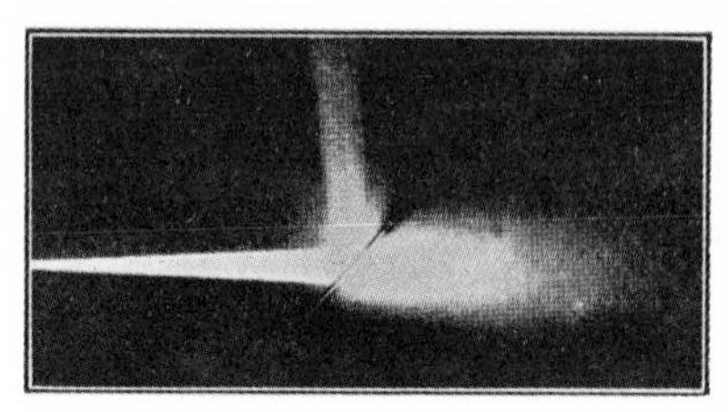

Etched glass: smooth side toward beam.

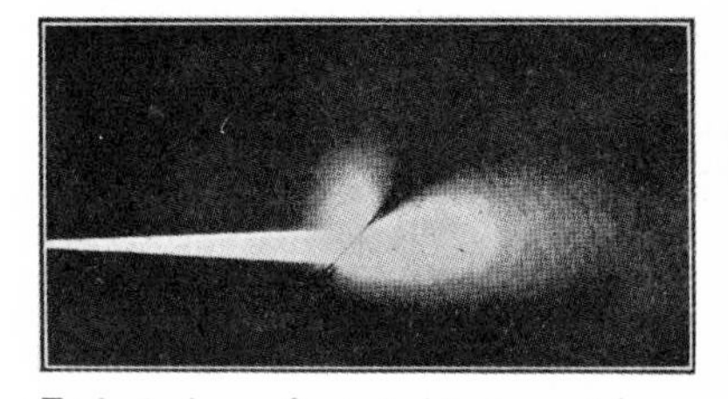

Etched glass: frosted side toward beam.

TYPES OF DIFFUSE TRANSMISSION.

Spread reflection results when the character of the reflecting surface is such as to break up the incident light and reflect it, scattered, in the predominant direction that the reflected ray would take in regular reflection. Thus spread reflection might be termed "directional diffused reflection." *Semi-matte* surfaces such as smooth, though not highly polished, bright metal surfaces exhibit this type of reflection. Its application on the stage includes the use of aluminum paint for the footlight and borderlight reflectors; the use of spun aluminum reflectors for the footlights, borderlights, and olivettes; and the bowed reflector disks, covered with silver leaf, used by David Belasco in place of borderlights.

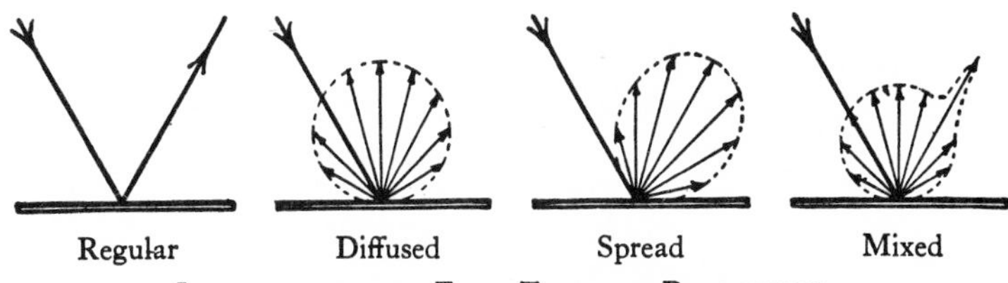

ILLUSTRATING THE FOUR TYPES OF REFLECTION.

Mixed reflection results when the character of the reflecting surface is such as to break up the major portion of the incident light and reflect it, scattered, in all directions (just as with diffuse reflection), but to reflect the remaining portion of the incident light according to the law of regular reflection. *Glossy* surfaces, such as a piece of white blotting paper covered with a thin sheet of clear glass, or a sheet of white glossy, calendered paper, exhibit this type of reflection. Porcelain-enameled steel reflectors, sometimes used in footlights and borderlights, represent the application of this type of reflection to the stage.

F. REFRACTION

When a beam of light strikes the surface of a transparent object, such as a piece of clear glass, the major portion of the rays is trans-

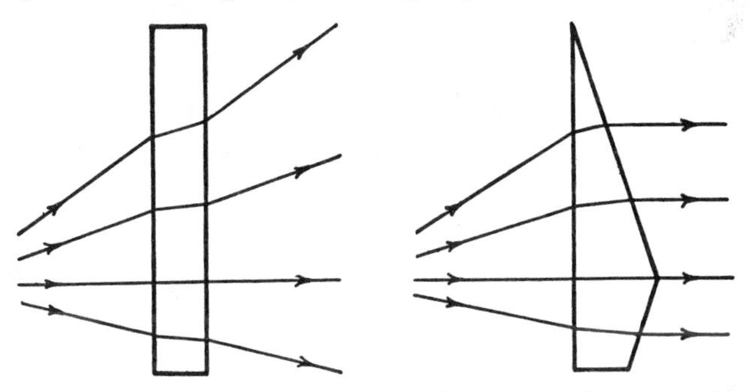

Illustrating how light rays are refracted in passing from one medium to another. The first diagram shows the effect of a sheet of glass with parallel sides; the second shows the effect of a sheet of glass, the sides of which are not parallel, and which represents in an elementary fashion the effect of a lens.

mitted, and much smaller portions are absorbed and reflected. When a ray of light passes obliquely from one transparent medium to another, as from air to glass, or vice versa, its direction is considerably changed. This phenomenon is called *refraction*, and finds its principal application in lenses, which are used for redirecting and controlling beams of light. When a ray of light passes obliquely from a rarer to a denser medium, as from air to glass, it is bent *away from* the dividing surface upon entering the second medium. Conversely, when a ray of light passes from a denser to a rarer medium, as from glass to air, it is bent *toward* the dividing surface upon entering the second medium. Of course, if a ray strikes this dividing surface perpendicularly, it enters the second medium without its direction having been changed. The extent to which a transparent object changes the direction of a ray of light, entering it obliquely from the air, is termed its *refractive index*. The higher the refractive index of a substance, the greater the bending effect it exerts.

Refraction of a beam of light by a glass prism.

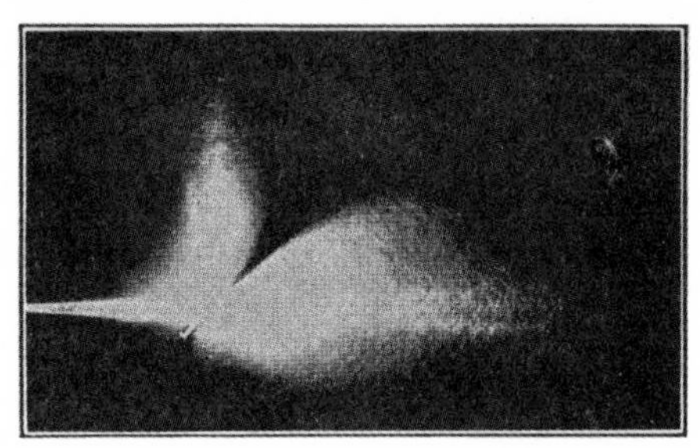

Illustrating how a sheet of prismatic-ribbed glass spreads a narrow beam of light into a wide "sheet" of light.

G. REFLECTORS

A mirror, in general terms, is a reflecting surface that operates in accordance with the principle of regular reflection. Glass mirrors are made of a high quality of smooth polished glass, coated on one side with a thin layer of chemically deposited silver. The ray of light passes through the glass, is reflected by the silver coating, passes again through the glass and emerges from the mirror. A metal mirror is usually made of thin copper or brass, highly polished,

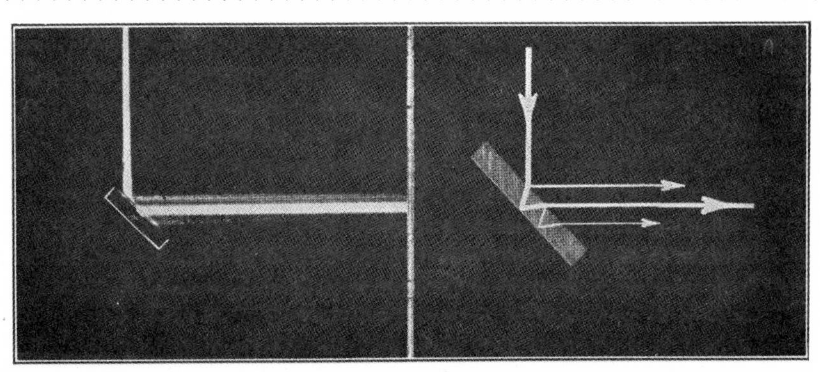

Regular reflection from a plane glass mirror: the diagram on the right explains the existence of the two minor reflected beams, the upper of which is caused by direct reflection from the surface of the glass, and the lower by double internal reflection within the glass. The major portion of the beam is, of course, reflected by the silvered back surface of the mirror.

which is coated on the reflecting side with a plating of silver from which the rays of light are reflected directly.

A *spherical mirror* is usually made of glass, its reflecting surface being a sector of a sphere. Such a mirror has a special property which makes it particularly useful for light projection apparatus. If a light source be placed at the geometrical center of the sphere of which the mirror is a sector, the light rays will be reflected back on

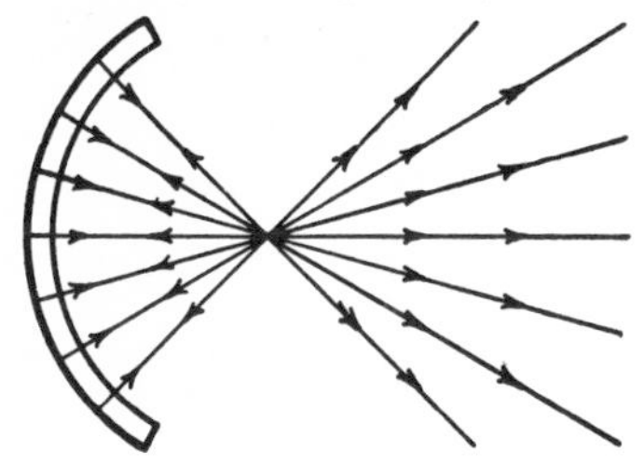

SPHERICAL MIRROR

Illustrating the manner in which a spherical mirror reflects back on themselves the rays emitted by a light source placed at the focal point of the mirror.

themselves, since they strike the mirror perpendicular to the tangent at the point of contact. Thus they return to the light source, greatly to increase the intensity originally emerging in the opposite direction.

A *parabolic mirror* is usually made either of glass or of metal, its reflecting surface being a sector of a paraboloid. When a light source is placed at its focal center, all reflected rays are parallel to each other. Since all the light rays emitted in the direction of the reflector are collected to form the beam, it is very powerful. A

Mangin mirror, made of glass, has two spherical surfaces, the inner one being of lesser radius than the outer one, which is silvered. This

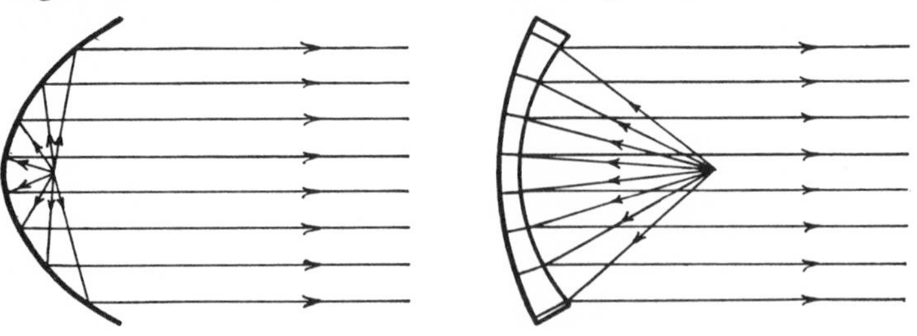

Illustrating the manner in which a parabolic reflector and a Mangin mirror redirect, in parallel lines, incident rays emitted by a light source placed at the focal point of each.

mirror, which takes into consideration the refraction caused by the glass of which it is made, also produces a parallel beam. Searchlights and floodlights which must be projected from a long distance, as in the lighting of outdoor pageants, employ the parabolic and Mangin types of mirror.

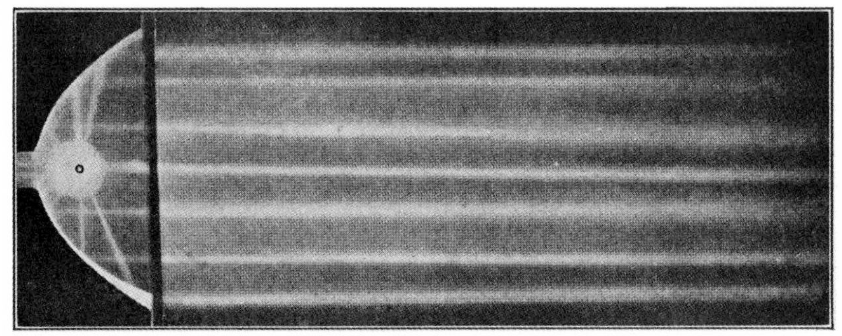

Illustrating the action of a parabolic reflector in producing a parallel beam of light when a light source is placed at its focus.

H. LENSES

A lens is a transparent body, usually made of glass, having one or both of its opposite faces curved, which employs the phenomenon of refraction for the purpose of controlling the direction and shape of the beam of light passing through it. The degree of divergence or convergence of light rays caused by a lens depends largely upon the curvature of the faces of the lens, and, to a lesser extent, upon the index of refraction of the particular type of glass of which the lens is made. The curvature of the faces is almost invariably spherical. The *optical axis* of a lens is the straight line passing through the center of the lens in a direction perpendicular to its transverse axis.

The *focal length* of a lens is the distance from the center of the lens to the point (outside the lens, on the optical axis) at which rays of light (which were parallel with the optical axis before entering the lens)

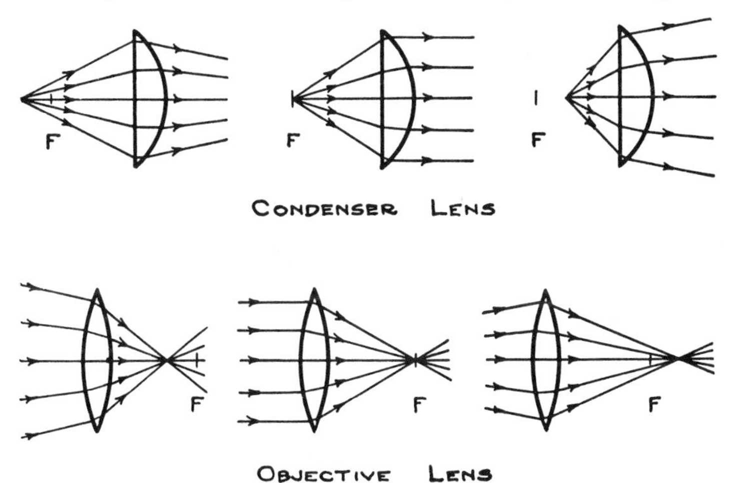

Illustrating the manner in which a condenser lens refracts the rays of light emitted from a light source placed beyond, at, and before its focal point; and the manner in which an objective lens redirects incident rays of light through points before, at, and beyond its focal point.

are made to meet, or *focus*. The lenses commonly used on stage-lighting equipment are the plano-convex, or *condenser lens*, and the double-convex, or *objective lens*.

I. LIGHT PROJECTION

Methods of light control for stage lighting are almost all comparatively simple. How the various types of reflection — regular, diffuse, spread, and mixed — are employed has already been indicated. The use of lenses is perhaps a trifle involved. Lens systems on the stage are used mainly in spotlights and in sciopticons.

The lens system used on spotlights is the simpler. Since light travels in straight lines, it would be necessary, in order to produce a spot of light, only to mount a light source of small dimensions, a spotlight lamp, for instance, in a suitable housing in one end of which is a circular hole. Only the light emanated in the direction of the hole would escape, and this would form an enlarged image of the hole on the surface at which the spotlight was directed.

However, as the light source emanates light in all directions, and as the hole is comparatively small, only a small proportion of the total light available would be utilized. This can be represented as being contained in the narrow cone whose base is the circular

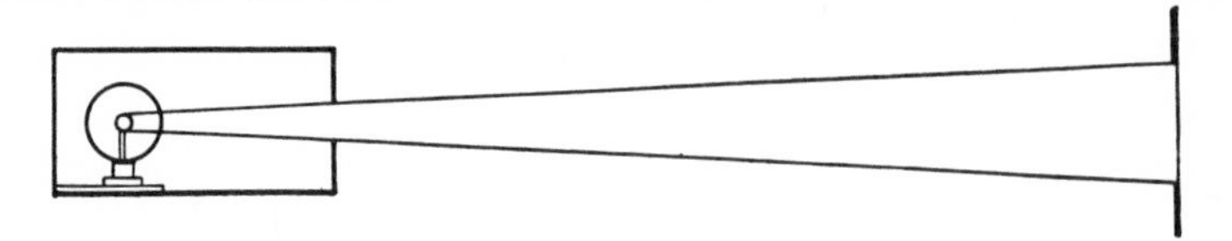

hole, and whose apex is the lamp filament. It is highly desirable to increase the amount of light used, in order that a brighter spot may result from the same consumption of electric current. This is accomplished by the use of a condenser lens, which, because its diameter is larger than that of the circular hole used previously, will intercept a much greater portion of the emitted light and bend the rays so that the resulting spot will be the same size as before.

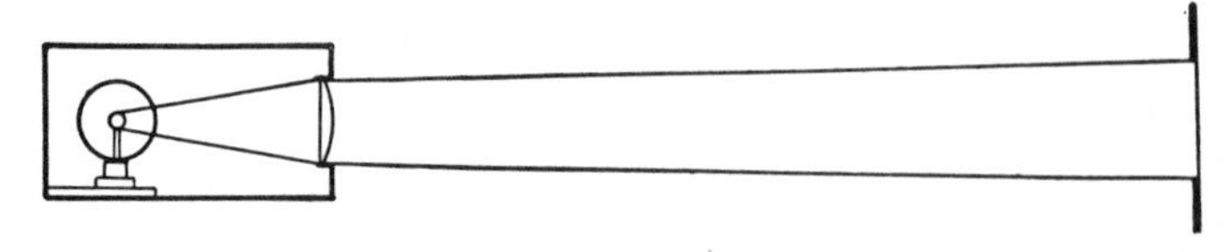

In this manner the quantity of emitted light that is effectively utilized, contained in the now much wider cone, will be increased more than tenfold. (It must be remembered that these sketches present a section only, and that a ratio of the solid apex angles of the two cones is greater than is apparent at first from their sectional area.) Even this effective utilization of the emitted light can be greatly increased by the use of a spherical mirror, so positioned behind the lamp that the filament is at the focal point of the mirror. Then a portion of the backward rays of light, that would otherwise be wasted, will be reflected back again, through the open spaces in the filament. The spot will therefore be much brighter, for the same electric current consumption, than it would be if the mirror were not used.

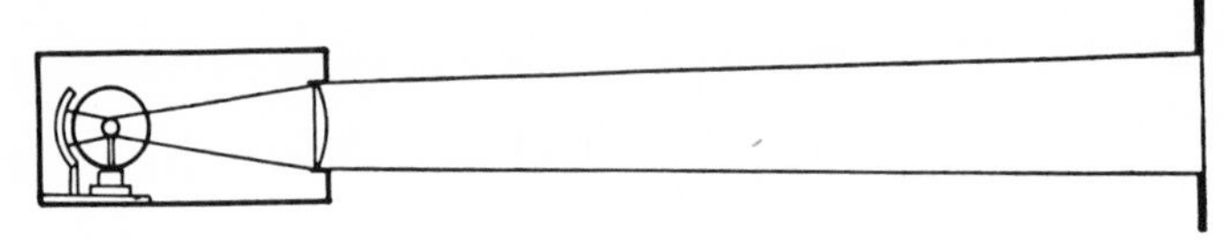

If the carbon arc is used as the source of light, the nature of its mechanism will usually preclude the use of a spherical mirror. However, arc spotlights are used but to a limited extent, and when they are used, they are usually brilliant enough not to require the "backing" which a spherical mirror provides. But every incandescent spotlight should be equipped with such a mirror, because a great and unnecessary loss of light takes place unless one is used.

The size of the spot produced by a spotlight can be changed by varying the distance from the lamp to the lens. When the lamp is far back in the housing, as pictured in the previous sketches, the beam of light will be narrow, and the resultant spot of light will be correspondingly small. If the lamp is close to the lens, as pictured below, the spot produced will be large. Of course, the spherical mirror must be fixed to the same movable plate, or rod, to which are fixed the socket and the lamp, and the combination must move as a unit, because the effectiveness of the mirror depends upon its being always at the correct distance from the lamp filament.

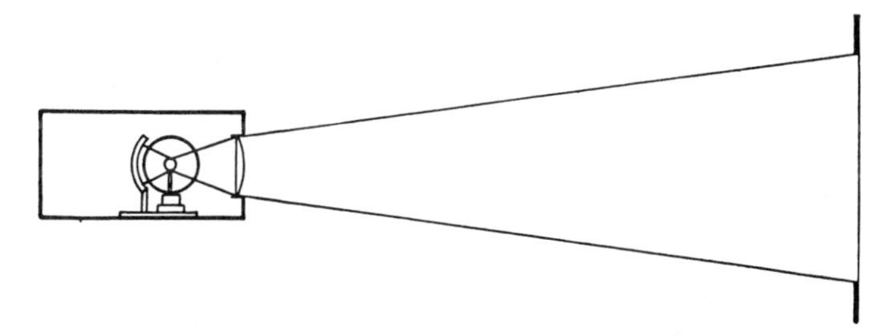

The size of the spot produced depends also upon the focal length of the condenser lens used. For the same distance between the lamp and the lens, a lens of short focal length will produce a narrow beam, and hence a small spot, and a lens of long focal length will produce a wide, spreading beam, and hence a large spot (see table on page 186). Needless to state, the discussion in the several foregoing paragraphs presupposes that the distance between the spotlight and the surface upon which the spot of light falls is the same in all cases. Naturally, the greater this distance, the larger the spot will be.

The other lens system used in stage lighting is an extension of that just described, and hence is somewhat more involved. It is used for projecting, on a screen or backdrop, greatly enlarged, sharply defined images of designs and pictures, either transparent, or opaque cutouts. This lens system is employed in the old-fashioned "magic lantern", the stereopticon, the motion-picture machine, and in the stage adaptation of these devices — the *sciopticon*. In this system, two condenser lenses, the transparent slide, or opaque cutout, bearing the design or picture, and a set of objective lenses are used, in addition, of course, to the light source and its spherical mirror. The two condenser lenses, mounted close together at a fixed distance, serve to pick up the maximum amount of light possible and project it through the slide, which is placed close to the condenser lenses. The image produced by the slide (that is, the light passing through the slide) is then enlarged and projected on to the screen or backdrop by the objective lenses, which are mounted together, as a unit, in a brass cylinder, at a fixed distance apart. The rays of light, after passing the condenser lenses, converge and meet at a point situated between the two fixed objective lenses. For this reason, the screen

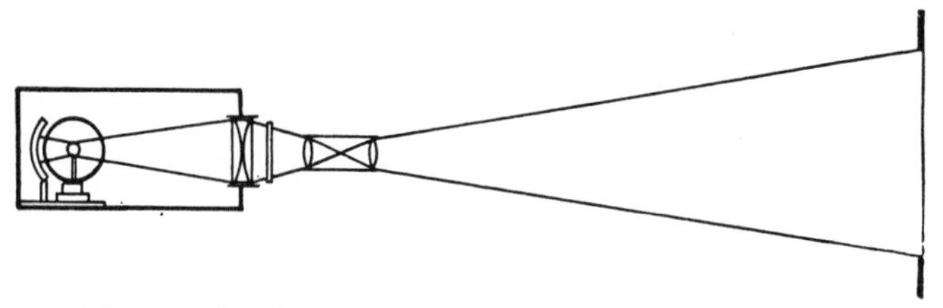

or projected image is always reversed, in both vertical and horizontal directions, as compared with that on the transparent slide. The distance at which the set of objective lenses is placed in front of the slide depends upon the composite focal length of these lenses, the size of the projected picture desired, and the distance from the screen or backdrop (see table on page 197). All the elements that constitute a stereopticon lens system are fixed, except the set of objective lenses, which are adjusted to the position at which the sharpest projected picture results. This process of adjustment is called *focussing*. In the case of the objective lenses, the shorter the composite focal length, the larger the picture, and vice versa. Thus if it is desired to project a large scene on a backdrop from a very short distance, such as might be available backstage, an objective lens of very short focus must be employed.

A *sciopticon* is the adaptation of a regular stage spotlight, by means of standard accessories, to the purposes of stereopticon projection. If a slide is inserted in the beam of light produced by a spotlight, only a very blurred image, if any at all, will result, because the enlarging and clarifying power of the objective lenses is lacking. However, to the standard spotlight (which already has the light source, the spherical mirror, and a single condenser lens) may be affixed a second condenser lens, a slide carrier (a simple device for conveniently holding the slide or cut-out), and a set of objective lenses, movable, for focussing. This converted spotlight now constitutes a sciopticon. If in place of the slide there is substituted a revolving transparent disk, one side of which passes before the condenser lens in a continuous direction, moving "effects", such as clouds, rain, fire, and a host of others, more or less satisfactory, can be produced. These are discussed in Chapter X.

A light projection system which must not be confused with the sciopticon is one which is an importation from Europe but which at present is coming into more common use in this country — the Linnebach lantern. This is used to project very large "still" scenes, usually from behind, on to a transparent drop. It uses neither lenses nor mirrors — merely a concentrated source of light, and a very large glass slide upon which the scene is painted. This apparatus depends on only the rectilinear propagation of light for its operation, whereas the spotlight and sciopticon employ also the phenomena of reflection and refraction.

Proper optical alignment and cleanliness of the component parts of any lens system are essential to its efficient and satisfactory operation. Slight films of dust and finger marks on the surfaces of the mirror, the lamp bulb, the transparent slide, and the lenses will cause such an absorption of light that the brightness of the final projected image will sometimes be reduced by more than half. The sharpness of the image will also be reduced because of the distortion of the light beam. If any of the lenses, or the lamp, or the mirror, are not in alignment, that is, if they are not centered on the optical

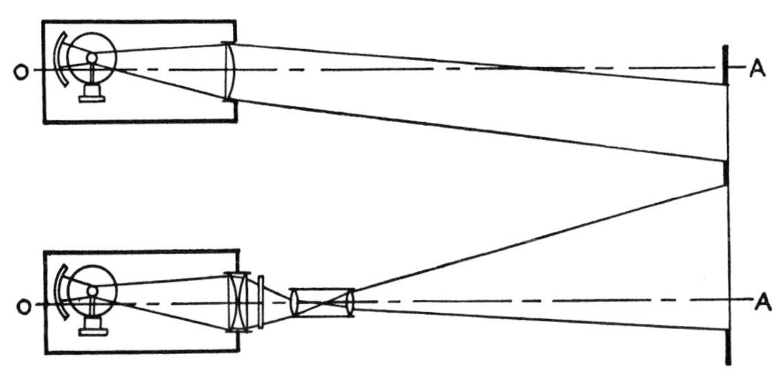

axis of the lens system, not only will a great loss of light result, but the spot or picture will be "spotty" (very irregular in brightness), and proper control and focussing of the light beam will not be possible. Normally, spotlights, sciopticons, and other light projection apparatus are so constructed that the lenses are correctly placed. The slide holders are so adjusted that the slide is in the proper position in relation to the lenses. The light source, however, is subject to variation, and its character and position are of particular importance. The ideal light source for projection purposes would be a brilliant *point source*. The nearest practical approach to this ideal is the concentrated filament of the spotlight lamp, which is closely coiled and crowded into the smallest practicable space. This concentrated filament must be placed on the optical axis of the lens system. Since these lamps are supplied with a standard *light center length* (the distance from the bottom of the base to the center of the filament), every spotlight is equipped with a socket so positioned that, when the lamp is screwed in, its filament will be in optical alignment with the lens. The spherical backing mirror is usually adjustable, and can most easily be placed in the proper position by directing the spotlight beam on a white surface and moving the mirror about in all directions until the spot appears brightest. Carbon arcs are provided with a rack and pinion mechanism for adjusting the light source and for keeping it properly in focus.

II. Subjective Light

The physical, the scientific, aspects of light and their particular relation to stage lighting work have now been discussed. The subjective aspects of light, which include mainly the relation of light and its antithesis, shade, to the process of visual perception, find their definite relation to stage lighting work in the extent of their relative importance, their contribution, to each of the five functions of stage lighting as a whole.

A. COLORLESS VISUAL SENSATIONS

There are two types of visual *sensations* — those which are colorless (recording black, white, grays, and contrasts between them), and those which are colored. The latter, which are relatively of much less importance in the human visual process, will be discussed in the chapter following. The former, the colorless sensations, are of far greater value for the discernment of objects than are the colored sensations. The case of color-blind persons, who experience no visual difficulties, and who are unaware of their deficiency until they compare notes with persons possessing so-called "normal" vision, or until they engage in some operation that depends upon the discernment of color for its successful execution, affords ample proof of the contention that color is but subordinate to light and shade for the purpose of visual perception.

1. *Brightness*. Hence vision is primarily dependent upon whites, blacks, and grays, the gradations of which are termed brightness. Brightness is difficult to define without recourse to scientific units, but it may be said to be the degree of luminosity of an object — the intensity of light reflected by it to the eye. Naturally, then, the average brightness of any object is dependent upon two factors — first, the *intensity of illumination*, or the amount of light incident upon the object, and, second, the proportion of this amount of incident light which the object reflects to the eye, or its *coefficient of reflection*.

However, unless the surface of the object exhibits diffuse reflection, the apparent brightness will depend also to a large extent upon the angle at which the surface is viewed. Referring to the sketches on page 79, it will be noticed that if the spread reflection surface is viewed from the right side, its apparent brightness will be much greater than if it were viewed from the left side, since much more of the incident light is reflected toward the right. And if a regular reflection surface be viewed from any angle but the angle of reflection, it will appear to have hardly any brightness whatsoever. If a mixed-reflection surface be viewed from the angle of intense reflection, it will appear to have a much higher brightness than when it is viewed at any other angle. Only a diffuse-reflection surface will exhibit the same brightness when viewed at almost any direction, because from such a surface the incident light is reflected virtually equally in all directions.

2. *Coefficient of Reflection.* The coefficient of reflection of any surface — the ratio of the amount of incident light to the amount of reflected light — must lie between two definite limits, namely, zero (none of the light reflected) and unity (all of the light reflected). An object with a reflection coefficient of zero, since it reflects no light to the eye and hence causes no visual sensation, is called *black.* At the other end of the scale, an object with a reflection coefficient of unity, since it reflects all of the incident light to the eye and hence causes the maximum visual sensation (for a given intensity of illumination), is called *white.* Between these limits are the gradations, really infinite in number, called *grays.*

Actually, no objects that reflect absolutely all of the light incident upon them, or that reflect absolutely none of the light incident upon them, are ever encountered. The practical approaches to these limits are, for *white,* a freshly scraped surface of magnesium carbonate, and, for *black,* a piece of heavy black velvet. The coefficients of reflection of the objects, as well as a representative intermediate range, are given, approximately, in the following table.

Material	Coefficient of Reflection
Magnesium carbonate	.95
White plaster	.90
White blotting paper	.85
Heavy pure white silk	.80
White bond stationery	.75
Newspaper	.50
Dull copper	.25
Chocolate	.05
Black cambric	.02
Black velvet	.004

All of the objects listed in the table possess a fairly diffuse reflection. As pointed out above, surfaces with other types of reflection vary in brightness, depending upon the angle at which they are viewed.

3. *Intensity of Illumination.* The other factor that enters into the brightness of any object — the intensity of illumination — is equal in importance to the reflection coefficient. It has, for its lower limit, zero, no illumination at all, but it has, theoretically at least, no upper limit; that is, there is no limit to the amount of light that can be used to illuminate any object. The apparent brightness of any object is directly proportional to the intensity of illumination on it. For instance, an object having a reflection coefficient of only .25, would be about equal in brightness, when illuminated to 10 foot candles, to an object with a reflection coefficient of .50 that was illuminated to only 5 foot candles. However, the eye is not equally sensitive to equal variations in brightness under different intensities of illumination. For example, every one notices that it is difficult clearly to distinguish objects in moonlight, because, under this low intensity (about .05 foot candle), the eye can differentiate between only the brightnesses of very wide variation. This characteristic of the eye is called *brightness sensibility*. For intensities lower than one foot candle, the brightness sensibility of the eye is generally rather low. Under the range of illumination intensities to which the eye has accustomed itself through ages of use, namely from one to ten thousand foot candles, the brightness sensibility of the eye reaches its highest value. In fact, it reaches a practicable maximum at about 100 foot candles: that is to say, very high intensities of illumination (above 100 foot candles) can accomplish little more, as far as vision is concerned, than is accomplished at 100 foot candles. This is about the maximum intensity that is ever required in the course of the lighting of the average play.

B. LIGHT AND SHADE

That the brightness of any surface depends upon the intensity to which it is illuminated, and upon its coefficient of reflection, has already been demonstrated. Black and white have been defined in terms of the physical properties of the objects which are so described. Between black and white, there are, of course, innumerable gradations of gray. These shades of gray, sometimes known, especially to the designer and to the painter, as "value", can also be described by reference to the reflection coefficient of the object to which the term is applied. It has been proposed [1] to establish a standard scale of values: the value, or shade of gray, of any surface being determined by the range within which its coefficient of reflection lies.

[1] M. Luckiesh, "Light and Shade and Their Applications", page 61.

This proposed scale of values was formulated after there had been carried out an exhaustive scientific examination of the widely differing, inconsistent, arbitrary value scales that are used in art courses and that are made by various artists. The nomenclature of light and shade would benefit considerably by the universal adoption of such a standard, since a definite and uniform basis for discussion and instruction would be provided. This standard scale of values, with the seven designations of value between black and white in common use by designers and painters, is as follows:

Value		Range of Coefficient of Reflection
Black		0.00–0.10
Grays	Low dark	.10– .20
	Dark	.20– .30
	High dark	.30– .40
	Medium	.40– .50
	Low light	.50– .60
	Light	.60– .70
	High light	.70– .80
White		.80– .90

These several values or shades of gray are absolute; that is, they are inherent in the objects themselves and are independent of the illumination. However, the terms "light" and "shade", when used in relation to each other, have no absolute meaning; they indicate merely a brightness comparison. A surface would be called "light" in comparison with another surface that was only half as bright as itself, but would be called "shade" in comparison with still another surface that was twice as bright as itself.

C. METHODS OF ACHIEVING BRIGHTNESS CONTRASTS

These differences in brightness, upon the perception of which the process of vision depends, may be produced by any one of several methods, either singly, or in combination. Those methods suited to use on the stage are three in number. The first two involve the use of plane surfaces, the other involves the use of three-dimensional, or solid, objects.

1. *Uniform Illumination.* Of the two methods involving plane surfaces, one is generally typical of the older stagecraft, the other typical of some phases of the newer stagecraft. The former achieves brightness contrasts on a plane surface by providing the surface with areas of different and varying values and illuminating the entire surface diffusely to a uniform intensity. As the illumination is

uniform over the entire surface, the brightness contrasts depend altogether upon the differences in the reflection coefficients of the various parts of the surface. This method is that used for pictures — pencil, charcoal, ink, and crayon sketches; photographs, and reproduced halftones such as those that appear in this volume; and also, in a more limited sense, line drawings and even printing. The various portions of the sketch or picture reflect the incident light in proportion to their value, and so build up the contrasts in brightness that are received by the eye and registered as a composite visual sensation. The application of this principle to the stage is particularly characteristic, especially when used by itself, of the older stagecraft, which profusely employed flat surfaces such as wings, drops, and borders to represent, by means of painted light, shade and shadow, three dimensional objects, all parts of which were illuminated to the same intensity by the indiscriminate use of the footlights, several sets of borderlights, and other equipment.

The light and shade and perspective effects of this older stagecraft are incongruous and grotesque. They will always appear futile when they are gauged (as at once they must be) against the living actor who plays in the midst of them. The perspective is violently distorted except for the few spectators so positioned that they occupy approximately the original point of view of the person who executed the setting; the light and shade, particularly the painted representations of shadows (including the necessarily heavy make-up on the actors), are completely irreconcilable both with the objects and the light sources that are presumed to give rise to them, as well as with the actual light sources used on the stage, which, when they really do cause shadows, provide shadows that are quite at variance with the painted ones. Happily, the use of painted shadows has almost disappeared — from the serious theatre, at least; yet its persistence on a small scale may occasionally still be seen in interior sets — particularly the painted panelings and moldings with their curious array of inverted-L-shaped painted representations of shadows.

2. *Uniform Value.* The second method of achieving brightness contrasts is more adapted to some phases of the newer stagecraft. Although this method also involves plane surfaces, it is quite the reverse of the method just discussed, inasmuch as the surface is of uniform value (usually white), rather than made up of many patches, or areas, of differing value. In this case, then, since the surface is of uniform value, the brightness contrasts can be produced only by the other factor involved, namely, by differences in the intensity of illumination over the surface. It is this method which is used for showing "magic lantern" slides, stereopticon pictures, and motion

pictures. The patches of light of various intensities strike the diffusely reflecting surface, or "screen", and are all reflected, with the true brightness contrasts between them still maintained, to the eye, where the first step in the formation of the complete composite visual sensation takes place. This second method is applied to stage lighting in the form of the cyclorama and the sky dome (where, although the surface is curved instead of plane, the principle still holds true) and the effect and scene-projecting apparatus such as the sciopticon, "effect machine", and Linnebach lantern. The cyclorama or the sky dome is a surface of uniform value, the texture of which is such as to provide diffuse reflection, and which, when lighted to various and carefully graded intensities by virtue of the position and direction of application of each of the light sources used, produces the illusion of distance without the revealing effect of unnatural and distorted perspective. The sciopticon, "effect machine", and Linnebach lantern, all produce the patches of light of various intensities by virtue of a painted or photographed "slide" which is inserted in the beam of light to modify the various portions of it as desired. These pieces of apparatus may be used to project their light either from before on to a diffusely reflecting surface, or from behind, on to a translucent, or diffusely *transmitting* surface, in order to convey the image, or picture in light, to the spectator.

3. *Solid Objects*. The third method of achieving brightness contrasts involves not plane surfaces but solid objects — objects in three dimensions — the illusion of which, on two dimensional surfaces, is the aim and purpose of the two methods just discussed. Except in unusual cases no one of the three methods of achieving brightness contrast is ever used alone; the three methods are usually used in conjunction with one another. But one is always predominant. Thus the first method is predominant in the older stagecraft, the second for certain phases of the newer stagecraft, and the third for the general phases of the newer stagecraft. With the introduction of the newer stagecraft this third method has become the most important of the three. No longer are architectural features of the stage setting, even furniture and properties, painted on backdrops, wings, and borders. They are actually present in three-dimensional form, and therefore require the proper type of lighting, the type that will best cause their appearance to conform to the effect, as a whole, that is being striven for. This method employs all the possibilities of the two factors that enter into brightness contrast — the value of the surface of the object (it may be uniform or not) and the intensity of the illumination (it may be uniform or not: it usually is not).

D. SHADOWS

Variations in this last-named factor — the intensity of illumination — take the form of shadows. A shadow is the darkness (or lack of light), either partial or complete (though seldom complete), caused by the interception of light by solid opaque objects, or by certain portions of them. Thus in three-dimensional visualization there are light and shadow, which quite correspond to the light and shade

Lighted from below, as from footlights. Lighted from above, as from borderlights.

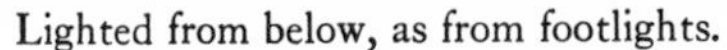

Illustrating how shadows caused by light from an obviously unnatural direction can distort the appearance of the human face.

of two-dimensional visualization. A study of shadows is most interesting, as, except under the simplest conditions, the character of a shadow can hardly be determined in advance. Such determination is difficult because the formation of a shadow depends upon so many variable factors — the properties of the surface it falls upon (the receiving surface), the object that casts it, and the light source. Nevertheless, a few general rules regarding the formation of shadows may be given, as follows.

The larger the light source, and the closer it is to the object, the more *diffused* its light is (and hence the larger the solid angle subtended by the light source), the softer will be the shadows cast. (Under a perfectly diffused light, no shadows at all can be cast.) Thus, an olivette equipped with a frosted gelatin in the slide grooves will cause much softer shadows than it would cause if the frosted gelatin were not used. A spotlight, being almost a point source of light, will produce hard, sharp, well-defined shadows. The optical system of a "soft-edge" spotlight is so arranged as to give the more diffuse effect of a larger light source, and hence provides softer shadows. The less the distance from the light source to the object, and also the greater the distance from the object to the receiving surface, the larger will be the shadow cast. Thus, the closer an actor moves to the footlights, the larger will become his shadow on the rear wall of the set or on the cyclorama; and, conversely, the farther an actor moves away from a spotlight, the smaller his shadow will become.

If, as is usually the case on the stage, more than one light source is employed, multiple shadows of each object, equal in number to the number of light sources, will be cast. Each shadow cast by one of the light sources will be lighted by the remaining light sources, and therefore its brightness contrast will be lowered. When other light sources, especially those of a much higher intensity, light a shadow to the extent that its brightness contrast with its surroundings is no longer perceptible, the shadow may be said to have "faded out", or to have been "killed." On the other hand, where multiple shadows cross or overlap, they will strengthen each other and build up a greater brightness contrast.

E. HIGHLIGHTS

An important factor in brightness contrast on solid objects is the highlight, which is most pronounced on surfaces exhibiting regular reflection, mixed reflection, or both. A highlight is usually a well defined area of comparatively high brightness, and is really the regularly reflected image of the light source; its shape depends on that of the light source itself, and on that of the reflecting surface of the object. With several light sources, an object is likely to show several distinct highlights.

F. VISUAL PERCEPTION OF OBJECTS

The third method of achieving brightness contrasts, namely, through the use of three-dimensional, or " solid," objects, is perhaps the most important of the three, not only on the stage, but for all purposes of visual perception, since by it one is enabled to perceive all objects that the eye encounters.

It has been pointed out that all objects (except, of course, self-luminous ones), are *visible* by virtue of the light they reflect to the eye. But they are *identified*, made recognizable and distinguishable, by virtue of the manner in which they reflect this light, and by the manner in which they are illuminated. Vision is essentially a process that involves the perception of differences in brightness, but the appearance of objects, the form they assume in the human consciousness, is essentially a matter of the arrangement, the composition, the distribution of these brightness variations — the light, shade, shadow, and highlights — over the surface of the object viewed. Three-dimensional objects such as a sphere, a cube, a cylinder, a cone, and irregular forms are recognized as such because the observer takes into account (unconsciously, of course) the position and character of the light source, the character and distribution of the patches of varying brightness on the object itself, and the character of the shadow cast, and links up his visual impression thus gained with the memory of past visual experiences that through constant repetition have become associated with definite three-dimensional forms.

The appearance of any object is determined by the resultant of many involved factors. The more important of these influencing factors, which may be classed as indicated, in three groups, are as follows:

FACTORS INFLUENCING THE APPEARANCE OF AN OBJECT

Pertaining to the object
1. Dimensions
2. Shape of outline
3. Contour of surface
4. Reflective nature of surface
5. Color
6. Environment

Pertaining to the illumination
7. Predominant direction
8. Degree of diffusion
9. Color
10. Intensity

Pertaining to the observer
11. Position
12. Previous visual experience
13. Acquaintance with object
14. Visual sensibility

Of the factors listed above, the fifth and ninth, relating to the effect of colored light on colored objects, will be discussed in the next chapter. The influence of the first factor, that of the physical dimensions — the actual size of the object — is so apparent as to require no comment. The second and seventh factors together will determine the shadow of the object that is cast on the surroundings, but even this is subject to variations because the surroundings will exert a considerable influence (sixth factor) on the cast shadow, par-

The human figure as it appears under light from various directions: in the center picture the statuette is lighted uniformly from all directions, and, as a result, its plastic nature is unrevealed.

ticularly if they are uncommon in nature. The reflective nature of the surface and its contour, in combination with the direction of the light (third, fourth, and seventh factors), together are the most important set of factors, since they will determine, in large measure, the distribution — the arrangement — of light, shade, shadow, and highlights over the surface of the object, by means of which its identity is revealed to the observer. The twelfth and thirteenth factors are important in this connection, because an observer must depend upon his familiarity with the object, or at least with that type of object, if he is quickly to recognize it and form a definite visual conception without detailed observation; if the object is new to him, he must rely upon his previous visual experience to indicate the nature of the object he is viewing under the lighting conditions that prevail. Of course, if his visual system is not "normal" (fourteenth factor) because of defective eyesight or color blindness, the object will assume (for him) a distorted and untrue appearance. The observer's position (eleventh factor) in relation to the object and the light source will determine that portion of the object visible to him, and hence the appearance of the object as a whole. As has already been pointed out, the more diffused the illumination (eighth factor) the softer the shadows; and the lower the intensity of illumination (tenth factor) the lower the brightness sensibility of the eye, and hence the less distinct the appearance of the object. When one takes into account these various factors, the relation of objective light to subjective light may therefore be summed up, diagrammatically, as follows: Light > illumination > brightness > contrasts in brightness > vision > visual identity.

G. CONTRIBUTION OF SUBJECTIVE LIGHT TO EACH OF THE FUNCTIONS OF STAGE LIGHTING

The foregoing material has been discussed in detail principally in recognition of the vital importance of the part played by subjective light (that is, the light and dark, the colorless, the brightness, sensations — not including the color sensations, which will be taken up in the next chapter) in the development of the stage picture, and of the necessity of a thorough working knowledge of the basic characteristics of light, on the part of the present-day stage worker, if he is to make the fullest possible use of the potent force that is now so conveniently at his disposal. Perhaps the most effective method of indicating the direct relation of subjective light to stage lighting is to point out its contribution to each of the five functions of stage lighting, as outlined in the first chapter: illumination, realism, composition and design, plastic expression, and psychological expression.

Illumination. This primary function of stage lighting is not always the easiest to accomplish, especially if any of the other functions of stage lighting are dominant in the lighting design of any production. Usually, however, no difficulty should be experienced in rendering visible to the spectators the actors and their actions and the other components of the stage picture. The factors that make for satisfactory visibility have just been discussed in detail. Since the human visual system has been evolved under natural daylight conditions, it is usually sufficient, for purposes of visibility, roughly to approximate these conditions. Of course, it is not necessary to provide the extremely high intensities of natural daylight — as pointed out on page 90, the practicable range of intensities for good visi-

The human face as it appears under light from various directions: in the center picture the head is lighted uniformly from all directions, and, because of the resultant lack of shadow, the features seem flat and expressionless.

bility is from ten to one hundred foot candles of illumination. The *predominant* direction of the light is the factor next in importance, and, again, if natural conditions are consulted as a criterion, a predominant downward direction will be found the most conducive to good visibility conditions. The quality of the illumination, or its degree of diffusion, is also important, inasmuch as the eye has become accustomed to viewing objects under light that is fairly diffused. If the light is not sufficiently diffused, sharp, harsh, and unnatural shadows will result; on the other hand, too much diffusion will destroy the very shadows that are so essential to vision.

Realism. Although realism in stage lighting can only seldom be achieved with any distinctive degree of success, there are a great many plays that will permit of no other method of treatment. Since the sun is the primary light source in nature, all considerations of outdoor natural illusive lighting must logically begin with it. It is almost impossible satisfactorily to simulate sunlight itself on the stage. The remoteness of the sun causes those of its rays that strike any restricted area such as may be represented on the stage, to be virtually parallel, and hence to cast parallel shadows. The close proximity of light sources on the stage is betrayed by the widely divergent shadows that it causes. Hence, the most satisfactory simulation of sunlight can be secured only by placing the light source at as remote a distance from the stage as possible, or by using reflectors of either the parabolic or Mangin type (properly equipped with louvers that will prevent any side spill of light), that provide parallel rays of light. The direction of sunlight is, of course, an indication of the time of day. At noon the sun is virtually overhead and casts very short, if any, shadows. At dawn and dusk its rays are almost horizontal, and consequently cast long shadows. Thus in its course across the sky, the sun (and the moon also, for that matter) casts shadows of varying length, according to the time of day. The stage shadows of the sun (or moon) are therefore very useful for indicating the hour of the day.

But light from the sun is never alone in nature: it is supplemented considerably by light from the sky, which serves as the most important of the secondary natural light sources. Skylight is at a minimum when the sky is blue, clear, and cloudless, and at a maximum when the sky is overcast with fairly heavy, white clouds that act as a diffusely transmitting medium for the sunlight behind them. The latter condition, that of an overcast sky, eliminates direct sunlight altogether and provides highly diffuse, almost non-shadow-forming light of much lower intensity than direct sunlight, and usually prevails when inclement weather is present or imminent. Usually, the thicker the clouds, and hence the lower the intensity of the natural light, the more inclement is the weather. Direct sunlight, with a clear sky, causing sharper and more intense shadows, is always indicative of fair weather. Furthermore, during the summer months, natural light is of higher intensity than during the winter months. Still another factor enters into natural outdoor lighting, and that is the reflected and multiple-reflected sunlight and skylight from surrounding objects, such as trees, grass, buildings, and pavement, which constitute another secondary source of natural light and provide an added element of diffusion and a more horizontal component of natural light direction. Thus, by adjusting the direction, the diffusion, and the intensity of light, it is possible to suggest place, hour, weather, and season. Of course, with the supplementary effects provided by proper lighting of the cyclorama and by mechanical "effect" apparatus — lightning, clouds, and so forth —

the possibilities for refinement of this suggestion of natural lighting conditions are almost limitless.

Natural lighting indoors is perhaps even more difficult to simulate than natural lighting outdoors. All the conditions discussed in the previous paragraph apply to it, with the added restriction that the natural light is admitted to an interior only through the usually comparatively small apertures such as doors and windows. Almost invariably interior natural lighting has a noticeably predominant direction from one side, since generally diffused light would result only in the case of a room that has equal window space on each wall, through which it receives light from an overcast sky. This predominant direction is about horizontal, especially at points remote from windows. Natural light indoors is also reflected and multiple-reflected from the objects in the room, and from the walls, the ceiling, and, to a lesser extent, the floor; however, only a moderate degree of diffusion prevails. Because of this comparative lack of diffusion, realism must occasionally be sacrificed to visibility in simulating natural lighting indoors. *Actually*, the face and figure of a person facing away from a window are rather dark, yet *practically*, on the stage, it becomes necessary to front-light actors who are facing the audience and who have their backs turned to the window or door in the rear wall of the set, to a higher intensity than true realism would permit. Of course, the presence of windows in the traditional missing front wall of the set might be assumed, but actual rooms that have windows facing each other from opposite walls are rare. Although on the stage the source of light should be implicitly apparent by means of the arrangement of the brightness contrasts that prevail, conditions of realistic lighting that prevent the spectators from easily viewing the characters and the objects on the stage should, as a rule, be overcome by the careful application of light intended for the purpose of visibility only. Realism in natural indoor lighting is so difficult to achieve that, unless the spectator is able to see simulated sunlight or the sky through a door or window, he is very likely to assume the result to be artificial indoor lighting.

Artificial indoor lighting is easiest to simulate because in this instance stage conditions most closely approach actual conditions. Actual light sources consist of fixtures suspended just above the face level, wall lights approximately at face level, and portable floor and table lamps just below face level. As the lights are usually shaded, and as they are usually several in number, they provide a moderate degree of diffusion, which is augmented by multiple reflections from objects in the room and from the walls, ceiling, and to a less extent, from the floor. The prevailing general directional effect is thus a soft, diffused, face-level lighting, which can be rather easily achieved on the stage by the judicious, balanced use of borderlights and footlights, or more effectively by front-of-house lighting with spotlights equipped with diffusing screens. Although this front-of-house lighting is nearer the horizontal in direction than the light from the borderlights, it is not quite horizontal, and for best results should strike the stage at an angle of about thirty degrees above the horizontal. This angle of application is usually sufficient to prevent unnatural and betraying shadows from falling on the rear wall of the set.

When all factors are considered, this front-of-house lighting will usually be found most satisfactory for realistic lighting in general, since a diffused face-level lighting, with a predominant direction, is its general requirement. There is no excuse for attempting an exact reproduction of the actual lighting conditions encountered in real life, because, as has been pointed out, it is practically impossible of accomplishment, and even if accomplished, it would very likely prove unsatisfactory, especially from the standpoint of visibility.

Composition and Design. Since the composition and design of the stage picture are left entirely to the individual discretion of the stage designer, little can be said regarding them except to point out the adaptability of light and shade to their purposes. Most stage designers rely primarily upon the design, the composition, and the coloring of the setting, the properties, and the costumes as the chief factors in achieving the effectiveness of the stage pictures that they create. For these, light is prepared to act as a unifying medium that will bind together all of those artistic forces, the combined effect of which will constitute the scene, — the stage picture. Perhaps the most important precept for obtaining this unifying effect of light is that stage light should have a predominant direction. Only a predominant direction of the light can give this unity of effect, because to give rise to unified brightness contrasts — light, shade, shadows, and highlights — a single unit light source (presupposed by a predominant direction of light that, however, may be obtained, if necessary, by several light sources, properly focussed, positioned, and directed) must be used rather than a number of scattered light sources in widely varying positions, which will result in conflicting, confusing, multiple light-and-shade effects that lack this desired unity. For this unifying effect, light that has a predominant direction may be either soft and diffused, in which case the result will be quiet, restful, charming, and beautiful; or it may be more uni-directional in nature, casting clearer and sharper shadows, rather bold and forceful, more powerfully unifying, so similar to the familiar effect of a typical Rembrandt portrait.

When stage designers definitely avail themselves of light and shade as contributory factors to the appearance of their stage picture, most of them employ light and shade in the rather supplementary manner just indicated. Many have begun to realize, however, the value of light and shade *per se*, and often build up their stage picture with comparatively neutral and simple surroundings and depend upon the correct application of light and shade to emphasize and high-light those features of the scene which are to be predominant, and to cast into a background of darkness less important features. Also, with patches of light and shade, properly graded and arranged, they create brightness contrasts according to a definite scheme of composition and design just as a painter creates them, for the same purpose, with pigments on canvas. If light is to be used in this manner, a large number of small individual light sources, preferably small spotlights, each susceptible to complete independent control — focussing, positioning, and directioning — are more useful than a fewer number of large light sources, all with a predominant direction. Although the artist in pigments has the advantage that lies in his product being lasting and permanent, the artist in light has all the advantages of applying to three-dimensional space a medium that is capable of a far wider range of adaptability and that is part of life itself. And furthermore, the artist in light has available the art of *mobile* design and composition in light which has only begun to be developed and which shows promise of untold possibilities.

Plastic Expression. Closely allied with the use of light for building up a stage picture through proper brightness contrasts is the use of light for giving relief, plasticity, solidity, to solid objects, for bringing out their three-dimensional features in a manner compatible with the general effect desired of the scene of which they are a part. The older stagecraft attempted, by means of painted light, shade, shadows, and highlights, to give a semblance of plasticity to the representations of solid objects on flat surfaces. The newer stagecraft, especially that phase of it which tends always towards greater realism, provides real objects which require real shadows for their proper appearance and identification. Appia was perhaps the first stage worker to draw attention to this formative power of light, and to prescribe for its effective use on the stage. For this purpose of plasticity, light is used as a sculptor would use his chisel and mallet — it is used to model the form of the objects to which it is applied. Just as a diffused, general illumination renders objects *visible*, so a sharper, more directional component of light renders these objects not only distinguishable, recognizable, identifiable, but also *expres-*

sive. Changing the direction of the light that strikes an object can radically change the appearance, and hence also the expression, of the object.

Footlights, projecting their light from below, have always been found unsatisfactory because the direction of their light produces shadows that cause the appearance of objects on the stage, particularly the features of the actors, to be unpleasantly and unnaturally distorted. Thus, very intense footlights illustrate the perverted use of this highly important formative, or statuesque, power of light. On the other hand, if the upward light from the footlights is balanced by downward light from the borderlights, an almost shadowless and flat condition results that is characteristic of the older stagecraft — a condition, in fact, that forced the older stagecraft to resort to painted shadows and to rather violent make-up on the actors. Light from overhead, as from the borderlights, causes heavy downward shadows and produces a massive, sculptured effect. Although this effect is somewhat fantastic, it is not nearly as unnatural and ugly as that caused by upward light from the footlights. Thus it is evident that this plastic power of light can be used to its greatest effectiveness only if the choice of the position and direction of the light sources is carefully made.

Psychological Expression. The production of mood, atmosphere, and feeling is chiefly dependent on color. The colorless visual sensations, those caused by light and shade, seem to be very restricted in their power to arouse emotional feeling. Only very broadly can light and shade aid psychologically in the interpretation of a play. As a crude, basic illustration: a dimly lighted scene will inspire gloom and suggest murkiness, tragedy, loneliness, suspicion, and so forth; a brightly lighted scene will give rise to a cheerful feeling and suggest wholesomeness and gayety. The form and the distribution of brightness contrasts in a scene also aid in conveying mood and symbolism. Brightly lighted objects before a dark background, dark objects before a light background — these conditions are indicative of the range of mood and expressiveness available. The plasmic powers of light, discussed above, can be invoked to change the appearance and expression of actors, properties, and setting to create a desired mood. The burden of mood creation, however, rests mainly on color. The almost unbelievably facile power of color for the expression of mood, feeling, and atmosphere will be discussed fully in the next chapter.

CHAPTER V · COLOR

Objective color — nature, propagation, the spectrum, production, complementary hues, terminology and units, color mixture, color diagrams; subjective color — colored visual sensations, effect of the color of light on the appearance of colored objects, psychology of color, color harmony, contribution of subjective color to each of the functions of stage lighting.

COLOR can be discussed similarly to light — that is, first from the objective point of view, and then from the subjective point of view. The statement is often made that color is unqualifiedly physiological, subjective, in nature; that color exists as a sensation only; that color has no purely physical significance. It is true that what is called "color" must be translated into nerve sensations by the retina of the eye and must activate certain brain cells before it be recorded, or impressed, on the visual consciousness. Until then it cannot really be said to exist — it is not humanly perceptible. But the properties of the natural phenomena that give rise to sensations of color constitute what may be termed the *objective* phase of color. The color sensations themselves, and the physiological and psychological reactions that they entail, constitute what may be termed the *subjective* phase of color. However, it is not quite as easy to segregate these two phases of color as it is to segregate those of light.

I. Objective Color

A. NATURE

Light has already been defined as "radiant energy", to which the visual organs respond, ranging in wave length from 0.35 micron to 0.75 micron. It so happens that light of one small range of wave lengths, from 0.40 micron to 0.43 micron, for instance, gives rise to a definite hue sensation, that light of another small range of wave lengths gives rise to another definite hue sensation, and so on. Under ordinary conditions, the eye can distinguish from twenty-five to thirty different hues. Under carefully arranged experimental conditions, however, visual systems that are high in hue sensibility can segregate over a hundred distinct hue sensations. When these different hues are arranged in the sequence of the wave lengths of the light that gave rise to them, they form a continuous, smooth gradation of hues that constitutes what is termed the *spectrum* of light. Each separate and distinct band of monochromatic light that causes a distinguishable hue sensation is termed a *spectral hue.* The composite hue sensation caused by several adjoining spectral hues, by light of a comparatively extended range of wave lengths, is termed the *dominant hue* of that particular range of wave lengths.

B. PROPAGATION

Monochromatic light, light of a spectral hue, of a dominant hue, are all subject to the same conditions that govern the propagation and other optical characteristics, such as reflection and refraction, of "white" light. Colored light, therefore, will behave identically the same with mirrors and lenses as will white light. So-called "white" light was that discussed in the previous chapter. White light is light that is composed of equal portions of all the spectral hues and that gives rise to a colorless light sensation.

C. THE SPECTRUM

The spectrum was first studied by Isaac Newton in 1666 when he decomposed a beam of white light into its spectral components by means of a glass prism. He observed that the hues he obtained were the same as those in nature's spectrum — the rainbow — and were

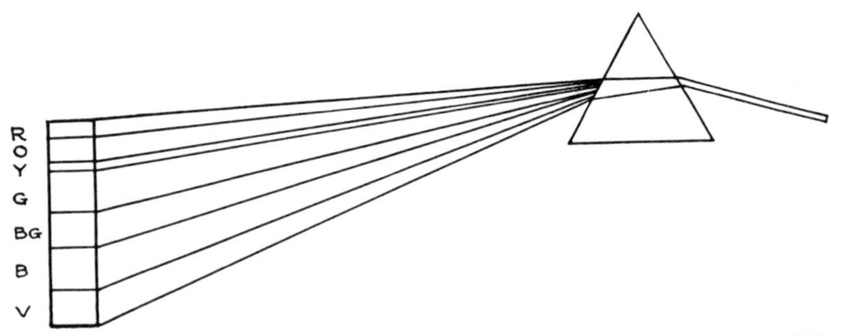

Illustrating the manner in which a glass prism resolves a beam of incident white light into its constituent colored rays. The red rays are refracted the least and the violet rays are refracted the most.

arranged in the same sequence. Violet, indigo, blue, green, yellow, orange, and red — in this order — were the principal hues that he distinguished. This decomposition of a thin beam of white light by a glass prism is possible because the various hues are not equally susceptible to the refractive, or bending, powers of the glass prism.

The violet rays are the most susceptible to refraction; each hue, in order, is less susceptible; and the red rays are the least susceptible. Hence the light rays of various wave lengths, that is, of various hues, are bent apart and can be separately observed. However, the ratio of wave length to degree of refraction does not decrease uniformly

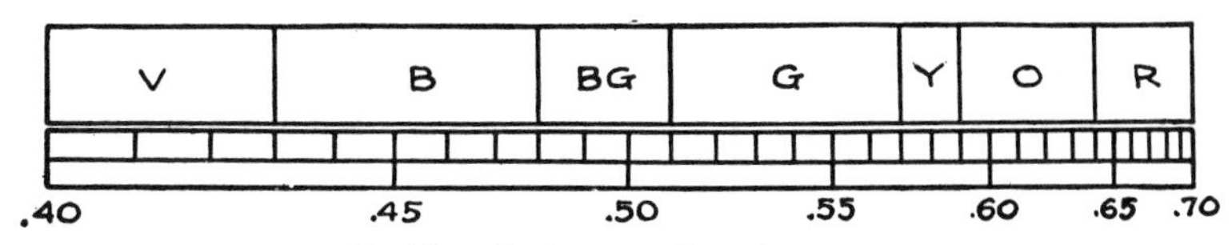

a. Position of colors on prismatic spectrum.

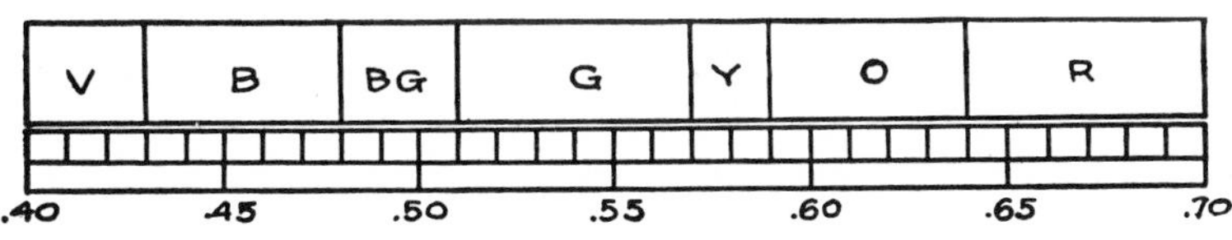

b. Position of colors on diffraction spectrum.

Spectrum diagrams. These diagrams will be found a convenient reference whenever the wave length of hues is mentioned in this volume. Wave-length units are expressed in microns, and the hues are, in order, violet, blue, blue-green, green, yellow, orange, and red.

— it changes more rapidly at the violet end of the spectrum than at the red end. As a result, the violet, blue, and green hues occupy much more space on the *prismatic spectrum* than is proportional to their actual presence — they seem to preponderate — their presence is unduly emphasized. However, the spectrum produced by a diffraction grating allots proportionate spaces to the various hues in accordance with a uniform scale of wave lengths. The *diffraction spectrum* is therefore a true spectrum.

Although wave lengths of 0.35 micron and 0.75 micron mark the extreme limits of the visible spectrum, the range for ordinary visual conditions is more truly from 0.40 micron to 0.70 micron. These even limits also help to simplify discussion. Radiant energy of wave length lower than 0.40 micron is termed ultra-violet; that of wave length higher than 0.70 micron is termed infra-red. Both the ultra-violet and the infra-red are ordinarily invisible.

Few investigators agree either as to the number of major hues segregated or as to the exact wave-length limits of each hue. This is due to the fact that there is really no marked division between the spectral hues — they blend into each other so gradually and so almost imperceptibly that an indefinite number of major hues can be chosen, and only arbitrary wave-length limits assigned to each. Perhaps the most convenient (though somewhat arbitrary) spectrum division for the purposes of this volume is one that chooses major hues and assigns wave-length limits to them as follows:

Hue	Wave-length Limits (in Microns)
Violet	0.40–0.43
Blue	.43– .48
Blue-green	.48– .51
Green	.51– .57
Yellow	.57– .59
Orange	.59– .64
Red	.64– .70

Present practice, it will be noted from the above table and from the foregoing spectrum diagrams, has abandoned the *indigo* of Newton and has established another hue — *blue-green*. The realization of the importance of the blue-green hue is constantly growing. It is to be regretted, none the less, that its name is a compound one rather than a more desirable individually descriptive one.

D. PRODUCTION

There are several methods of producing color. Two of them — refraction and diffraction — have already been mentioned. But these are not practicable methods. The method commonly used is *absorption*. Color production by absorption can take place either by selective transmission or by selective reflection.

In order to understand correctly the principles of color production by absorption, it is necessary to lay aside the popular impression that colored light is white light that has been changed, or transmuted, into colored light, or that it is white light that has been made to appear colored by "coloring it", or by "adding color to it." White light — theoretical white light, at least — contains equal amounts of light of all wave lengths, equal proportions of all the spectral hues. All the hues balance or neutralize each other, and the resultant light is colorless or "white." Therefore, white light, although it appears colorless, really contains all colors. It is possible to isolate any desired color, to produce any color, merely by absorbing, from the white light, all the hues except the one desired. If green light is desired, for instance, it can be obtained by absorbing the violet, blue, blue-green, yellow, orange, and red rays from the white light, thus leaving only the green light. The removal of the undesired hues is the particular function of a "color medium", which it performs by "selecting" the color desired and eliminating, by absorption, the remainder of the spectrum. This absorption can be accomplished by two methods, either by *transmitting* the white light through a thin sheet of transparent material such as colored glass or colored gelatin, or by *reflecting* it from an opaque surface, such as colored paper or colored silk. The former method constitutes *selective transmission*, the latter, *selective reflection*. Both methods, however, function by virtue of the absorption of the undesired hues in the incident white light.

Most color media or colored pigments or dyes used in practice do not completely absorb *all* the undesired hues. Nevertheless, those hues that they transmit or reflect combine to form a *dominant hue* which is equivalent in appearance to a single spectral hue, and which proves quite satisfactory for most purposes. The color produced by the usual type of color media, then, does not consist of a pure spectral hue, but of a number of hues, the proportions of which are such that together the several constituent hues form the desired dominant hue. For instance, a *pure* red color medium will transmit only a spectral red, whereas a regular commercial red color medium will transmit spectral red and also lesser amounts of the orange and yellow hues, but its dominant hue will be red. The usual blue color medium will absorb the yellow and orange hues, not quite all of the red hue, and will transmit mainly the blue and violet hues, and also some of the blue-green and green hues, but its dominant color will be blue.

Naturally, an illuminant which emits light that is rich in yellow, orange, and red rays, and poor in blue and violet rays, and which is therefore predominatingly yellow in hue, cannot be expected to provide as satisfactory a blue light, or as great a relative quantity of it, as white light would provide, when both are used in conjunction with a blue color medium. However, such yellowish light would provide excellent, and much, yellow, orange, or red light when used with the proper color medium. It is necessary, then, in order to produce light of any hue, that this hue be present in appreciable quantity, or that the hues combining to form an equivalent dominant hue be present in appreciable quantities, in the incident light delivered to the color medium. To this extent is the production of colored light dependent upon the spectral character of the illuminant used.

Direct noon sunlight is perhaps the nearest natural approach to a pure white light, although even it is a trifle yellowish. The light from a clear blue sky, on the other hand, is predominantly blue. Light from an incandescent lamp filament also contains light of all different hues, but it contains less light of the violet, blue, blue-green, and green hues than of the yellow, orange, and red hues. This explains its decidedly yellowish appearance when it is compared with sunlight. Of the light emitted by the three types of incandescent lamps, that of the obsolete carbon lamp is very yellowish, that of the tungsten vacuum (Mazda B) lamp is less yellowish, and that of the tungsten gas-filled (Mazda C) lamp is least yellowish. Although the light emitted by the last-named type of lamp is deficient in violet, blue, and blue-green rays, it is the nearest practicable approach to white light that is available at the present time. For this reason it is the most satisfactory to use for color production, especially for stage work. When any incandescent lamp is dimmed, the proportion of yellow, orange, and red rays will increase, until, when the lamp is dimmed almost to "black out", its filament will be a dull red. As the lamp is dimmed, therefore, its ability to produce blue light will be greatly reduced. Conversely, if an incandescent lamp is burned at "over-voltage", the proportion of violet, blue, and blue-green rays in its emitted light will be increased, making it possible to obtain more light of these hues from it. However, such practice tends to reduce the life of the lamp, and should be employed carefully, and only in cases of necessity.

Inasmuch as color production involves the absorption of light, it is only natural that a decrease in the intensity of light results if a color medium be placed before an incandescent lamp. To maintain a certain intensity of light it becomes necessary to provide a higher total wattage of the lamps used to produce the colored light. That portion of the light that is absorbed is changed to heat. This explains why a color medium in use, or any other object, in fact, that is absorbing light, is always of a higher temperature than that of non-absorbing objects.

Any color of light, then, may be produced, provided it be contained in the illuminant used. It may be segregated either by selective transmission or by selective reflection. The former process consists of the absorption of the undesired hues and the *transmission* of the desired hue. The latter process consists of the absorption of the undesired hues and the *reflection* of the desired hue, and is usually carried out by opaque materials. The property of selective *transmission* is what renders gelatin and glass color media, such as are used on the stage, so valuable for the convenient production of color when they are used with a light source such as the incandescent lamp. The property of selective *reflection* is the basis of the Fortuny system of stage lighting and is also used by David Belasco in his system of indirect stage lighting. The practical phases of color production by means of color media are treated at length in Chapter IX.

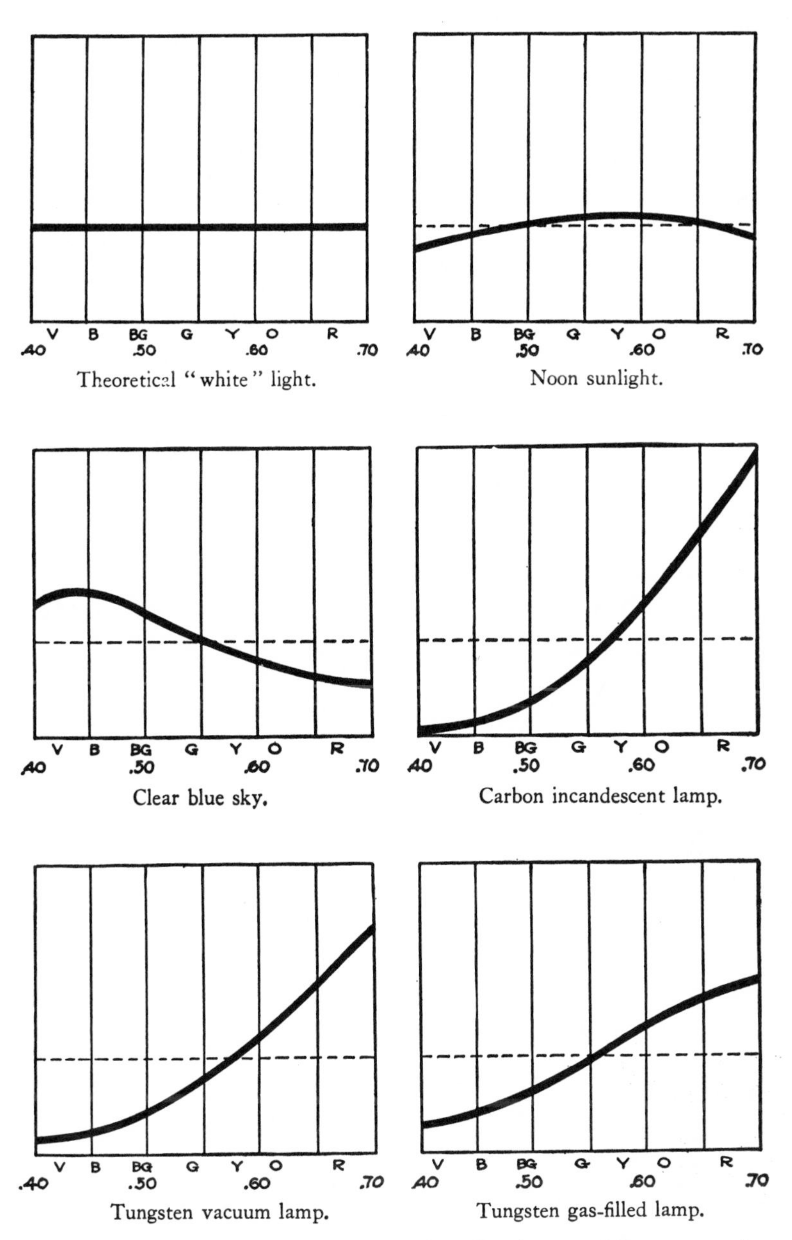

Theoretical "white" light.

Noon sunlight.

Clear blue sky.

Carbon incandescent lamp.

Tungsten vacuum lamp.

Tungsten gas-filled lamp.

Spectroscopic curves of the light emitted by various illuminants. These curves show the proportionality of colors in each illuminant. Wave-length units are expressed in microns.

E. COMPLEMENTARY HUES

Two hues of light that, when combined, form white light, are *complementary* to each other. If white light is projected through a color medium, the hue of the transmitted light is exactly complementary to the hue of the light absorbed by the color medium, since together these two hues had formed white light. If the major hues

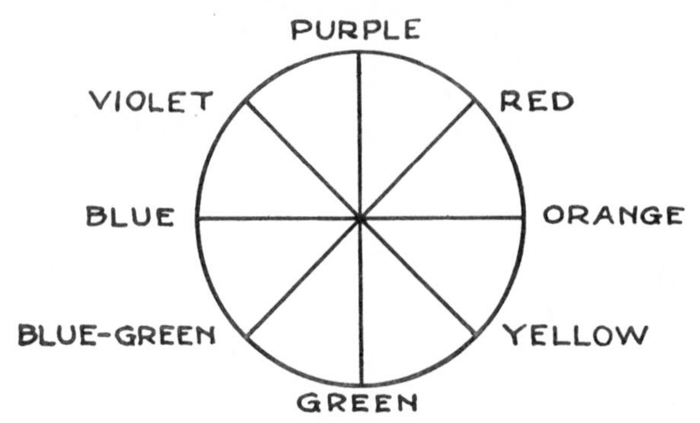

The color circle. By "bending the spectrum" around the circumference of a circle, and leaving space for the mixture of the end-hues, complementary hues will be found diametrically opposite each other.

of the visible spectrum — violet, blue, blue-green, green, yellow, orange, and red — are spaced equally around the circumference of a circle, and space left for the newly formed hue resulting from a mixture of the spectral end-hues, violet and red, the hues situated diametrically opposite each other are complementary. With the exception of the purple hues, any hue in existence can be exactly matched by the hue at some point in the spectrum. The purples are formed by the mixture of hues at the end of the spectrum, and are the only ones that need be "artificially" created — the only ones not found within the range of the visible spectrum.

F. TERMINOLOGY AND UNITS

Colors, in their many ramifications of tint and shade, are so numerous, so varied, so vague and indefinite, so affected by environment and by the quality of the illumination by which they are viewed, that it might seem as though no fixed terminology of color, no orderly arrangement, no systematic description, could be arrived at. But such is not the case. Each color possesses three characteristics by which it can be accurately described. These descriptive characteristics of color are *hue*, *saturation*, and *brightness* — the three color constants.

The most common property of color relied upon for the purpose of description is its *hue* — its spectral hue — its exact position within the range of the spectrum or, if it be a purple, the exact position, within the spectrum, of its complementary hue. "Hue is that property of color by which the various spectral regions are characteristically distinguished." Hue is known to the layman as the "*color*", such as blue, yellow, green, and so forth. Hue is the name applied to light of a certain wave length, or to light whose wave length, or range of wave lengths, lies between closely fixed limits, such as those of the major spectral hues. The accurate designation of the dominant hue of any color consists of the wave length of the equivalent spectral hue, or if it be a purple, of the wave length of the equivalent spectral hue of its complementary. Thus, the hue of sulphur is designated as 0.571 micron, and that of Paris green as 0.511 micron.

The second descriptive property of color is its *saturation*. Saturation of a color is "its degree of freedom from admixture with white." A pure spectral hue is considered to be fully saturated — its saturation is said to be 100%. If a pure spectral hue is diluted, so to speak, by admixture with white light, it becomes unsaturated. As more white light is added, the hue becomes fainter and fainter — the saturation decreases — until it becomes almost completely desaturated and virtually disappears. White, therefore, might be considered as the limiting color having no hue and having zero saturation. Saturation is designated by percentage. Thus, if a color contain an admixture of 25% of white light, its saturation is said to be 75% (100% − 25%). An unsaturated hue is termed a *tint* — thus the series of pinks are reds at various degrees of saturation, and the color of a clear blue sky is a blue of wave length 0.472 micron at 40% saturation.

The third characteristic of a color that enters into its description is its *brightness*. Brightness in relation to colorless visual sensations has been discussed in the previous chapter. Its relation to color sensations is quite similar. If the inherent color of a surface or of a pigment, viewed under white light, be referred to, its *relative* brightness is designated by its coefficient of reflection — the ratio of incident light to reflected light, irrespective of the color of the latter. If colored *illumination* be referred to, its brightness may be expressed in foot candles. If colored *light* be referred to, its brightness in any direction may be expressed in candle power. The *absolute* brightness of a colored surface, regardless of the illumination, may be expressed by the amount of colored light it emits per unit area (the unit is the *lambert* — one lumen per square centimeter).

Thus the unit of measurement for the brightness of any color depends upon the occurrence of the color — upon the form in which the "color" manifests itself. The brightness of a color is termed its *value*, or its *shade*. Navy blue is a very dark shade of blue, the hue of which is 0.472 micron, and the brightness (expressed as the coefficient of reflection) only 0.019. Sulphur is a rather light shade of 0.571 micron yellow, its brightness (also expressed as the coefficient of reflection) being as high as 0.80.

Variations in saturation and brightness can be very easily and vividly demonstrated with the aid of two spotlights, each on a dimmer. The first spotlight should be equipped with a gelatin color medium of a fair degree of purity (red will prove the most satisfactory). The second spotlight should have no color medium and should provide only clear light. Both spotlights should be directed on to a diffuse white surface, and should be so adjusted that both spots of light are equal in size and are superimposed on each other. With the first spotlight at "full on", and the second at "black out", a spot of light of a fairly pure hue will be projected on the screen. The saturation of this color can be changed, and tints produced, by adjusting the dimmer on the second spotlight. This will dilute the pure hue with clear light. The brightness of the color can be changed by adjusting the dimmer on the first spotlight. This changes the intensity of the colored light itself. Thus can the entire range of both saturation and brightness of a single hue be demonstrated.

Colors are analyzed — their hue, brightness, and saturation are determined — by means of delicate and expensive precision instruments such as spectroscopes, spectrophotometers, and colorimeters. Perhaps the most effective method of illustrating the use and usefulness of these three color constants is to present actual, concrete values for colors of materials that are universally familiar. The values given in the following table have all been determined by careful investigation on the part of scientific color experts, mainly by Messrs. Nutting, Abney, and Jones, and have been selected from condensed versions of their original reports.

An intelligent study of this table will reveal many interesting, and even absorbing, facts regarding the colors encountered in everyday life, and will help render the subject of color composition and nomenclature easily comprehensible by virtue of the relation it indicates between casual observation and scientific determination. *Bearing in mind* the spectrum diagram on page 107, a few of the more obvious and significant comments that interpretation of the values in the table might inspire are as follows.

QUANTITATIVE ANALYSIS OF FAMILIAR COLORS

Material	Hue (Wave Length in Microns)	Saturation (Per Cent)	Brightness (Coefficient of Reflection)
Ruby (glass)	0.622	98	0.131*
Vermilion (pigment)	.610	97.5	.148
Chocolate	.595	30	.05
Orange (pigment)	.5915	96	.62
Gold	.591	36	.21
Chrome yellow (pigment)	.5835	74	.77
Dark brass	.583	39	.25
Butter	.580	72	.64
Light brass	.575	40	.32
Sulphur	.571	52	.80
Bottle-green (glass)	.551	69	.106*
Emerald-green (pigment)	.522	41	.227
Paris-green	.511	44	.386
Signal-green (glass)	.510	39	.194*
Ultramarine-blue (pigment)	.472	39	.044
Navy-blue	.472	10	.019
Cobalt-blue (glass)	.4675	58	.038*
Illuminants			
Candle	.593	87	†
Carbon incandescent lamp	.597	75	†
Tungsten vacuum lamp	.586	66	†
Tungsten gas-filled lamp	.584	47	†
Clear blue sky	.472	40	†

* Coefficient of *transmission*.

† Since the brightness of the color of illuminants depends upon their intensity, which is not fixed, no values can be given.

From the wave length of the dominant hue, it is evident that the hue of ruby glass is really more of an orange-red than a red. Vermilion is still more orange. Ruby glass and vermilion and orange pigments are almost completely saturated — they are almost the pure hues of their respective wave lengths. They differ greatly in brightness, however, the orange pigment being by far the lightest color of the three. It seems strange that chocolate, orange pigment, and gold, all differing so widely in appearance, have colors almost identical in hue. This difference in appearance can be accounted for by the high brightness and saturation values of the orange pigment, and by the fact that the color of gold is more than four times as bright as that of chocolate. Similarly, the hues of chrome-yellow pigment, dark brass, and butter are almost the same. The similarity in appearance between chrome-yellow and butter is explained by the fact that their hue, saturation, and brightness values do not lie so far apart. The dark brass has much lower saturation and brightness values, but because these values lie so close to those of gold, there is but a slight difference in appearance between these two materials. This difference in appearance is perceptible mainly because the color of gold is slightly richer — it tends a little more toward the red end of the spectrum than does the color of dark brass. Light brass and sulphur differ in appearance mainly in brightness and less in saturation. Incidentally, sulphur is the brightest material listed in the table. The hue of bottle-green glass is positioned about midway in the spectrum, and therefore is a good example of a green hue that is uninfluenced by the blue or yellow on either side of it in the spectrum. The hue of emerald-green pigment is more blue than that of bottle-green, and the hue of Paris green and signal green is hardly more than a blue-green. The two latter colors differ principally in brightness. Navy blue is exceptionally low, both in brightness and saturation, a fact that explains its almost black appearance. Ultramarine-blue pigment is the same as navy blue in hue, but is almost four times as saturated, and more than twice as bright. It is a strange fact that the colors of ultramarine-blue pigment and of a clear blue sky are virtually alike in hue and saturation. The great difference lies, of course, in the brightness, which in the case of a clear blue sky is exceptionally high. This fact would seem to indicate that ultramarine-blue pigment, if used on the sky drop or cyclorama on the stage, would give an excellent sky effect, *provided* that it could be illuminated to a high enough intensity with clear light.

The difference in the color, or spectral quality, of the light furnished by the carbon lamp, the tungsten vacuum lamp, and the tungsten gas-filled lamp, is explained by the color analyses. The hue of the light from the carbon lamp is more red than that from the tungsten vacuum lamp. The latter, however, is still more yellow than the light from the tungsten gas-filled lamp. That the tungsten gas-filled lamp gives the "whitest" light of the three types of lamps is again strikingly evidenced, this time by the saturation values. These show that light from the carbon lamp contains the least proportion of white light (because its hue is the most saturated); that light from the tungsten vacuum lamp contains a greater proportion of white light; and that light from the tungsten gas-filled lamp contains the greatest proportion of white light. Light from the candle is shown to be of almost a pure orange-yellow hue.

It is interesting to observe that the colors of dark brass, signal-green glass, and ultramarine-blue pigment, which differ so widely in appearance, are of exactly the same degree of saturation. It will be noticed that the pigments, as a class, have about the highest average saturation and brightness. This is only natural, since these properties — purity and brightness — are what make colored materials particularly suitable as pigments. The colored glasses also have a high average saturation, but they achieve this purity of color only by their comparatively high density, and, consequently, at a great sacrifice in brightness.

Thus will a study of the table of color analyses help to create in the mind of the reader a clearer conception of the combined influence of hue, saturation, and brightness on the ultimate appearance of colors. The limited number of color analyses presented in this table shows how definite and accurate can be the description of a color if it be given in terms of the three color-constants. It may seem nothing short of sacrilege to reduce to numerical quantities the infinite possible variations of the beautiful, living, dynamic force that color is. And this is decidedly not the present recommendation. It cannot be denied, however, that there exists a crying need for a really usable nomenclature of color. A widespread genuine appreciation of color, and a full development of the art of color, cannot take place until some effective system of color notation is devised, recognized, and universally adopted. It is necessary that such a system of color notation take into account the three color-constants. These may be expressed numerically, perhaps, if it is found impossible to express them otherwise. The present method of designating colors employs vague and meaningless terms, such as old rose, orchid, cardinal red, ecru, dawn, coral, peach, apricot, salmon, bisque, nude, tan, maize, jade green, Nile green, powder blue, French blue, and navy blue — all of which have been transcribed from the carton containing a packet of popular dye. Many attempts have been made, and are being made, to devise a satisfactory color notation, but so far none has been successful to the point of having been accorded universal acknowledgment and adoption. It would seem that almost any organized system of color nomenclature would be preferable to the haphazard one that now prevails — one that must call upon almost every thing and condition in existence for assistance in describing color.

G. COLOR MIXTURE

As a result of numerous experiments and attempts made to establish a system of color notation, it has been definitely ascertained that the two spectral end-hues — violet and red — and the spectral mid-hue — green — constitute a set of color primaries of light, in terms of which any color of light can be expressed. The term violet has become generally supplanted by the term blue, so that now the *light color primaries* may be said to be *blue*, *green*, and *red*. The exact hue, the spectral position, the wave length of each of these three light primaries, is a moot question which is still to be definitely settled. For the purposes of this volume, however, it will be simplest and most convenient to assume, arbitrarily, as concepts of the three primary colors of light, the following: For *blue*, the dominant hue of light of wave length ranging from 0.40 micron to 0.50 micron; for *green*, the dominant hue of light of wave length ranging from 0.50 micron to 0.60 micron; for red, the dominant hue of light of wave length ranging from 0.60 micron to 0.70 micron.

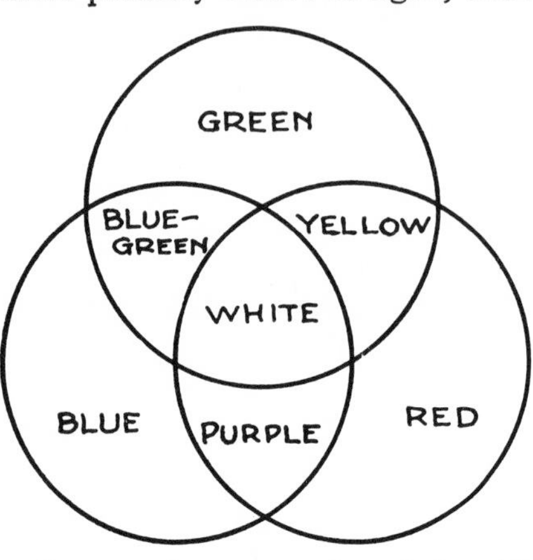

A diagrammatic representation of the additive method of color mixture, that applies to mixtures of colored light.

By mixing light of these three primary colors in the proper proportions, light of any color can be produced. If equal portions of the three primaries are mixed, white light will result. If equal portions of the light primaries are mixed in pairs, the color secondaries will result. Blue and green form blue-green; green and red form yellow; and red and blue form purple. Thus the *light color secondaries* are blue-green, yellow, and purple. Of course, with varying proportions of the three light primaries, it is possible to produce light of any color. Such color mixture is possible mainly because the eye is synthetic rather than analytic in its action. The ear, for example, is capable of sound analysis, since it can distinguish in music the individual tones that comprise a chord. But the eye cannot distinguish between a yellow that is a pure monochromatic spectral hue, and one that is a well-balanced mixture of red and green.

Each light primary is complementary in hue to a mixture of the two other light primaries, since together all three form white light. Thus, blue is complementary to yellow (green and red); green is complementary to purple (red and blue); and red is complementary to blue-green.

It is quite possible to obtain these color-mixture results in practice, but it is necessary to use color media that provide light of a fair degree of purity. Gelatins made by Munroe R. Pevear are of a very high purity, and serve excellently. Since 1913 he has been making absolutely pure primary light filters, mounted upon glass, for special laboratory use. If each of three spotlights is equipped with a pure primary color media, and the beam of light from each is directed to overlapping areas on a white surface, it is possible, by adjusting the intensity of each light by means of a dimmer, to demonstrate very simply the fundamental principles of light color mixture. This method of color mixture is known as the *additive method* of color mixture, because it forms colors by direct addition and combination of the three light primaries. The additive method of color mixture applies only to light.

The other method of color mixture is known as the *subtractive method*, and applies to pigments and dyes. Because of the inherent relation existing between the two methods of color mixture, the secondaries of the additive method serve as the primaries of the subtractive method. That is, the light secondaries — blue-green, yellow, and purple — are the pigment primaries. Because of the lack of a definite color notation, the pigment primaries, which have been much more widely known and used than the light primaries, have been erroneously termed blue, yellow, and red. The pigment primary commonly known as blue is not a pure blue, but is actually a blue-green; the pigment primary commonly known as red is not a pure red, — it contains blue, and is actually a purple. The yellow has been correctly named. The *pigment primaries*, therefore, are *not* blue, yellow, and red, but *blue-green*, *yellow*, and *purple*.

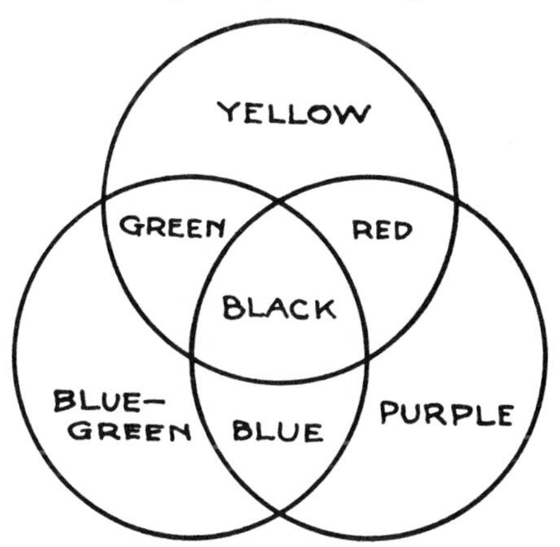

A diagrammatic representation of the subtractive method of color mixture, that applies to mixtures of colored pigments.

Pigment color mixture acts by subtraction. The color of a pigment, or of a mixture of pigments, is due to the reflection of residual rays of colored light after the subtraction of the remaining rays from the incident light. This subtraction takes place by virtue of absorption. The reflected rays form the dominant hue of the color. If white light strikes a yellow surface, the blue rays are subtracted from the white light — absorbed by the pigment — and only the red and green rays are reflected to the eye, where together they give the sensation of yellow. Similarly, then, blue-green pigment subtracts the red rays, and purple pigment subtracts the green rays. Therefore, if white light strikes a mixture of yellow and blue-green (commonly termed blue) pigments, the yellow will subtract the blue rays, the blue-green will subtract the red rays, and only the green rays remain to be reflected. This explains why yellow pigment and so-called blue pigment (really blue-green) produce green upon being mixed. Similarly, yellow and purple will produce red, and purple and blue-green will produce blue. Thus, the pigment secondaries are blue, green, and red (the *light* primaries). Each pigment primary subtracts one of the light primaries from white light. Hence a mixture of the three pigment primaries would reflect no light at all, and would appear black.

To sum up: The *additive method* of color mixture is fundamental in nature. It governs the mixture of colored *light*. Its primaries are blue, green, and red; its secondaries are blue-green, yellow (red-green), and purple (blue-red). A mixture of the three light primaries always tends toward the formation of *white*. The *subtractive method* of color mixture is really based upon the additive method. It governs the mixture of pigments and other coloring materials, which depend for their perception upon the colored light they produce. Its primaries are blue-green (commonly but erroneously termed blue), yellow, and purple (commonly but erroneously termed red); its secondaries are blue, green, and red. A mixture of the three pigment primaries always tends toward the production of *black*. These two methods may be said to be the converse of each other, the additive method being of basic importance.

The methods of color mixture, both for light and for pigments, are extremely valuable in designing stage lighting. Especially will a knowledge of these two methods enable the stage designer to understand the often mystifying action of colored light in changing the appearance of colored objects. It will therefore help him to plan intelligently the color of his settings, his costumes, and his lighting, so that these important factors will be sure to work together harmoniously and add to the effectiveness of a scene rather than detract from it.

H. COLOR DIAGRAMS

Perhaps the most effective method of aiding in the visualization and conception of the subject of color, especially of its physical basis, its objective phase, is to present several sketches that diagrammatically represent the factors that enter into color appearance, and the relation of these factors to the general scheme of color formation.

The first of these diagrammatic representations is the *color triangle.* The three light primaries — blue, green, and red — are considered to be situated exactly at the corners of an equilateral triangle. The three hues are present in equal amounts, and each

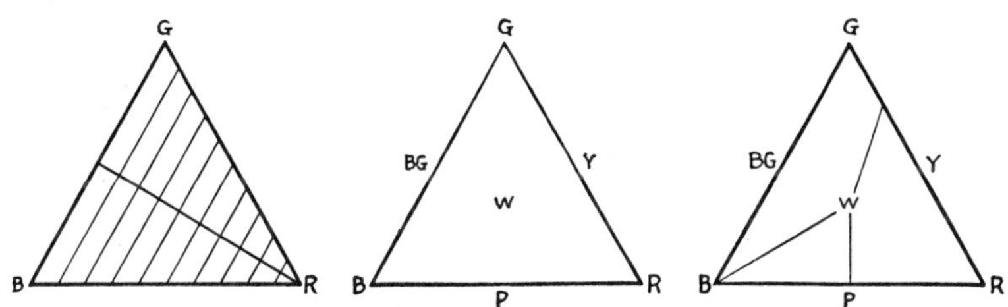

A color triangle. The first diagram represents the position of the three primary colors of light — red, green, and blue, each at the apex of an equilateral triangle. The mixitive influence of the red hue can be represented as decreasing from maximum to minimum along the central line of the triangle. Along the other lines perpendicular to the central line the influence of the red hue has the same value. The mixitive influence of both the green and blue hues may be represented in a similar fashion. The second diagram shows the secondary hues, blue-green, yellow, and purple, at the center of each of the sides of the triangle along which the fully saturated hues are found, and white at the center of the triangle. In the third diagram along the lines radiating from the "white position" to the sides of the triangle, may be found the various degrees of saturation of the hues represented by the respective perimeter positions — blue, purple, and yellow-green.

exerts its greatest influence at the corner at which it is situated. As the distance from the corner of a primary hue increases, in the direction perpendicular to the opposite side, the influence of that hue decreases at a uniform rate, until, at the side opposite the corner, the influence of the hue is just zero, along that entire side. The influence of any hue, then, is unity at its corner, is zero along the entire opposite side, and is equal along lines parallel to this opposite side. The exact degree of influence along any one of these parallel lines is dependent upon the distance of the line from the hue corner (the greater the distance, the less the influence).

Then, for any point within the color triangle, the influence of each hue may be expressed in the form of a triple ratio whose components will total unity. At the center of the triangle, where the influence of each hue is the same, white light will result. It can be expressed as $\frac{1}{3}$ blue, $\frac{1}{3}$ green, $\frac{1}{3}$ red. Along the perimeter of the triangle, where only two colors are mixed (the influence of the third being zero), all the saturated hues are found. At the centers of the three sides are found the light secondaries. Purple, for instance, would be expressed as $\frac{1}{2}$ blue, 0 green, $\frac{1}{2}$ red. Any pure, fully saturated hue has a position on the perimeter of the triangle. Therefore, on a line joining the perimeter position of any pure hue with the center of the triangle are found all the degrees of saturation of that hue, from one hundred per cent saturation at the perimeter, to zero saturation at the center of the triangle. Thus the position of any color in the color triangle is an index to its hue and saturation. All the colors in any color triangle would, naturally, be of the same brightness.

The theoretical color triangle for light color mixture, as just described, can be roughly approximated for practical experiment and demonstration by mounting small incandescent lamps (40 watt for red, 50 watt for green, and 60 watt for blue), properly shaded, at the corners of an equilateral triangle about two feet on a side. The lamps may either be colored with lamp dip, or be provided with small reflectors and gelatin or glass color media. The surface of the triangle should be a diffuse white — white blotting paper will serve well. By this means may be demonstrated the color triangle for light, which is a convenient help for theoretically visualizing the influence of each of two of the three color constants — hue and saturation.

Variations of the remaining color constant — brightness — cannot be represented on the color triangle, which is a two-dimensional plane surface. Another dimension is needed. In conjunction with the color triangle, this third dimension, vertical downwards in direction, will form a color solid — an inverted pyramid. The base of this *color pyramid* is the color triangle itself, and the apex is situated directly below the center of the color triangle. This apex can then represent black, and since the center of the basic triangle represents white, all the shades of gray from white down to black are found on the vertical line joining these two points.

The hue and brightness of a particular color are represented by a point in the color triangle at the base. Hence, on a line joining this point with the apex are situated all the brightnesses, all the shades, of that color, the hue and saturation remaining constant. On the intersected triangles parallel to and below the base are found the shades of the colors in the base color triangle, still in their relative positions. As the apex is approached — as the shades grow darker — the triangles become smaller. This crowding together of colors near the apex is representative of the decreased ability of the eye to distinguish between colors whose shades are very dark. All colors of zero brightness merge into black at the apex. On the three faces of the pyramid are found the varying shades of the saturated hues situated on the perimeter of the triangle. Thus any possible color of light, of any hue, saturation, and brightness, as well as white, grays, and black, can be represented by a point either on or within the color pyramid for light.

This scheme of diagrammatic representation is often used for color of light. In counterpart form it can also be used to represent the color of pigments. It has been pointed out that additive light color mixture always tends toward the formation of white, whereas subtractive pigment color mixture always tends toward the formation of black. Accordingly, therefore, a color triangle for pigments, similar in principle to that for light, can be hypothetically assumed with the pigment primaries—blue-green, yellow, and purple—at the corners. The center of the triangle would represent *black*. Hence, the color triangle for pigments would represent pigment colors of all hues and brightnesses, but of uniform, full saturation. A third direction, vertical upwards, would form a color pyramid for pigments that would have *white* as its apex. The vertical direction would then represent various tints, various degrees of saturation, of the colors whose hues and brightnesses are represented in the base triangle.

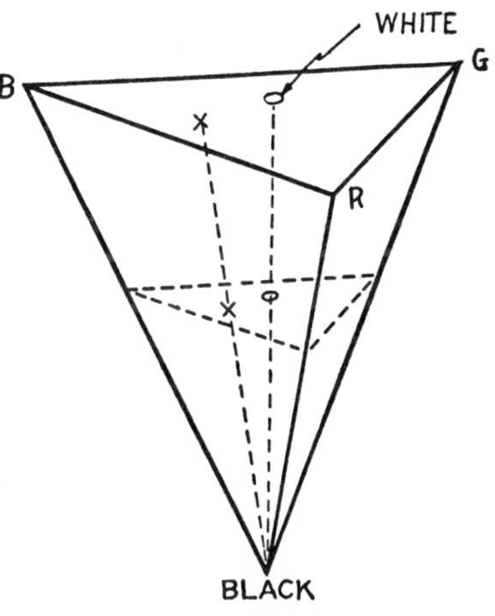

Color pyramid. An extension of the color representative system of the color triangle. The apex of the pyramid represents black, and on lines extending from it to various points within the color triangle may be found all the shades, the hues and saturation remaining constant, of the colors represented by the respective points in the color triangle.

These color diagrams are meant only as an aid in the visualization of the objective phase of color and should not be interpreted as an attempt to set forth a diagrammatic color notation. For the latter purpose, the diagrams would have to be considerably modified to compensate for various physiological and psychological phenomena—hue sensibility and brightness sensibility of the eye, the color sensation values of the various spectrum wave lengths, the effect of environment on color appearance, and many others. Perhaps the fundamental reason for the failure of many proposed schemes of color notation lies in the fact that an attempt has been made to force the subject of color into some rigid, uncompromising, arbitrary geometrical or mathematical form, whereas, in the last analysis, color is a human sensation, and is therefore subject to the vagaries of human processes and reactions. Although some material that is arbitrary appears on the foregoing pages of this chapter, its presence can perhaps be justified by the necessary rôle it assumes in the presentation of an elementary concept of so involved and indeterminate a subject as that of color.

II. Subjective Color

It has been pointed out that the colorless visual sensations, those involving only the perception of brightness differences, play a much more important part in the human visual process, in the discernment of the presence and the size and shape of objects, than do the sensations of color. But color is beyond all doubt the far superior medium for the creation of appearances that possess a variety of appeal, that can be esthetically pleasing and expressive, that can be impressive, effective, and emotive in their action on the human consciousness.

A. COLORED VISUAL SENSATIONS

The exact physiological process by which the human visual system accomplishes the perception of color has not yet been definitely and finally determined. One of the most plausible theories of color vision is the Young-Helmholtz theory, which presupposes the existence of three substances or sets of nerves in the optical system, each of which is stimulated by one of the three primary colors of light — blue, green, and red. These three sets of nerves build up a composite color sensation, and hence perceive color, by acting together, in accordance with the laws of additive color mixture, and in combination with a fourth set of nerves which registers brightness sensations. Thus in the Young-Helmholtz theory, which is basically physical in principle, the three sets of "color nerves", as they might be called, register the hue and saturation of a color, and the fourth set of nerves registers the brightness. Another important theory of color vision, the Hering theory, explains color vision more from the physiological and psychological points of view, more directly in terms of the sensations of color. Other color vision theories involve the "gray molecule", the "rods" and "cones", and the "visual purple." Although several of these theories are highly plausible, no one of them is entirely successful in explaining several visual phenomena that are irregular, or exceptional, in nature.

Hue sensibility, the ability of the eye to distinguish between hues that are adjacent in the spectrum, varies for different parts of the spectrum. The eye can distinguish the greatest number of hues in the yellow portion of the spectrum, less in the green, still less in the blue, and least in the red. Under good conditions the eye can distinguish, altogether, approximately 125 perceptibly different hues (including the extra-spectral purple hues); it can distinguish approximately twenty different steps of saturation, from zero to one hundred per cent; and it can distinguish approximately one hundred different degrees of brightness. Thus it is possible for the eye to perceive and distinguish the enormous total of 250,000 colors.

Hue visibility, or hue luminosity — the degree of luminous sensation produced by light of any hue — also varies for different regions of the spectrum. The maximum hue sensation is produced by a yellowish-green hue of wave length approximately 0.55 micron — the mid-point of the spectrum. On either side of this spectrum midpoint, approaching the ends of the spectrum, the hues gradually become "less visible"; that is, the visual sensation they produce is weaker, until at the ends of the spectrum the hues fail to produce any sensation. Thus a yellowish-green hue produces the strongest visual sensation, and deep blue and deep red hues produce the weakest visual sensations. The reason that the usual red color appears so much brighter than the usual blue one is that commercial red pigments and color media reflect, or transmit, besides red, also an appreciable amount of the more luminous yellow rays. However, a deep pure red color is just as dense as a pure blue color. The fact that yellow and red rays preponderate in present-day light sources has also the effect of intensifying the luminosity of the yellow and red hues.

Chromatic adaptation of the visual system is another important physiological problem that affects the final perception, or rather, the appearance, of color. If the eye is exposed for some time to light of any hue, the set of nerves used for the perception of that hue becomes fatigued. Colors viewed immediately after this exposure will be affected to the extent of appearing to contain less of the original hue viewed than they actually contain. For example, if the eye has become accustomed to the yellowish light of artificial illuminants, even the slightly yellowish sunlight will appear blue. These after-sensations always tend toward the complements of the hues just previously viewed, and disappear as the eye grows accustomed to the changed surroundings. The persistence of the after-sensation increases with the intensity and duration of the original exposure. This phenomenon explains why, for dark outdoor night scenes, or even moonlight scenes, on the stage, light of some color of blue is always used rather than merely a low intensity of clear light, which would produce a composition of grays, as is really the case, physically speaking, in nature. This practice is due to the fact that the eye, having become accustomed to the pale-yellow color of sunlight, and of artificial light indoors, has become unable to perceive the low intensity of the yellow component of dim, clear light, and registers a blue (complement of yellow) sensation when it is afterward exposed to little or no light. If the effect of night vision out-of-doors is to be represented on the stage, the effect presented to the spectators must be in keeping with this visual effect, or illusion, as it might be called, that they have accepted as customary. The blue light so used on the stage is often too bright — too pronounced — a common error which causes such lighting to defeat its own ends.

Another visual phenomenon, somewhat similar in nature to that of chromatic adaptation, is the effect of *simultaneous contrast*. When two colors are placed in juxtaposition, each will not have quite the same appearance that it would have if viewed alone. Usually a color will be "heightened" in effect when placed alongside another, especially if the latter is complementary in hue. It seems that each color registered on the retina of the eye "induces" a complementary hue adjacent to itself on the retinal area, and that the appearance of each color whose image falls adjacent to that of the first color is influenced by the faint induced complementary hue. Thus a gray patch appears a faint purple, or pink, when it is surrounded by a large area of green. Some of these effects of simultaneous contrast are very involved and are difficult to explain, and their insidious action will often make or mar the color composition of any picture or scene. These effects, which defy description, constitute an important factor in color harmony, and hence also in the design of settings and costumes for the stage. A good understanding of them is indispensable to every artist and designer, and is acquired only through experience.

B. EFFECT OF THE COLOR OF LIGHT ON THE APPEARANCE OF COLORED OBJECTS

But perhaps the most striking, the most important, visual phenomenon, the one that applies most directly to the subject of stage lighting and stage design, is the effect produced upon the apparent color of objects by the color of the light under which they are viewed. Every stage worker should be thoroughly familiar with these effects, for so much that is vitally important in stagecraft depends upon them. The most beautiful scenery and costumes may be utterly ruined in appearance if they are used under stage lighting for which they were not designed. On the other hand, they may appear altogether unsuitable, and even dull and ugly, until they are viewed under the proper lighting.

The principle underlying the action of colored light on the appearance of colored objects is very simple, even though its practical application is somewhat involved. It has been pointed out that objects are visible only because they reflect light to the eye. Colored objects appear colored because they selectively reflect the incident light under which they are viewed — because they absorb all the colors of the spectrum except their own color. That is, they pick out certain rays from the light that falls upon them, reflect these rays to the eye of the observer where the color sensation is created, and absorb all the other rays that are not so reflected.

An example of the simplest case — a pure color viewed under pure white light: White light contains equal portions of light of all hues; all hues are present in it. Suppose the object is green. By virtue of its physical nature, its inherent characteristics, this object is incapable of reflecting any but green light. The green light in the incident white light is, therefore, reflected alone to the eye — all other colors in the white light are absorbed by the object — and the color of the object is said to be "green." Similarly, a pure red object reflects only red rays, a pure blue object reflects only blue rays, a pure yellow object reflects only yellow rays, and so forth.

Conversely, a white object viewed under colored light will appear the same color as that of the light that falls upon it, because a white surface reflects all colors of light with equal facility. If green light fell upon a white surface, the green light would be reflected in full value, its character would be unchanged, and the surface would appear green. A pure black object, on the other hand, will always appear black, regardless of the color of the incident light, because a black object absorbs all light, and hence, all colors, that strike it, and reflects none to the eye, thereby causing a sensation of blackness. A gray surface would cause an intermediate effect, depending upon its shade, because gray may be considered as a mixture of black and white; a gray surface, then, would assume the hue of any incident light falling upon it, but in a darker shade, since the gray would not reflect the incident colored light in full value; there would be some absorption.

An example of another case — a pure color viewed under pure colored light: If the object is green, and the incident light is green the light will all be reflected by the object to the eye. The object will thus, of course, appear green. But if the incident light is red, or blue, or any color other than green, it will be completely absorbed by the object (which reflects only green rays), and none of it will reach the eye. The object will thus appear black.

An example combining those cases just discussed: If a square of pure green color be placed on a white background, and both flooded with pure green light, the green square will be invisible, for both the green and the white surfaces will reflect the green light in full value, affording no contrast, so necessary for visibility, between the green and the white. If, however, a square of red also be placed on the white background (under the green light) it will be visible — not as red, of course, but as black — because it cannot reflect the green light, and will afford a sharp contrast against the green-lighted background and itself. If red light be substituted for the green light, conditions will be reversed. Now, for similar reasons, the red will be invisible and the green will be visible. A black or a gray square would be visible under both lightings. Extensions of these simple manifestations of fundamental principles have been used for novel and startling effects — "changing scenery with light", and so on. This principle is also the basis of "pointillage" scene painting, which is discussed later in this chapter.

But these illustrations are based upon the use of *pure* colors, both of pigments and of incident colored light. By a "pure" color is meant a single spectral hue — completely free from traces of other hues and completely saturated — undiluted with white. Needless to say, colors of such absolute purity are never met with in practice; and colors of even a fair degree of purity are very rare. The usual commercial pigments and color media are never pure; they contain colors other than the dominant color by which they are known and for which they are used. Thus virtually all the blues contain red, and many also green; the greens contain yellow and blue; the yellows contain much green and red, and sometimes blue also; the reds contain considerable yellow; and the purples also contain yellow. All such colors are always unsaturated; they are diluted with varying amounts of white that range from two or three per cent to as high as sixty per cent.

Although most available pigment colors and light colors are impure, from the standpoint of spectral color analysis, their impurity does not detract from their value as art media. In fact, the subtle, almost indescribable difference between the many colors — which lends variety, interest, charm, beauty, vividness, to the use of color — is due to varying amounts of these impurities. But when colored light is used in conjunction with colored pigments, the composition of each, and the action of each on the other, must be very carefully considered in advance, or the apparent visual results are likely to prove disastrous to the effect sought for. For instance, the use of a tan or buff drapery for a cyclorama on which blue light will be projected (not at all a rare choice for the inexperienced — intrinsically, under white light, the color might seem a most desirable one) will probably result in a dark, muddy appearance. Incidentally, this dark, muddy appearance, in some form or other, is the tendency of many unplanned and untried combinations of colored light and colored pigments. Except for the basic principle that a pigment will reflect light of the colors that compose the pigment, in proportion to the amounts of those colors present in both the pigment and in the incident light, no rule-of-thumb can be given that will gauge the action of colored light on colored objects, as found in practice. But without spectral analyses of both pigment and light, this principle is usually of no avail. Red light, for instance, might make a yellow object appear yellow, or orange, or red, or some intermediate shade, depending upon the composition of both light and pigment. There is but one safe way of determining results exactly, and this is by means of direct experiment that reproduces actual conditions. This fact cannot be stressed too strongly.

From time to time, however, there have appeared various tables and charts listing the probable resultant appearance of pigments of various colors under light of various colors. But there is not a sufficient consistency in the composition of colored pigments and dyes and color media in common use to render any such table better than a very rough and occasionally misleading guide to probable results. Besides, the chaotic state of color nomenclature also helps to reduce the effectiveness of these "color and light" tables. Neither would it help appreciably to reproduce, in actual colors, the various series of effects. Individual samples of a single dominant hue, exactly alike in appearance, may differ widely in actual spectral composition, which is the final determinant of their reaction under colored light. Hence such a reproduced color chart would not be universally applicable with success — its usefulness would be restricted to actual conditions that duplicated exactly the conditions under which the chart was prepared. Actual experiment and experience can alone be relied upon for definite and accurate knowledge of what the appearance of a dyed fabric, a piece of painted scenery, or perhaps even an actor's make-up will be under the light produced by any color medium, or by several color media. However, many stage workers have not had the opportunity to observe in detail this important effect of colored light on the appearance of colored objects, and must rely to some extent upon a prepared table for help in planning the lighting, the settings, and the costumes for a production. For their use, the two tables on the following page are presented. The first, "Table A", has been compiled as a sort of composite of tables already published, and includes eight standard pigment colors and the four light colors commonly used on the stage. The second, "Table B", more detailed than the first, though fundamen-

PROBABLE APPEARANCE OF PIGMENTS UNDER LIGHT OF VARIOUS COLORS

TABLE A

COLOR OF PIGMENT	COLOR OF LIGHT			
	Blue	Green	Amber	Red
Violet	Bluish violet	Dark blue	Dark orange	Reddish purple
Blue	Intense blue	Blue-green	Dark yellow-green	Bluish violet
Blue-green	Dark greenish blue	Green	Yellow-green tint	Blue-black
Green	Dark blue-green	Intense green	Intense yellow-green	Dark red
Yellow	Dark yellow-green	Yellow-green	Intense yellow	Orange
Orange	Very dark orange	Greenish yellow	Intense orange	Scarlet
Red	Dark reddish purple	Dark orange	Intense orange-red	Intense red
Purple	Purplish violet	Dark purple	Dark crimson	Purplish red

TABLE B

COLOR OF PIGMENT	COLOR OF LIGHT							
	Violet	Blue	Blue-green	Green	Yellow	Orange	Red	Purple
Violet	Deep violet	Dark violet	Dark violet	Violet	Dark brown	Dark brown	Dark gray	Dark violet
Blue	Light blue	Deep blue	Light bluish gray	Light blue	Dark bluish gray	Black	Gray	Blue
Blue-green	Dark blue	Very dark blue	Dark bluish gray	Dark green	Greenish blue	Dark greenish brown	Black	Dark blue
Green	Bluish brown	Light olive-green	Light greenish gray	Intense green	Bright green	Dark green	Dark gray	Dark greenish brown
Yellow	Scarlet	Greenish yellow	Greenish yellow	Greenish yellow	Intense yellow	Yellow-orange	Red	Orange
Orange	Scarlet	Light brown	Light brown	Light brown	Orange	Intense orange	Intense orange-red	Scarlet
Red	Scarlet	Purplish black	Dark maroon	Maroon	Bright red	Orange-red	Intense red	Red
Purple	Reddish purple	Dark violet	Maroon	Purplish violet	Light brown	Maroon	Reddish brown	Deep purple

tally no more reliable, was compiled by the writer, using ordinarily available gelatin color media, and the specimen pigment colors in the old edition of the Prang Standard of Color.

The color booth. The results given in these two tables are only roughly reliable and should not be depended upon when accuracy and nicety are important factors in the color design of any setting. Actual trial and experiment can alone be relied upon as a safe guide in the selection of colored fabrics and pigments for use under colored light upon the stage. Every producing organization, large or small, should have a *color booth* as a standard piece of workshop equipment. In this color booth the stage designer can carefully test out samples of costume and drapery fabrics, trial results of dyes and pigments for settings — even the actor's make-up — to determine their appearance under different lightings. With the color booth he can choose the pigment or fabric for use with the stage lighting that has been planned, or he can plan the color and intensity of the stage lighting by adjusting it to suit the setting and costumes he has chosen, or he can adjust each to the other by experimental, or "cut-and-try", methods which are not awkward and cumbersome in their manipulation. Whichever method he uses, he can be reasonably certain of the final resulting appearance, for he sees it in miniature before him — nothing is left to chance. Material is not purchased, costumes are not made up, scenery is not painted, draperies are not dyed, until exactly the proper conditions have been determined. The slight expense of a color booth is amply repaid not only in the saving of time and trouble and the avoidance of possible disappointment, but also in the saving of money spent for material and work that might prove to be unsatisfactory.

A color booth, to be successful in operation, should provide a sample (as representative a one as possible, especially in regard to color) of the actual lighting conditions of the stage in conjunction with which it is used. It is necessary, therefore, that the number of color circuits and the color media on each, in the color booth, correspond *exactly* to those used on the actual stage. The relative position of the light sources is not so important. The principal function of a color booth is to provide, on a small scale, light in the various colors and intensities that the regular stage equipment can provide. This, however, does not necessitate the construction of the lights in the color booth on a model scale — regular, full-size material should be used, but less of it.

A typical color booth might be made three feet wide, in front, three feet high, and two feet deep. A large packing box will very likely prove suitable. Except for two strips, each six inches wide, across the top and bottom, for shielding the rows of lights, the front face should be open. Two rows of lamps, one above and one below the front opening, will be enough. If color-dipped lamps are used on the actual stage, these must also be used in the color booth, *with the same dip applied.* The sockets for the lamps can then be fixed directly to the upper inside and lower inside edges, to simulate the borderlights and footlights respectively. But if individual compartments, or reflectors of some sort, and gelatin color media are used on the stage, this condition must be approximately reproduced by constructing a small compartment for each lamp in the color booth. These compartments may be constructed of light wood, or of thin copper or other metal, and should be painted white inside, and should each be provided with a light-tight holder, or with a groove, for holding the small gelatin color medium in place. Each color circuit on the stage should be represented, *in proportionate wattage*, by at least two lamps (in order to secure a fair distribution of light of each color) in the color booth. The smaller sizes of incandescent lamps, 40, 50, or 60 watt, are convenient. Small portable reflectors, with small lamps and gelatin color screen holders, are useful where it is desired to simulate the localized effect of olivettes and floodlights. Each color circuit in the top and bottom row of lights should have a switch, and in the more elaborate color booths, also with a miniature dimmer (laboratory sizes of slidewire resistances supplied by Biddle, of Philadelphia, serve admirably, as do also small home-made devices prepared in the manner recommended for home built dimmers on page 375). The entire inside surface of the booth should be painted a dead black (except that, if open dipped lamps are used, the space behind them should be painted white). Non-gloss prepared paint known as Venetian black does very well. Or the inside of the booth may be lined with black velvet.

Properly constructed, such an apparatus can provide faithful reproductions of actual stage-lighting conditions, under which samples of fabric, paint, and other stage materials may be tried out. Effects should not be viewed too closely, but rather at a distance of ten or a dozen feet, preferably in a darkened room. A color booth will prove invaluable to the stage designer who must know with certainty just how his stage materials will appear under stage-lighting conditions, or who wishes to select the most suitable materials to use under a specified lighting.

C. PSYCHOLOGY OF COLOR

Undoubtedly the most subtle, least explored field of color is one that embraces what might be termed its psychological effect (aside from what psychological reaction, if any, is involved in the mere reception of color sensations). An exact choice of term would depend upon whether color is fundamentally regarded from the physical or from the physiological point of view — the popular term is simply "the psychology of color." The psychology of color is that property of any one color which causes it to be regarded, by the majority of observers, as being, for instance, warm, or cold, or stimulating, or sedative. It is unreasonable to suppose that colors — ether vibrations of narrow ranges of wave length — can be directly cold, stimulating, and so on, physiologically speaking. Colors can only exert this affective influence, then, by virtue of their psychological effect. Broadly speaking, the *emotive value* of colors ranges from warm and stimulating at the red end of the spectrum to cold and sedative at the blue end. This general statement is subject to modifications, of course; under various conditions of color composition and contrast perhaps blue might be called stimulating, and red sedative.

In addition to the emotive value of color, and closely associated with it, as a psychological effect, is the *symbolic value* of color: what conditions, what atmosphere colors suggest, what impressions they give rise to. These subtle attributes of color — the emotive and the symbolic — are of inestimable and unplumbed value in the service of the newer stagecraft, especially in combination with the mobile quality of light. The old practice of using a bright stage for comedy and a darkened one for tragedy constituted a crude attempt on the part of the older stagecraft to avail itself of the symbolic aspects of light and color. But the intelligent application of light and color for such purposes requires greater refinements. A closer study shows that at various times all of the colors have been used as symbols of happiness and all as tokens of death. For example, black is the usual symbol of death and purple of royalty; yet the Chinese use white and yellow, respectively, as these symbols.

These psychological attributes of color — the emotive and the symbolic — are sufficiently similar in cause and in final effect to justify their being discussed jointly. Their existence, in almost every case, may be traced to the relation to each other of some independent, otherwise isolated, mental processes. This relation, usually known as *association*, is defined as "the functional inter-connection of objects of experience." Thus throughout the ages, association, relating colors to objects and conditions, both those of Nature and those created by man, has gradually developed in the human consciousness this psychological susceptibility to color which modern stagecraft is just learning to utilize for its own purposes.

Man's primary color associations are undoubtedly due to the influence of Nature. The colors of objects of Nature — of the sky, the clouds, the earth, the vegetation, the rocks — being indicative of the conditions and moods of Nature — the time of day, the weather, the season of the year — have impressed themselves indelibly upon the mind of Man and have created the fundamental psychological reactions to color. The association of the *color* of an object with the object itself has induced the association of this color with the conditions surrounding the object, with the *characteristics* of the object.

Blue has been called a "sedative" color. Blue is the color of the clear sky, and nothing in Nature presents a more serene, sedate, satisfying, tranquillizing appearance than an unclouded sky. Blue is "cold." Cool shadows in Nature receive light from the blue sky only; very deep blue skies are characteristic of cool late October days; bodies of water, invariably cold, have a bluish tinge. *Green* is considered a "neutral" color, because of the vast areas of green vegetation in Nature to which Man's visual system has had to adapt itself. *Yellow*, the color of sunlight, and more so, of artificial light, has come to be regarded as "cheerful" and "warm." More "cheerful" and more "warm" are *orange* and amber, the colors of flame. "Hot" and "stimulating" is *red*, the color of glowing coals and embers. Purity, innocence, and truth are suggested by *white*, the color of snow. The *grays* of rocks and of storm clouds suggest severity and turbulence. The darker grays of winter weather and the *black* of night suggest gloom, despair, infinity. In this manner have the colors of Nature influenced the emotional make-up of mankind.

Secondary color associations — the less common and less important ones — have been brought about through the activities of Man (in contrast to the primary color associations, to which Nature's objects and conditions gave rise). Although some of these secondary color associations may be traced to the intentional, arbitrary, deliberate assignation of certain colors as symbols of special conditions and qualities, the majority of them may be traced to unintentional, accidental occurrences of collective individual experience. In the former class may be included the attributes of colors used for ceremonial purposes as recorded in mythology, and as practiced in religion and government. For example, purple (in early times the most costly dye obtainable) has come to signify royalty and riches; blue, the color of the heavens, suggests divinity, truth, and constancy; yellow, deceit and jealousy; gray, penance and sadness; and red, martyrdom. In the second class are color associations that have their origin in common collective experience — long contact with conditions with which incidental colors have become associated. Thus red is universally accepted as a symbol of danger, fire, bloodshed, and warfare; yellow of sickness and disease; green of peace, safety, and victory; and so forth.

The effectiveness of the more subtle and delicate phases of color psychology as employed in the theatre is dependent in large measure upon the extent and depth of the experience of the observer, and upon the degree of imagination and intelligence with which he is endowed. Of course, there are many cases of color reactions, usually very pronounced, that have their origin in some striking, unusual, and highly impressive individual experiences. Since color in stagecraft must present a unified appeal to the composite group of spectators that view it, the existence of this individual phase of color psychology is unfortunate, because its manifestations tend to confuse, and detract from, the value of the general and more common color reactions to which the majority of persons are susceptible.

Color reactions of such an individual type usually take the form of like or dislike. Yet color preference, less pronounced in character, also exists as a collective color reaction. Experiments have shown that pure colors are generally preferred in this order: red, blue, violet, green, orange, yellow; tints in this order: blue, violet, red, yellow, green, orange; and shades in this order: violet, blue, red, green, orange, yellow. The preference for a color is of use only for creating the feeling of pleasure or displeasure; it is no index to the emotive value of the color. The emotive value of a color varies directly as its purity. That is, a tint or shade of a color has less emotive value than the pure color undiluted and unsubdued. Thus red is symbolic of lustful, violent, consuming, passionate love; pink, a tint of red, is symbolic of a love that is more ideal, more modest, more gentle, more pure. If two colors are mixed, the attributes of one will usually influence those of the other. Thus purple, a mixture of red and blue, in addition to its own symbolisms, may partake of the attributes of either red or blue, depending upon the proportions of the mixture — whether the purple is a reddish-purple, or a bluish-purple. The attributes of a color are also influenced by those of colors adjacent to it in the spectrum.

A summary of a few of the more common psychological influences of various colors might seem superfluous in view of the fact that emotive and symbolic attributes of color must, *ipso facto*, be common knowledge if their use is to prove at all effective. Yet such a summary is here presented in the belief that many stage workers will find in it useful suggestions that might otherwise escape them in a moment of need. The reader is deliberately warned against regarding the following summary with any great degree of seriousness. It is hardly necessary to point out that this summary, with its many seemingly arbitrary assignations of psychological attributes to the several colors (not to mention its uncanny resemblance to the classical type of phrenological chart!), is nothing more nor less than a simple list of psychological attributes that the colors, under widely varying sets of conditions, have definitely been observed to possess. This list does not undertake to serve as a treatment of color psychology; its explanations are entirely superficial, and it is meant only as a guide, as a reminder, as the indication of a range of possibilities. The care and discretion that are necessary in the consideration and use of this summary are evidenced by the several conflicting, if not directly contradictory, statements that it contains. The reasons for these contradictions will perhaps be revealed if the several contributing causes, in each case, are carefully scrutinized.

Red is commonly known as a hot color, exciting in effect. Many of its psychological attributes are due to its suggestion of blood and of fire. For this reason, it symbolizes blood, war, tragedy, martyrdom, danger, destruction, fire, heat, courage, valor, bravery, strength, power, revenge, cruelty, hatred, shame, anger, rage, passion, lust. Although occasionally deep red might be somewhat subduing and dignified, red is usually considered as being loud, raging, bloody, vigorous, manly, passionate. *Pink*, a tint of red, is less vigorous in its suggestions, symbolizing love, truth, beauty, bashfulness, health. *Scarlet* is especially suggestive of blood, anger, glory, and beauty; and *crimson* of beauty, generosity, and courtesy.

Orange is known as a warm color, stimulating in effect. The association of orange with autumn and with flame is largely responsible for its psychological attributes. Thus it symbolizes autumn, harvest, fruition, plenty, contentment, happiness, laughter, warmth, heat, fire. It is lively, stimulating, warm, glowing, satisfying.

Brown, a rather dark shade of orange, is subduing in effect, and suggests rest, studiousness, sluggishness, melancholy, strength, maturity, solidity, as well as deceit, inconstancy.

Yellow, particularly orange-yellow, is known as a mildly warm color, cheering in effect. Its symbolism may be traced mainly to the association of it with the sun, and to its relatively high luminosity. It symbolizes sunlight, brightness, luster, brilliance, richness, cheerfulness. It is gaudy, joyous, gay, lustrous, enlivening. The brighter shades of *greenish-yellow* symbolize youth, cheerfulness, peace, faith. The dingier shades, perhaps from association with the complexion of diseased persons, suggest sickness, decay, and morbidity, as well as indecency, cowardice, inconsistency, and deceit. They are usually disagreeable, or even repulsive, in effect.

Green is regarded as a neutral color, probably because of Man's enforced adaptation to ever-present large areas of it in vegetation. Green is neither warm nor cold, neither stimulating nor sedative. As the color of springtime it suggests freshness, youth, vigor, inexperience, immaturity, faith, hope, contemplation, victory, peace. Green is neither sad nor cheerful — it is peaceful and perpetual, though when tinged slightly with yellow it becomes smiling, cheerful, and promising.

Blue-green partakes of the attributes of both blue and green. It is a cool color, somewhat sedative in effect. It suggests semi-mystery, aloofness, distance, idealism. Although it is occasionally characterized as symbolic of song and poetry, it is, on the whole, rather subduing and depressing.

Blue is decidedly a cold color, sedative in effect. As the color of the sky and the heavens, it has come to symbolize spirituality, divinity, mystery, severity, sedateness, serenity, dignity, coldness, melancholy, hope, constancy, love, fidelity, generosity. Blue is retiring, soothing, tranquillizing, cooling, sobering; and in its darker shades, subduing and depressing.

Violet is usually cold and depressing. It suggests sadness, sentimentality, piety, suffering, passion, love, truth. It is sad, hard, unyielding, gloomy.

Purple may be warm and stimulating, or cool and subduing, depending upon the proportions of blue and red in its composition. Usually it is emblematic of royalty, riches, wealth, affluence, pomposity, stateliness, sedateness, dignity.

Although black, gray, and white are, physically speaking, not colors, they share with color the property of being able to exert a psychological effect.

Black is really the absence of light, and as such has come to denote night, darkness, gloom, witchcraft, mystery, infinity, sleep, death, despair, woe, dread, terror, wickedness, crime. It is undoubtedly subduing and depressing in effect.

Gray is cool and retiring, the color of winter skies. It denotes melancholy, sadness, sobriety, solemnity, prudence, secrecy, calm, quiet, coolness, winter, severity, storm, age, decrepitude.

White is cool, refreshing, and cleansing. It is symbolic of winter, sacrifice, humility, integrity, truth, light, peace, purity, innocence, modesty, chastity, femininity, delicacy, and weakness.

Because of present-day limitations imposed by lack of a suitable color nomenclature and by the lack of a more definite knowledge of color psychology, this brief summary of the more important of the psychological attributes of color can be little more than a collection of nouns and adjectives. It will serve, however, as a practical basis upon which the stage designer can build a more comprehensive and detailed analysis which will be applicable to his particular problems.

D. COLOR HARMONY

Perhaps the simplest definition of color harmony, taken in its broader sense, would describe it as an arrangement or combination of two or more colors that gives rise to a feeling of ease, of satisfaction, of completeness, in the mind of the observer. Color harmony, therefore, constitutes a most intricate subject, depending, as it basically does, upon color preference, the emotive and symbolic attributes of color, the effect of simultaneous contrast — the apparent effect of mutually adjacent colors on each other's appearance — and other similar factors. Since color harmony must be inherently felt by both designer and observer, no hard and fast rules for achieving color harmony in stage design can be laid down.

To achieve color harmony in any color composition, a balance must be struck between the colors that comprise it. The greater the number of colors, the more involved the problem. There are two fundamental methods of obtaining harmony between colors of different hue: one employs complementary hues, the other employs hues adjacent to each other on the color circle. The former results in contrast; the latter in what might be called true harmony.

Contrast is achieved directly through the use of complementaries (situated diametrically opposite on the color circle); or, more subtly, with split combinations, by the use of mutual complementaries. A mutual complementary is a hue that serves as a joint complementary to two or more hues.

A true harmony will result only if not less than three adjoining hues, within the range of half the color circle (similar to the one shown on page 112, but with a greater number of intermediate hues), are used. If more hues than those within half a color circle are used, one or more complementaries are unavoidably included, and the balance of true harmony is overthrown.

It is also possible to achieve monochromatic color harmony by the use of a single hue, but in a variety of shades and tints (brightnesses and saturations).

In each of these three methods of obtaining color harmony, the purity and luminosity of the hues employed, and the relative areas occupied by each of the hues, are important factors. For instance, yellow is a relatively luminous color compared with its complementary, blue, and hence, for a good balance, the area of the yellow should be smaller than that of the blue. And, as a general rule, small areas of pure colors (high in saturation and brightness) should be used to balance large areas of colors lower in saturation and brightness. The areas of each color should be, roughly, inversely proportionate to the purity and luminosity of each color.

The more neutral a color is, the more safely can it be used with other colors without clashing. Neutrality of a color, when used in reference to color combinations, refers not so much to the psychological aspects of the color as to its value — its shade, its brightness. Strictly speaking, a neutral color is one that has been "neutralized" by the admixture of its complementary color, a process that does little else but reduce its brightness — "make it muddy", in some instances. Navy blue, brown, tan, buff, gray, black, white, and colors with metallic lustre, such as silver and gold, can be used as part of almost any color combination without disastrous results.

However, as has been pointed out, color harmony is the result of the application of taste, judgment, and experience to a problem of color composition. No set rules can be given that will hold true in all cases. The few broad generalities which have been stated above are for the guidance of those stage workers who desire a fundamental knowledge of color harmony that will serve as a starting point for their own work and experiments.

E. CONTRIBUTION OF SUBJECTIVE COLOR TO EACH OF THE FUNCTIONS OF STAGE LIGHTING

The material on objective and subjective color has been discussed somewhat in detail because only a thorough understanding of it, rather than a set of superficial rules and a few vague, general statements, can form the basis of the intelligent application of color, and more particularly, of colored light, to the purposes of present-day stagecraft. As with subjective light (discussed in the previous chapter), the best method of pointing out the importance of subjective color in relation to stage lighting is to discuss its contribution to each of the five functions of stage lighting — illumination, realism, composition and design, plastic expression, and psychological expression.

Illumination. As has already been pointed out, color is only of secondary importance in the process of visual perception. From the standpoint of visibility on the stage, it is sufficient that a reasonable amount of light, properly distributed, be applied to a scene; the color of the light does not matter much. However, some combinations of colored light and colored scenery and costumes, chosen, perhaps, for psychological effect or for esthetic reasons, are very likely to alter and distort the true, desired, appearance of a scene. This is another case where a compromise must be affected when light applied to carry out any one of the several functions of stage lighting interferes and conflicts with other light whose contribution to the ultimate effect is desired. Thus the contribution of color to visibility might really be considered as negative, since it cannot improve on the visibility afforded by white—or unmodified—light, and, under certain conditions, it might actually prove troublesome.

Realism. As regards realism, however, color makes a distinct contribution. Nature herself is a most skillful colorist, and any attempt to reproduce her conditions upon the stage must rely heavily upon color if it is to prove at all adequate. (It cannot prove wholly successful; conditions are too different.) Light from the sun — the primary light source of Nature — is almost a pure white at midday (it is generally regarded as having a slightly yellowish tinge). Both earlier and later in the day it strikes the earth at sharper angles and is refracted as it passes through the atmosphere. Such refraction causes sunlight to appear more red. This effect is, of course, most pronounced at sunrise and at sunset. On cloudy, misty, and stormy days the sunlight is filtered through large layers of clouds that remove its cheerful colors, making it appear dull and gray. In winter the sun retreats to the south, and less of the warm yellow rays reach the earth. On very clear, cloudless days, the blue color of the sky (one of Nature's secondary light sources) is predominant. Because of the chromatic adaptation of the eye, the low intensity of clear moonlight causes it to appear a faint blue-green. For the same reason, dark nights appear a deep, dense blue. These few statements prove that color can be very useful on the stage to indicate, and to simulate as well as possible, hour, season, and weather. Of course, it can accomplish this only when it is properly used in conjunction with other attributes of light, such as direction, intensity, and quality (degree of diffusion). Less easily can colored light be used to indicate place, but even here, subtly controlled color can simulate Nature's conditions in so far as natural light is modified in color and quality by surroundings — the green vegetation in the forest, the walls of buildings, and so on.

A very useful stage device for simulating Nature is the cyclorama, when properly constructed and lighted. On it can be pictured all of Nature's moods and varying conditions, such as those of time of day, season, and weather, to which the sky is a faithful index. In addition, a cyclorama is most useful for creating within the narrow confines of a stage the illusion of great distance.

Cycloramas are made in various shapes — flat, curved, and quarter-spherical (dome-shaped). Where permanently installed, they may be constructed of concrete and plaster; where they must be raised and lowered, or otherwise disposed of, a heavy quality of linen can be used, or a light, reinforced framework of wood may be rigidly constructed, to which may be applied a smooth cyclorama surface of "compo" board or three-ply veneer. Plaster cycloramas should never be given a smooth finish; a rough surface is best for diffuse light reflection. Canvas possesses a suitable surface after it has been properly painted, but folds should be carefully eliminated, as these always cause undesirable and illusion-destroying shadows. The question of the color of the cyclorama surface is a very important one. Blue, of course, is the predominant color of light used on a cyclorama. Although white plaster or canvas can be satisfactorily lighted to a blue tint, the effect is heightened and the degree of illusion is increased, if the surface is water-painted (or preferably sprayed) a flat tint of light blue. The exact tint might be described as that of a clear noon sky in midsummer, viewed at an angle of about 45 degrees from the horizontal. Under no circumstances should a cyclorama be colored yellow or buff, as it will take on a muddy appearance when flooded with blue light.

In the realistic simulation of artificial lighting, especially of that indoors, color plays a large and easy part, because here stage conditions most nearly coincide with the actual conditions that are being simulated. In fact, the wide variety of color media that are now available for practical stage use makes it possible for the stage designer to reproduce almost every existing color of light, and therefore also the accompanying conditions and effects. Colored light makes it possible to achieve a fairly high degree of realism, in cases where realism in stage design is necessary or desired.

Composition and Design. Many scenes, many stage pictures, rely almost entirely for their effectiveness upon the coloring of their component parts — the setting, the costumes, the lighting. In the older stagecraft, color was dependent upon but one factor, namely, the actual pigment — the paint, the dye — that was used. At the present time stage colors depend not only upon the pigment, but also (and perhaps to a greater extent) upon the lighting. In the hands of the stage designer colored lighting is a medium that, either alone or with conventional stage accessories, can be used to create stage compositions in color that surpass in beauty and distinction the highest achievement possible with pigments alone. Colored light has two advantages over pigments; it is easily mobile, and it is animated, vibrant in quality. Unaided pigment is lifeless; when used with the proper colored light it lives.

The principles governing color harmony apply with equal force to both colored pigments and colored light. The stage designer who uses colored light must bear in mind and keep distinct the two methods of color mixture — the additive for colored light, and the subtractive for colored pigments. He must remember that no colored pigment is visible (as a color) until it is "picked up" by, and responds to, light of its own hue, either alone or in combination with others. This important principle has been discussed previously in the present chapter as "the effect of the color of light on the appearance of colored objects."

This principle is the basis of that much discussed but relatively little used complex system of coloring known as *pointillage*. Briefly, pointillage consists of covering scenery with tiny, closely crowded spots of pigments of several colors. Each color of pigment will respond to the same color of light, but will otherwise remain invisible. The space between the spots of one color is so small as to cause the spots to blend together and present an unbroken surface, whose color is that of the light applied to the pointillage. By applying two colors of light to the pointillage, two pigment colors will respond, and the composite color will be an evenly blended mixture of the two (by the additive method, since the reflected light, rather than the pigments, is mixed). By using varying proportions and purities of pigment colors on the scenery, and varying combinations of the applied light, results can be secured that appear to be nothing short of magical. The effectiveness of pointillage depends not only upon the application of general principles, but also upon study and experiment with the actual pigments and colored lights used. If the spots in pointillage be arranged according to definite designs and representations, still more startling effects can be secured.

Where true pointillage is used in play production, the play is sure to suffer by contrast. Although there is much that is beautiful and artistic in the too often startling and bizarre effects that the system of pointillage affords, such effects are really not consistent with the purposes of serious dramatic production, and are as out of place there as would be, perhaps, a sleight-of-hand performer, or a trapeze act, out of vaudeville. Pointillage is novel and sensational, and should prove excellent for ballet and revue purposes.

Modifications of pointillage, adaptations of its underlying principle, are, however, very useful in the service of true play production. Such familiar devices as stippling over a neutral (well shaded) ground color, the use of broken color, and the use of homogeneous mixtures of pigments in place of solid, unmixed pigments of direct color, have been developed and adapted to stage work solely because of their effectiveness when used with colored light. A gray obtained by mixing the three pigment primaries has a much more living and vibrant quality than has a flat gray obtained by the use merely of a solid black such as lampblack.

Fabrics also, for costumes and draperies, are dyed with special regard to their appearance under colored light. Proper dyeing and lighting of ordinary, inexpensive fabrics will endow them with a rich and gorgeous appearance. For example, a piece of heavy unbleached muslin dyed first in a red and blue mixture of cotton dyes, then redipped in a royal purple basic dye, will take on the appearance of a brocaded velvet robe when made into a costume and lighted with the right color. A piece of cheap sateen dipped unevenly into a bath of chrysoidine (a deep orange basic dye), when roughdried and subjected to the proper lighting, has the quality of panne velvet. The property of colored light is of special importance where expense as well as appearance is a factor in play production.

The surface character of the material to which pigments are applied, and the manner of the pigment application itself, also tend to influence the appearance of the color. As a general rule, the softer, the more textural, the more porous and unsmooth the surface, the deeper and purer will appear the color, since the rays of incident light are purified by repeated diffuse reflections in the porous material before they escape and are finally reflected to the eye of the observer. This fact accounts for the particular suitability, from the standpoint of color, of the distemper water colors used in stage painting. Pigment applied in the form of an air spray is more porous, and hence, deeper and richer in color, than brush-painted pigment.

All these complexities attendant upon the use of color in pigment and light, in play production, indicate the desirability, if not the necessity, of providing for the unified and centralized design of all the components that enter into the stage picture, such as the settings, costumes, properties, and lighting.

In addition to aiding in the achievement of realism, the cyclorama is also very useful to the stage-lighting artist, for pure artistic or esthetic purposes. It serves him as a sort of canvas, a large area whereon he can paint important parts of his color designs and pictures in light, and fully avail himself of the two most important properties of light — its vibrant, living quality and its mobility.

Although, as has been already pointed out, colored light is one of the most useful adjuncts of realism, many stage designers believe that it is more effective when used for the sake of its own virtues — as an important element in the composition and design of the stage picture — as an art medium *per se*. Of course, every stage designer must make his own decision and must make it for each individual problem he encounters. There is always the possibility of a too attractive stage picture drawing the spectators' attention away from the play for which it is meant to serve as a background or setting. But this danger is also present with realism, which offers the temptation to overemphasize it or carry it out to a distracting extent. Irving Pichel, who always expresses his stimulating ideas on stage lighting with refreshing clarity and candor, discusses this problem that faces the stage designer. He says[1] ". . . we must settle whether we are to try to reproduce nature or attain a correlative beauty. To me the beauty of a stage sunset has rarely been the beauty of a real sunset; it has been the beauty of rosy light. If anything, the unreality of the sunset has stood in the way of my appreciation of the reality of red. The beauty of red was accidental, and not the artist's intention. It could not have been avoided, for it is germane to sunset, but the fact remains that the artist achieved something other than he set out to achieve. It would have been better to go in for red and attain it than to go in for sunset and attain red. If blue light intimates the moon, well and good. It is beautiful itself and does not awaken marvel at the cleverness with which we have contrived an effect. Whereas a nicely operated moonrise, or a jiggling procession of stereopticon clouds, leaves us gaping while the tragedy hobbles, unattended, to its close."

Plastic Expression. Color can add little or nothing to what light and shade accomplish in giving plasticity to the several components of the stage picture. The plasticity of an object is revealed by the brightness contrasts — the light and shade, and high lights and shadows — that prevail over its surface. Thus the intensity, direction, and quality of light, rather than its color, carry out this sculptural effect — this important function of stage lighting.

Psychological Expression. But as a potent medium to help express the pervading mood or thought of a play — to create in the consciousness of the spectator a psychological background for the work of the actor — to reinforce and help draw out the real inner content of a play — color, and more particularly colored light, is unsurpassed. Music is, of course, the obvious exception. But there is no reason that, in due time, color should not become equal to music in effective value, and perhaps eclipse it, since, compared fundamentally to light, sound is sluggish, restricted, feeble.

[1] "Modern Theatres," page 66.

To the stage designer who employs colored light for psychological effect, there are available the infinite and, for the most part, well-defined color associations, of symbolic and emotive value, that have gradually accumulated through the ages, and which may now be conveniently applied to stage production by virtue of the comparatively recent mechanical and electrical advances in stage-lighting appliances.

The psychological attributes of color have already been considered. Although applicable also to costumes and settings, they are primarily of value as forming the basis for the use of colored lighting on the stage for mood creation. Such lighting is most effective when used by itself, without the hampering restrictions imposed by realism and its distracting influence. But it can also be used, very subtly and effectively, in conjunction with a realistic treatment of the stage picture.

In the former case, its use is obvious and admitted. The playgoer before whom it is presented must be sympathetic enough unresistingly to allow his own consciousness to play its emotional part in the production. He must attend a play so treated in the spirit in which he has been trained, or grown accustomed, to attend a symphony concert or, more apropos, really dramatic opera. Otherwise, he might be antagonized. In such a play production, where realism has been dispensed with, and where the lighting is depended upon to help greatly in reinforcing the mood of a play, the cyclorama is invaluable as the principal means of presenting the mobile color and light to the spectators. Area of color is an important factor in psychological lighting; so is position, relative to the spectator. The cyclorama presents a large surface upon which color may be applied with light, and, by virtue of its position, it surrounds and envelops, and serves as a literal background for the action of the play, but never interferes with it. The greater the area of color, and the purer the color, the more pronounced will be its emotive effect. Colored light, then, must not be used with the reserve that characterizes its use for purposes of realism, or of composition and design, but boldly and broadly and vividly, if its maximum effect is sought. The value of accessories to colored lighting, such as high lights, and shade and shadows, must not be underrated. Their proper use adds greatly to the effect of colored light alone.

When used for psychological effect in conjunction with a realistic treatment, colored light must be used cautiously and subtly, and in such a way that its contrast to realism is not too noticeable. In other respects, however, its use with realism should be similar to its use alone. Undoubtedly, it is in careful conjunction with the usual, popular realism that the playgoer will grow accustomed to the mood-creative possibilities of color and colored light, and accept their aid as emotional stimulants just as he now accepts the aid of music at the opera, or more popularly and poignantly, at the motion pictures.

Excellent examples of the use of color, both of lighting and setting, for emotive and symbolic effect, are given by H. K. Moderwell. These were the work of Leon Bakst, a stage designer whose reputation is largely founded on "his bold use of intense tones and his inexhaustible ability to manipulate color effects in the service of the inner drama. . . ." Mr. Moderwell discusses[1] these two continental productions as follows:

One of the dances[2] which the Russian Imperial Ballet has been performing in all the European capitals, tells the story of a Caucasian queen who lured strangers into her palace and, having made them drunk with her orgies, put them to death. The erotic intensity of the whole scene was suggested in the fierce warmth of the oranges and reds of the setting and costumes, only slightly modified by the greens toward the centre. Only through the window was a cold violet-blue. This afforded not merely a contrast in feeling, setting off the warmth of the room, but a true complement of the principal colours, setting off the fierce yellow and orange of the costumes. At the end, after the orgy was over and the traveller had been put to death, the whole scene, even including the sky outside, was bathed in hot reds, suggesting the weariness and sweat following an intense period of passion.

A most remarkable example of the use of symbolic colour was given in the Paris production of d'Annunzio's play, "La Pisanelle." Perhaps never before in the history of the modern stage have the principles of colour been carried so far. A somewhat detailed description of the colour schemes will suggest the use of colour in imaginative works.

The stage was divided literally in half, the front section being decorated in black and gold (harmonizing with all colours) and always in view of the audience, since the main curtain was behind it. This neutral section was conceived in the Byzantine spirit which dominated the whole and made an excellent frame for viewing all the acts. The drop curtain (a real curtain hanging loosely with real folds and not painted ones) was of gold and black.

The prologue and the three acts were conceived each with a definite tone. And for each there was a special curtain revealed some

[1] Page 97, "The Theatre of To-day," by Hiram Kelly Moderwell; published by Dodd, Mead and Company.

[2] "Thamar."

two minutes before the commencement of the act by the raising of the drop curtain.

The drama played in Cyprus during the late crusades, when all the civilizations of Europe and Asia — Saracen, Byzantine, Italian, Norman, German, and Pagan Greek — were mingled pellmell. In the prologue we were shown what might be called an interior view of these civilizations. The colour scheme, as may be imagined, was far from simple. Yet all the chief hues were somehow set off with their complements, and the warmth of the picture centred downstage where most of the important action took place. The general colour scheme of the setting was deep purple and luminous green (complements enriched freely with designs of gold). Just what the scene represented was not clear, nor was it meant to be, but the effect was that of a richly decorated interior, dominated by a sort of primitive ecclesiastical mood. A blue light thrown from the side completed the cold unity of the background. The costumes were of nearly all colours, but rich oranges and reds dominated, contrasting with the coldness behind. With a wealth of variety in the costumes it was easy for the producer to emphasize pictorially any important dramatic effect by grouping or "spotting" these costumes. At the close of the scene, the chief dramatic conflict was between the prince and the queen, his mother. The queen, who had been pictorially inconspicuous, was clad in a brilliant yellow, and the prince, whose outer garment was of a somewhat neutral shade, confronted her, managing to display the inside of his garment — a most brilliant reddish violet. These two colors, the most brilliant and luminous of the whole act, were nearly enough complements to set each other off vividly; the attention was bound to be centred on these two confronted colours — where the dramatic interest also was centred. This was a perfect example of the use of symbolic colour for dramatic effect.

The motive of the first act was the diverse outer life of Cyprus. The scene was the quay. The back drop, rather crudely painted, showed the harbour, a confusion of heavy black lines, with a vessel at anchor in a slip. The whole curtain (quite at variance with nature) was suffused with a warm though low-toned red-orange, except for the small bit of water which was a vivid greenish-blue — the complement. The movement of the first part of the act was a riot of rich and contrasting colours. Various passionate suitors pleaded for the love of the slave girl. Then came the prince. He loved her chastely, as something holy. He was mantled in white and rode upon a white horse. At the moment when she accepted him as a "bride in Christ", — at the moment, that is, when her meaning in the drama changed — she was covered with the prince's white robe and was carried off the stage on the white horse.

The second act was at a convent garden. Its "motive" was peace and retirement. The curtain for the act was a restful pure blue, with a repeated design in white. The background, rather conventionally painted, was a neutral blue-green, with a touch of red-orange (a complement) in the centre. The nuns were in pure blue and white. La Pisanelle was clad in a greyish white. When the convent was violated by the entrance of the Prince of Antioch with his courtesans, brilliant, profane colour broke in upon the scene.

In the third act we are back in the pomp and cruelty of the court, in which La Pisanelle is to die through the intrigues of the queen. The curtain for the act was an intense green with a stiff gold design. The colour scheme of the whole was too complex to be explained in words. But one brilliant device must be mentioned. La Pisanelle is to be smothered under a mass of flowers. Now we have noticed repeatedly throughout the act a peculiar red in various shades, usually of a low tone and verging toward purple — in the costumes of the ladies in waiting, in the doorway, in the garden behind. As denouement approaches, reds come upon the scene, each more intense and more purplish. Finally the slaves enter, and, with a mass of flowers of the most intense and hot red-violet, smother the Pisan girl. This gradual crescendo of a dominant colour up to one almost too powerful to be endured was an effect which can never be forgotten.

CHAPTER VI · STAGE-LIGHTING EQUIPMENT

Classification of equipment; light sources; footlights; borderlights; strip-lights; olivettes; spotlights; sciopticons; the Linnebach lantern; cyclorama lighting equipment; lighting equipment for outdoor productions; accessories; European equipment.

ACCORDING to a statement credited to Harley Granville-Barker, the lighting equipment is the Achilles' heel of almost every stage. There is much truth in this classical comparison. And how often does this delicate heel go unshod, or, at best, poorly shod, because of unintelligent manipulation of what lighting equipment a stage may possess? Stage-lighting equipment must be handled with intelligence, with discretion, with patience, with care, with due appreciation of its possibilities and limitations, and with a sound practical working knowledge of its fundamental operating principles. If an operator possesses these qualifications and attributes, he can produce results with obsolete or crude stage-lighting equipment that will compare very favorably with the results he can produce with more modern and efficient equipment. On the other hand, a full set of the most modern equipment is not necessarily a guarantee of successful results. The principal advantage that modern equipment affords is a greater convenience of manipulation. And it is this factor of convenience, which includes ease and speed of operation, so important to work on the stage, that justifies the use of the most modern equipment, of the highest quality, that conditions (usually financial) will allow. At every period in theatre history, stage workers have made use of all the mechanical developments, pertinent to their work, that were available to them at the time. There is every reason why stage workers of to-day should press into service every modern mechanical or electrical improvement that can advance their art, or make their work simpler and easier.

The general, the more abstract, aspects of stage lighting have already been discussed, as have also the fundamental principles of electricity, of light, and of color that apply especially to stage lighting. In this chapter will be discussed the actual equipment, the mechanisms, the instruments, that are available, or standard, for stage lighting — of what they are constructed, how they operate, what they are capable of doing, why they are useful, and how they can be applied. With a full knowledge of these features, the operator of stage lighting can adopt standard equipment to the requirements of any particular problem.

I. Classification of Equipment

A survey of recent productions at metropolitan theatres indicates a strong tendency toward flexibility in stage-lighting equipment — a tendency that is gaining more and more momentum. For those productions in which lighting receives any respectful attention at all, the lighting requirements of each are carefully studied as an individual problem. A special set of standard equipment is assembled for each production, and only those necessary units of equipment are set or hung in place to be used throughout the performance. If such a production is sent on tour, it carries with it this same equipment. Less and less reliance is being placed on the standard house equipment, such as the footlights and borderlights. In some cases, occurring not infrequently, special apparatus is developed and constructed to meet some special requirements of the production.

Formerly, a definite classification of stage-lighting devices could be made. The footlights, borderlights, and striplights could be classed as those providing general, diffused, "flat", illumination; the olivettes and the various types of spotlights could be classed as those providing localized, directional illumination. The present tendency is to use a large number of devices of the latter type, and so build up a *general* illumination with several small areas of *localized* illumination. This practice has the decided advantage of allowing the stage worker to light each one of the various small areas, and hence also the actors and objects in it, to an intensity, color, direction, and quality of light independent of the light on the remainder of the stage, so that each of these small areas may contribute, in the most correct and desirable proportions, to the effect as a whole.

This tendency to abandon the footlights and borderlights, as such, may be traced in no small measure to faulty design and inherent cumbersome properties, which rendered them less and less fitted for work of the type demanded by the increasingly critical appreciation of stage effects on the part of the theatre-going public. However, a more logical conception of the functions of these units, and recent radical changes in design (as, for example, the indirect footlight and the revolving borderlight) that provide for a more accurate control of light, along with improvements in color media and the more general use of the efficient higher wattage incandescent lamps, have produced footlights and borderlights more capable of creating effects that measure up to the higher standards that prevail to-day. For this reason, good types of these units should not be omitted from any permanent installation of stage-lighting equipment. The correct type of footlight or borderlight, properly wired and equipped, has a distinct field of usefulness.

Despite the gradual abandonment of the older classification of stage-lighting equipment, it has seemed wise to retain it for the purposes of this chapter. Out of the confusion that is attending the assignment of new uses to the old, accepted forms of equipment, no definite, final classification has yet evolved — at least none that conveys as much meaning to most persons as does the old footlight-borderlight-striplight-spotlight-olivette classification.

Each type of stage-lighting equipment, or stage-lighting *instrument*, as it is sometimes termed, will be discussed from the point of view of application, construction, and operation. Under *application* will be discussed the uses of the instrument, its functions, its possibilities, and its limitations; under *construction*, its general assembly, the lamp, the reflector (if any), the lens (if any), the provision for color modification, the wiring, and the mounting; under *operation*, its method of control of light (intensity, color, direction, quality), and its maintenance. Then special types of each particular instrument will be discussed. In addition to the standard types of instruments — footlights, borderlights, striplights, olivettes, and spotlights — there will be also discussed the special-purpose instruments, such as sciopticons or "effect machines", Linnebach lanterns or "scene projectors", and cyclorama lighting equipment, and also equipment or devices that are accessory to the instruments themselves. Equipment for use with outdoor productions will be described briefly, and the design and construction of "homemade" equipment by the worker in the amateur theatre will be taken up somewhat in detail in the next chapter. Stage wiring and centralized control (by means of the switchboard) for the instruments described in the present chapter, and the color media to be applied to these instruments, as well as the methods, or "practice", of using them, will all be treated in following chapters.

In all descriptive catalogues, and glossaries, and definitions of stage-lighting equipment, the light source, either the carbon arc, or, more generally, the incandescent lamp, is invariably classified as an "accessory." Such classification is not correct. The light source is *not* accessory to any piece of stage-lighting equipment. In fact, if the question be at all logically considered, it is evident, that, strictly speaking, the *equipment* is accessory to the light source rather than the reverse being true. The light source, to-day usually the incandescent lamp, is the starting point, the basis, of stage-lighting equipment design — all the physical characteristics of equipment depend upon the device which produces the light in unmodified, or "raw" form. For this reason, light sources will here be considered in advance of the stage-lighting instruments the existence and usefulness of which they make possible.

II. Light Sources

The light sources used on the stage to-day are virtually confined to the electric carbon arc and to the electric incandescent lamp. Although gas lighting and the limelight are still used, in rare instances, their use is so limited as not to merit consideration here.

The carbon arc. The heating effect of an electric current jumping, or "arcing", across an open-air gap between two hard carbon rods is the basis of the electric carbon arc. A depression, or "crater", is formed at the tip of each carbon rod by the action of the arc. These craters of carbon become heated to incandescence, and are the actual sources of light from the carbon arc (that is to say, the prevailing type of carbon arc used for stage purposes to-day). With direct current, the crater on the positive carbon is by far the larger of the two, and emits the major portion of the total light of the arc. With alternating current, the craters are each of the same size, and each emits about half of the total light. All other conditions being equal, the alternating current arc is much less efficient than, does not emit as much light as, the direct current arc.

The operating voltage of carbon arcs is usually between 50 and 75 volts. Since the usual line voltage of electric current supplied by central stations is in the immediate neighborhood of 115 volts, a resistance, usually a winding of thin metallic ribbon, must be placed in series with the arc in order to reduce the line voltage to the proper voltage required by the arc. In arc spotlights used on the stage this resistance is usually present inside a perforated sheet-iron housing, surrounding the vertical pipe support, or "standard", at the base of the mounting.

Direct current, because of its efficiency and greater quietness, is mostly used for carbon arcs. The positive carbon that is used is approximately twice the diameter of the negative carbon. With alternating current, the carbons used are approximately of the same diameter. The gradual volatilization of the carbons by the intense heat of the arc requires that they be pushed toward each other at frequent intervals in order to maintain fairly constant the distance between their tips. And then both carbons must be so adjusted simultaneously, as a unit, that the incandescent craters remain in optical alignment with the lens system (carbon arcs on the stage are now used almost entirely in spotlights). And then the axial position of each carbon in respect to that of the other must also be carefully adjusted in order to maintain the proper light efficiency.

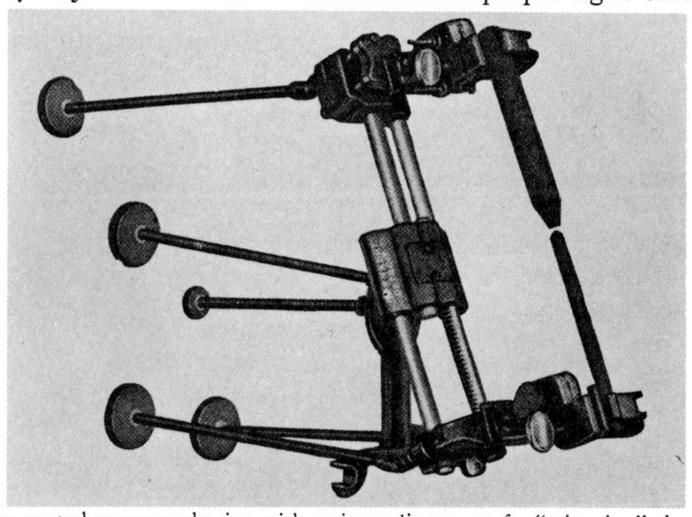

A 100-ampere carbon arc mechanism with various adjustments for "trimming" the carbons and controlling the manner of burning and for positioning the light source in proper relation to the optical system.

Provision for all this multiple adjustment is obtained by clamping the carbons tightly to insulated metal holders (to each of which a flexible wire carrying one side of the electric current is attached) which slide on guide rods. These carbon holders may be moved together or apart (and, hence, the arc distance regulated), when they are actuated by rack and pinion mechanisms which the operator controls by means of revolving handles on rods that extend outside the spotlight housing. Although the carbons are sometimes mounted vertically and sometimes horizontally, they are usually mounted at an angle, so positioned that the greatest possible area of the upper (positive) carbon is exposed to the spotlight lens.

Carbon arcs are available in a variety of sizes. The smallest practicable size of arc for use on the stage is rated at 25 amperes. As this is operated at about 60 volts, it consumes about 1500 watts (exclusive of current consumption by the resistance coil). Carbon arcs are available in intermediate sizes up to as high as 200 amperes (about 12,000 watts), which is the largest size used for stage lighting. The larger the arc, the thicker must be the carbons used. Their range of diameters is, roughly, as follows: on D.C., positive, $\frac{5}{16}''$ for

25 amperes to $\frac{3}{4}''$ for 200 amperes, negative, $\frac{5}{8}''$ for 25 amperes to $1\frac{1}{2}''$ for 150 amperes; on A.C., each, $\frac{5}{8}''$ for 25 amperes, to $1''$ for 125 amperes.

Although the smaller standard sizes of arc spotlights are sometimes still used directly on the stage (the Metropolitan Opera House still uses many in such fashion), the majority of the carbon arcs used for stage lighting are used for long-distance spotlight projection (as from the balcony, or from the projection booth of a motion picture "super-super" theatre) where an exceptionally bright spot is desired.

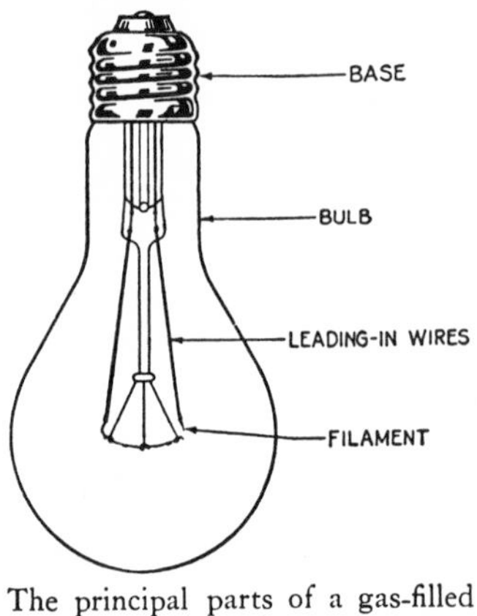

The principal parts of a gas-filled tungsten incandescent lamp.

Thus it is seen that the carbon arcs take up their work where incandescent lamps leave off — that is, the field of usefulness of arcs is virtually limited to "spotting" and "flooding", at high intensities and at long "throws", for which no incandescent lamp yet developed is both powerful and practicable enough.

The carbon arc possesses several drawbacks which account for its very limited use in the theatre. (1) It cannot be dimmed, except by the mechanical interposition of a screen, or cut-off, or iris diaphragm. If its voltage is reduced by any appreciable extent it is abruptly extinguished. (2) In order to achieve proper adjustment, each arc requires the virtually constant attention of an operator. In fact, most municipal ordinances and fire regulations demand that an operator be provided for each arc light used upon a stage, from the standpoint of safety. In view of the high labor costs that prevail in the professional theatre, this feature involves undue expense. (3) The arc is somewhat noisy and sputtering and flickering in operation. The alternating current arc hums very perceptibly. (4) The quality of light produced by the arc is rather unpleasant—it has a "cold" and harsh quality when it is unmodified.

Because of the photographic quality of the light they produce, carbon arcs were once used extensively in motion-picture studios for lighting the productions when they were being filmed. But with the almost simultaneous advent of talking motion pictures, which demand absolute quiet during their filming, and of panchromatic film, which registers colors over the entire spectrum range in their true proportionality, the incandescent lamp in special large sizes is rapidly replacing the carbon arc equipment in motion-picture studios.

The incandescent lamp. The heating effect produced by an electric current in overcoming the resistance of a thin metallic filament through which it passes is the basis of the electric incandescent lamp. The filament is heated to incandescence, and thus becomes a source of light. The fundamental parts of an incandescent lamp are the filament, the bulb, and the base. The *base* is a thin brass shell, in the form of a coarse screw thread, which can be fastened into a

The most common sizes of screw bases used on incandescent lamps: mogul, medium, candelabra, and miniature (full size).

socket and which thus provides a convenient means of holding the lamp firmly and of conducting the electric current, by means of *leading-in wires*, to the *filament*, which is a thin tungsten wire. The incandescent filament is protected from the oxidizing action of the air by enclosure within the glass *bulb*, which is hermetically sealed and fixed to the base. In the smaller sizes of lamps the air is exhausted from the bulb, and the filament operates in a vacuum (*vacuum lamp*). In the larger sizes of lamps the bulb is filled with an inert gas, such as nitrogen or argon, so that the filament can operate more efficiently (*gas-filled lamp*).

The various types, styles, and sizes of lamps are virtually without number. Of these, two or three dozens serve the majority of stage-lighting requirements. Incandescent lamps of the smaller sizes, especially up to 100 watts, generally used for domestic purposes, are universally procurable from neighborhood dealers in electrical merchandise and hardware. The larger lamps, and those for use in spotlights, are not in such common use, and must usually be procured from more fully stocked dealers, such as those specializing in stage-lighting material. The greater portion of incandescent lamps in use in this country are known as "Mazda" lamps. The term "Mazda", although it has come to be popularly applied to

DATA ON MAZDA LAMPS FOR GENERAL STAGE-LIGHTING SERVICE
(115-VOLT RANGE)

TEXT REFERENCE NUMBER	WATTS	BULB	TYPE	DIMENSIONS, INCHES			BASE	LUMENS OUTPUT	LUMENS PER WATT	HOURS LIFE	POSITION OF BURNING
				Bulb Diameter	Over-all Length	Light Center Length					
(a)†	(b)	(c)	(d)	(e)	(f)	(g)	(h)	(i)	(j)	(k)	(l)
(1)	10	S-14	B	$1\frac{3}{4}$	$3\frac{1}{2}$	$2\frac{1}{2}$	Medium	70	7.0	1500	Any
(2)	15	A-17	B	$2\frac{1}{8}$	$3\frac{5}{8}$	$2\frac{3}{8}$	Medium	126	8.4	1000	Any
(3)	25	A-19	B	$2\frac{3}{8}$	$3\frac{15}{16}$	$2\frac{1}{2}$	Medium	232	9.3	1000	Any
(4)	40	A-21	B	$2\frac{5}{8}$	$4\frac{7}{16}$	$2\frac{7}{8}$	Medium	396	9.9	1000	Any
(5)	50	A-21	C	$2\frac{5}{8}$	$4\frac{15}{16}$	$3\frac{3}{8}$	Medium	515	10.3	1000	Any
(6)	50	S-19	B	$2\frac{3}{8}$	$5\frac{3}{16}$		Medium	515	10.3	1000	Any
(7)	60	A-21	C	$2\frac{5}{8}$	$5\frac{1}{4}$	$3\frac{3}{4}$	Medium	672	11.2	1000	Any
(8)	60	S-21	B	$2\frac{5}{8}$	$5\frac{1}{4}$		Medium	624	10.4	1000	Any
(9)	75	PS-22	C	$2\frac{3}{4}$	$5\frac{7}{8}$	$4\frac{3}{8}$	Medium	930	12.4	1000	Any
(10)	100	A-23	C	$2\frac{7}{8}$	$6\frac{1}{16}$	$4\frac{3}{8}$	Medium	1310	13.1	1000	Any
(11)	100	PS-25	C	$3\frac{1}{8}$	$6\frac{15}{16}$	$5\frac{1}{4}$	Medium	1340	13.4	1000	Any
(12)	150	PS-25	C	$3\frac{1}{8}$	$6\frac{15}{16}$	$5\frac{1}{4}$	Medium	2310	15.4	1000	Any
(13)	200	PS-30	C	$3\frac{3}{4}$	$8\frac{1}{8}$	6	Medium	3240	16.2	1000	Any
(14)	300	PS-35	C	$4\frac{3}{8}$	$9\frac{7}{16}$	7	Mogul	5280	17.6	1000	Any
(15)	500	PS-40	C	5	$9\frac{13}{16}$	7	Mogul	9500	19.0	1000	Any
(16)	750	PS-52	C	$6\frac{1}{2}$	$13\frac{1}{8}$	$9\frac{1}{2}$	Mogul	14775	19.7	1000	Any
(17)	1000	PS-52	C	$6\frac{1}{2}$	$13\frac{1}{8}$	$9\frac{1}{2}$	Mogul	21000	21.0	1000	Any
(18)	1500	PS-52	C	$6\frac{1}{2}$	$13\frac{1}{8}$	$9\frac{1}{2}$	Mogul	33000	22.0	1000	Either *
(19)	2000	PS-60	C	$7\frac{1}{2}$	$15\frac{1}{8}$	11	Mogul	45000	22.5	1000	Either *

* Lamps numbers (18) and (19) are available either for base up or for base down burning, but not for universal burning in any position.

† See note on opposite page regarding these columns.

all tungsten filament incandescent lamps, strictly refers only to lamps manufactured by two well-known firms, whose combined research efforts have been largely responsible for the rapid development and present status of the incandescent lamp.

For purposes of stage lighting, lamps are most conveniently classified into two main groups (depending upon their filament construction) — those for *general lighting* and those for *spotlighting* (or for other service where a point source of light is needed). Other classifications within these two large groups are as follows: (1) whether the lamp is a *vacuum*, or type "B" lamp; or a *gas-filled*, or type "C" lamp; (2) the *size*, from the standpoint of electric current consumption, and hence also of roughly comparative light-producing power (expressed in watts); (3) the *rated voltage* at which the lamp was expressly designed to be operated (expressed in volts); (4) the *shape and size of the bulb*, expressed as a letter and number (the letter designates bulb shape: thus P and PS = pear-shaped, S = straight side, G = globular, and A = curved-side type, inside frosted; the number designates maximum bulb diameter in eighths of an inch); (5) the *size of the screw base* (*medium*, 1″ in diameter, for the smaller lamps, and *mogul*, $1\frac{1}{2}$″ in diameter, for the larger lamps); and

DATA ON MAZDA LAMPS FOR SPOTLIGHT SERVICE
(115-VOLT RANGE)

TEXT REFERENCE NUMBER	WATTS	BULB	TYPE	DIMENSIONS, INCHES			BASE	LUMENS OUTPUT	LUMENS PER WATT	HOURS LIFE	POSITION OF BURNING *
				Diameter Bulb	Over-all Length	Light Center Length					
(*a*) †	(*b*)	(*c*)	(*d*)	(*e*)	(*f*)	(*g*)	(*h*)	(*i*)	(*j*)	(*k*)	(*l*)
(20)	100	P-25	C	$3\frac{1}{8}$	$4\frac{3}{4}$	3	Medium	1270	12.7	200	Base down
‡ (21)	250	G-30	C	$3\frac{3}{4}$	$5\frac{1}{8}$	3	Medium	4175	16.7	200	Base down
§ (22)	400	G-30	C	$3\frac{3}{4}$	$5\frac{1}{8}$	3	Medium	7440	18.6	200	Base down
(23)	500	G-40	C	5	$7\frac{1}{16}$	$4\frac{1}{4}$	Mogul	9750	19.5	200	Base down
(24)	1000	G-40	C	5	$7\frac{1}{16}$	$4\frac{1}{4}$	Mogul	22000	22.0	200	Base down
(25)	1000	G-40	C	5	8	$5\frac{3}{16}$	Mogul	22000	22.0	200	Base down
(26)	1000	G-48	C	6	$8\frac{5}{8}$	$5\frac{1}{4}$	Mogul	22000	22.0	200	Base down
(27)	1500	G-40	C	5	8	$5\frac{3}{16}$	Mogul	34200	22.8	200	Base down
(28)	2000	G-48	C	6	$8\frac{5}{8}$	$5\frac{1}{4}$	Mogul	47000	23.5	200	Base down

* All spotlight lamps can be burned in any position except within 45° of vertically base up, as described on page 161.

† The numbers in column (*a*) serve merely as a convenient reference to text discussion, and have no other significance. In column (*b*) is listed the most commonly known of lamp characteristics — the wattage consumption of electric current. In column (*c*) are listed the various bulb shapes — the letter denoting the shape of the bulb and the number denoting the maximum diameter in eighths of an inch. The letters in column (*d*) denote whether the lamp is a vacuum lamp (type *B*), or a gas-filled lamp (type *C*). The dimensions in column (*e*) are the maximum bulb diameters. The dimensions in column (*f*) are the over-all lengths. The over-all length of each lamp is the distance between the extremities of the lamp, measured along the lamp axis. The light-center length, values for which appear in column (*g*) is the distance between the center of the filament and the contact tip on the base of the lamp, measured along the lamp axis. In column (*h*) appear the base sizes. In column (*i*) appears the initial light output of each lamp, expressed in lumens (see page 75). The efficiency of each lamp is listed in column (*j*), and is expressed in lumens of light output per watt of electric current consumption. In column (*k*) is listed the designed average life of each lamp. In column (*l*) is listed the burning position in which each lamp can be operated. All the values given in the above tables are for lamps of the 115-volt range. Lamps of the 230-volt range (seldom used for stage lighting) have slightly different values for each lamp characteristic.

‡ Lamp number (21) is also available with a mogul base, with an over-all length of $5\frac{9}{16}$″ and a light center length of $3\frac{3}{8}$″.

§ Lamp number (22) is also available with an over-all length of $5\frac{15}{16}$″ and a light center length of $3\frac{3}{4}$″.

(6) the *color* of the lamp bulb, and the *type of coloring* (most lamps for stage lighting have clear glass bulbs — the question of coloring is discussed in Chapter VIII). Other properties of incandescent lamps that must be considered are (7) the *over-all*, maximum, *length* (upon this dimension depends the size of the equipment housing any lamp or group of lamps), and (8) the *light-center length* — the distance from the contact tip at the bottom of the base to the center of the filament (upon this depends the design of reflector and lens systems, and consequently, of equipment housing them). All these data, for the lamps commonly used for stage lighting, are given in the two accompanying tables.

The first table lists the lamps used for general lighting purposes. These may be termed "regular" or "standard" lamps. Since the common voltage supplied by central stations throughout the country is within the 115-volt range (that is, between 110 volts and 120 volts), no voltage is mentioned for the lamps listed in the table. All the lamps described in the tables are for use on such 115-volt service. Each lamp listed in the tables has been numbered for

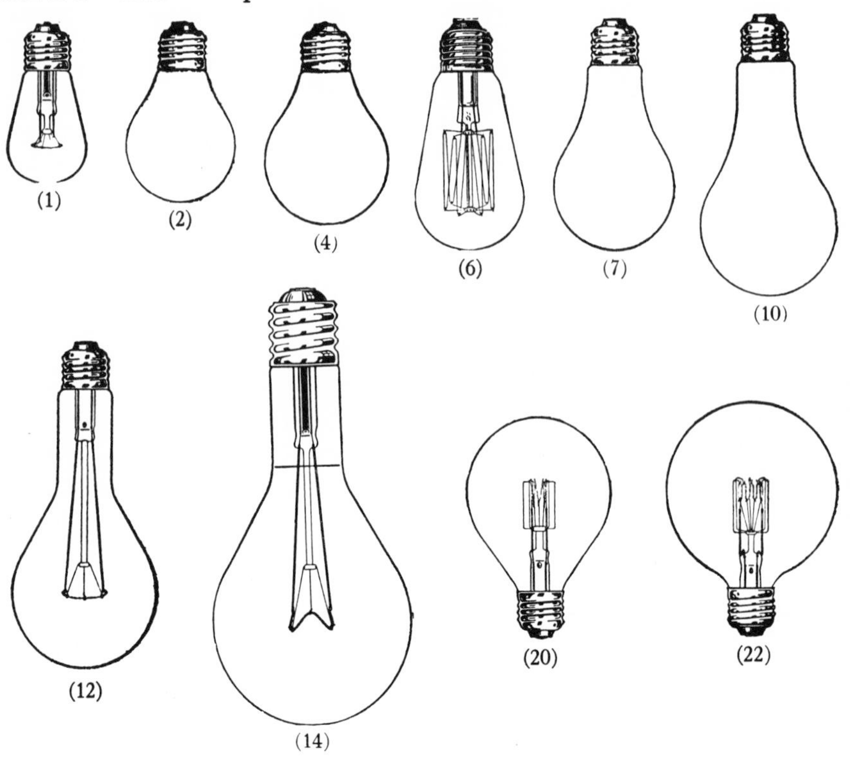

Comparative sizes and various bulb shapes of incandescent lamps. The number designations are the text reference numbers in column (*a*) of the tables on the two preceding pages. (Quarter size.)

present purposes — to facilitate reference and to simplify discussion. These numbers have no other significance. Lamp number 1 on the list is the smallest size of lamp made for use on 115-volt service. Lamps of such small size are useful where just a touch of light is required, without the use of a dimmer. Lamps listed as numbers 2, 3, 4, 5, 7, and 10 are of the latest type, having not a clear glass bulb, but one frosted, or etched, on its inside surface. This "inside frost" serves as an excellent diffusing medium, and such lamps provide light of a good quality, with an appreciable degree of diffusion, which makes them particularly suited to certain stage-lighting requirements. Lamps of 100 watts or under are used mainly in the footlights, borderlights, and striplights of the open-trough type. However, lamps numbers 5 and 7 are type "C" (gas-filled) lamps, and cannot be colored with lamp dip because of the rather high temperature of some portions of their bulbs — particularly opposite the filament and at the neck. Where it is necessary to color-dip lamps of these two sizes, lamps numbers 6 and 8 (which are of the older style — vacuum, type "B") must be used. For color modification with all gas-filled, type "C" lamps, either external color screens, such as gelatin sheets or glass plates or color caps, must be used, or the lamp bulb itself will have to be of natural colored glass. Lamp number 11 must be used in preference to lamp number 10 in conjunction with mirror reflecting devices, such as "X-Ray" borderlights, because such devices depend for their proper operation upon the sharp source of light (placed in the same position, with regard to the reflector, that the lamp filament of lamp number 11 occupies) which the inside-frosted lamp does not provide. If used with a $\frac{7}{8}''$ socket extension, the light-center length of lamp number 10 is made equivalent to that of lamp number 11, and the former lamp can then often be used, with fairly satisfactory results, with some types of mirrored-glass reflectors. Lamps number 9 to 13 are commonly used in footlights and borderlights of the compartment and mirrored reflector types. Lamps numbers 13 to 19, the larger sizes, are used mainly in very large sizes of borderlights, in olivettes and various other types of floodlights, and in cyclorama lighting equipment. It will be noted that, in addition to the several classifications of lamp characteristics outlined above, the actual light output (in lumens) of each lamp is given in the tables. This affords an excellent comparison of the greater light-producing power of the larger lamps. Thus a 1000-watt lamp gives, not 100 times as much light as a 10-watt lamp, but 300 times as much. The larger the size of the lamp, the greater the efficiency. This indicates that, very often, better effects at lower costs are possible with the use of the larger lamps as compared with the smaller ones. All lamps for general lighting purposes have an approximate average life of 1000 hours. That is to say, of a reasonable quantity of lamps, the *average* life of each lamp (until burn-out or other failure occurs) will be at least 1000 hours. Few lamps fail before 1000 hours of burning, and many continue to give service for longer periods.

The second table lists the lamps that are used in spotlights, tormentor hoods, and other instruments requiring a point source of light. These lamps have "concentrated" filaments, which are closely coiled and crowded into the least possible space so as to provide the practicable "point source" of light which is the basis of proper light projection with mirror or lens systems. These lamps are known as "spotlight lamps." They are designed especially for stage-lighting purposes and must not be confused with "flood-lighting lamps" or with "projection lamps", which also have concentrated filaments but which, for various reasons, are not altogether suitable for use in spotlights. Flood lighting lamps emit less light and have not so concentrated a filament; projection lamps have a much shorter average life (only 50 hours) and can be burned only within a very limited range of positions. Lamps for general lighting purposes, outlined in the previous paragraph, cannot be used in spotlights, because their filaments are not concentrated. All spotlight lamps are type "C", gas-filled. They should never be color-dipped. They all have an approximate average life of 200 hours. This shorter life (as compared with that of the regular lamps) is due to the rigorous conditions that the filament concentration gives rise to. Lamps numbers 20, 21, and 22 are usually used in baby spotlights and other small sizes of spotlights; lamps numbers 23, 24, and 25 are used in standard small spotlights; and lamps numbers 26, 27, and 28 are used in standard large spotlights. The question of light-center length is more important in the case of spotlight lamps than in the case of regular lamps, for it is essential that the filament be accurately positioned on the optical axis of the spotlight. Although limited final adjustments can be made by slightly shifting the socket that holds the lamp, it will be noticed that lamps designed for one size of spotlight (20, 21, and 22; 24 and 25; 26, 27, and 28) have approximately the same light-center length.

Incandescent lamps, compared with other illuminants, are "fool-proof"; they require a minimum of attention and maintenance, they are compact, unified, and easy and convenient to handle and install. But there are several reasonable precautions to be observed in regard to the lamps, which will enable the stage-lighting worker to obtain full value and effective results from their use, and to receive the full benefit of their advantageous features.

For instance, lamps must be of proper voltage — the designed or "*rated*" operating voltage of the lamps must be the same, or as nearly as possible the same, as their *actual* operating voltage — the voltage of the circuit on which the lamps are operated. Discrepancies between actual and rated operating voltage cause disadvantageous results for the user of the lamps. If the rated voltage is lower than the actual voltage, the life of the lamp is materially shortened. Thus a 110-volt lamp operated on a 120-volt circuit will burn out rapidly. On the other hand, if the rated voltage is higher than the actual voltage, the lamp will be inefficient: it will not emit its full quota of light for the current it is consuming. Thus a 120-volt lamp, operated on a 110-volt circuit (a discrepancy of only about 7%) will produce less than 80% of the light it would produce if it were used with the voltage for which it was designed — a loss of over 20%. Besides, under such a condition, the light becomes decidedly yellow in color. This "normal voltage" factor

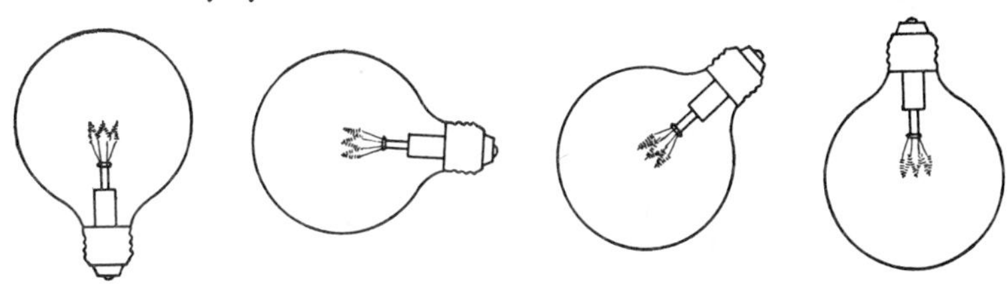

Correct and incorrect positions for burning spotlight lamps. The first two positions are quite safe; the third is the angular limit of burning (45 degrees of vertically base up); the fourth is an unsafe position.

is an important one but is seldom given proper attention. The actual voltage of any electric service can be obtained directly with a voltmeter, or by inquiry of the central station, or electric service company, that supplies the current. The rated voltage is etched on the glass bulb of every lamp. In the 115-volt range, lamps are regularly procurable in rated voltages of 105, 110, 115, 120, 125, and 130 volts. Lamps whose rated voltage is nearest to the actual voltage should be the ones chosen. If the actual voltage is difficult to ascertain, or fluctuates unduly, the choice of lamps rated at 115 volts is perhaps the safest.

Burning position is an important factor in the case of spotlight lamps. Regular lamps, for general lighting purposes, may be burned in any position (except in the special cases of lamps numbers 18 and 19, as noted on the table). Spotlight lamps should be burned "base down" if possible, but they can be burned in any position except within a range of 45° of vertically "base up." They should never be burned directly "base up", because, as they have no neck for ventilation and cooling, the heat of the filament will most likely soften the cement that holds the base and bulb together, and allow the lamp to fall apart.

The fact that such heat is liberated when an incandescent lamp is burning requires that stage-lighting equipment have adequate means of ventilation — for keeping the lamp cool. Although their fire hazard is virtually nil, the larger lamps should never be allowed to come into direct contact with fabrics and draperies, which they might char or otherwise discolor.

Incandescent lamps are, especially when new, very rugged, and require only reasonable care in handling. Severe shocks, however, which they might receive when lighting equipment is being hurriedly and rashly moved about the stage, may break the thin filament, especially after the lamps have been burned for a length of time and their filaments have become somewhat brittle. Of course, the glass bulb of a lamp is easily shattered, and for this reason it is desirable to equip open-trough borderlights and footlights with removable wire screens or guards that will protect the lamps in them.

It is not always economical to operate lamps until they burn out. As a lamp ages, especially after its designed life has been passed, the bulb gradually becomes blackened and the lamp grows less efficient. Although a lamp might actually burn for thousands of hours, it should be discarded as soon as it has become appreciably or visibly blackened, because its light output is far below what it was initially. As a general rule, it is decidedly disadvantageous to operate lamps for a period much longer than their designed life.

In order to secure the proper type of lamp, then, it is necessary to take into consideration the following facts, and to cite them when purchasing or ordering lamps: the wattage, the voltage, the bulb designation, and (if for other than general lighting) the particular service for which they are to be used. Thus, for example, 100-watt, 110-volt, A23 lamp; and 500-watt, 115-volt, G40 spotlight lamp.

The incandescent lamps discussed above compose the bulk of the lamps used on the stage, but there are dozens of miscellaneous types for other special purposes. There are decorative types of lamps, natural-colored glass bulb lamps, sprayed colored lamps, lamps with candelabra, intermediate, and miniature screw bases, tubular lamps, special-shaped lamps, and so forth. These will be discussed individually in connection with any piece of stage-lighting equipment that requires their use.

III. Footlights

The footlights are perhaps the most misused, misunderstood, and abused unit of stage-lighting equipment. Along with the borderlights and proscenium striplights, they helped furnish the blast of *raw* light, indiscriminately applied, that characterized the productions of the older stagecraft. They were an essential part of a system that employed multi-directional bright light and that gained its plastic effects unnaturally and unconvincingly by the use of paint on the scenery and heavy make-up on the actor. In the case of stages with wide aprons, they were also necessary as being the only equipment that could apply light for the actor who ventured forward of the proscenium arch. Because of their location, footlights provide light with an upward direction that often (and unfortunately) succeeds in brightly lighting the under sides of tables, the chins and nostrils of actors, and the ceilings of box sets (not to mention the proscenium frame and the ceiling of the auditorium), and in casting huge shadows on back walls and cycloramas.

These disadvantages of footlights were largely responsible for the ably press-agented wave of antipathy toward them which not so long ago inundated the ranks of professional producers, and which resulted in their abandonment in several metropolitan theatres. But it is interesting to note that in these cases, almost without exception, the footlights have been unostentatiously replaced. Persons considered as authorities who previously led the opposition to footlights have admitted that the footlights are not only useful but often necessary. These results of practical experience are perhaps the most cogent reasons for recommending that footlights be not omitted from a complete set of permanently installed stage-lighting equipment. The criticism of footlights should have been directed not so much against the footlights themselves (although, more often than not, their design was faulty) as against the method of using them, and the end to which they served as a means. A well-designed set of footlights, rather than an "old string of lamps behind the time-honored tin trough", used with the discretion that should characterize the use of every piece of stage-lighting equipment, and susceptible to adequate control, should be available.

Unless face-level lighting from the auditorium, subtly applied and skillfully manipulated, is used, footlights are necessary to balance the plastic distortion, particularly that on the faces of the actors, and to overcome the annoying expressionless silhouette formed by the actors playing far downstage, caused when overhead lighting, such as the borderlights provide, is used alone.

Nevertheless, even under the best conditions, footlights have a tendency to cause huge shadows of objects on the stage to loom up on the cyclorama or the rear wall of an interior set. In order to minimize this ever-present possibility, the footlights should never be very bright, and they should approximate as closely as possible a continuous, unbroken strip of light, diffusive in quality. Thus, instead of a series of multiple shadows from a few separated bright light sources in the footlights, a broad, very faint, continuous shadow will be formed, which will blend into the other lighting on the stage and which will then be hardly noticeable. For this reason, low-wattage lamps, spaced closely together in a well-designed trough, with a white-painted diffusely reflecting lining, are perhaps better for footlight use than a less number of high-wattage lamps in compartments, spaced farther apart and acting more as several individual light sources than as a continuous strip. The indirect type of footlights approximates most closely of any type the ideal condition of a continuous strip of light of diffusive quality.

Footlights are of three principle types, the open-trough type, the compartment type, and the indirect type.

The *open-trough type* consists of a simply constructed sheet-metal trough, sunk at the outer edge of the stage floor (but still protruding four or five inches above its level) and extending almost the full width of the proscenium opening. Porcelain sockets (medium base) are mounted in the bottom of the trough. These are spaced from three to five inches apart, depending upon the size of the lamps to be used — the lamps being crowded together in a row as closely as is practicable — the larger the lamp, the farther apart, necessarily, the sockets. *Lamps* up to and including the 150-watt size are used in the open trough footlights. The lamps are inclined slightly in order that the maximum light flux may be utilized in the desired direction — on to the stage at an angle of from ten to twenty degrees above the horizontal. For large stages, two rows of lamps are sometimes used. In some types of open-trough footlights the lamps are inverted, *i.e.*, base up, which practice provides no special advantages, except that it minimizes the possibility of light escaping to the auditorium ceiling. The surface of the trough is utilized as a diffusive *reflecting medium*, and is therefore painted flat white. A special magnesia paint is used which remains fairly permanent and clean in spite of its close proximity to the lighted lamps. The trough incline, leading from the stage floor down to the lamps, is painted a flat black to prevent the diffusion of light back on to the auditorium ceiling or the proscenium frame. *Color modification* is the weak point of the open-trough footlight. Either one of three methods must be used: (1) the lamps may be color-dipped if they are of type "B" (vacuum lamps); (2) the type "C" (gas-filled) lamps may be of the rather expensive, difficult-to-obtain variety with natural-colored glass bulbs; (3) clear lamps (of type "B" or "C") may be equipped with glass color caps, which fasten mechanically to the lamp bulb,

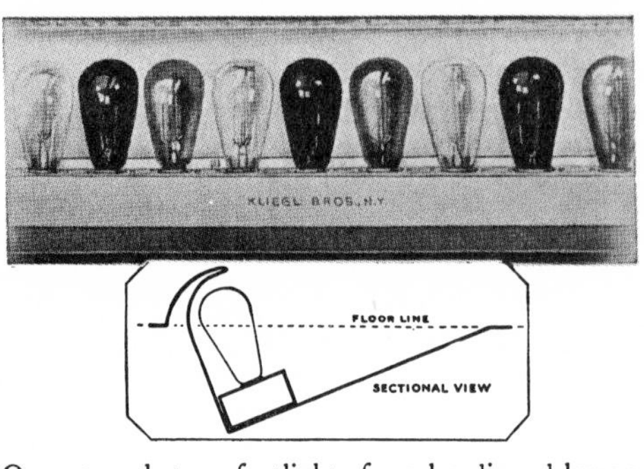

Open-trough type footlights for color-dipped lamps.

or with glass color globes, which fasten to spring-clip holders attached to the footlight trough. But whichever method is employed, the various-colored lamps or color caps are mingled together. Hence some light is lost by reflection from and transmission through adjacent lamp bulbs or color caps, either directly or after being reflected from the trough. For the same reason, strict purity of color cannot be obtained. The *wiring* is contained in an enclosed metal wiring channel directly beneath (or in the case of inverted lamps, above) the sockets. Wire with slow-burning insulation, wired directly to the sockets, is used. Since footlights are usually permanent, a splicing box is provided for making a permanent connection between the footlight circuits and the supply mains from the switchboard. Footlights can be wired for any number of color circuits. Usually, the old-fashioned, inadequate, patriotic red, white, and blue circuits prevail. But at least four, and preferably five circuits should be provided, so that red, green, blue, and clear (white) light may be available, with the fifth circuit for amber. The number and size of lamps on the several color circuits must be so adjusted that the total wattage load on each color circuit is approximately inversely proportional to the absorption factors of the color media employed. If feasible, the footlight circuits should be divided into two and preferably three sections, rather than have each circuit extend the entire length. With this sectional arrangement, part of the footlights can be kept dark while the other parts are kept light; part may be of one color and part of another color.

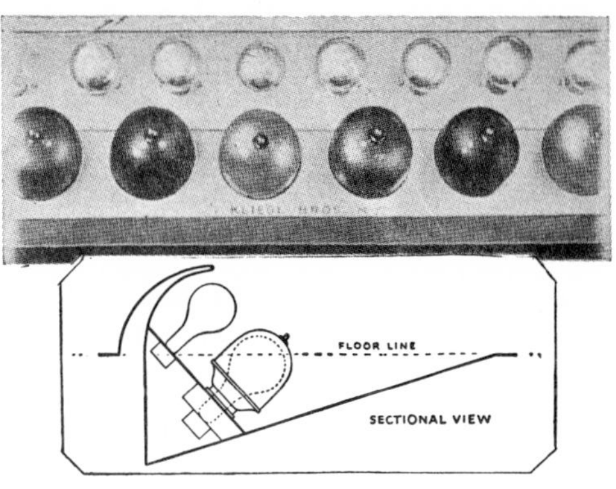

Open-trough type footlights with color caps.

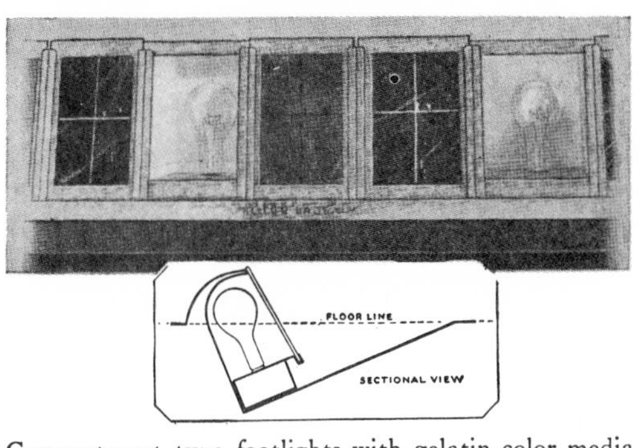

Compartment type footlights with gelatin color media.

The *compartment type* of footlights was developed as a result of the introduction of higher wattage lamps. Since it was a direct outgrowth of the older open-trough type, it is very much like the latter except that each lamp is partitioned off by a separate compartment, also of sheet iron, with the open side facing the stage. Although any size of *lamp* may be used, the compartment type of footlight is intended mainly for 75, 100, and 150-watt type "C" lamps. The lamps, if of the sizes mentioned, are usually spaced about 6″ apart. The width of the compartment is approximately the same as the lamp spacing. The simpler forms of compartment type footlights employ a coat of white paint on the inside surfaces of the compartment as a *reflecting medium.* The more elaborate types, however, are equipped with specially designed reflectors for each of the lamps. The reflectors are mounted inside the compartments, and are made of either ribbed silvered glass (mirrored), ribbed silvered metal, spun aluminum, or porcelain-enameled steel. Each of these types of reflectors has its own characteristics: the silvered glass is efficient, but cannot withstand rough treatment; the silvered metal is also efficient, but under certain conditions is likely slowly to tarnish; the spun aluminum gives an excellent spectral quality and diffusion of light, but is not quite so easily kept clean and bright; the enameled steel is comparatively inexpensive, but does not give so good a diffusion as the other types of reflectors. The white painted metal is least expensive and gives a good diffusion, but is not as efficient, not as permanent, as the more costly silvered reflectors. *Color modification* is effected by inserting color media in light-proof slots, or grooves, before the openings of the compartments or the reflectors. These color media are occasionally small sheets of natural-colored glass, but more usually they are gelatin color media in suitable sheet-metal holders, or frames. Color-dipped lamps or natural-colored glass bulb lamps are not ordinarily used in compartment type footlights. With the color medium in place, the lamp is entirely enclosed. This gives rise to the problem of proper *ventilation*, which is not present in open-trough footlights, in which the lamps are exposed to the air. Ventilation is secured by means of holes, $\frac{1}{2}''$ to 1″ in diameter, punched in suitable parts of the sheet-metal hood or compartment, and so shielded that, while air may find easy passage, light is completely prevented from escap-

"X-Ray" compartment type footlights with ribbed silvered glass reflectors and glass-plate color media.

ing. The *wiring* of compartment type footlights is not appreciably different from that of open-trough footlights. The same principles of division into color circuits and sections prevail.

"Aluminide" compartment type footlights with spun aluminum reflectors and gelatin color media.

A new type of footlight, an elaboration of the compartment type, is the removable unit footlight. This consists of a sheet-iron wiring channel, in the face of which are mounted a row (in the larger sizes, two rows) of flush plug receptacles (very similar to the small electric appliance receptacles used in the home), and a series of deep-bowl, long-stemmed spun-aluminum reflectors, equipped with prong connectors which fit into these receptacles. Each reflector is an independent unit, and can accommodate a 75, 100, or 150-watt lamp. The mouth of each reflector is provided with a ribbed channel and a stout wire spring, which together hold a standard convex railway color lens, or "roundel", for the color circuits. The principal feature of the removable unit footlight is its extreme compactness. The removable reflectors make replacements and color screen changes easy, and, by the removal of several adjacent units, can provide space for the location of footlight baby spotlights without exposing them to the view of the audience. The spotlight can then be plugged into any one of the footlight circuits from which the reflectors have been removed, or it may be plugged into a separate circuit, individual receptacles for which are spaced at intervals on the face of the wiring channel.

An installation of removable-unit type footlights.

Both the open-trough and the compartment type of footlights are available in forms that can be sunk below the level of the stage floor, completely out of sight, when they are not being used. This form is known as the disappearing, or flush, type of footlight. This type is particularly well suited to platforms and stages in assembly rooms or auditoriums of schools and other buildings in which play production is not carried on continuously, or where the platform or stage is used for purposes other than play production. The footlights are exposed only when they are actually in use; otherwise, they are sunk beneath the floor, covered over by hinged or removable sections of the flooring, and locked, if necessary. Thus there is less likelihood of lamp breakage and of unauthorized use of the equipment.

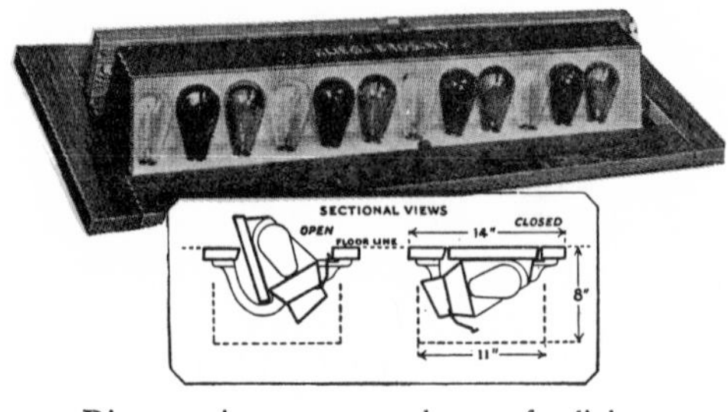

Disappearing open-trough type footlights.

Portable footlights, in either the open-trough or compartment type (though more usually the former), are also available. They are very useful where a stage or platform has not been equipped with a permanent, built-in installation of footlights. Some varieties may be simply placed, or set, at the front edge of the stage floor; others may be hooked over the front edge of the stage. The latter type allows the use of more, or larger, lamps without causing the footlight to project unduly above the stage-floor level and interfere with the view of the spectators. Most portable footlights, however, are nothing more or less than regular striplights pressed into service as footlights.

The *indirect type* of footlights represents the latest and most promising development in footlight design. It provides what is perhaps the nearest approach to the "ideal footlight" — a source of light in the shape of a continuous, unbroken strip, of relatively low brightness, and just wide enough to afford a reasonable degree of diffusion and at the same time preserve a predominant direction. Although the indirect type of footlight has been used to some extent in Continental theatres, it has just recently been introduced into this country. Nevertheless, results already obtained with the very few present installations make it not unreasonable to predict that this type will become increasingly popular with stage workers who desire to use footlights in a manner compatible with the advanced standards of modern stagecraft. The indirect type of footlight provides just the correct quality, direction, and intensity of light necessary to reveal most successfully the plastic nature of objects on the stage, principal of which are, perhaps, the features of the actors. In addition, the indirect type of footlight permits a better and more thorough mixture and blending of colors than does the usual direct type; it minimizes the unsightly shadows on the rear wall or cyclorama; its light is more subdued and more generally "pleasant" in quality; and it is decidedly less trying on the eyes of the actors. The indirect type of footlight is also, inherently, an aid to realism, because all natural lighting from below, either indoors or outdoors, is subdued, and is reflected (from the floor, or pavement, or other low objects), and never emanates primarily from bright light sources such as constitute the usual direct type of footlight.

There are two forms of indirect footlights, one employing low wattage lamps, and the other higher wattage lamps in compartments. The former consists of what is practically an open-trough footlight, mounted beneath the stage floor, emitting its light flux in a direction slightly upwards, and *toward* the auditorium. This emitted light is directed on to a curved, white-painted metal, diffusively reflecting shield, which is placed lengthwise before the row of lamps in the trough. This reflecting shield is partly below and partly above the stage-floor level, and projects through a long slot in the floor near the front edge of the stage — in the position usually occupied by the regular type of direct footlights. Although the light reflected from this shield is diffusive in quality, it has a predominant direction, which can be adjusted, slightly, by changing the angle of tilt of the shield, which is hinged. Color circuits are arranged just as in the direct type of footlight. The indirect type of footlight employing the higher wattage lamps is similar to the open-trough type just described, except that the lamps are in compartments, and gelatin sheets or glass plates are used for color modification. A most practical and interesting elaboration of the indirect type of footlights is a combination of both the direct and indirect types. In this self-contained and removable combination unit the lamps are mounted in a white-painted, metal reflecting trough of special design, which in turn is so mounted that it may be revolved on its longitudinal axis. In addition, there is also a white-painted metal shield as used with the totally indirect type of footlights. The row of lamps may be locked in position either below the stage floor and facing the auditorium (in which case totally indirect lighting is produced), or above the stage floor and facing the acting area (in which case totally direct lighting is produced). The row of lamps may also be fastened in any intermediate position between these two extremes. Thus combinations of both direct and indirect lighting may be produced, with the desired proportions of each.

All types of footlights are subject to centralized control, that is, from the switchboard. Light intensity is controlled by the dimmers;

color is controlled by a graded mixture of light from the various color circuits at the proper intensities. The distribution and quality of light from footlights are fixed, and are not subject to control (except,

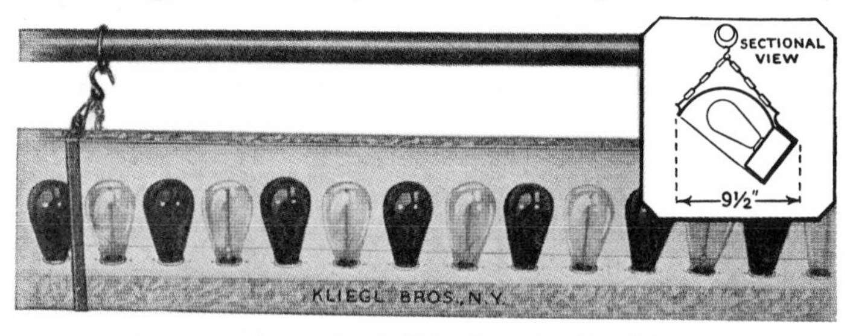

Open-trough type borderlights for color-dipped lamps.

of course, in the case of the indirect footlight, with the adjustable metal reflecting shield, and in the case of the combination direct and indirect type of unit footlight).

Footlights should never extend across the entire front of the stage, but should extend only to three or four feet within the proscenium opening. They should be so designed that no stray light is "spilled" on the frame surrounding the proscenium opening, or up on to the ceiling of the auditorium. Such spill light is always annoying to the spectators and always reduces the effectiveness of the stage picture. In open-trough footlights, the hood should extend sufficiently over the lamp to prevent light from striking the auditorium ceiling or the top of the proscenium arch. It is more difficult to prevent light from striking the sides of the proscenium. Trough footlights should be equipped with several shields (or "fins", or "baffles", as they are sometimes called), at each end of the trough,

Open-trough type borderlights with color caps.

spaced about eighteen inches apart and placed between adjoining lamps. If the baffles are painted a dull black, they will minimize the side escape of light on to the proscenium frame. With the compartment type of footlight, particularly those equipped with reflectors, it is obvious that the correct placing and directioning of the footlights will prevent any undesirable escape of light.

In new construction of stages, the exact footlight equipment must be decided upon before the front edge of the stage floor is planned

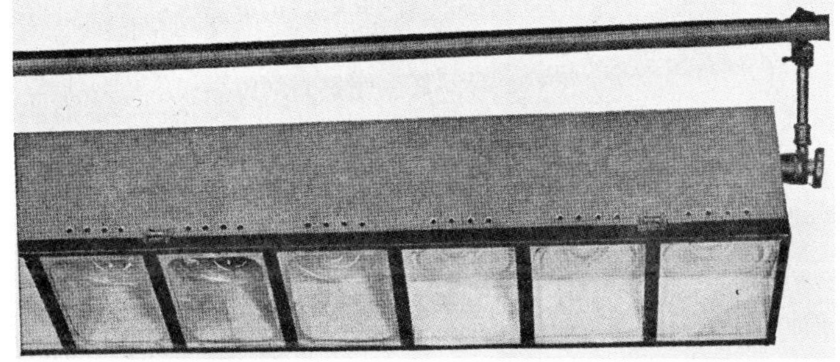

"Aluminide" compartment type borderlights with gelatin color media.

or built, since the supporting beams must be so spaced as to allow for the depression, or recess, necessary for the footlights. The permanent type of footlights, for permanent installation, are never carried in stock by dealers or manufacturers, but are made up to specifications such as length, size and spacing of lamps, wiring, color circuit arrangement, and number of sections.

IV. Borderlights

Borderlights are the companion equipment of footlights. They, too, provide general illumination, but from a more natural direction, that is, from overhead. Borderlights therefore are virtually inverted footlights, suspended from the gridiron at variable heights and parallel to the front edge of the stage. Construction of borderlights corresponds to that of footlights, except with a difference in

"X-Ray" compartment type borderlights with gelatin color media.

actual details made necessary because of the inverted position and the suspended mounting. As with footlights, there are two general types of borderlights — the older open-trough type and the newer compartment type. In each type the *lamps* almost invariably are burned base up. The size and spacing of lamps in open-trough borderlights are much the same as those in open-trough footlights; the compartment and reflector type borderlights, however, usually accommodate lamps up to and including the 200-watt size, the

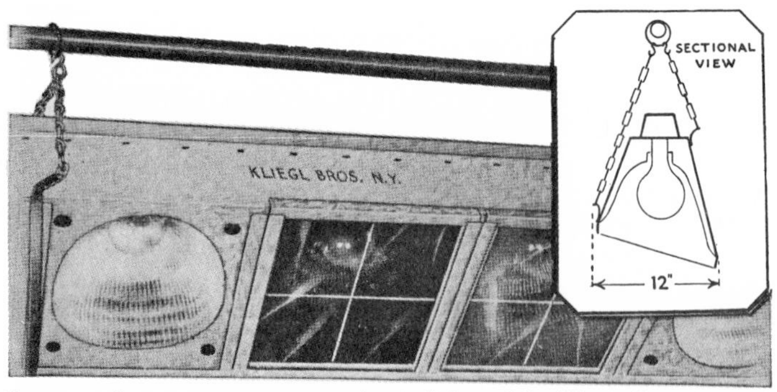

Concentrating compartment type borderlights with ribbed silvered metal reflectors and gelatin color media.

spacing varying from six to twelve inches, depending upon the type of reflecting medium. The same types of *reflecting media* are used: the simple white-painted sheet iron of the trough, or the inner surface of the compartments, or mirrored ribbed glass, or silvered ribbed metal, or spun aluminum, or porcelain-enameled steel. There is also a removable unit type of borderlight, similar to the removable unit type of footlight previously described. Means of *color modification* are the same — namely, color-dipped lamps, natural-colored glass bulb lamps, glass color caps and globes for the

Distributive compartment type borderlights with ribbed silvered metal reflectors and gelatin color media.

open-trough type; and sheet gelatin and glass plates for the compartment and reflector types. The same principles of *ventilation* prevail. *Wiring* is also carried in channels, directly above the lamps, and is permanently connected, in the splicing box, to the mains from the switchboard. Because of the variable height of the borderlights, the switchboard mains for any borderlight unit cannot be brought directly to the splicing box in rigid or permanent wiring form — they can extend only to a secondary splicing box midway up on the side wall of the stage, opposite the borderlight. At that point they are connected to flexible, multi-conductor borderlight cable (similar to regular two-conductor stage cable) which in turn is connected to the lamp circuits in the splicing box on the borderlight. This borderlight cable is of such length as to allow the borderlight to ascend or descend freely to its full limits of vertical traverse, and still be under complete control from the switchboard. The borderlight cable must be protected from the stress caused by its own weight by being securely fastened to the borderlight batten with a special cable support, and must be prevented from kinking by the use of a cable cradle. The principles of division into color circuits and sections that apply to footlights are equally applicable to borderlights. *Mounting* of borderlights is effected by chains or pipe clamps which are secured to the borderlight housing at intervals of about six feet. These are hung over, or firmly clamped, to the batten (usually a length of 1″, or $1\frac{1}{4}$″, or $1\frac{1}{2}$″ iron pipe) which is, in turn, suspended by the regular set of lines (usually three in number; on very large stages, four), from the gridiron, counterweighted, and secured ("tied-off") at the pinrail. If flexible steel cables are used for the lines (instead of manila hemp rope), strain insulators must be used close to the borderlight batten to prevent the transmission of any possible electrical ground in the borderlight to other parts of the stage where it might prove dangerous or cause trouble.

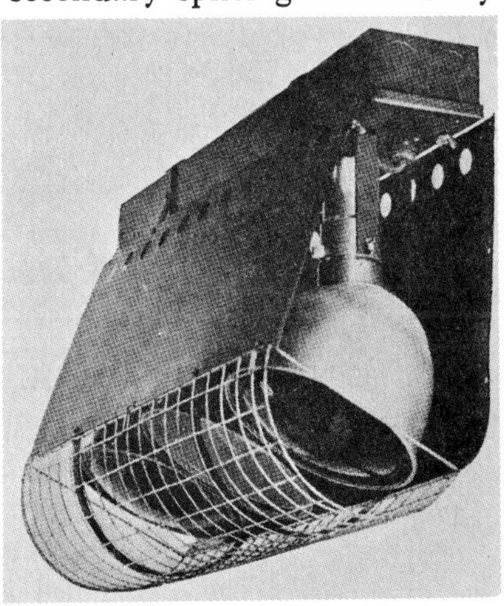

Removable-unit type borderlights.

Individual spun aluminum reflector with lamp, round glass color plate, and spring holder, as used in removable-unit type borderlights.

Borderlights were originally used to illuminate not only the stage, but also the hanging strips of canvas, known as "borders", that were formerly in such common use to represent ceilings of interior scenes and skies and foliage of exterior scenes. Hence the name "borderlights." The old-fashioned borders are nearly obsolete, but the term "borderlights" has remained, although the functions of the unit has changed somewhat. As a result, many improvements in design have resulted. For some productions, the regular installed borderlights are not used. In their place are substituted a number of spotlights, or of olivettes, or of both, each unit individually controlled, mounted on pipe battens wherever desired or needed. Thus there has been developed the spotlight cradle, which is described later.

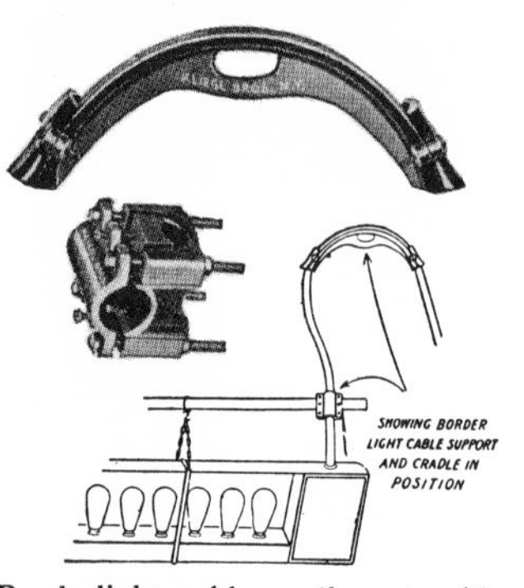

Borderlight cable cradle and cable support.

In place of the usual type of borderlights, David Belasco now uses a sort of indirect borderlight, consisting of twelve individually controlled spotlights, each of which is directed downward toward the auditorium, and permanently focussed upon a bowed circular disc coated with silver leaf. The silver leaf provides a semi-diffuse reflection, and being bowed, shapes the reflected light into a strip about six times as long as it is wide. The position of the disc controls the direction of the light strip, and the spotlight dimmer controls its intensity. Color modification is obtained by coating the silver leaf with colored French varnish, which acts as a color medium by reflection. Thus the stage scene is painted with what might be termed brush strokes of light, which, taken together, constitute a most natural and realistic effect. Belasco has also frequently used, with very effective results, a miniature borderlight consisting of a bank of twenty-five or thirty very small mirrored glass reflectors, each with a small 25-watt lamp. Banks of teaser lens units, a form of soft-edge spotlight, are also coming into wider use, replacing the borderlights, and in some cases supplementing and reinforcing them.

The old-style open-trough borderlights are objectionable because of improper distribution of light, low efficiency, and undesired mixing of color. The newer forms of borderlights are correspondingly similar in design to the newer forms of footlights. As the borderlights must be able to provide a much higher intensity of light than the footlights, the use of higher wattage lamps in compartments or reflectors in the borderlights is very widespread. Open-trough borderlights with low wattage lamps are now rapidly becoming obsolete, except for a new and compact type of "rotating borderlight." These units are placed close to the teaser and are used, in conjunction with teaser and tormentor lens units, to blend or modify

A bank of six spotlights with bowed circular reflector discs, used by David Belasco in place of the usual borderlight equipment.

color over the acting area. Through adjustable rotation about their longitudinal axis their light may be eliminated from ceilings or the back walls of interior scenes, and, in general, directed where it is most desired.

Borderlights, in contrast to footlights, should extend two or three feet beyond the side limits of the stage area; that is, for permanent installations. Temporary installations, of several portable borderlight units, for special purposes or single productions, should, of course, be only of the total length required for the immediate needs. They should be so designed that their light flux is emitted in a downward and backward direction, without having too sharp a "cut-off." One of the common and serious faults of most compartment and reflector types of borderlights is their tendency to "cut off" sharply — that is, the limit of their light flux is sharp and clearly defined. This causes a harsh shadow (running downwards and backwards on the side walls of interior sets, and horizontally along the back wall), where the sharply defined area of light projected by the borderlights does not merge, or blend, into the other lighting on the background from the other lighting units.

The number of sets of borderlights necessary to light satisfactorily the entire playing area of a stage will, of course, depend upon the depth of the stage. Usually, the first set of borderlights is placed directly in back of the act curtain, as closely as is possible without fouling the curtain. This first set is the most important of all. Obviously, it is the only one that can be used with an interior box set with a ceiling. For small stages, not exceeding about 15 feet in depth, this first set of borderlights, formerly sometimes called the "concert border", is sufficient. For larger stages, it is customary to use one set of borderlights for every 8 to 12 feet of stage depth. Always, on each set of borderlights, there should be left space for three or four 200-watt lamps, equipped with porcelain-enameled, steel reflectors, without color media, on a circuit entirely apart from the regular stage-lighting circuits. These are useful for general utility purposes — "work lights" for lighting the stage when construction work or rehearsals are being carried on, or when the stage is being set or cleared. Their use will help conserve the lamps and color media and reflecting surfaces on the regular stage-lighting equipment. As borderlights are subject to jars and hard knocks from contact with "flied" scenery, the color media, lamps, and reflectors must be protected by placing on the borderlight housing several suitable curved guards that will fend off the battens, drops, and other pieces of scenery as they are being raised into the fly loft.

Borderlights of special lengths are not regularly stocked by dealers and manufacturers, but must be made up to specifications, just as the footlights. Borderlights in standard unit lengths of 3, 6, and 9 feet are, however, usually available. Several of these convenient lengths may be fastened to a batten to make up the required total length. Individually mounted work lights may then be placed between them. These short lengths are usually considered as being portable, and they may be conveniently used as desired, in positions other than mounted on the battens. These borderlight units are often carried on tour by traveling productions. Portable striplights, such as are occasionally used as footlights, can also be used as temporary borderlights when they are properly mounted and suspended.

V. Striplights

The term "striplights" is applied generally to rows of lamps mounted either in an open trough or in compartments. They are usually portable and are useful for providing illumination (either general or local, depending upon whether the striplight is a long or a short one) in various places on the stage where a broad but not too powerful a light source is necessary. Striplights are similar in design to the various types of footlights and borderlights. Thus

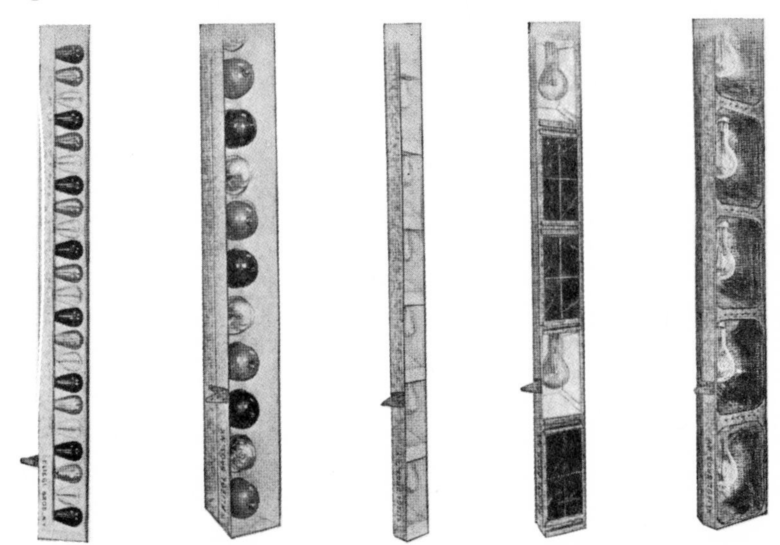

Several varieties of striplights, which offer a direct comparison between the essential characteristics embodied in various types of general stage-lighting equipment.

there are striplights of the open-trough type, using color-dipped lamps, natural-colored glass bulb lamps, or color caps and color globes on the color circuits; and of the compartment type, using sheet gelatin and glass color media. Besides the white-painted metal, reflectors of mirrored glass, silvered ribbed metal, porcelain-enameled steel, and spun aluminum are used. Lamps similar in size and spacing to those in corresponding types of footlights and borderlights are used. At present there is no indirect type of striplights, but there is no logical reason why there should not be. *Proscenium striplights* are mounted vertically, ranging in height from about eight feet to the full height of the proscenium arch, hinged so as to be adjustable in a horizontal plane, just behind the sides of the proscenium frame. They are the only type of striplights that are permanently installed. They are used to light the "first entrance" on each side of the stage. Although formerly much in vogue, proscenium striplights are rapidly becoming obsolete, being replaced by vertical banks of small spotlights, or by banks of tormentor lens units, a form of soft-edge spotlight, each unit of which is operated individually for flooding or spotting certain stage areas.

Portable striplights are available in several lengths, ranging from 18″ to 8 feet or more. They can be adapted to a number of uses on the stage. They can be set on the floor between ground rows, to illuminate them, or before the cyclorama, to supply tinting effects such as dawn and sunset, or at the front edge of the stage, as temporary footlights; hung from battens or parts of scenery by a pivoted hook near one end, they can light entrances, "wings", masking pieces, and dioramic scenery or "transparencies"; or suspended horizontally from battens, they can serve as temporary borderlights. Since portable striplights are used only for special purposes, they are hardly ever wired in more than one or two color circuits. Instead, they are equipped with lamps, or color media, of the desired color. If several colors are necessary, more than one strip is used. Portable striplights are wired in a wiring channel, but have no splicing box for permanent connections. Instead, each circuit in a striplight unit is provided with a short length of cable and a male cable connector by which it is plugged into a length of stage cable, which, in turn, is plugged into a stage pocket or into a switchboard receptacle, and controlled from the switchboard. A "skeleton striplight" is simply a row of sockets mounted in a wiring channel without any compartments or reflecting hood. It is of limited use, but is convenient as a holder for type "B" lamps when they are being color-dipped.

Striplights in standard lengths, both open-trough, and with painted metal compartments, wired in one circuit, are usually stocked by dealers and manufacturers. The more elaborate types, and odd lengths, must be made up to specifications. Several striplights, of various lengths, will often be found useful in lighting a production, especially for odd requirements for which other types of stage-lighting instruments are not so suitable or adaptable.

Footlights, borderlights, and striplights (with the exception of very short striplights, and divided sections of footlights and borderlights), supply a light that is general in character. Considered as a source of light they are in the form of a strip — long and narrow in shape. Hence their light is diffusive, non-directional, in planes parallel to and passing through their longitudinal axes. But in planes perpendicular to their longitudinal axes, their light is predominantly directional. Hence the necessity of footlights from below and borderlights from above to counteract, to some extent, the vertical directionality of the light from each other. But the light from olivettes and spotlights, each of which forms a more compact light source, is directional in all planes. Spotlights project a comparatively narrow beam of light, which is highly directional, as spotlights are virtually point sources of light. Olivettes project a wide beam or flood of light, which is slightly more diffusive, though still directional, in nature. Thus olivettes and spotlights, used for local lighting, find their most effective use in bringing out the plastic qualities of the stage picture.

VI. Olivettes

These are said to have derived their rather uncommon name from that of the production in which they were first used. They are sometimes known as "open-box lights", or "floodlights." Of all stage-lighting instruments, the ordinary type of olivette is perhaps the crudest, or at least the simplest, in design, construction, and use. It is essentially an open-faced sheet-iron box, containing a mogul socket for accommodating a lamp of high wattage. The open face of the metal box is about 18″ square, and the side walls converge to the back wall, which is only about six inches wide but is just as high as the open face—about 18″. Inside, at the top, is fastened a porcelain mogul socket, which accommodates, base up, any lamp ranging in size from 300 to 2000 watts. For its reflector, the common type of olivette utilizes its inside surfaces, painted with a flat white diffusely reflecting paint which is fairly resistant to the intense heat of the lamp. Nevertheless, it requires occasional cleaning and repainting. The more modern type of olivette has a parabolic-shaped reflector of spun aluminum incorporated in the sheet-metal housing. The reflecting surface of the aluminum is protected by a coat of lacquer, which prevents it from oxidizing or discoloring. The reflector of spun aluminum is not only more efficient than the white painted metal (since it reflects a greater proportion of the light emitted by the lamp), but it also provides light that is much "whiter"

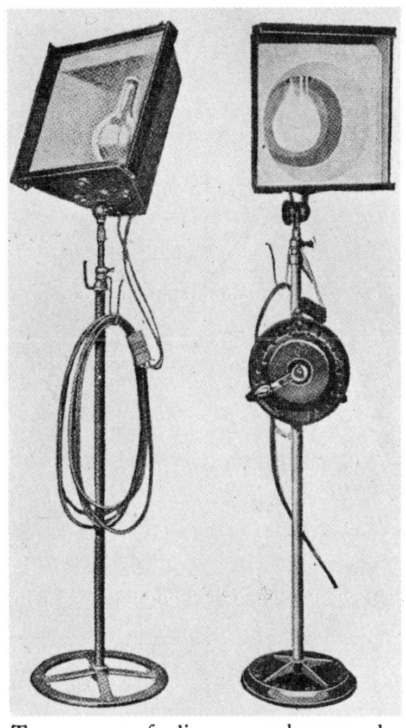

Two types of olivettes: that on the left is of the simple open-box type; that on the right is equipped with a spun aluminum reflector. The latter is shown with a small round-plate dimmer, on the pedestal standard, for the local control of light intensity.

in quality. It also provides a good degree of diffusion. Color modification of light from an olivette is achieved by means of gelatin color media, usually in wooden frames, that cover the entire open face of the olivette. These color frames are held in place by grooves at the top and bottom of the olivette. Usually two sets of grooves are provided in order that two color frames can be accommodated simultaneously. There is a tendency for stray white light to escape at the vertical sides of the color frames. Some olivettes are equipped with hinged side covers for the color frames, which prevent the "spill" of light that often spoils the effects sought for. A "combination olivette" is equipped with two medium sockets, in addition to the single mogul socket. These extra sockets are placed on a separate circuit, and in them smaller sizes of lamps may be used when just a touch of light is desired, without the use of a dimmer. Ventilation of olivettes is important, as the heat generated by the large lamps (totally enclosed, with the color frame in place) must be dissipated. The top and bottom, as well as part of the sides of the olivettes, are made double-walled, both pierced with $\frac{3}{4}''$ diameter holes, so placed in relation to each other that air is allowed a free passage from the bottom to the top of the olivette, without any attendant escape of stray light. The wiring is simple. Short lengths of flexible asbestos-covered wires leave the olivette at the bottom and are attached to a male cable connector. An olivette is usually mounted, by means of an adjustable swivel joint, on an adjustable telescopic extension standard with a heavy circular cast-iron pedestal. Several holes near the circumference of the base permit its being fastened rigidly to the stage floor with stage screws. The swivel joint permits

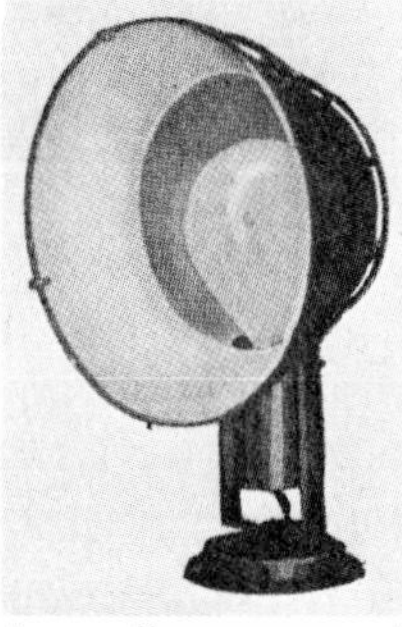

A small, unmounted size of spun aluminum olivette.

"Wellesley" combination box light: a type of olivette with which may be used three interchangeable polished metal reflectors (two parabolic and one cylindrical) depending upon specific requirements. This unit is especially useful for simulating a beam of sunlight or moonlight. The concentric fins, or "louvers", eliminate undesired spill light.

adjustment of light direction in a vertical plane, and the extension standard permits adjustment in a horizontal plane, as well as permitting adjustment of the olivette height within a range of from 4 to 8 feet. This constitutes the so-called "pedestal mounting." Banks

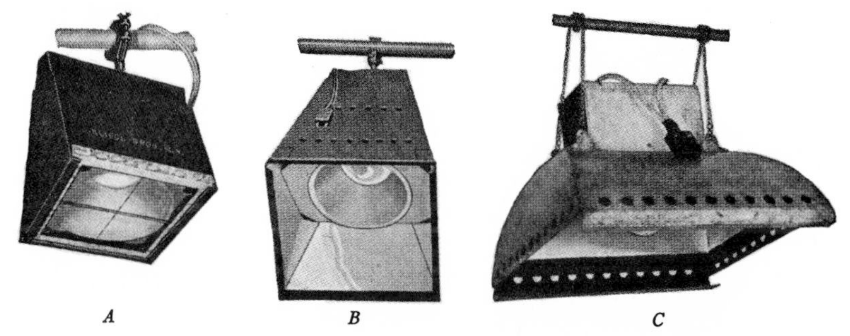

A *B* *C*

Several types of olivettes, or floodlights, for suspension mounting employing reflectors of: *A*, ribbed silvered metal; *B*, spun aluminum; and *C*, polished metal.

of several olivettes, mounted vertically on heavy pipe standards with bases, are also available and are principally useful for side-lighting of back drops and cycloramas, and for other purposes where a large volume of light is necessary. By means of a swivel-joint pipe hanger and a pipe clamp, it is possible to mount the usual type of pedestal olivettes on a pipe batten. Thus mounted, olivettes are often used as needed, singly or in groups, and occasionally for supplementing, or sometimes altogether replacing, the usual borderlights. Because of this increasing use on battens, some olivettes are designed primarily with chain or pipe hangers, exclusively for such service. Smaller sizes of these "suspension type" olivettes, as they are called, for lamps up to the 200-watt size, are equipped with silvered, ribbed, metal reflectors, and may be considered as a single compartment of a borderlight. Dismounted from the pedestals, olivettes are often laid on the floor and used to light the bottoms of back drops and cycloramas. With the pedestal type of olivette, it is possible to mount an enclosed switch and a slide-wire dimmer on the extension standard, for local control of light intensity. Or, olivettes may be subjected to centralized control from the switch-board. Various types of commercial flood-lighting units, particularly several special types, are often used on the stage, with excellent results, for fulfilling the functions of olivettes. Their chief advantage (discussed in the section describing lighting equipment for outdoor productions) lies in the high degree of light control (compared to that of olivettes) that they afford. These floodlighting units, with the exception of the "Wellesley" and "Pilgrim" theatre and pageant projectors, require special mounting and special means of applying color media, with which they are not originally equipped. The painted-metal type of pedestal olivette is available in only one size, although lamps ranging in size from 300 to 1500 watts can be used in it. The spun-aluminum olivettes, however, are made in several sizes, depending on the maximum size of lamp they can accommodate. Thus there are 300-watt, 500-watt, and 1500-watt sizes, and also several small units (not mounted on pedestals) using 100-watt and 200-watt lamps.

A 100-ampere carbon arc spotlight with access door open, showing the arc mechanism. The built-in framing shutters before the lens are shown partially closed.

Although olivettes, employing a single lamp of high wattage, have rendered the old-fashioned "bunchlight" almost obsolete, a few of the latter are still in use, and are still available. A bunchlight is simply a square open-faced sheet-iron box, painted white inside, in which ten or twelve medium sockets are mounted to provide for an equal number of lower-wattage lamps. Grooves for color frames extend across the top and bottom of the open face. Because it uses a number of low-wattage lamps instead of a single high-wattage lamp, the bunchlight is very inefficient. It still finds favor to a very limited extent, nevertheless, principally because of the mistaken idea that, with the small lamps, current consumption and lamp replacement costs are lower (ultimately, both are really very much higher) and because, if a regular dimmer is not available, a dimming effect can be achieved, in a crude jerky fashion, by removing or replacing one lamp at a time (even this cannot be carried out if a color frame is in place). Olivettes employing the electric arc as a light source are still used, but to even a less extent than are bunchlights.

VII. Spotlights

These are also known sometimes as lens lamps or by similar names. They employ scientific methods of light control to a greater extent

TABLE OF BEAM-SPREAD ANGLES IN TERMS OF "SPOT" DIAMETERS, FOR PROJECTION DISTANCE OF 100 FEET

(Values of Beam Spread Expressed in Angular Degrees; Those of "Spot" Diameters, in Inches)

Beam Spread Angles and "Spot" Diameters									
°	"	°	"	°	"	°	"	°	"
1	21	21	445	41	897	61	1414	81	2049
2	42	22	467	42	921	62	1442	82	2086
3	63	23	488	43	945	63	1470	83	2123
4	84	24	510	44	970	64	1500	84	2160
5	105	25	532	45	994	65	1529	85	2199
6	126	26	554	46	1019	66	1559	86	2238
7	147	27	576	47	1044	67	1589	87	2277
8	168	28	598	48	1069	68	1619	88	2317
9	189	29	620	49	1094	69	1649	89	2358
10	210	30	642	50	1119	70	1680	90	2400
11	231	31	664	51	1145	71	1712	91	2442
12	252	32	687	52	1171	72	1744	92	2485
13	273	33	710	53	1196	73	1777	93	2528
14	294	34	733	54	1223	74	1810	94	2573
15	316	35	756	55	1249	75	1843	95	2619
16	337	36	780	56	1276	76	1876	96	2665
17	358	37	803	57	1303	77	1909	97	2713
18	380	38	826	58	1330	78	1943	98	2761
19	402	39	850	59	1358	79	1978	99	2810
20	423	40	873	60	1386	80	2013	100	2860

The above table gives values of spot diameters only for a 100-foot projection distance, or "throw." Values for any other projection distances can be obtained easily, as they will be in direct proportion to the values given above. Thus, for a 200-foot throw, the values above must be multiplied by 2; for a 20-foot throw the values above must be divided by 5. The above table can be used for determining the area lighted by the light beam from any lighting instrument whose beam spread is known. Thus, it can be used with floodlighting projectors, spotlights, and so forth. It is primarily intended to be used, however, in conjunction with the table on the opposite page. Examples of the use of both, together, are as follows:

(*A*) It is desired to find the size of spot which will be produced by a 6″ × 10″ condenser lens (one that is 6″ in diameter and 10″ in focal length) when the light source is 7″ from the lens, and when the spotlight is 25′ distant from the screen, or backdrop or other surface onto which the beam will be directed. Reference to the previous table reveals the beam angle as being 17°. The above table shows the size of spot for 17° beam spread to be 358″ for a 100′ throw. Hence, by direct proportion, it will be, approximately, 90″, or 7½′, for a 25′ throw.

(*B*) It is desired to equip a spotlight with a 5″ diameter condenser lens of such focal length that it will produce an 8′ spot at a 20′ throw, when the midpoint of the light-source traverse-range is 5″ from the lens. A spot 8′, or 96″ in diameter on a 20′ throw is equivalent to one 480″ in diameter on a 100′ throw. Reference to the above table reveals such a spot to result from a beam spread of approximately 23°. By using this figure, and the other data given, reference to the previous table will reveal a 5″ × 7½″ condenser lens to be the most suitable for fulfilling the required conditions.

sheet metal frames. The wiring of spotlights is very simple — the socket is connected to two asbestos-covered flexible wires brought through the spotlight hood and terminating a few feet outside it, in a male cable connector, by means of which the spotlight can be

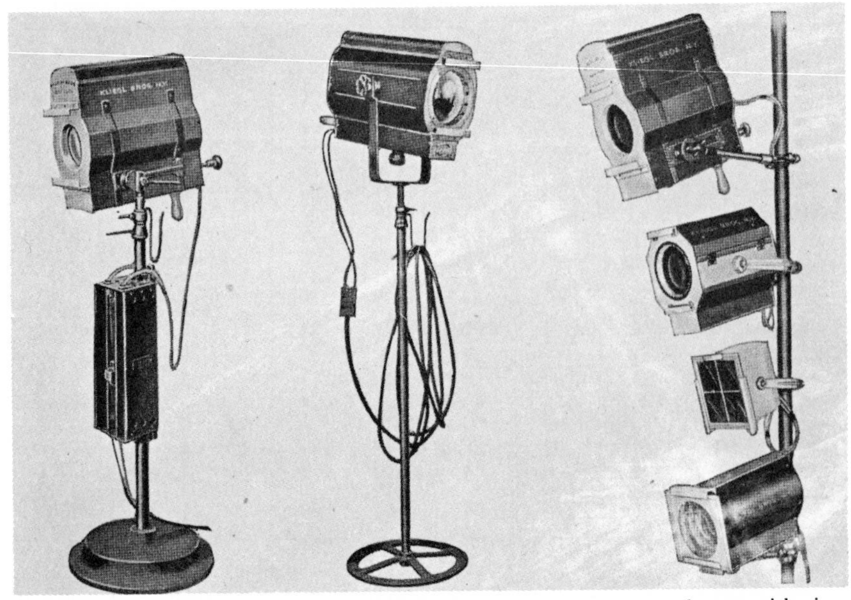

Two types of incandescent spotlights with pedestal mounting; and several types with pipe-clamp mounting for use on vertical pipe standards in the tormentor position or on a travelling spotlight tower. The spotlight on the left is equipped with a slider type dimmer for local control of light intensity.

readily connected to the stage mains from the switchboard. Although spotlight lamps are standardized to such an extent that, usually, no vertical adjustment of the lamp position is necessary to bring the lamp filament into optical alignment with the lens, the better grades of spotlights have their lamp sockets mounted so that, should it be necessary, any such adjustment can quickly and conveniently be made. Spotlights have two types of mounting — pedestal and suspension. Unless otherwise designated, they have the same mounting as have olivettes; namely, an adjustable swivel joint (attached to a heavy bracket on the side wall of the spotlight, opposite the access door), fastened to an adjustable telescopic extension standard on a heavy, circular, cast-iron pedestal. Thus the maximum adjustment of light direction and position is possible. Present practice utilizes, to an ever-increasing extent, spotlights mounted on pipe battens (usually the same battens from which the borderlights are suspended), or on a light-bridge directly behind the teaser, or on vertical pipe standards directly behind the tormentors. For such use, spotlights are available for suspension mountings. The same spotlights are used as for pedestal mountings, except that a swivel-joint pipe hanger and a pipe clamp is supplied in place of the telescopic standard. For permanent mounting (such as for front-lighting from the balcony or the rear wall of the auditorium) regular "suspension mounting" spotlights are used, with the pipe clamp replaced by a pipe "floor flange" which is fixed to the wall, or ceiling, or beam.

A footlight baby spotlight.

With the pedestal types of standard and baby sizes of spotlights, an enclosed switch and a slide-wire dimmer can be mounted on the extension standard, for the local control of light intensity. Otherwise, the spotlight can be controlled directly from the switchboard. Color control is, of course, provided by the color frames, and control of light direction by the swivel mounting. The size of the "spot" is controlled by varying the distance between the lamp and lens, which can easily be accomplished by adjusting a focus handle, or thumbscrew, that projects through the bottom of the housing.

There are many special types of spotlights, but almost all are variations or elaborations of the basic types mentioned above. One type is fairly distinctive — the footlight baby spotlight. As its rather cumbersome name indicates, it is placed in the footlights, and hence is small and compact. Because of its compactness, its range of focus is rather limited. In one type, the lamp socket is

A

B

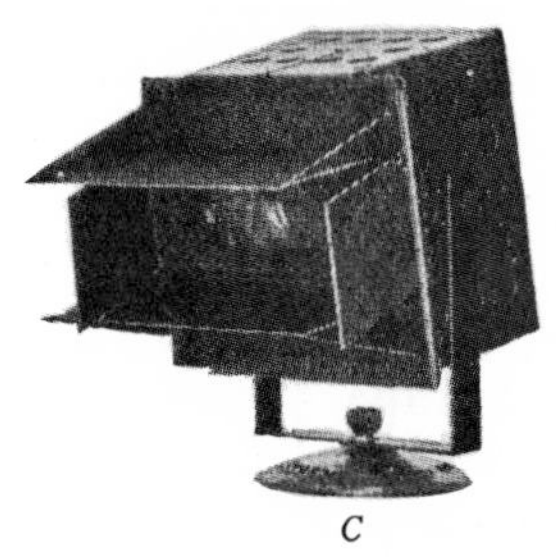
C

A 250-watt combination box light and lens unit: *A*, without lens, for use as a sort of small "floodlight"; *B*, with regular condenser lens, for use as a footlight baby spotlight; and *C*, with special wide-angle cylindrical lens, for use in balcony-front operation, for which purpose it is compact and powerful.

fixed in position, the focus range being adjusted by moving the lens. The footlight baby spotlight is useful where a small "spot" of mild intensity is desired. A compact and rugged type of baby spotlight is that made of cast aluminum and equipped with a yoke mounting and a swivel-joint pipe clamp. The lens, on this type of baby spotlight, is readily removable, thus converting the spotlight into a small open-box light, or floodlight. There is available a so-called "spotlight cradle", which consists of six small baby spotlights mounted

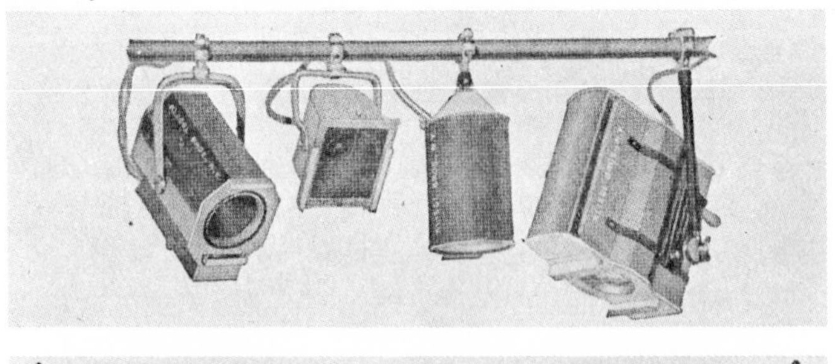

Spotlight equipment for supplementing or supplanting borderlights: above, several sizes of spotlights with suspension pipe-clamp mounting, for use on pipe battens, especially in the teaser position; and, below, a spotlight cradle consisting of six baby spotlights, each of which is susceptible to individual control.

together in a steel frame, each spotlight subject to individual control of direction, intensity, color, and focus. Two or three of these spotlight cradles are sometimes mounted on a batten, and thus used in place of borderlights. The use of a number of small individually controlled spotlights in place of borderlights is a practice that is constantly increasing in favor, primarily because of the highly individualized and flexible control of light that it affords. Another type of spotlight is the "suspension spotlight" (500 to 1000-watt size), cylindrical in shape and equipped with a pipe clamp, designed especially and exclusively for batten mounting.

A comparatively recent development of great importance to stage lighting, and of particular usefulness in the service of the newer stagecraft is the "soft-edge" spotlight. This instrument is somewhat similar to the standard type of spotlight, and is equipped with an internal sliding device (consisting of a special hand-ground glass diffusing medium and a metal diaphragm) which overcomes the hard, sharp edge of the ordinary "spot." The "spot" of light produced by the soft-edge spotlight is very dim at the edge and gradually grows brighter toward the centre. This feature makes the spotlight ideal for localized illumination, as the edges of the "spot" fade out into darkness, or blend into a low intensity of general illumination.

In addition, the spotlight beam can be dimmed uniformly over the entire lighted area, without sharp shadows and without the use of an electrical dimmer, merely by inserting an opaque screen in the color frame grooves of the spotlight. The color of the light beam may be changed, or tinted, or blended into each other in a similar fashion (also uniformly and without shadows), by sliding the color frames in the grooves, directly before the lens. The entire instrument can, of course, be subjected to centralized control from the switchboard. The soft-edge spotlight can be converted into a standard type of spotlight by the removal of the internal sliding device. The soft-edge spotlight is available in two sizes, one with a medium socket (accommodating spotlight lamps of 100, 250, and 400-watt size), and the other with a mogul socket (accommodating spotlight lamps of sizes larger than 400 watts). It is equipped for either pedestal, suspension, or permanent mounting.

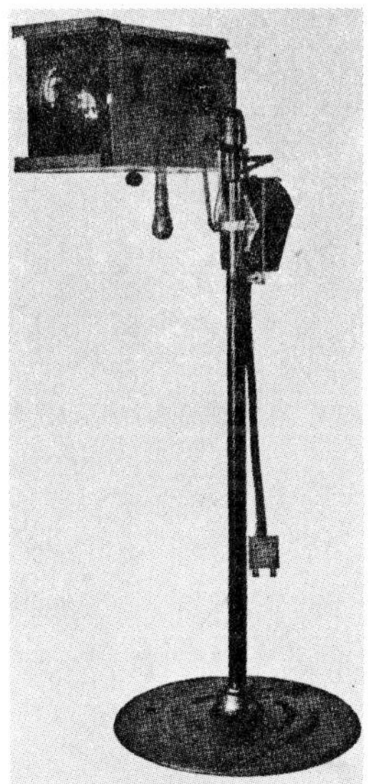

A 400-watt "soft-edge" spotlight with pedestal mounting and enclosed switch.

Another "soft-edge" instrument, somewhat similar to the soft-edge spotlight (designed especially for short projection distances), is the "tormentor lens unit", or, as it is sometimes called, the "tormentor hood." It is provided with a special polished metal reflector permanently mounted at the rear of the unit. Like the soft-edge spotlight, it is also equipped with a ground-glass diffusing medium and a metal diaphragm, as well as a large condenser lens. In addition, it is

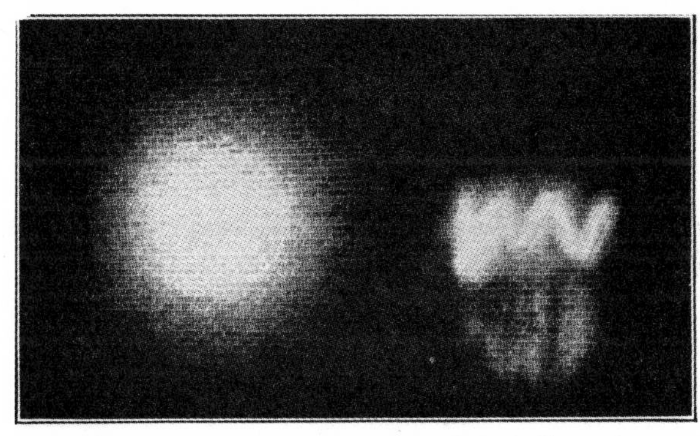

Comparison of "spots" produced by a "soft-edge" spotlight (left) and by a standard spotlight (right), both of the 400-watt size, at 40-foot projection distance, and at minimum focus.

equipped with a set of "blinders" and "shutters" for "framing", or restricting, the lighted area. It is provided with a yoke mounting, and by means of a special pipe clamp and "swinging arm" it can be mounted on a vertical pipe standard. Thus mounted, vertical banks of tormentor lens units, each unit subject to individual control, are placed behind the tormentors at each side of the proscenium opening. With a small "angle knee" attached to the yoke mounting, this same lens unit may be suspended by means of the special pipe clamp, from a horizontal pipe batten. In this form it is termed a "teaser lens unit." Mounted on a pipe batten directly behind the teaser, or limiting upper drapery of the proscenium opening, banks of these teaser units, each unit subject to individual control, are used in place of the usual type of borderlights. Soft-edge tormentor and teaser lens units are also available in two sizes (100 to 400 watts; and 500 to 2000 watts). Like the soft-edge spotlight, these lens units provide directional light that is diffused in character, and that hence forms shadows that are soft and pleasing.

A group of 400-watt yoke type tormentor lens units as mounted on a vertical pipe standard in the tormentor position.

As explained previously, incandescent spotlights, because of their many desirable qualities, have almost totally superseded arc spotlights for use on the stage. The use of arc spotlights is almost wholly confined to long-range projection. For such purposes, arc spotlights are generally available in the following approximate amperage sizes: 25, 35, 50, 75, 100, 125, 150, and 200 amperes.

VIII. Sciopticons

These instruments, sometimes known as "effect machines", are used for simulating various visual effects found in nature and various visual effects not found in nature. Primarily, though, they are used to simulate natural phenomena. Some are very ingenious and when cleverly constructed and manipulated, they produce results that seem amazingly real — so real, and so amazing, in fact, that their tendency to distract an audience is a matter of no small moment to be reckoned with whenever their use is planned. When used carefully, however, with taste and discretion, they often prove a very useful adjunct to play production. Although well over a hundred different effects are available — natural, fantastic, or otherwise —

A group of 250-watt yoke type teaser lens units as mounted on a pipe batten (with a special enclosed wiring channel) in the teaser position.

there are relatively few that are commonly used. Among these may be listed "moving clouds" (of several different formations), "rain", "snow", and "fire" or "flame" effects. As explained on page 86 a sciopticon is an extension, or adaptation, of a spotlight. A sciopticon must not be confused with an "effect head", or "effect casing", as it is sometimes called, which forms only a part of a complete sciopticon. To be operative, a sciopticon must consist of four major parts: a spot-light (most invariably a standard large spotlight), which serves as a light source; a second condenser lens (beside the one that is part of the spotlight); an effect head, or an effect casing, containing a painted or photographed transparent disc, and the mechanism for revolving it; and an objective lens for magnifying and focussing the image of the painted disc, and projecting it on to the screen or back drop or cyclorama. The *spotlight* has been discussed immediately above. When a spotlight is used as part of a sciopticon, the lamp should be focussed at about two thirds of its traverse distance away from the lens (with the lamp filament slightly "ahead" of the focal point of the lens), for best results.

Front view of a sciopticon, or "effect machine", consisting of a standard large spotlight equipped with effect apparatus.

The second condenser lens serves to redirect the diverging light rays of the spotlight, forming them into a convergent, or narrowing, beam of light. This lens is mounted in an aluminum holder which fits tightly (by means of a thumbscrew) into the color-frame grooves of the spotlight. A spring ring-collar which fits snugly against the front face of the spotlight housing prevents the escape of any stray light from the small space between the spotlight and the lens holder. This lens holder is itself equipped with a set of grooves (on the side opposite that having the ring-collar), in which the effect head is securely fitted. The combination of lens, lens holder, ring-collar, and grooves is termed an *effect holder*.

The *effect head* varies somewhat in design, depending upon the particular effect which it produces. Its principal function is to pass through the beam of light from the second condensing lens, at the proper speed and in the proper direction, a transparent slide or disc (or, in elaborate "effects", both slides and discs, each at its own proper speed and direction), on which is painted or photographed, in miniature, such designs as will provide the effect desired. The motive power for moving the slide or revolving the disc is usually furnished by an adjustable speed clockwork mechanism with a train of gears. In the case of simple effects, such as "rising moon" or "setting sun", the effect head consists merely of a painted slide that is moved slowly through the beam of light, its projected image moving across the backdrop, or cyclorama, at a speed proportionate to that at which the slide is moved through the beam of light. For most effects, however, such as "moving clouds," "rain or snow," where the motion must be more rapid, as well as continuous over an appreciable length of time, the designs are painted or photographed in continuous form, around a circular disc (usually 18″ in diameter). The disc is revolved, and a portion of it (that nearer the edge than the center) passes through the light beam, thus producing the continuous moving effect. The slide or disc is usually made of mica, the undesired portions being opaqued out with black paint or with a photographic emulsion process. Where color is desired in the resulting effect, transparent-colored paints are used. For some effects, a disc and a slide are used, or two discs, or two discs and a slide — each moving at its requisite speed and direction. For some effects, such as flames and water ripples, the secondary, quivering sort of motion is obtained by the use of a pressed glass plate of irregular density (of various thicknesses over its face, arranged in a more or less definite design) placed in the beam of light (in addition to the revolving disc). This causes a mobile distortion of light rays which produces a most realistic effect. Different designs of pressed glass are used for different effects. These glass plates, when used, are mounted directly in the effect head, in a fixed position. The "mask opening", or area of slide or disc exposed to the beam of light at any instant, is usually $2\frac{3}{4}'' \times 3''$. The disc, or slide (or both, or several of each — according to the effect), and the mask opening and pressed glass plate (if used) are all contained in a rigid sheet-iron housing, or casing, open, of course, on both sides where the beam of light passes through. The clockwork mechanism is mounted in its own housing, on the outside of the casing. The casing is equipped with a holding plate that fits snugly into the slide grooves on the effect holder. This holding plate is fastened to the effect casing by means of a swivel joint, which permits the casing to be turned in any position, so that the effect image may move in any desired direction across the screen or cyclorama—from left to right, from right to left, up or down, horizontally, vertically, or diagonally. Like the effect holder, the effect casing is also equipped with a set of slide grooves. These are for holding the objective lens in place. These various elements, then—the holding plate, the swivel joint, the effect casing, the effect disc or slide, the clockwork mechanism, and the slide grooves—together constitute what is usually known as an "effect head." Some modern types of effect heads use small, slow-speed electric motors in place of clockwork mechanisms for revolving the discs. These are adapted to remote control (from the switchboard, for instance), and require no attention, but are very likely to prove somewhat noisy, especially for use on small stages.

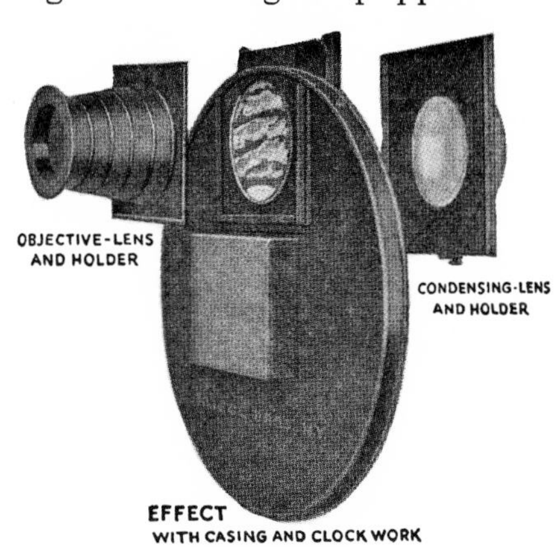

Disassembled effect apparatus: three accessories which convert a spotlight into a sciopticon.

For projecting stationary effects, such as clouds or a scene of any sort, painted or photographed on a lantern slide, the effect head of a sciopticon is replaced by a *slide-carrier holder*. Thus the sciopticon is converted into what is practically a stereopticon, or "magic lantern." Conversely, a regular sciopticon is virtually a stereopticon in which the lantern slide has been replaced by a moving slide or disc. Such a slide-carrier holder is equipped, just as is an effect head, with a swivel-joint plate holder for attaching it to the effect holder, and with a set of grooves for accommodating the objective lens in front.

The *objective lens* used with a sciopticon receives the image of the lighted slide or disc, magnifies it many times, and projects it on to the screen or backdrop or cyclorama. It consists principally of two convex lenses, mounted, a fixed distance apart, in a cylindrical brass

TABLE OF SIZES OF PROJECTED IMAGES PRODUCED BY A SCIOPTICON, WITH SPECIAL WIDE-ANGLE OBJECTIVE LENSES* OF VARIOUS FOCAL LENGTHS, AT VARIOUS PROJECTION DISTANCES

(ALL VALUES ARE EXPRESSED IN FEET, AND ARE BASED ON THE USE OF A CIRCULAR MASK OPENING IN THE EFFECT HEAD, 5″ IN DIAMETER. THE FIGURES REPRESENT THE DIAMETERS OF THE PROJECTED IMAGES)

FOCAL LENGTH OF LENS	PROJECTION DISTANCE								
	10′	15′	20′	25′	30′	35′	40′	45′	50′
4″	24	48							
6″	18	32	44	56					
8″	12	18	23	28	33	38	43	48	53
10″	8	12	16	20	24	28	32	36	40
12″	6	10	13	17	21	24	27	30	34

* The special wide-angle objective lenses scheduled in this table are designed for the projection of "effects" only, especially where a very large image must be obtained at a comparatively short projection distance. They cannot be used with satisfactory results for projecting lantern-slide or similar images, when sharp definition or accurate masking is required, as they distort the light beam somewhat because of the abnormal service exacted of the lenses. Hence all of the values given in this table should be considered as being roughly approximate only. For the projection of "effects" at long projection distances, or for the accurate projection of lantern-slide, or similar, images, the long-distance objective lenses scheduled in the table on the opposite page should be used.

tube or "barrel." This lens barrel telescopes within another brass cylinder (thus allowing for focus adjustment) which is fastened to a rigid conical sheet-metal holder that fits into the slide grooves on the effect head. An objective lens of given focal length has but a limited projection range. Conditions under which sciopticons are used vary greatly — especially as regards projection distance (from sciopticon to screen) and size of projected image desired. For this reason it is necessary to provide a sciopticon with an objective lens of a focal length suitable to the specific conditions of use. Objective lenses are available in a wide variety of sizes. The accompanying tables indicate lens sizes, focal lengths, and sizes of image at various projection distances. The importance of selecting the proper objective lens for sciopticon use cannot be overstressed.

These four parts, then - spotlight, effect holder, effect head, and objective lens — constitute a sciopticon. Lacking any one of these four parts, a sciopticon is totally inoperative. A separate effect head is required for each effect desired. As all effect heads are equipped with similar sets of grooves and holders, they are rapidly and conveniently interchangeable.

TABLE OF SIZES OF PROJECTED IMAGES PRODUCED BY A SCIOPTICON, WITH LONG-DISTANCE OBJECTIVE LENSES OF VARIOUS FOCAL LENGTHS, AT VARIOUS PROJECTION DISTANCES

(All Values Are Expressed in Inches, and Are Based on the Use of a Mask Opening 2¾″ High and 3″ Wide. The Upper Figure of Each Pair Represents the Height, and the Lower Figure Represents the Width, of the Projected Images)

Focal Length of Lens	Projection Distance											
	10′	20′	30′	40′	50′	60′	70′	80′	90′	100′	110′	120′
4″	77 84	154 168	231 252	308 336								
6″	55 60	110 120	165 180	220 240	275 300							
8″	44 48	88 96	132 144	176 192	220 240	264 288						
10″		66 72	99 108	132 144	165 180	198 216	231 252	264 288				
12″		55 60	83 90	110 120	138 150	165 180	193 210	220 240	248 270	275 300		
14″			71 77	94 103	118 129	141 154	165 180	189 206	212 232	236 257	260 283	
16″				83 90	104 113	124 135	145 158	165 180	186 203	207 225	227 248	248 270
18″					92 100	110 120	128 140	147 160	165 180	184 200	202 220	220 240
20″					83 90	99 108	116 126	132 144	149 162	165 180	181 198	198 216
24″						83 90	96 105	110 120	124 135	138 150	151 165	165 180
28″						73 79	84 92	96 105	107 117	119 130	131 143	142 155
32″							74 80	84 91	94 102	104 113	114 124	124 135
36″							64 70	74 80	83 90	92 100	101 110	110 120

"Effects" may be projected from several positions: some, such as "clouds" or "rising moon", from the light-bridge directly behind and above the proscenium opening (in a position similar to that of the first row of borderlights), on to the backdrop or cyclorama; or from behind on to a translucent drop or cyclorama; some, such as "rain" and "snow", from the balcony face, or rear wall of the auditorium, on to a gauze drop that completely covers the proscenium opening; and others, such as "flames" or "flowing water", from the front directly on to the stage setting itself. With several sciopticons, or "effect machines", in operation simultaneously, "the possibilities of effects are limited only by the imagination of the artist and by their contributory or distracting effect upon the audience."

IX. Linnebach Lantern

This unit, often termed a "scene projector", is used to project, by means of light, a scene or design on to a backdrop or cyclorama. The Linnebach lantern is extremely simple both in principal and construction. Its operation depends altogether upon the simple fact that light travels in straight lines. It consists essentially of a powerful, concentrated light source, a large glass slide upon which is painted the scene or design, and a suitable housing and mounting. The painted glass slide is placed in the path of the light rays emitted by the practicable point source of light, with the result that the image of the painted scene or design is projected, greatly enlarged, on to the desired surface. Because of the great magnification, the design painted on the glass must be clear and sharp, and the light source must be as concentrated and powerful as possible. No lenses are used in the Linnebach lantern. The light source commonly used is an incandescent spotlight lamp, of 1000, 1500, or 2000 watts, although a 30-ampere carbon arc is also used occasionally. With an incandescent lamp, a spherical mirror, properly focused, is usually used to achieve the maximum utilization of light. The housing of the Linnebach lantern is simply a large sheet-iron hood, in a form similar to that of a truncated rectangular pyramid lying on its side. At the narrow end of the housing is mounted the lamp (with provision for adequate ventilation); at the edges of the wide end, which is open, are provided grooves for holding in place the painted slide. The slide, which is approximately $2\frac{1}{2} \times 3\frac{1}{2}$ feet in size, is of thin, smooth, polished plate glass, in order to minimize distortion of the light beam, and is painted in transparent colors (except, of course, where opaque black is used for "masking"). As any light, except that emanating from the point source, would tend to blur the projected image, the entire inside surface of the Linnebach lantern is painted a dead black. The entire unit is mounted on a regular pedestal base — a telescoping extension standard such as spotlights and olivettes have — with provision for adjustment of height and vertical and horizontal angular setting for directioning the light beams. The Linnebach lantern is wired with short asbestos-covered wires and a male cable connector, by means of which it can be plugged into a stage pocket and controlled from the switchboard.

The Linnebach lantern has long been regarded as a most ingenious device — a contribution, by Continental theatre practice, to modern stagecraft — and its actual possibilities have been greatly overrated by the same enthusiasm that coined the now banal and meaningless phrase, "painting scenery with light." It is neither ingenious (it is simplicity, perhaps even crudeness, itself) nor are its possibilities unlimited. Its effective use is distinctly restricted to the stylized or symbolic method of mounting a play, and to plays which can be so mounted. The contrast between a projected scene and the actors who appear before it is likely to be very jarring to the spectator.

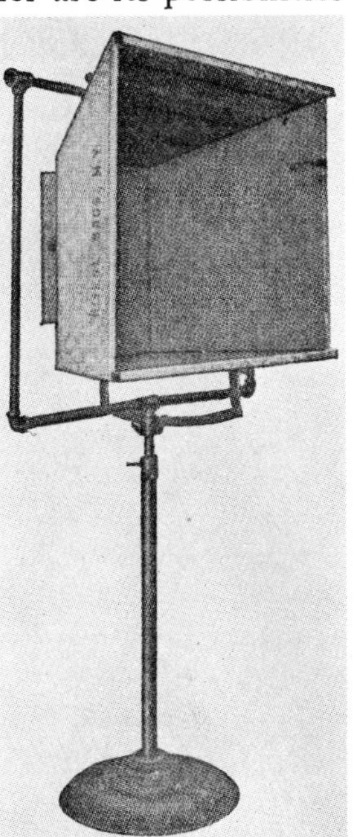

A Linnebach lantern, or "scene projector."

A special advantage of the Linnebach lantern is its wide angle of projection, which permits its use, for scenes as much as thirty feet wide (and proportionately high), at as little as ten feet away from the drop or cyclorama upon which the image is projected. Usually a translucent drop is used, and the scene projected from the rear, although the lantern can sometimes be used from the front (mounted on a batten or light-bridge) and the scene projected on to a solid cyclorama or opaque drop. The former method is perhaps the more satisfactory one, because it permits the actors to take any position, even directly in front of the drop, without casting shadows and spoiling the entire projected scene. One backdrop, or cyclorama, can be used for a limitless number of scenes thus projected. If two lanterns are used, each equipped with a dimmer, and a proper number of painted slides are available, scenes can be changed with startling effect directly before the eyes of the audience. Because of the great enlargement of the painted design that takes place in the Linnebach lantern, the scene projected can never be as clear and sharp as might be desired, even under the best of conditions, and, unless the projected scene is kept free from appreciable quantities of extraneous light, its effectiveness will be seriously impaired.

The picture on page 15 shows a particularly effective use of two Linnebach lanterns.

X. Cyclorama Lighting Equipment

On the whole, the important question of lighting cycloramas seems to have received but little serious attention from the designers of stage-lighting equipment. The problem of correctly lighting a cyclorama is a very special and distinctive one, and, in most cases, cannot be satisfactorily solved by the use of the usual standard equipment such as has been previously described. The present common practice is to light a cyclorama by means of several banks of olivettes, some mounted at the top and some placed at the bottom edge of the cyclorama, and by means of borderlights and striplights.

A valance type borderlight, equipped with shallow mirrored glass reflectors and glass diffusing screens, adaptable to some types of cyclorama lighting.

These methods are as wasteful and inefficient as they are (except for very small cycloramas) generally unsatisfactory. For lighting a cyclorama a powerful, comparatively thin "sheet" of light is usually needed. This sheet of light can only be obtained by accurate and scientific control of light, either by reflection, or refraction, or both. Besides the single outstanding development discussed below, there have been several units developed which serve the purpose of cyclorama lighting somewhat better than did any previous equipment, but which still are not satisfactory. One of these consists of deep-bowl spun-aluminum reflectors with high-wattage lamps (usually 500 watt). Mounted close together, these form virtually a powerful borderlight. Another is the so-called "valance borderlight" (designed primarily for use in motion-picture theatres to hang directly behind the valance and to light the front curtain, for spectacular effects). This usually consists of 500-watt lamps with shallow, concave reflectors, and glass diffusing screens. For lighting cycloramas, these units can be used, suspended at the top edge of the cyclorama, and placed on the stage floor at its lower edge. These units are wired in several color circuits.

But by far the most satisfactory instruments designed to light cycloramas are the so-called "cyclorama color-mixing units." These utilize truly scientific methods of light control. These units are available in standard lengths, depending on the size of lamps used. Each unit is similar to a compartment type borderlight, but is about half again as large in cross-section. However, instead of the inside of each compartment being of white painted metal, it is, in its entirety, a carefully designed and constructed polished metal reflector of the parabolic type. This reflector, which helps utilize virtually all of the light rays emitted by the lamp, redirects the rays striking it, in the form of a thin sheet of light. Each reflector employs a regular lamp (of the type used for general lighting purposes).

A close-up view of one of the cyclorama color-mixing units of the installation shown in the illustration on the following page. One color screen has been removed, showing the polished metal parabolic reflector and lamp in position.

These cyclorama color-mixing units are available in two forms, the "hanging type" and the "horizon type." The hanging type is designed for use at the upper edge of the cyclorama, where the units are mounted on a pipe batten that is suspended about three feet forward of the cyclorama and about two feet above it. The hanging type units are available in three sizes: for use with 200, 500, or 1000-watt lamps. Each unit contains six reflector compartments and is wired in three color circuits, which are intended for use with gelatin color media of the three primary colors of light — red, green, and blue. Thus, by proper mixture, these units can light the cyclorama in any desired color. The 1000-watt size of cyclorama color-mixing units, when used across the entire upper edge of the cyclorama, can effectively and evenly light a cyclorama as much as seventy feet in height. All the light emitted by the units is carefully restricted to the cyclorama, none being wasted or spilled on the acting area or other portions of the scene. The horizon type of unit is similar to the hanging type, except that it is inverted and is specially designed for mounting at the lower edge of the cyclorama, being either set directly on the stage floor or recessed in a "light pit", or trench, in the stage floor. The horizon type units are available in only one size: for use with 200-watt lamps. They direct their light upwards for about 18 feet on to the lower portion of the cyclorama. They are not used for actually lighting the cyclorama (this is accomplished by the hanging type

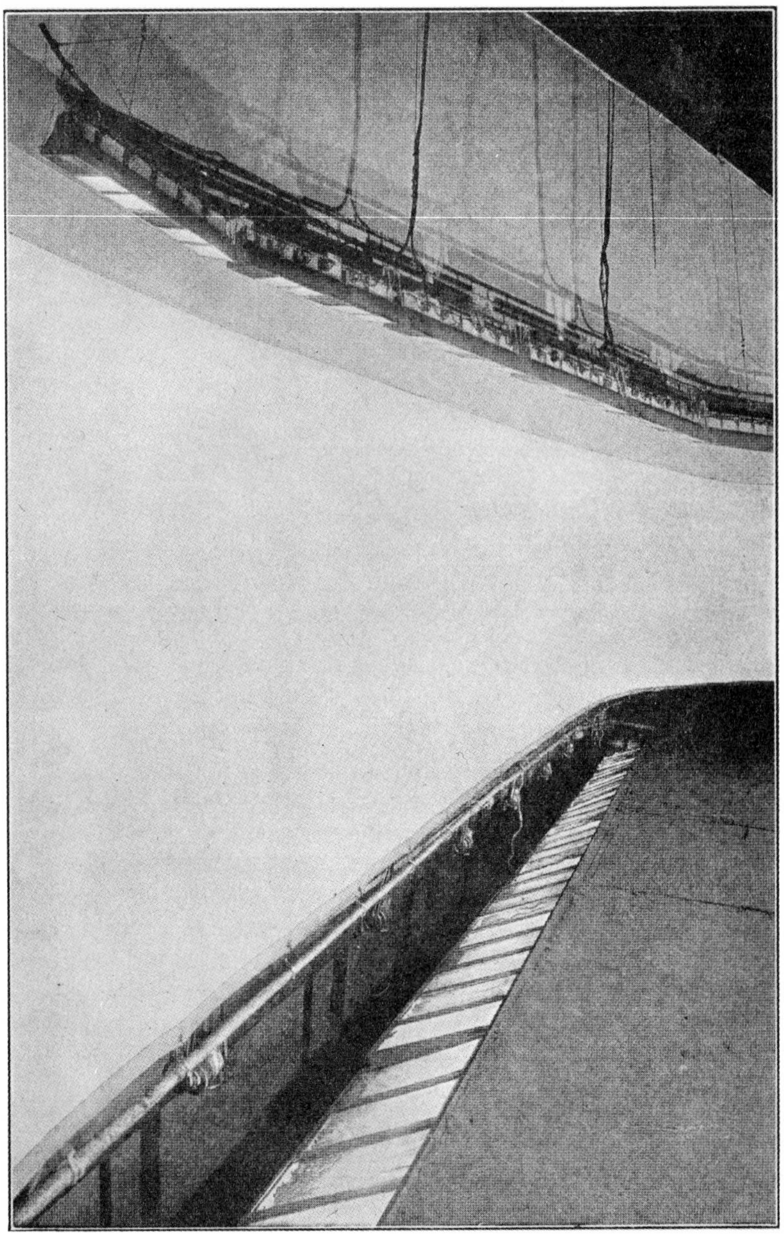

The installation of cyclorama color-mixing units at the Guild Theatre, New York. The cyclorama is more than seventy feet high, and the lighting equipment is ordinarily "trimmed" at its upper edge. The hanging units of the cyclorama lighting equipment are here shown lowered more than half-way. This was done in order to bring them within the picture limits. The horizon units are shown recessed in a pit in the stage floor that extends along the lower edge of the cyclorama.

units, unaided), but for providing contrasting horizon effects, such as dawn, sunset, or clear tinting. Each of these horizon type units contains eight reflector compartments and is wired in four color circuits, three of which are intended for use with gelatin color media of the three primary colors of light, and the fourth for unmodified, or clear, light. All these types and sizes of cyclorama color-mixing units are, of course, subject to centralized control from the switchboard.

XI. Lighting Equipment for Outdoor Productions

Although most of the regular lighting equipment for lighting indoor stages, such as has been discussed in the preceding sections of this chapter, can occasionally be used to advantage for lighting outdoor productions, there are several types of lighting equipment particularly suitable to such work. One of the principal requirements for outdoor equipment is that it should be weatherproof (or rather, waterproof, since protection against rain is the most important factor).

Perhaps the most useful unit for lighting pageants and other outdoor productions is the commercial type of floodlight that is used extensively for floodlighting building exteriors. These floodlights are made in an almost infinite number of types and styles and sizes. The principal classifications of outdoor floodlights are, (1) size — the size of lamp accommodated, and (2) beam spread, or beam angle — the degree of divergence of the light beam, and hence, the area it will cover at a given distance, and its brightness for a given size of lamp. Floodlights are available in sizes ranging from 100 to 1000 watts and with average beam spreads ranging from about 15 to 60 degrees.

A floodlight consists principally of two elements — a light source and a reflector. The light source is a concentrated filament floodlight lamp which is made especially for such service (a floodlight lamp has the same dimensions of a spotlight lamp of the same size, but its designed life is 800 instead of 200 hours, with a corresponding decrease in light output; it is used in floodlights to reduce the expense of maintaining a very large installation of the shorter life spotlight lamps). The reflector is usually a shallow parabolic one, of silvered glass or polished, silvered metal. The position of the lamp filament, in relation to the focal point of the parabolic reflector, is variable to a small extent and can be readily adjusted, thus providing a means of broadening or narrowing the floodlight beam (within the limits of only a few degrees, however — this control of beam spread in a floodlight must not be compared with that offered by a regular stage spotlight). Floodlights must be chosen carefully for their average beam spread — adjustable variation is limited. The reflector and lamp are mounted in either cast-iron or heavy sheet-steel housings, with a suitable ventilated lamp housing. The mouth of the reflector is closed by a heavy

Type "L-1"

Type "L-3"

Two Types of Outdoor Floodlighting Projectors.

iron door frame, hinged or bolted to the housing, in which is tightly mounted a heavy glass plate. Thus the entire unit is strongly built and well protected against inclement weather. Floodlights are available either with trunnion mounting (for fixing, by means of bolts or screws, to platforms, walls, or other permanent structures), or with pedestal mounting (similar to that of stage olivettes and spotlights) for portable use. Both types are provided with means for complete adjustment and setting of beam direction. Although floodlights are usually designed for permanent wiring, they can be provided by short cable leads and connectors for use in play production. Except in two of the most modern types of floodlights, means for color modification of the beam of light are lacking. However, the housings of most floodlights are so constructed that the attachment of color-frame grooves presents no special difficulty.

"X-Ray" outdoor flood-lighting projector.

Banks of floodlights, with a flexible system of control, constitute the principal equipment used for lighting outdoor productions. Where the lighting is done from a distant point, and a higher intensity of light is necessary for any small portion of the acting area or scene, as compared with the remainder, recourse must usually be had to carbon arc units, either to small searchlights, or to the more powerful of the long-distance spotlights that are used in large motion picture theatres.

"Pilgrim" outdoor pageant projector: in operating principles virtually a small searchlight, with a narrow (seven-degree) beam spread. This unit dims and color-changes manually, and is equipped with louvers for eliminating "spill" light.

Where it is possible to mount lighting equipment on or near the acting area, the so-called "giant" reflectors, consisting simply of large metal hoods, painted white inside and containing one or two 1000-watt lamps, will prove effective. These are equipped with an adjustable bracket by which they can be mounted on poles at the edge of the acting area. They provide a diffused light, but, ordinarily, are not equipped with color-frame grooves. They are also available for suspension mounting directly over the stage area. For lighting individual pieces of scenery, or trees, or shrubbery, there are available units of silvered metal reflectors (the same as are used in compartment type borderlights, but larger, and inverted) each with a 500-watt lamp, mounted in a waterproof sheet-iron housing with a wired plate glass front. Placed on the ground a few feet before trees, shrubbery, and other objects, they project a wide angle of light and serve to light them to a high intensity and to accentuate them in comparison to the remainder of the scene. Several of these units, which usually contain two reflectors, can also serve as large "footlights" for the scene to balance the downward lighting from beam floodlights placed at a distance. Although no special means for color modification are provided, it is possible simply to lay color frames over the inclined mouths of the reflectors.

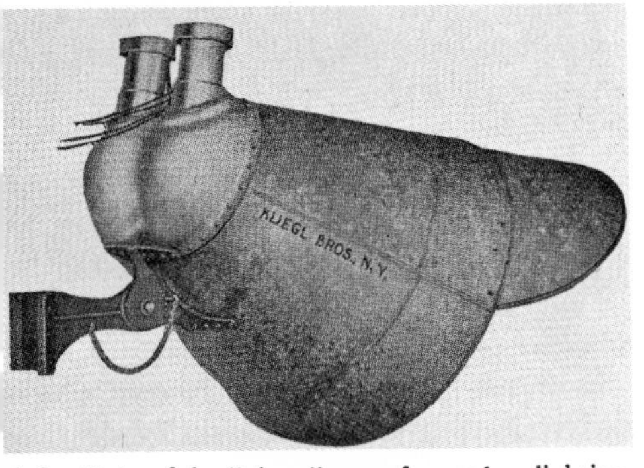

A floodlight of the "giant" type, for outdoor lighting.

XII. Accessories

The term "accessory" when applied to stage-lighting equipment, is usually made to include many devices which either are important or distinctive enough to warrant separate classification of their own, or which are already essential parts of stage-lighting equipment. Thus stage-cable connectors, pockets, and wiring devices, color media and frames and other color devices, lamps, lenses, and reflectors are often referred to as accessories, which, strictly speaking, they are not. An accessory is a device which can be applied to a standard stage-lighting instrument, increasing the range of usefulness of the instrument or its convenience of operation, or modifying its results in some desired manner.

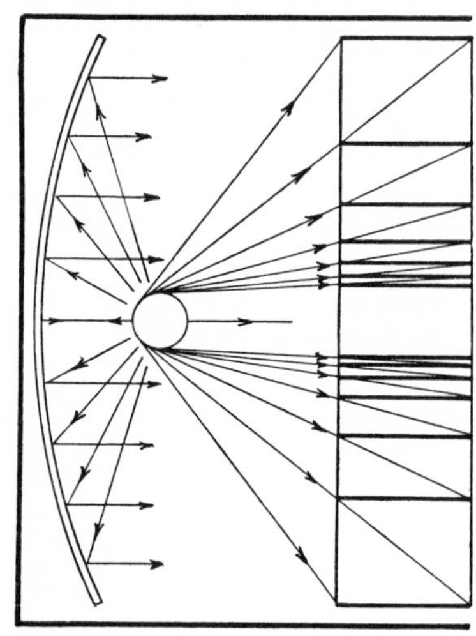

Illustrating the use of louvers for eliminating from a principal projected beam of light direct rays of light emanated by the lamp. The circle represents the extreme limits of the lamp filament.

Strictly speaking, effect holders, effect heads, and objective lenses are accessories to standard large spotlights. But since together they constitute sciopticons, they are not usually considered as accessories, even though they are separately available.

An *extension lens* (see page 185) is useful for increasing the projection range of a spotlight. It consists of a condenser lens mounted in a tube which fits into the slide grooves of a spotlight. It decreases the size of the spot ordinarily produced.

A *louver* is applied to an instrument producing a beam of light, for the purpose of removing from the beam all rays of light except those emanating from the instrument in the principal direction of the beam. In short, a louver cuts out, or absorbs, stray light. A louver consists of a set of thin metallic baffles, arranged usually in the form of concentric circles, or, occasionally, in the form of straight lines parallel to each other. The depth of the baffles is usually two or three inches. The baffles are painted flat black. When the louver is placed in a beam of light, all rays that are not essentially parallel strike the baffles and are absorbed, thus removing them from the beam. Louvers are used mostly with instruments that employ parabolic reflectors, as they cut out the bulk of the direct, unreflected, diverging rays from the light source, yet permit the free passage of the reflected, parallel rays. Obviously, then, louvers are never used with olivettes (except the straight, parallel baffles, under certain conditions) or with spotlights. The baffles, or fins, placed at intervals etween lamps at the end of an open-trough footlight, which pre-ent the spill of light over the sides of the proscenium frame, might lso be considered as louvers.

Shutters of various types are used in the grooves of spotlights to estrict the area of the light spot to a desired shape or size. These hutters are of many different types, depending upon the service or which they are to be used. The *iris shutter* consists of thin rass leaves mounted in a metal frame vhich fits into the spotlight slide rooves. Regulated by a single handle, hese leaves may be brought together, lecreasing the size of the spot, or may e fully opened, allowing the full size f spot. The iris shutter is especially iseful, when used with a tiny opening, or "finding" the object to be "spotted" that is, aiming the spotlight in the roper direction, on to the object) be-ore opening the shutter to the desired extent. *Framing shutters* are made of thin metal, with openings of various shapes, mostly adjustable, some fixed. When placed in he spotlight slide grooves they modify the shape of the light beam

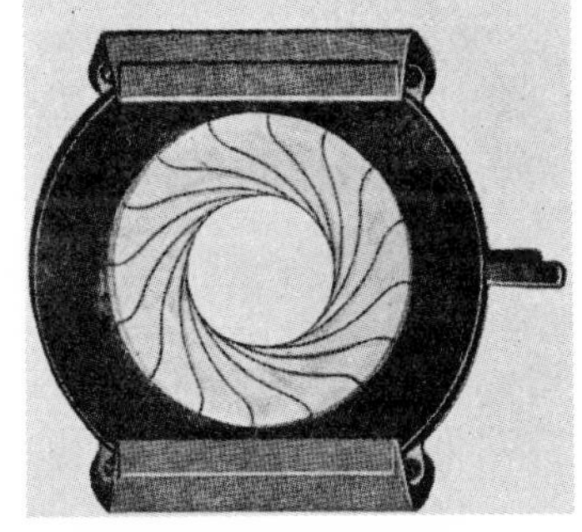

An iris diaphragm shutter.

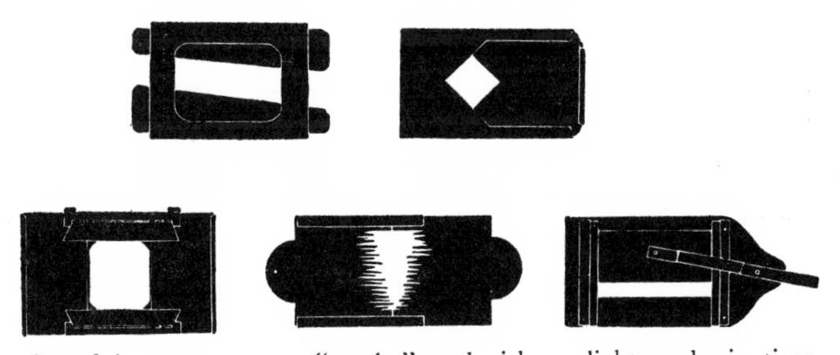

A few of the more common "masks" used with spotlights and sciopticons.

so that it will cover a desired area. Framing shutters are often used on balcony spotlights for restricting the light to the stage area and keeping it off the proscenium frame. *Curtain shutters* are framing shutters that enable the operator of a balcony spotlight to reduce the area of the spot of light as the curtain rises or descends, thus keeping the light off the curtain, but still on the visible portion of the stage. *Blinders*, or flippers, are similar to framing shutters in effect but different in action. They are hinged, flat, metallic plates, placed on two sides of a metallic frame that fits into the spotlight slide grooves. Tormentor lens units and teaser lens units are equipped with blinders and framing shutters as regular parts of the instruments. *Masks*, or *mats*, are similar to framing shutters, but have fixed openings, and are non-adjustable. They usually consist simply of a thin metallic plate, with the opening punched in it which fits into the spotlight slide grooves. Some masks are made especially for use with effect heads, to limit the size and shape of the area over which the effects are produced. These are usually built-in permanently with the effect head. Other masks are used for stationary effects in the lantern-slide carrier.

Another class of accessories, which increases the utility and convenience of a standard instrument, is the variety of mounting accessories. Although all types of portable equipment are available directly for suspension mounting, they are almost always desired with pedestal mountings. By means of various combinations of interchangeable pipe clamps and pipe hangers and swivel joints,

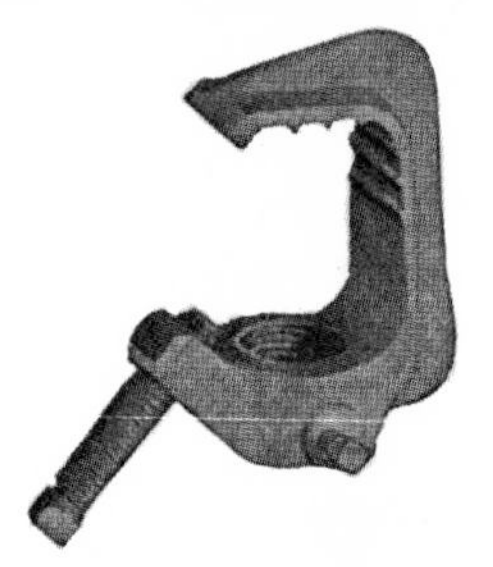

Two types of pipe clamps for mounting stage-lighting equipment on pipe battens, vertical tormentor pipe standards, light bridges, and so forth.

which have already been described, the units of pedestal-mounted equipment may be conveniently and expeditiously used for virtually any type of mounting — in any position, in any place, on any object.

XIII. European Equipment

Although European stage-lighting equipment is neither commercially available in this country, nor generally adaptable to the conditions of current American theatre practice, a brief description of it may prove interesting and not altogether out of place at this point.

Almost all the stage-lighting equipment of any significance used in Continental Europe is German in design and manufacture. In countries other than Germany little if any initiative seems to have been exercised in the matter of either stage-lighting equipment or practice. For this reason, a discussion of German stage-lighting

quipment constitutes virtually a discussion of representative
quipment, at least of the better and more modern type, used
hroughout all Europe. The German equipment is now being
dopted even in England.

For the considerations of stage lighting, continental theatres are
ivided into two general classes: those of the older type, which still
mploy the older stagecraft — painted drops, wings, borders and so
orth — *die Gassenbühne;* and those employing the newer stage-
raft, the principal mechanical feature of which is *der Horizont*, or
yclorama.

Stage-lighting equipment for theatres of the first class is similar
n principle and design to the major portion of the older type of
quipment used in America. Thus there are *die Rampe* — foot-
ghts; *die Oberlichter* — borderlights; and various *Versatzkörfer*
portable units) that correspond to striplights, olivettes, and bunch-
ghts. Although such equipment is also used to a limited extent
n the newer theatres, where the more modern practices prevail,
he characteristic equipment used on the modern stages embodies
ighly scientific principles of optical and mechanical design. *Die
cheinwerfer* — light projectors or spotlights; *die Spielflächen-
aternen* — acting-area lighting units; several types of *die Hori-
ontlaternen* — cyclorama lighting units; and various elaborate
nits of "effect" apparatus, principally *die Wolkenapparate* —
"cloud machines": these are examples of lighting equipment found
n the more advanced of the Continental stages.

The incandescent lamps (*Glühlampen*) used in Germany differ
nly in minor characteristics from those used in this country. They
re, however, commercially available in sizes ranging as high as
000 watts — both the concentrated filament lamps for projection
nd spotlight service and the lamps for general lighting service.
lso, in addition, tubular lamps, with straight line filaments, are
vailable in sizes up to and including 1000 watts. These line-
ilament lamps (which are not at present available in America but
which will probably be developed shortly), prove exceptionally use-
ul — the smaller sizes (up to 100 watts) being used in banks in some
ypes of footlights, borderlights, and striplights, and the larger
izes in the cyclorama lighting units. As in America, carbon arcs
Bogenlampen) have been generally superseded by incandescent
amps, and are used only to a limited extent.

The common type of *footlights*, known as *die Rampe*, are prac-
ically identical with the open-trough footlights used in America.
n addition, the compartment type and indirect type of footlights
re also used. There is also a combination of direct and indirect

types, producing results (though by a somewhat different method similar to those obtainable with the type described on page 169 (Incidentally, the use of indirect lighting for the stage has long been appreciated in Europe, whereas in America it is just being generally introduced.) Another type of footlight employs small line-filamen tubular lamps (*Rohrenlampen*) placed end to end in the footligh trough, thus forming a close approximation of the continuous unbroken strip of light which is ideal for footlight use. *Borderlights* known as *die Oberlichte*, or *die Sofitten*, are also very similar to cor responding types used in America. Such is also the case with the portable striplights. These are sometimes mounted in a vertica position on telescoping tripod standards for use as proscenium and "wing" strips. Other portable lighting units, known as *die Ver satzständer*, include instruments that correspond to the bunchlights and olivettes of this country.

The *spotlights*, known as *die Scheinwerfer*, are similar in principa to those used here, but are somewhat different in construction and appearance. They, too, have a spotlight lamp, a spherical mirror and a condenser lens, but the shape of the sheet-iron housing is usually cylindrical, contrasted to the narrow, almost rectangular shape of the housing of domestic spotlights. The *Scheinwerfer* are usually used with a telescopic tripod mounting, but the *Proszeniums-scheinwerfer* (spotlights used from the auditorium for lighting the stage and the fore-stage) are provided with permanent yokes de-signed for suspension mounting. German spotlights come in three major sizes — *kleiner*, *mittler*, and *grosser*, corresponding respec-tively to domestic baby, standard small, and standard large sizes. A miniature size, provided with a handle, but without mounting — *der Handscheinwerfer* — is meant to be held and directed by the operator.

A German stage-lighting instrument which has no direct counter-part among American equipment is the *Spielflächenlaterne* — acting-area floodlight. This employs a concentrated filament lamp placed at the near focal point of an ellipsoidal reflector. All reflected rays then pass through the far focal point. This arrangement permits the use of color media of small area. This is an advantage, because natural-colored glass plates (which are used almost exclusively — the use of gelatin color media is not nearly as widespread as in America) are both uneconomical and unsafe when used to cover the openings of large reflectors such as olivettes. Because of these characteristics, the *Spielflächenlaterne* appears as an inverted cone, truncated relatively near its apex. These units are invariably mounted on battens or beneath "light-bridges" and project their light vertically downwards. They come in two sizes, *grosser* and *kleiner*. Another and less popular type of *Spielflächenlaterne* is cylindrical in form, and has a lens instead of a reflector, and corresponds almost exactly to the American "suspension type spotlight." In the general scheme of German stage-lighting practice, these *Spielflächenlaternen* are of considerable importance, for the two great problems of stage lighting to a German producer are "first, to light the acting area, and second, to light the *Horizont*—the cyclorama."

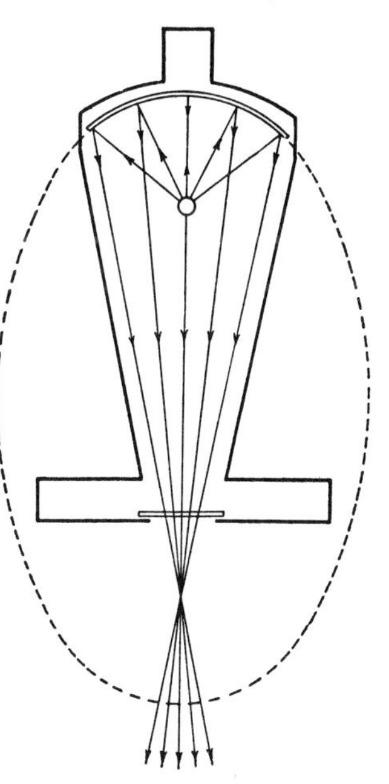

Diagrammatic sketch showing the principle of operation of the ellipsoidal reflector used in *Spielflächenlaterne*. The dashed curved line represents the complete ellipse of which the reflector is a small part. The small circle before the reflector represents the light source.

Slide holders and objective lenses are available which can be attached to the front of the *Scheinwerfer*, thus converting it into a *Bildprojektionsapparat*, or sciopticon. In German theatres very elaborate systems of fly galleries (*Arbeitsgallerien*), light-bridges (*Portalbrücken*), and traveling cages (*fahrbahre Scheinwerferbrücken*), provide useful vantage points from which these *Scheinwerfer* can be operated.

For lighting the cyclorama, or *Horizont*, several types of instruments, called *Horizontlaternen*, are used. The simplest and most used of these is the *Ovallaterne*. This consists principally of a tubular line-filament lamp (usually of the 1000-watt size) surrounded (lengthwise) on the front by a curved sheet of glass (semi-elliptical in cross-section — hence the name), and on the back by a diffusely reflecting white-painted sheet-metal surface. These parts are held in place by a well-ventilated housing, the glass safeguarded by a meshed-wire guard, and the whole equipped with a yoke for suspension mounting. Banks of these are mounted, usually three or four tiers high, on specially constructed steel frames, hung from the gridiron near the front of the stage, over the proscenium opening. As the banks of *Ovallaternen* project their flood of light downward on to the cyclorama from their elevated position, it is obvious that hanging scenery hung in the flies can be used not at all, or must be trimmed at an exceptionally great height, so as not to cast shadows on the cyclorama. But hanging scenery is automatically out of the question when a *festbahre Kupell-Horizont*, or permanent cyclorama, is used. Several other types of *Horizontlaternen* are also used, some equipped with three or four 1000-watt line-filament lamps. Special units, single and quadruple in size, are mounted in portable cradles to be placed on the stage floor at the lower edge of the cyclorama, for contrasting and tinting effects, such as dawn and sunset. Besides the usual type, some of these units provide for both direct or indirect lighting, and others are equipped with running parabolic reflectors for use with the line-filament lamps.

German stage technicians seem to have been endowed with a high order of mechanical and optical ingenuity, and no small part of this endowment has been lavished on one of their pet products — *der Wolkenapparat* — the cloud machine. Having established the *Horizont*, they have embellished it with clouds that represent the utmost in realism. Although *Wolkenapparate* come in several sizes and types, their basic principles are much the same. A cloud machine consists of a 3000-watt concentrated filament lamp about which revolves a number of sets (ranging from four to twelve) of condenser and objective lenses, each set equipped with a transparent photographic positive print of some actual cloud formation. Each set of lenses, in combination with the light source, corresponds to an American sciopticon with a cloud print in the lantern-slide holder. Each set of lenses forms its own cloud image as it passes in front of the light source, and projects the cloud image on to the cyclorama. The projected cloud image travels from one side to another as the sets of lenses slowly revolve about the lamp. Such is the basic principle, of which there are a great many variations and elaborations. Thus, by revolving some of the sciopticon lenses faster than others, two layers of clouds, each traveling at a different speed, give the illusion of atmospheric distance. Again, by reflecting the projected cloud images from flat mirrors, some of which are stationary and others of which have a gently undulating motion (perhaps even of various speeds) both the *ziehenden* and the *steigenden* clouds are formed. By using two or three machines simultaneously, the possible cloud effects are almost without number.

Various other "effects" are available, most of them being elaborate to a degree. The *Mondapparat* is particularly impressive in appearance, consisting of a large *Scheinwerfer* unit from which projects a well-braced sliding rack on which is mounted an objective lens, an iris diaphragm shutter, and a plane mirror.

In design and construction, the *Wolkenapparat* is, perhaps, fundamentally characteristic of most German stage-lighting equipment. The general impression which the German equipment creates is that, in its design, scientific optics and mechanics are present in enviable proportions, but that convenience and practicability have either been forgotten or deliberately sacrificed. Many instances may be cited as proof of this contention. For example, although the *Wolkenapparat* gives an effect that would satisfy the most ardent and critical realist, it is bulky and cumbersome and weighty — some types weigh well over a ton or two, and require special structural support and accommodation — *and* expensive. Again: for "following" a person with a spotlight, instead of handling the spotlight directly and simply as is American practice, the German technician will mount his *Scheinwerfer* rigidly, placing in its slide grooves a bulky reflector accessory with objective lenses and two plane mirrors that twice redirect the beam of light; and control the final direction of the beam with a handle on one of the mirrors. Still again: the practice of mounting all portable equipment on tripods (instead of on round-base pedestal standards) is admirable from several points of view — the weight of the equipment is well distributed, the instrument is firmly planted, it cannot tip over, and so forth — *but*, the tripod consumes valuable space on the stage, it is easily stumbled over, it requires several men to move it, and it is generally awkward and clumsy and inconvenient. In these and other respects, much of the German equipment gives the impression of being designed for scientific laboratory use rather than for practical use in play production. The adoption of scientific principles for stage-lighting equipment is earnestly to be recommended, though hardly at the expense of practicality.

CHAPTER VII · DESIGN AND CONSTRUCTION OF HOME-BUILT EQUIPMENT FOR AMATEUR USE

Necessary general considerations; construction of specific equipment; footlights; borderlights; striplights; spotlights, mounting devices; olivettes.

AT this point a discussion of "homemade" stage-lighting equipment, principally for the benefit of workers in the amateur theatre, may not be out of place. The fundamentals of electricity and light have been covered, and the many types, styles, and sizes of standard stage-lighting instruments have been discussed and illustrated in sufficient detail to give the reader a general idea of their most important characteristics. This information is essential as a basis, as a starting point, for any practical work in the construction of "home-built" stage-lighting equipment.

Without question, lack of funds with which to buy available standard equipment is the principal reason why amateurs desire to build their own apparatus. Accordingly, the recommendations outlined in this chapter have been prepared with the necessity for a minimum of expenditure as an important consideration. To a lesser extent, amateur workers build their own equipment simply for the fun of doing it themselves, for the joy of thorough accomplishment, and for the satisfaction of knowing that whatever merit in stage lighting they achieve is as much the result of their own direct experimental efforts as it is possible for it to be. Such workers will find in the following paragraphs a few suggestions that will indicate methods of more advanced design and construction. Home-built equipment is of two general classes: first, that quickly put together, of readily available materials, for a single occasion — merely to serve as a temporary makeshift; and second, that built for regular continuous, permanent use, or, at least, permanent until circumstances favor the acquisition of better equipment.

No recommendations can be given for devising temporary makeshifts, since their construction depends entirely upon the particular needs of the moment, the particular materials and facilities directly at hand, and the ingenuity of the maker. A few odd bits of advice that may prove useful in such cases, however, are included in the appendix under "*Miscellaneous Notes for Amateur Workers.*" Although the construction of the more permanent home-built equipment is also dependent upon available facilities and materials and the experience and ability of the maker, more definite suggestions and plans can be offered that will prove of help. For purposes of discussion, such home-built apparatus of a permanent nature is most conveniently divided into two classes: first, and most usual, that which is virtually an assembly of various standard devices that are readily obtainable commercially; and second, that which embodies, in appreciably greater measure, originality in design and construction, both as a whole and in its component parts. The latter type is usually out of range of the average amateur workers, owing to the lack of knowledge of practical construction details, lack of practical mechanical working experience, and lack of suitable facilities — workshop, tools, and so forth. The bulk of the following discussion, therefore, will take up the construction of apparatus that makes no unreasonable demands on the amateur worker in the way of technical knowledge, experience, facilities, or expense.

There is one important matter that every builder of homemade equipment must be cautioned to bear in mind, and that is the possibility of coming into conflict (1) with state or municipal regulations governing (*a*) electrical practice in general and (*b*) theatre practice in particular; and (2) with underwriters' regulations (as embodied in the National Electrical Code), if the building in which the home-built equipment will be used is protected by fire insurance. Although most of the home-built apparatus described in detail in ensuing paragraphs complies with the requirements governing electrical equipment in general, little of it complies with the requirements governing electrical equipment for specific use in theatres. This fact, however, will not prevent its use by the great majority of amateurs who produce their plays in buildings other than those legally classified as theatres. And, as a general rule, those amateurs who use a building that is legally considered a theatre have reached a point where they can afford the regular, standard equipment, which is always built to comply with the most stringent of regulations. This question of compliance with government and code regulations is here again emphasized as a serious one, to which proper attention should be given. Amateur stage workers who are in doubt as to any point should apply to the proper local official or local underwriters' agent for a ruling covering the particular case in hand, well in advance of the performance date on which the equipment is to be used. Otherwise, it is quite possible that a police officer or fire department inspector will walk upon the stage just as the curtain is about to rise and forbid the performance unless changes are made that will remove the violations. Even though such emergencies can almost always be overcome by means of the old, effective, time-honored method, they are likely to prove somewhat discouraging. They can be avoided by practicing a little foresight.

I. Necessary General Considerations

Every stage-lighting instrument consists of several fundamental parts — the light source (incandescent lamp), its holder (socket), the means of supplying it with electric current (wiring), the means of controlling the light it emits (reflectors, lenses, and housing), the means of color modification (color-screen slide grooves, compartments, and so forth), and the means of mounting (clamps, battens, pipe stands, and so forth). After the type of instrument which is to be built and the service it must render have been decided upon, the next step in its construction is a consideration of each of the parts just enumerated, preferably in the order given, since the determination of each, in most instances, will depend upon that of those preceding it. The design must then be arrived at by substituting, for the most desirable choice of materials and their construction, the best that is possible with the availability of materials, facilities, and experience that prevail. The more common of the commercially available *materials* for each of the principal parts of stage-lighting equipment listed above is as follows. *Lamps* have been discussed at length in a previous chapter. *Sockets* of various types are available at the local electrical shop or hardware shop, or, in emergencies, even at the "five and ten-cent store." It is sometimes difficult to obtain locally the types of sockets that lend themselves most conveniently to this work, but a glance through the electrical dealer's trade catalogues will aid in the choice of the most suitable type, which the dealer can order through his supply jobber with but little trouble and delay. The sockets are easily mounted by means of small screws or stove bolts, to either the housing, the base, or the portion of the equipment that proves most convenient. Care should be taken to use the correct size of socket, either medium or mogul — depending upon the size and type of lamp to be used, and the correct type of socket — porcelain, keyless sockets. Brass sockets, especially those with key switches or pull-chain switches, should never be used in stage-lighting equipment. If a shadeholder is to be used to mount a reflector, the porcelain socket must be equipped with a shadeholder groove. For porcelain sockets without a shadeholder groove, the so-called "emergency shadeholders", which fasten to the screw shell of the socket, can be used; but unless the entire electrical system is a grounded one, their use should be avoided if possible. If a silvered glass or polished metal reflector, or a lens is to be used in conjunction with the lamp, it is essential that the socket be so mounted that the lamp filament will be in optical alignment with the reflector, that is, in the regular light-source position for which the reflector was designed to be used. The light-center length of the lamp to be used is an important dimension in determining the exact mounting position of the socket with reference to the reflector. *Wiring* should always be done with single conductor wire (always of a size large enough to carry the anticipated current load — see table on page 64 — and never smaller than No. 18 in size) that has *slow-burning* insulation, or, even better, *asbestos* insulation. It should be of the flexible, stranded type, if possible, though the solid type will do. The local electrical dealer seldom carries a stock of slow-burning or asbestos-covered wire, so this will also probably have to be ordered. Asbestos-covered *heater cord*, if of the proper size, does very well. This is the flexible cord used to connect electric flat-irons and heaters such as are used in the home. This comes twisted, in pairs, but the outer braid can easily be removed and the single wires untwisted, ready for use. Heater cord can always be obtained from the local electrical dealer. If any appreciable amount of work is planned, however, it is best to order a short coil of wire with slow-burning insulation. The usual type of wire, with rubber-covered insulation, should never be used, except in cases of emergency, and even then it should never be overloaded or be so placed that it will be exposed to the full heat of the lamp, as the insulating compound may melt and may even burn, causing a great volume of dense black smoke and perhaps even a fire.

Many types and sizes of *reflectors* that prove quite suitable for stage-lighting apparatus are commercially available. Thus there are the porcelain-enameled steel reflectors such as are used principally for industrial purposes in workshops and factories, and the silvered glass and silvered metal reflectors that are used for commercial lighting, and, in particular, for show-window lighting. Almost all of this large variety of reflectors may be procured from the local electrical dealer — if not directly, at least by ordering them through him from his supply jobber. Other reflectors for special purposes are, unfortunately, not generally available. Small silvered glass spherical reflectors, for use in spotlights, are obtainable from the larger dealers in stage-lighting equipment. They are usually listed as accessory apparatus. Reflectors of special design must be made to order — most conveniently, perhaps, by "spinning" thin sheet metal over a "chuck" which has been constructed with the designed contour of the reflector. The metal used is usually copper or brass, which is later plated with nickel or silver, and is then highly polished and lacquered. The use of chromium as a plating material for reflecting surfaces is also becoming widespread. For diffuse reflection, bright aluminum can be used, and carefully lacquered to prevent tarnishing. Bright, non-corrosive, and non-tarnishable metals, such as Monel metal, that are capable of taking a high polish (without any superficial plating) are also coming into wider use.

The design of special reflectors by amateur stage workers is an exceptionally interesting and noteworthy undertaking for the persons involved, and is really to be greatly encouraged. However, it is likely to prove just a bit expensive, that is, unless an appreciable quantity of the reflectors are to be made and used. The principal item of expense is the cost of the chuck, which, of course, can be used repeatedly. But it is frequently possible to find, stored on the dusty shelves of some local metal-spinning shop, a chuck that has been used previously in some reflector-manufacture operation or for some other purpose, and which might prove to be suitable, or at least adaptable, with slight changes, to the needs at hand, at a relatively low cost. Reflectors that are not surfaces of revolution must be accurately formed in sections, by hand operations, to templates of the designed outline, and then carefully fastened or mounted together. In many types of stage-lighting units only a white, diffusely reflecting surface is necessary. In such cases the inner surface of the housing can be used to advantage, and painted flat white. The usual type of oil paint should be used only in emergencies, and never when the painted surface is exposed to too great a temperature (from a large lamp close by), as the paint will very likely disintegrate and discolor, and give off an offensive odor. Special white reflector paint, which can be obtained from the larger stage-lighting equipment dealers, is the best for such use. Ordinary whiting, dehydrated lime, glycerine and water, when mixed together in suitable proportions to form a thick paste, serve very well as a diffuse white reflector paint. Aluminum paint such as is used for "silvering" radiators also provides a fairly good reflecting surface and produces light that is more directional and less diffusive in character than does the flat white paint. Some reflectors (especially the porcelain-enameled steel industrial type, and the silvered show-window type) may be mounted directly on to the socket that holds the lamp. The reflector is thus positioned permanently in correct relation to the light source. These and other types of reflectors may be mounted, by such means as small clamps, screws, bolts, or rivets, directly to the housing of the stage-lighting instrument. But whatever type of mounting is used, care must be taken to position the reflectors so that the relation between light source and reflecting surface is, as practically as possible, the same as that for which the reflector was designed. It is advisable to allow for a reasonable adjustment in position of either the socket or the reflector (preferably the latter) in order to compensate for any irregularities in light-center length, and filament position, of the lamp used.

Where *lenses* are to be used, the amateur builder (unless he be a manufacturing optician) is quite dependent upon optical supply companies and the larger dealers in stage-lighting equipment. Lenses, in the more commonly used sizes, at least, are comparatively inexpensive. If possible, only those lenses that are ground directly from optical glass should be used; the so-called "cast lenses" are cheaper but of much poorer quality. Condenser lenses are naturally the only ones about which the amateur builder need trouble himself; these are available in a very wide variety of diameters and focal lengths. The table on page 186 lists only the more common sizes. Lenses are easily mounted. If within a cylindrical space, they can be held in place against three or four protruding offsets by a circular spring clip that fits into a shallow channel; if "on the flat", against a circular opening (slightly smaller than their diameter, of course), they can be held in place by four small bent-metal clips spaced equally around their edge — three permanent, the fourth removable by screw or bolt, for replacements.

On the sizes of the lamp, of the lamp-position range (in spotlights and other adjustable-focus lighting units), of the socket, of the reflector (if any), and of the lens (if any), depend the dimensions and principal structural features of the *housing* of a lighting unit. In planning the housing for a piece of stage-lighting equipment, ventilation is perhaps the most important consideration. Enough open space for the free passage of air should be provided to dissipate the heat of the lamp to such a degree that the housing will not become unreasonably hot. This open space should total at least one square inch (for each inlet and outlet of air) if feasible, for each 100 watts of electricity consumed by the lamp enclosed in the housing. This open space, usually in the form of punched or drilled holes in the housing, should be so distributed that a current or draft of air is created which can carry off the heat of the lamp. Suitable provision should be made to prevent the escape of stray light from the lamp through the ventilation space. This is usually accomplished by means of a shield or baffle, placed either inside or outside of the hole, and about $\frac{1}{2}''$ before it, or by some sort of chimney and cowl arrangement, either of which methods prevents the passage of light but does not materially obstruct the current of air passing through the open space.

Suitable provision for lamping must also be made. That is, enough space must be allowed for "backing" the lamp out of the socket and removing it from the housing. Perhaps this precaution appears unnecessary, but it is a matter of fact that a not unknown manufacturer of stage-lighting equipment once turned out half a dozen large spotlights, the housings of which had no provision for admitting lamps of the proper size. The housing of any piece of equipment should also be so constructed as to provide a means of firmly securing the lamp socket (or, in a spotlight, the sliding base), reflector, lens, and color-screen slide grooves, and of fastening the mounting device, either for pedestal or batten mounting.

The simplest *housing* would consist merely of some opaque, rigid material that would exclude the light of the lamp from where it was not wanted, and also provide a means of mounting the important parts of the instrument so as to form a complete unit. Sheet metal is the best material for this purpose — blued sheet steel, in particular, in several thicknesses, gauge 20, 22, 24, 26, and 28, depending upon the strength required. Sheet steel, however, except for small work, requires special machines to bend and form it, because of its stiffness and rigidity. Sheet copper, in the same thicknesses, is much easier for the unequipped mechanic to "work", but it is not quite as rigid as sheet steel. Where it is absolutely necessary to use sheet steel for the housing of any stage-lighting equipment, it is advisable to plan it thoroughly and carefully, to draw a sketch of it, drawn to scale, showing clearly all the dimensions and physical characteristics, and then to have it made up at the local "tinsmith's" or "sheet-metal works", not neglecting, of course, to seek the advice of this artisan regarding details of construction, and to accept his suggestions, provided they do not conflict with the basic features of the design of the equipment. For home-built apparatus of a less permanent nature, sheet-metal vessels, with necessary modifications, will often prove satisfactory. Discarded metal containers (heavy cans and boxes), pails, kitchen utensils, old-fashioned wash-boilers, and a score of other humble domestic articles that can be obtained at the local hardware or house-furnishing store, will often prove just the thing for some special purpose. Thin wood, especially whitewood, or soft, clear pine, about $\frac{1}{2}''$ thick, is easily "worked" and always proves useful.

As a construction material, wood is perhaps the most convenient for the builder of amateur stage-lighting equipment. However, wood must always be protected from the heat of the lamp by having tacked to it a lining of thin asbestos paper (about $\frac{1}{8}''$ thick, comes a yard wide, and may be obtained at well-stocked hardware stores). Often this asbestos-paper lining can serve as a reflecting surface, painted with a flat white diffusely reflecting paint. It is also well to paint or spray all wood surfaces with any one of the standard fire-proofing liquids, such as are applied to the wood used for scenery construction. Incidently, the heat of the lamp precludes the use of solder on metal housings. Either small stove bolts or rivets (or, if done in a professional shop, electric spot welding) must be used to fasten the metal parts together.

Provision for color modification can, in most cases, be very easily applied to home-built stage-lighting equipment. For instruments with regular enclosed housings it is only necessary to provide two horizontal grooves (on the front face of the housing, one just above and the other just below the open mouth of the unit) which will accommodate the color-screen frame. Difficulty will be experienced in applying these color-frame grooves to the porcelain-enameled, steel, industrial type reflectors mentioned above. The accompanying sketches illustrate in detail what is perhaps the most convenient method of devising and fastening color-frame grooves for these reflectors. The types of enameled-steel reflectors most suitable for use as part of amateur stage-lighting equipment are those known as the "RLM" standard dome, the deep bowl, and the angular circular. These reflectors are available in several sizes, depending on the size of the lamp they accommodate.

All such reflectors have a beading around the edge for strength. This beading provides for the color-frame groove shield a convenient and firm securance that the smooth, enameled surface of the reflector would not otherwise afford. The metal shield having the color-frame grooves at top and bottom can be made from any available, reasonably rigid, sheet metal — sheet copper, galvanized sheet iron; or "sheet tin" (the kind that roofers use) will serve well. The external diameter of the reflector, *not including, but just behind,* the beading, should be carefully measured and scribed, as a circle, on the surface of the metal with a pair of dividers or with a sharp-pointed tool or nail tied to a short piece of string. Since the shield must bear against the beading, which is never large, it is important that this dimension be accurate, or at least be too small rather than too large, for obvious reasons. Another circle, concentric with the first, should then be scribed on the metal. The diameter of this second circle depends upon the size of the reflector. For large reflectors, it should be about two inches less than that of the first circle; for small reflectors about an inch less. Radial lines, from the center of the circles to points about an inch apart on the outer circle, should be scribed on the metal within the inner and outer

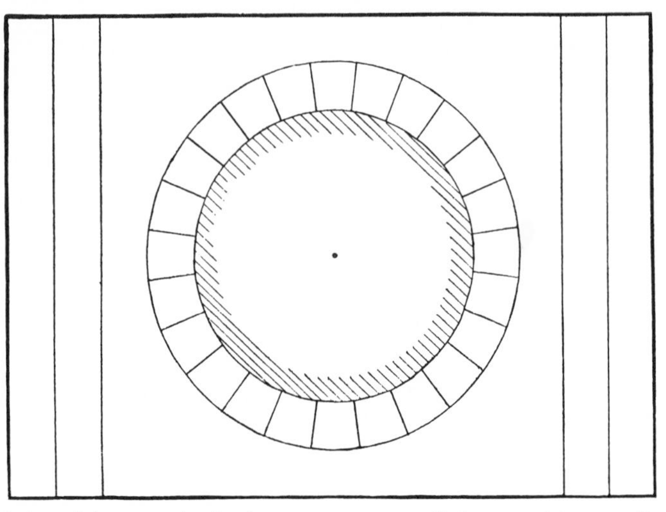

Developed view of sheet metal color-frame grooves as applied to porcelain-enamelled steel reflectors, indicating the cutting and bending lines to be scribed on the metal. Quarter size.

circles. The small areas of metal thus formed will constitute the "ears" for holding the shield in place around the edge of the reflector. A square should then be scribed about the circle, with its sides about an inch from the nearest points on the circle. The space for the slide grooves should be scribed at opposite sides of the square — two parallel lines for a single groove (as shown on the sketch) and five for a double groove (not shown here; see section view of double groove on page 273). The size of the grooves depends on the type of color frame — for thin metal frames, half-inch spacings of the lines are enough; for larger wooden frames, one-inch spacings are necessary. The sketches show desirable proportions of all dimensions, and have been designed for a reflector with an 8″ diameter opening, and for one-inch grooves. The scribings on the metal having set the limit of material needed, the metal should be trimmed down to the limiting marks with a pair of metal shears. Then the metal within the smaller circle should be cut, also with the shears. The cut can be started with a gash made by a sharp cold chisel. The ears should then be cut *carefully*, on the radial lines, just to the outer circle. No cutting should be done on the outer circle. The ears should be bent up (about halfway — not straight up) on its circumference. The grooves should then be formed by bending down (each 90 degrees — a right angle) first the outer strips, then the inner strips, as scribed on the metal. Bending along these straight lines should be done with the aid of pieces of hard wood with sharp edges. This will help achieve "clean" bends of the metal along the scribed lines.

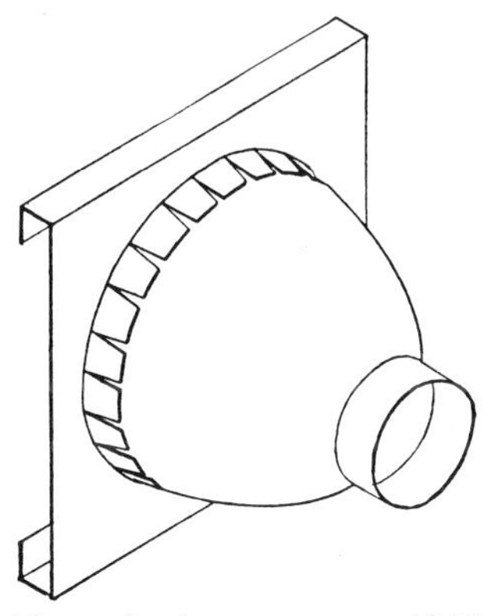

The color-frame groove shield mounted on a deep-bowl reflector. One-eighth size.

Next should be prepared a number of small clamps, one for each four or five inches of reflector circumference. These can be made of sheet metal, appreciably heavier than the material used for the shield. Strip copper or brass, about a half-inch wide and from $\frac{1}{32}''$ to $\frac{1}{16}''$ thick, will serve well. The clamps should have a flat surface about $\frac{3}{4}''$ long, and at one end should be bent into a hook, as is shown in the full-sized section sketch. This bending can be done easily and simply with a pair of pliers. A $\frac{1}{8}''$ or $\frac{3}{16}''$ hole should be drilled (or, if the metal is thin enough, punched, with a nail, and the

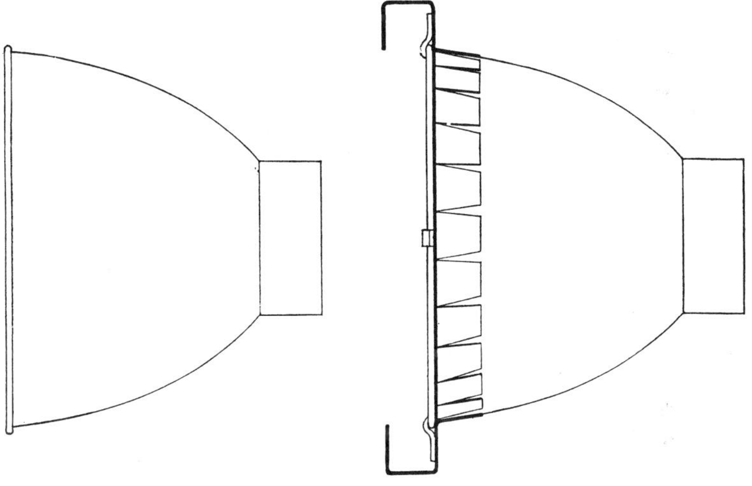

Method of holding the color-frame groove shield firmly to the edge of the reflector. Quarter size.

burr flattened) in the center of the flat part of each clamp. The sketches show how the shield is forced over the reflector hood against the beading and how the small clamps hold it in place by means of a

$\frac{1}{8}'' \times \frac{1}{2}''$ stove bolt on each clamp. The holes in the shield should be drilled or punched only after the exact location of each has been determined by trial — that is, scribed on the shield with the clamp in place. When all the clamps have been bolted tightly in place (spaced equally about the circumference of the reflector mouth), the shield will be held rigidly to the reflector. It is important that the clamps be properly bent, otherwise the shield is likely to be buckled out of shape when the bolts are tightened.

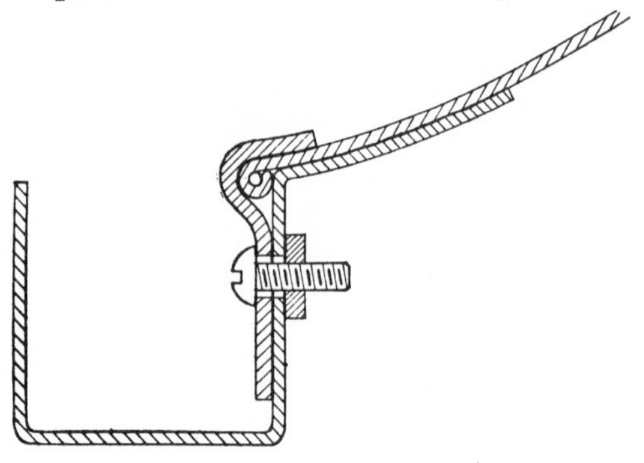

Small clamp used to grip the color-frame groove shield firmly against the beading at the edge of the reflector. Full size.

Strengthening can be provided, if found necessary, by bolting a thin strip of metal to each end of the upper groove and extending the strip to the lower groove and bolting it in place there in the corresponding position. A neat coat of flat black paint should be applied to the entire surface, both inside and out, of the shield and grooves. This will minimize any light leakage, besides providing a respectable appearance.

Steel reflectors are really very useful for amateur stage-lighting work — the amateur builder should familiarize himself with the simple trick of providing them with means for color modification. The method outlined above is both simple and substantial, and can even be used on borrowed reflectors, as it does not entail their mutilation in any way.

When used for stage-lighting purposes, reflectors of glass, or of rather thin, fragile metal, should always be enclosed in a housing for proper mechanical protection — the color-frame grooves for each reflector can then be mounted on the face of the housing. If the reflectors are being used open, temporarily, without a housing, the color-screen frames can be fastened, as best as possible, to the sockets, or to shade holders, or to the ventilation holes in the reflectors, by means of thin wire or stout twine. All color-frame grooves should be made to fit the housings or the reflectors snugly, so as to prevent the escape of unmodified white light. Flat black paint on the grooves and on the color frames will aid materially in reducing any small light leakage. When designing a set of instruments of various types it is well to arrange the color-frame grooves so that the frames will be interchangeable between several types of instruments —

that is, the various sizes of color frames that it is necessary to keep on hand should be reduced to a minimum; no more than three or four standard sizes should be used.

The problem of proper, secure *mounting* is always a difficult one for the amateur builder to solve satisfactorily. Mounting must be such that a reasonable range of movement is provided in which the instrument may be "aimed", or directed, and still be such that the instrument can be fastened firmly and safely in any position where it may be necessary to place it. It is advisable for the amateur builder to procure the small fittings, such as pipe clamps, stud brackets, swivel joints, leather washers, and lever set-screws, from the larger stage-lighting equipment dealers (who list them as accessory supply parts) if he wants his home-built apparatus to be most conveniently mounted. However, many ingenious and satisfactory substitutes for them can be devised from ordinarily available pipe fittings, hardware, and other material. If the housing of any instrument is firm and rigid enough, the mounting may be fixed to it directly; if not, bracing or strengthening (either internal or external: iron strips for sheet-metal housings; wooden cleats for housings made of wood) will have to be made part of the housing, and the mounting fixed to the bracing instead. This latter method removes the mounting stress from a small part of the housing, and distributes the stress over a wider area. Individual mounting problems are discussed in the following paragraphs that deal with the construction of specific equipment.

Upon the *facilities* available to the amateur builder will depend, in no small measure, the effectiveness of his product. Although elaborate facilities are not necessary, there should be at his disposal at least a reasonable space (hardly less than 100 square feet of floor area) which is exclusively for his own use and in which he can work undisturbed by other production activities, and an assortment of necessary tools, which is likewise dedicated to his exclusive use. This workshop may very well constitute the regular "lighting room" of the playhouse. It should be equipped with a fair-sized, sturdy workbench and with suitable cabinets for the storage of tools, materials, lamps, color media, and small odds and ends of lighting equipment and accessories. An ample source of electric current should be available for experimental work, for testing, and for other necessary purposes. Lists of tools necessary for various types of work will be found in an appendix to this volume.

Much will depend upon the amount of *experience*, of practical sense, and of mechanical ingenuity which the amateur builder of stage-lighting equipment can bring to his avocational activity.

Lack of experience alone is no great drawback, provided the worker is of a practical turn of mind and possesses a fair store of the elusive "common sense" in regard to mechanical and technical matters. It is often wise for the amateur producing group to enlist the interest and aid of local craftsmen — electricians, carpenters, metal workers, and so forth — for executing — or, at least, for directing — technical work that lies in their respective fields. But, as pointed out in a previous chapter, these craftsmen should be offered the opportunity to apply their knowledge, experience, and skill to the problems of the theatre only if they are willing and able to do so from the "theatre angle", and with a frame of mind that entails a thorough understanding of and compliance with the peculiar conditions and demands of theatre practice. If they are unable to acquire the theatre point of view, their services had better be regretfully but firmly declined or dispensed with, and replaced by those of rank amateurs — but *theatre* amateurs — who, if they are of the proper type, will find the acquisition of technical experience not, in the main, too slow or too difficult a process.

Inasmuch as the descriptions of stage-lighting instruments given in the preceding chapter have been compiled with a view to acquainting the reader with the fundamental characteristics of the construction and operation of each instrument, they will also serve as a guide to the amateur builder of equipment. Catalogues of the several larger dealers of stage-lighting equipment, both in America and abroad, are recommended to the amateur builder for the innumerable suggestions and specific bits of valuable information that the discerning reader of them will receive. However, nothing can be as satisfactory as the actual examination and use of standard commercial equipment as a guide for the person who wishes to construct his own instruments.

To the greatest degree possible, of course, home-built equipment should possess the desirable characteristics of good commercial equipment. *It should be simple* in design and construction — as simple as is compatible with satisfactory performance. Elaborate mechanical devices should not encumber it if simpler ones will serve the same purpose. "It should be painted black where black paint is necessary, painted white where white paint is necessary, and not painted at all where no paint is necessary"; this concise statement embodies a principle that should be applied, with equal force, to all phases of stage-lighting equipment construction, and, in fact, to all stage construction in general. *It should be sturdy* enough, without being cumbersome, to withstand the rigorous handling to which all stage equipment is invariably and unavoidably subject. A common fault of most home-built stage equipment is that its fragility, demanding care and attention almost as delicate as that bestowed upon an invalid, stands in the way of its fullest and most effective utilization. *It should be efficient* — as efficient as possible from the standpoint of the service for which it is designed to be used. Reflectors should be of the correct type and size and should be properly positioned; lenses should be of the correct size and focal length, and should be properly positioned; in other words, the design of the instrument should be such that, for a given service to be performed, the utilized portion of the light emitted by the lamp will be at a maximum. *It should be convenient* to manipulate — it should be so arranged that positioning, mounting, aiming, relamping, and its operation in general can be carried on with a minimum of time and trouble. Home-built equipment is usually too likely to require nails, screws, ropes, wires, and other makeshifts to hold it in place, and thus to require unusually inconvenient and lengthy methods for its most simple and necessary manipulations. *Finally, it should be safe* beyond reasonable doubt — safe from the standpoint of human safety: it should present no fire hazard or embody no violations, or, at least, no major violations, of municipal and underwriters' codes that apply to it; and safe from the standpoint of reliability in operation: it should be incapable of defection or breakdown at a moment when it is being heavily depended upon. Nothing is more deplorable than a serious accident, or more annoying than a mishap that interrupts the smooth running of a performance, especially if either could have been prevented by reasonable attention beforehand.

The most satisfactory lighting equipment, then, is that in which a fair balance, or compromise, has been arrived at between the several characteristics outlined — simplicity, sturdiness, efficiency, convenience, and safety.

II. Construction of Specific Equipment

The general considerations and principles underlying the construction of "home-built" equipment have been presented and discussed at what might seem to be too great a length. But it is felt that the amateur worker who undertakes to build his own lighting equipment will derive far more benefit, and many more suggestions, from such a thorough discussion of fundamentals, in conjunction with a reasonably detailed description of standard, commercial equipment, than he would from merely a few bits of information concerning the construction of specific apparatus, alone. It cannot be over-emphasized that a thorough consideration and planning, in accordance with the suggestions embodied in the above discussion, of at least the several important features, should precede any actual construction work on a piece of stage-lighting equipment. A few of the more simple and obvious methods, within reach of the amateur, of building the several types of equipment are outlined below.

For the major portion of the amateur-built equipment to which the following detailed descriptions and instructions apply, wood has been chosen as the principal material of construction; it is everywhere available and is most easily "worked." Specific designs, giving detailed dimensions, have been avoided, for the simple reason that prevailing conditions are never the same in any two instances. Rather, *methods* have been worked out that have a general application. The series of accompanying sketches have been very carefully planned. All represent, substantially, amateur equipment that has actually been built and that has proved practicable and has given at least fairly satisfactory results. These sketches are not given primarily for their value as specific designs (which, incidentally, they do possess, to a certain degree) but rather, in conjunction with the text descriptions and instructions, as a help in realizing, understanding, and solving the various problems that enter into the design and construction of stage-lighting equipment in general — amateur or professional, simple or elaborate. Although the sketches do not carry dimensions, they are reproduced exactly to scale (which is mentioned in each case), and readers who care to rely upon them more fully can calculate dimensions according to the scale of reproduction used, or they can resort to the dimension scales given on page 274. In the few instances where perspective is used in the sketches, it is the conventional "isometric perspective" rather than "true perspective." Thus it is possible to scale off dimensions on all vertical lines and 30° receding lines on these sketches — a convenience which true perspective does not permit. No set of instructions is complete in itself, except perhaps the first — that dealing with the open-trough type of footlights. The several descriptions have been arranged in the order of the difficulty of construction of each piece of apparatus; hence the instructions are progressive, and each set of instructions depends upon a full comprehension of those preceding it.

III. Footlights

Perhaps the simplest method of making serviceable footlights consists of mounting a row of sockets on a strip of wood, to the edge of which is fastened a suitable reflecting shield. But even such a simple operation should not be carried out haphazardly; it should receive reasonable and careful planning.

Open-trough footlights. One of the first and most natural considerations in the planning of equipment is the type and size of lamp to be used. This choice depends on several factors. Since footlights are non-focussing, it is obvious that general lighting service lamps are suitable. But what about size? This depends, for one thing, upon the means of color modification to be used. In the open-trough type of footlight, either glass color-caps, natural-colored glass bulb lamps, or colored lamp dip can be used. For amateur use, the latter is decidedly the cheapest and least expensive. The use of colored lamp dip automatically limits the size of lamp to 40 watts in the new A-style bulb, or 60 watts in the old S-style bulb. And this choice of a small lamp should prove quite acceptable from other standpoints: (1) footlights should not be too bright, and (2) they should provide a continuous strip of light (such as will be obtained from many small and adjacent sources of light) rather than from a few bright, isolated sources.

What shall be the size of the footlights? Obviously the *cross-section* will depend upon the size of lamp and socket to be used; the *length* of each unit will depend upon convenience in handling and construction. Permanent footlights in large theatres are usually built and installed as one complete unit; amateurs who must attach their footlights to the front edge of a stage will find that breaking up their footlights into units, each about six feet long, will prove most convenient. And then, if the front edge of the stage is curved, even shorter units will be necessary, in order that the footlights may conform more closely to the curved edge.

Except in certain cases where restricting conditions demand first attention, the size of the lamp and its socket should form the basis of lighting equipment design. After the lamp has been decided upon, the socket must be chosen. For open-trough work almost any kind of medium "cleat" socket will serve. The style known universally as Number 50715 is about the best type, but any socket approximating it in design will do. Certain types of sockets, especially those designed for the old-fashioned wooden-molding type of wiring, can be fastened to wood and have concealed contacts: these two features make them ideal for the present purpose, but they are rapidly becoming obsolete and difficult to obtain. Cleat sockets have exposed wiring contacts — an unsafe condition, but one which can be readily overcome by covering these contacts with some insulating material, as will be shown later. When the socket and lamp have been chosen, the design can be begun. It is well to work out the design in full size on a large sheet of paper, with the aid of a few simple drawing materials — a pencil and ruler will suffice.

First a "lamp template" should be made, and then a "lamp-in-socket template." The first is made by drawing, on a sheet of heavy paper or light cardboard, the outline of the lamp. Data for this can be obtained from the table on page 156. This outline is then cut out. The lamp-in-socket template is similar, but should be from *actual measurements* from the lamp screwed in the socket. It is important that the *actual* measurements be obtained from the actual lamp and socket to be used, as any error is likely to render the entire work useless. A sample of both lamp and socket had best be procured before the full supply necessary is purchased. From the lamp-in-socket template it is now easy to trace around, on paper, the outline of the lamp and the socket, and to draw around it a trial cross-section of the footlights. Several of these trial cross-sections can be made and the most desirable design found by the "cut and try" method. An effort should be made to design the cross-section of footlights so that (1) their height above the stage-floor level be at a minimum; (2) the angle of light cut-off (determined by drawing a line that connects the extremity of the light source with the limiting edge of the reflecting shield) be such that no direct rays of emanation from the lamp will fall upon the edge of the proscenium opening or upon the auditorium ceiling, but at the same time be such that the face of an actor standing reasonably close to the footlights will not be in absolute shadow; (3) the maximum amount of emanated light will be utilized; (4) sufficient space for relamping be provided; (5) each unit have sufficient rigidity and strength; (6) a convenient means of wiring be afforded, with no exposed live contacts or any other unsafe conditions; and (7) each unit may be conveniently mounted, or fastened, to the front edge of the stage. In connection with (3) it must be borne in mind that the maximum of light emanation from a lamp takes place in a plane perpendicular to the axis of the lamp, at the light center. This point can also be determined from the table on page 156, which gives the light-center length for all the lamps except those with the old-style "hairpin" filament. The light-center length is measured along the lamp axis, from the contact tip on the end of the base. For (4), the lamp template, in conjunction with the lamp-in-socket template, is useful. To achieve (5) it is best to use 1″ wood as the mounting base of the

Outline of lamp template for use in the designing of lighting equipment. Quarter size.

sockets. The back and top shields can be made of ½″ wood. For (6), ⅛″ asbestos paper is very useful. It can be used to cover the contacts completely, as well as all the wiring, and at the same time provides a diffuse reflecting surface. In the open-trough type of footlight, all the lamps are exposed, hence there is no problem of ventilation. With these few conditions and facts in mind, and with just a little ingenuity, it should be easy to arrive at a satisfactory design.

Lamp-in-socket template which serves as a basis for the design of lighting equipment. Quarter size.

The next problem is the purchasing of material. The style of lamp and socket have been chosen. The quantity of each must be determined. As the A-21 lamp has a maximum diameter of 2⅝″, it is possible, by careful crowding, to place the sockets 3″ apart, or as it is termed, to space them "on 3″ centers." This will allow a space of ⅜″ between lamps, which is quite satisfactory. Lamps should not be placed closer together than this distance. In order to accommodate more lamps per linear foot, recourse is sometimes had to staggered spacing, so

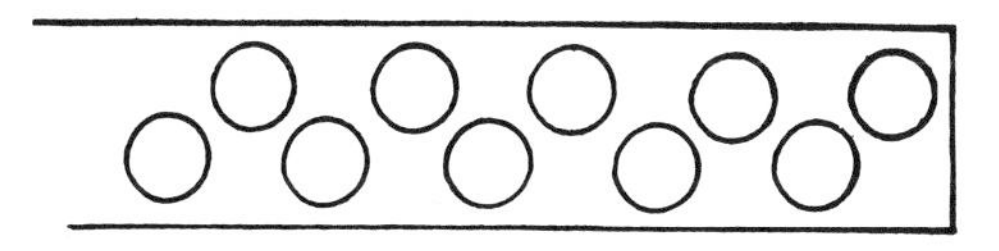

instead of spacing along a straight line, so

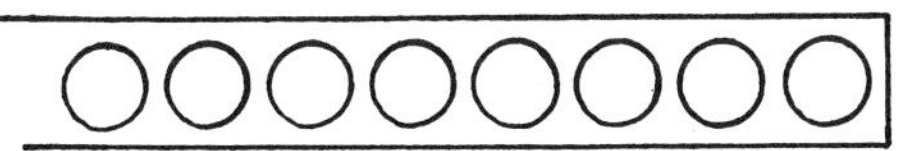

But the staggered position should not be used unless it is absolutely necessary, as the forward lamps will cut off some light from the lamps behind them. Very close crowding of lamps should be avoided. But, on the other hand, the mistake of placing the lamps too far apart should not be made; the closer the lamps, the closer the approximation to an ideal "strip" of light. And it must be remembered that, with three or four color circuits, the lamps on any one circuit will not be less than 9″ or 12″ apart (which is somewhat isolated, if only one color circuit is in use). The row of footlights should extend only to a point about three feet within the proscenium opening. For a stage with a straight front edge the total footlight length would be about six feet less than the width of the proscenium opening; for a curved, or apron-front stage the distance would be slightly greater, depending upon the degree of curvature.

Obviously, the number of sockets and lamps necessary may be calculated by dividing the lamp spacing into the total footlight length. As an example, a straight-front stage with a twenty-four foot opening would require about eighteen feet of footlights — three six-foot lengths would be satisfactory. With 40-watt A-21 lamps on 3″ centers, 72 sockets and lamps would be required. Once again it is pointed out that care should be taken to procure lamps of the proper rated voltage.

For the wiring, asbestos insulated or slow-burning wire should be used, as has been explained. The size of wire depends on the load it must carry, and can be determined from the table on page 64. The load each wire must carry depends upon the wattage and number of the lamps on the circuit it supplies. The wattage has already been determined, but the number of lamps depends upon the arrangement of color circuits. This is discussed on page 165. As the footlights should never give more than a low intensity of light, it is hardly necessary to supply a much greater proportionate wattage for the green and blue colors. If the 40-watt lamp is the largest to be used, a satisfactory proportion would be as follows (assuming an equal number of lamps on each color circuit): for the clear and amber, 25-watt lamps; for the red, green, and blue, 40-watt lamps. Certainly not less than three color circuits should be provided for the footlights, and more desirably four, or even five. With three circuits, amber, red, and blue is a good combination; with four circuits, red, green, blue, and clear; and with five circuits, red, green, blue, clear, and amber. An average of 40 watts per foot per color will provide a footlight intensity that is more than ample for the requirement of regular dramatic productions. Continuing the example started above: with four circuits in an eighteen-foot footlight, one hundred forty-four feet of single conductor wire is needed; for three circuits, one hundred eight feet. This wire is for internal wiring only — for connecting the sockets together. It is wise to procure an excess (at least 10%) of all materials needed for such small jobs, to compensate for any shortage, breakage, or miscalculation, and to provide for any necessary future replacements.

The amount of wood necessary can be calculated from the unit lengths and from the designed cross-section, remembering to make proper allowance for the end pieces of each unit, which should be of 1″ wood. The end lamps of each unit should not be closer than $\frac{3}{8}$″ to the wood end pieces. If six linear feet of lamps are desired in each unit, the total length of each unit will then be a few inches in excess of six feet. This length should be the length of the base and of the back and of the top shields. A soft wood, such as whitewood, or clear-grained white pine, should be used. The harder woods, especially in the $\frac{1}{2}''$ thickness, are likely to split when screws are inserted in them. Soft woods are also much easier to work with — to saw, and plane, and bore, and so forth. If the lumber necessary has been carefully planned, it is quite possible to obtain it in convenient widths and lengths that will not entail much waste or much labor in shaping it to the desired size. Only wood that has been completely dressed (planed smooth on all sides) should be used. In planning, it must be remembered that dressed wood of nominal 1″ thickness is really only about $\frac{7}{8}''$ thick, and nominal $\frac{1}{2}''$ wood is only about $\frac{7}{16}''$ thick. This factor (the difference between the so-called "nominal" and the actual dimensions) often causes an appreciable error if it is not taken into consideration when planning anything made of wood. Wood screws for inserting into the edge of $\frac{1}{2}''$ wood should be of Number 6 thickness — heavier ones are likely to split the wood; lighter ones will not hold securely enough. For other purposes, Number 8 screws are of the most convenient weight. An assortment of screws, with an ample supply of each size, should always be kept on hand. They should be bought by the gross — it is much cheaper to do so, rather than to "break" a carton quantity.

To insulate the wiring and the exposed socket contacts, as well as to protect the wood from the heat of the lamps, and provide a reflecting surface, sheet asbestos, or asbestos paper, as it is variously called, is the most useful and satisfactory material. It may be obtained at well-stocked hardware stores. It is available in several thicknesses and usually comes a yard wide. The $\frac{1}{8}''$ thickness is most suitable for use in home-built stage-lighting equipment that is made of wood. In the open-trough type of footlight it should cover the entire inside of the unit, extending from the front lower edge to the front upper edge, as shown in the sketch, with holes cut in it through which the upper part of the sockets can protrude.

To strengthen each unit, it is well to fasten a small bent angle iron about every two feet along the top and bottom *inside* edges, where two pieces of wood are joined at right angles. For the bottom edge, $3'' \times \frac{3}{4}''$ bent angles are of about the correct size, and for the top, $2'' \times \frac{1}{2}''$. These bent angles will help hold the bottom, side, and top of each footlight unit at right angles to each other, especially if the wood should tend to warp and if the edges have not been planed exactly straight and smooth.

For mounting the footlights on the front edge of the stage, a length of strap iron, about 1″ wide, and $\frac{3}{16}''$ or $\frac{1}{4}''$ thick, should be bent to hold the footlight, as is shown in the sketch. The portion of this "mounting hook" which rests on the stage floor should have a hole drilled in it through which a standard stage screw may be inserted for fastening the entire unit to the front edge of the stage. The portion upon which the bottom of the footlight rests should have two holes drilled in it to take wood screws, not for purposes of strength, but simply to hold the mounting hook in place. One mounting hook should be provided for each three feet of footlight length, and, of course, not less than two for each unit. On a six-foot unit, for example, two mounting hooks, each positioned 18″ (one fourth of the unit length) from each end of the unit, should be provided for mounting.

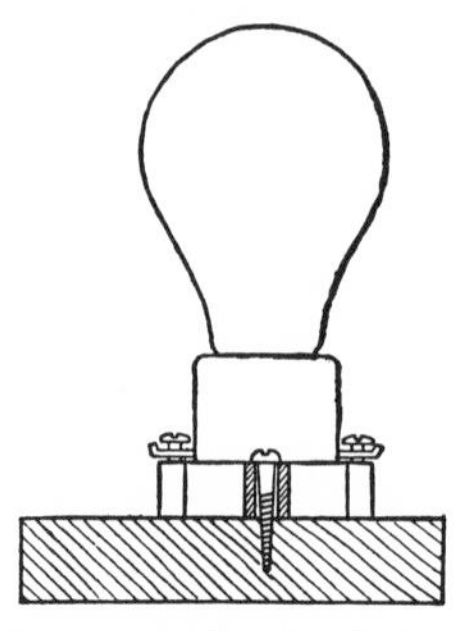

Open-trough footlight: lamp and socket mounted on footlight base. Quarter size.

When all of these details have been thought out and planned for any particular design, the actual construction is a comparatively simple matter. On the other hand, for any one to build equipment without first thoroughly considering all the factors involved is deliberately to court failure. The first step in the construction of the home-built open-trough footlight is to prepare the base carefully, according to the determined dimensions, and to mount on it the sockets, with the contact screws on the sides of each socket all in line, to facilitate wiring — that is, all the contact screws on one side of the sockets should be near the front edge of the footlight unit, and all those on the other side should be near the back edge. For mounting the sockets, 1″ Number 8 round-head wood screws should be used. Next, the back shield should be screwed to the back edge of the base. Care should be observed, whenever screws are inserted near the edge of thin wood, to prevent the wood from splitting. This can best be done by drilling a hole just large enough to accommodate the shank of the screw through the thin wood, instead of making the thick, heavy, unthreaded shank of the screw force aside the wood fibers. Thus the wood is prevented from splitting. These holes can most conveniently be drilled, at both the top and bottom edges of the back shield, before the shield is attached to the case, while it is lying flat on the workbench. For such thin wood $1\frac{1}{4}$″ Number 6 flat-head wood screws are of a suitable size and should be spaced about 8″ apart at both edges. When the back shield has been attached, the two end pieces of the unit should be fastened in place. These end pieces, as may be seen from the sketch, fit *inside* the base, back, and top pieces, and should be carefully prepared according to the dimensions, as upon their outline depends, in great measure, the actual final shape of the footlight unit. To fasten the base to the end pieces, 2″ Number 9 flat-head wood screws may be used, and $1\frac{1}{4}''$ Number 6 flat-head wood screws for fastening the other pieces. The $3'' \times \frac{3}{4}''$ bent angle irons should next be fastened into the corner formed by the base and the back shield — one angle iron should be placed at about every two feet. To fasten the angle irons to the thin shields, $\frac{1}{2}''$ Number 7 flat-head wood screws should be used, and 1″ Number 9 flat-head wood screws used to fasten the angle irons to the heavier base. Perhaps the $\frac{3}{4}''$ wide angles will not fit — the sockets used may be too close together; in that case, $3'' \times \frac{1}{2}''$ angles should be substituted.

Just after the back shield has been fastened to the base and to the end pieces is the most convenient time to do the wiring. The internal wiring can be done very simply and quickly. At this point the external wiring (that which connects the units together, and the whole footlight to the switchboard, a stage pocket, or other source of current) must be decided upon. If it is desired that each separate section, or unit, of the footlights, and each color circuit in it be subject to individual control, it will be necessary that as many individual leads, or lengths of stage cable as there are color circuits be brought from each footlight unit to the switchboard. Such "sectional" control, while it will often be found a very useful refinement, is thus seen to require wiring that is just a bit ponderous and which will require an auxiliary distributing panel at the switchboard. If the sectional control is desired, it will be necessary to bring the pair of wires connecting the sockets of each color circuit through either of the footlight end pieces (through the end piece nearest the side of the stage in which the switchboard is located) and to terminate it in a male cable connector, to which point the current can be carried from the switchboard by a length of stage cable equipped with the necessary connectors. This must be done for each color circuit on each footlight section, or unit, thus:

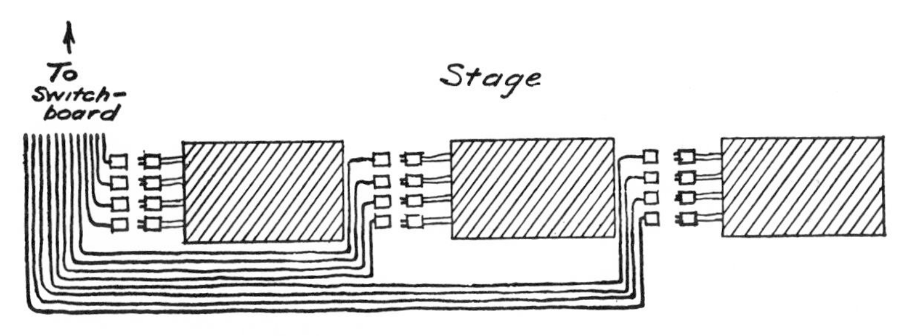

If, however, only individual color circuit control is desired — that is, each color circuit in the entire footlight controlled as a unit — the wiring will have to be arranged so that the color circuits of each footlight unit can be connected to the respective color circuits of the adjacent unit or units, and so that each color circuit so connected together can, in its entirety, be connected to the switchboard. For simple color-circuit control it is necessary that the wiring be arranged as follows: for the footlight unit farthest away from the switchboard side of the stage, each pair of color-circuit wires should be brought through the end piece on the switchboard side and should be terminated in a male connector; for the remaining footlight units, each pair of color-circuit wires should be brought through both end pieces and should be terminated (1) on the switchboard side, in a male connector, and (2) on the opposite-switchboard side, in a female connector, thus:

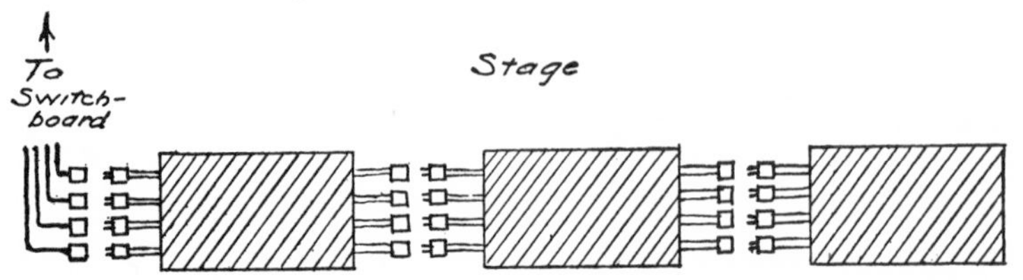

If the wires used for wiring the sockets are of the flexible type, each pair may be brought out, for a distance of about 18″, through a hole in the end piece, and connected directly to the cable connector. If the socket wires are solid, and hence rigid, it is best to terminate them within the footlight unit, and introduce a short length of cable, through a hole in the end piece, to which they may be joined by a well-made "splice" — the wires twisted tightly together, soldered, and bound with rubber tape and with friction tape. To the other end of the short length of stage cable, outside the unit, may then be affixed the cable connector. The holes in the end pieces through which the wires or cables pass should be smooth and carefully rounded, in order that the insulation of the wires may be protected from abrasion. It is well to line each hole with a porcelain bushing or with a piece of flexible "loom", both of which may be obtained from the local electrical dealer. In connection with the wiring of footlights (and borderlights and striplights as well) it must be remembered that the Code limit is 1320 watts, or 32 medium sockets on a branch circuit. If the wattage or number of sockets on any footlight circuit exceeds these limits, the circuit must be split up into two sections, each of which must be fused separately (see diagram on page 62).

The cable connectors should be of the regular type designed for stage service, as should be also the cable itself. Small cord connectors such as are used to connect small household electrical appliances should not, in most cases, be used for stage work. Under certain conditions, however, these small cord connectors can be employed on very small stages, where the load they must carry is light (they are usually rated at 6 amperes) and where they will be but seldom used, and then very carefully handled (they are of molded composition and will not withstand heavy usage, being liable to break open and expose their current carrying parts, which will cause a short circuit should these parts touch each other). In conjunction with such small cord connectors, for light loads, and with careful handling, heavy reinforced cord, Number 16 or Number 18 (depending on the load to be carried — see table on page 64) can be used on very small stages, in buildings not legally classified as theatres. Of course, the use of cable connectors as recommended above is for conditions where portability and flexibility of equipment are desired, as in many cases of amateur production. If the footlight units are to be permanently installed, the expense of the cable connectors may be saved by joining the wires permanently in the form of regular soldered-and-taped splices. It is wise, however, to use the cable connectors if possible; the moderate extra expense entailed will be more than compensated for by the resulting flexibility of equipment, which is always a most desirable characteristic, especially of equipment for amateur use. It should also be borne in mind that many municipal and state laws prohibit the installation of wiring of a permanent character by other than duly licensed electricians. If the equipment and wiring are portable, they may be set up and taken down, in any desired combinations, not only conveniently, but also without violating the law, which, in some instances, might lead to embarrassing situations.

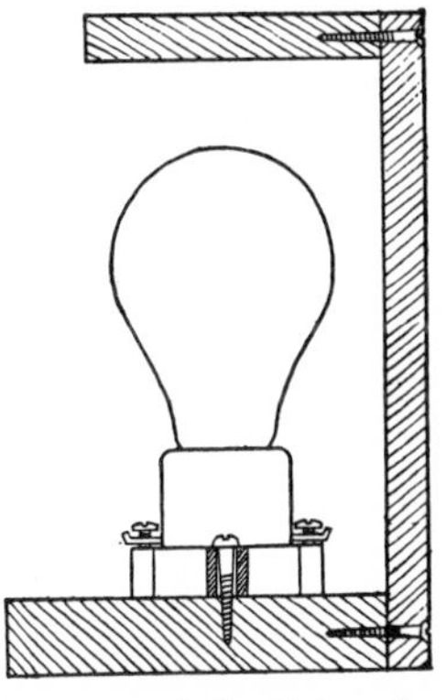

Open-trough footlight: the back and top shields added to the base. Quarter size.

When the wiring of the footlight has been completed and thoroughly tested to see if all circuits have been properly connected, the top shield can be fastened in place. For this purpose, $1\frac{1}{4}''$ Number 6 flat-head wood screws are of a suitable size. The $2'' \times \frac{1}{2}''$ angle irons should then be fastened into place in the corner thus formed. Next, the mounting hooks should be prepared and fastened to the footlight unit, as shown in the sketch. The final major operation in the construction of the footlight unit is putting the asbestos paper in place, running it the entire inside length of the footlight unit. Just how the asbestos papers may be tacked to the wood in such a manner as to protect the exposed socket contacts and provide space for the wiring is shown on the sketch. Small carpet tacks, size Number 4 or Number 6, are suitable for tacking down the asbestos paper, which should be applied also to the inner surface of the end pieces of each unit. The holes in the asbestos, through which the upper parts of the sockets protrude, should be cut to fit the sockets snugly. They may be cut with a sharp, pointed knife. The size and location of these holes had best be determined by trial, using a sheet of paper large enough to cover three or four sockets and to extend from the lower to the upper edge of the unit. The edges of the asbestos lining should not be cut exactly to size in advance; rather, an excess of $\frac{1}{2}''$ should be allowed, which can be neatly trimmed off after the asbestos has been tacked down. The reflective efficiency of the asbestos paper will be greatly increased if a coat or two of flat white diffusely reflecting paint is applied to the asbestos surface, after it has been fixed in place. The outside surfaces of the footlight unit should be sandpapered smooth and clean, whereupon the unit can be stained or painted to match the wood finish of the surroundings amidst which it will be used, or it can be painted a dull flat black, which will prove a neat and unobtrusive finish for most conditions. The footlight is then complete and ready for use.

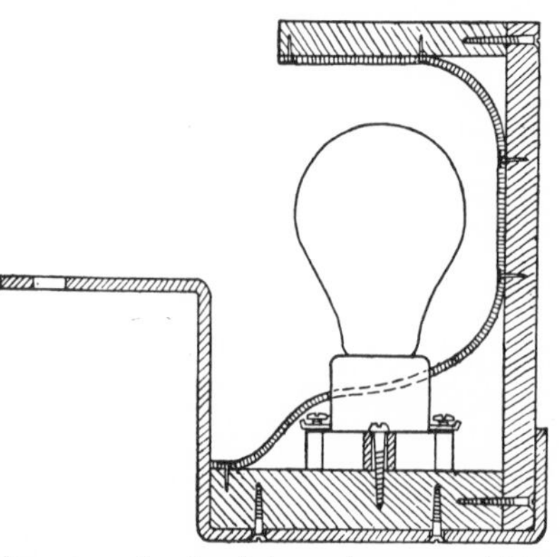

Open-trough footlight: the top shield added, the asbestos lining in place and the mounting hook attached. This view shows a cross section of the complete open trough footlight. Quarter size.

If the front edge of the stage is curved, or if it is embellished with a decorative molding, the front edge of the footlight base will not be able to fit snugly against the front face of the stage, and undesired light leakage will take place. This condition can easily be anticipated and can be avoided by adding to the footlight unit a low front shield, the upper edge of which is level with the stage floor. The asbestos lining should then also cover the inner surface of this front shield. (This front shield is not shown on any of the accompanying sketches.) If the front edge of the stage projects out from the proscenium wall for more than a few inches, side spill of light on to the sides of the proscenium opening is sure to take place. This can be avoided, or at least minimized, by the use of several fins, or baffles, near each end of the entire set of footlights. These fins should be made of thin sheet metal, and they should be placed in an upright position between pairs of two adjacent lamps in the footlights, perpendicular to the back shield. Their outline should be such that they fit snugly against the top and back shields of the footlight, with their lower edge level with the stage floor and with

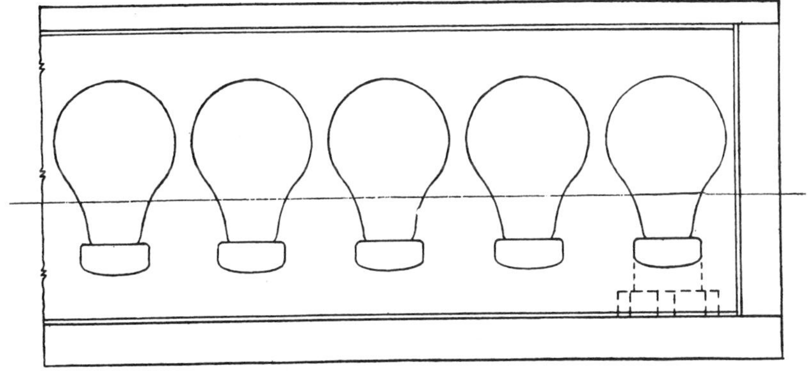

Open-trough footlight: front view of right end showing lamp spacing and general appearance when complete. The center line represents the stage floor level. Quarter size.

their front edge at an angle corresponding to that of the footlight end piece. Each baffle may be held in place by bending, on its back edge, a $\frac{1}{2}''$ ear in which two holes are punched. This ear can then be screwed against the back shield of the footlight with $\frac{1}{2}''$ Number 5 round-head wood screws. The number of these baffles necessary to prevent light spill from the ends of the footlights, and their exact position, will depend upon specific conditions, and can best be determined by trial, with the footlights in place and all lamps lighted. Small pieces of cardboard can then temporarily be inserted between the lamps at intervals that give the minimum light spill, and later replaced with the permanent metal baffles. Usually three or four baffles at each end, spaced from 12″ to 18″ apart, will be found sufficient. The baffles should be painted flat black on both sides, or, if desired, black on the side facing the nearest proscenium wall and white on the other side.

In such manner, then, is the typical design and construction of simple open-trough type footlights carried out. The above discussion gives an idea of how the many factors involved must all be taken into consideration, and how the various problems can be solved. Estimated costs for specific conditions can easily be calculated from the individual design if everything is carefully planned in advance. A host of minor problems, not touched upon in the description above, are certain to arise in the course of the work, but are equally certain to suggest their own solutions. Many details of construction have been pointed out that will, perhaps, prove of value to the less experienced amateur workers. These details will not, of course, be repeated in the following descriptions of other equipment. Neither will the general principles of design that have been discussed be again touched upon — only the more advanced phases of the work will be taken up.

The *compartment type of footlight* is useful where a high intensity of light is necessary, or if color modification by means of gelatin color media is desired. The size of lamp to be used is limited only by the

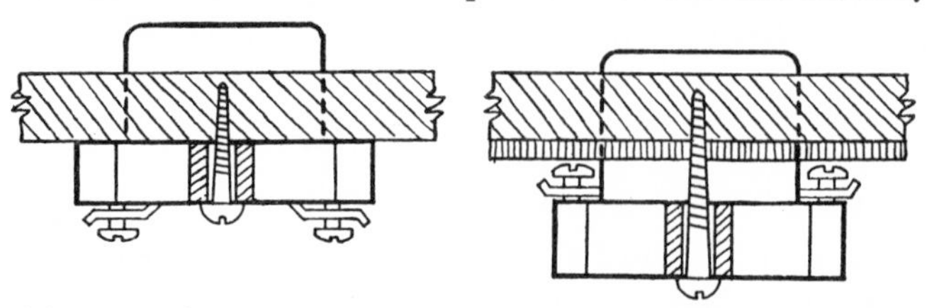

At left, special wooden sign socket particularly useful for compartment type lighting equipment made of wood. (See illustration on page 66.) At right, ordinary 50715 cleat socket adapted for use with compartment type equipment made of wood. Half size.

necessity for keeping the external dimensions of the footlight unit at a reasonable minimum. 150-watt lamps are usually the largest used for a stage of average size. In this type of footlight each lamp is completely enclosed in its separate compartment. This at once creates the problem of ventilation. It is also necessary that there be provided some means of holding a color frame in place before the mouth of the compartment which will not permit the leakage, or escape, of clear, or unmodified, light from the lamps or from the interior reflecting surfaces. Except for these two factors — ventilation, and means of color modification — the design of a compartment type footlight differs but little from that of an open-trough type of footlight. Lamp spacing is greater, of course, and depends not only on the size of the lamp, but also upon the necessity for allowing enough room on all sides of the lamp for the free passage of a cooling current of air. For lamps up to the 150-watt PS–25 size, a spacing of 6″ on centers will usually be found satisfactory.

As before, the first step in the design should be the making of a lamp template and a lamp-in-socket template. And this immediately raises the question of the proper type of socket to use. As each compartment is enclosed, with partitions separating the lamps, open wiring (such as was done in the open-trough footlight) is impracticable, as it would be necessary for all the wires to pierce all of the partitions. However, if it is possible to obtain a socket with the wiring contacts on the *bottom* instead of on the sides, the sockets can be protruded through wide-enough holes in a strip of wood, and fastened to the under side of the wood, and the wiring done below it in a continuous and hence convenient form, and the compartment partitions built *above* the strip of wood. Such a socket is made, but is not commonly available. It is known as a "wooden-sign socket", and may be ordered through the local electrical dealer.[1] However, if it is impossible to obtain this particular type of socket, recourse may be had to the same type used for the open-trough footlight — the type used for "cleat wiring", with the contact screws on the side. This type of socket can also be fastened to the under side of a strip of wood and protrude upwards through a hole. However, the wiring must be completed before the socket is screwed down, and the under side of the wood must be covered with an insulating material (asbestos paper will serve) that will prevent the live contact screws from touching the wood. This cleat socket is not as convenient to use as the regular wooden-sign socket, but it is a very effective and easily obtainable substitute.

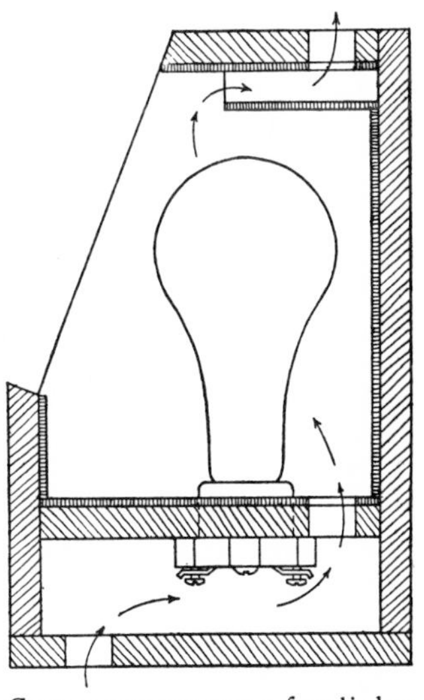

Compartment type footlight: cross-sectional view showing general construction, wiring channel, wooden sign socket with 100-watt A-23 incandescent lamp, and provision for ventilation as described in detail in the text. Quarter size.

With the proper templates made, the design can be begun. The accompanying sketches of the compartment type footlight are based on the use of 100-watt A-23 lamps with the regular wooden-sign sockets. If the 100-watt, 150-watt PS-25 lamps are to be used, correspondingly more space will have to be allowed in the compartment height for relamping, as these lamps are $\frac{7}{8}''$ greater in over-all length. In order to protect the wiring, a double bottom will have to be added below the "socket strip" (the strip of wood on the underside of which the sockets are mounted). This space between the socket strip and the bottom piece constitutes the "wiring channel."

[1] Its General Electric Company catalogue number is GE 170. Incidentally metal-sign sockets (see page 66), in three or four different styles, both split and solid, are very generally available, and can be used if sheet metal, rather than wood, is used as the construction material. The above description, however, is based on the use of wood as the construction material.

The wiring channel offers a convenient means of solving at least half of the ventilation problem. Ventilation holes can be bored in both the socket strip and the bottom strip, and if they are positioned as shown in the sketches, they will admit a current of air, but at the same time will allow no light to pass out of the bottom of the footlight unit. The remaining half of the ventilation problem can be solved by boring holes in the top shield and placing, a half-inch below the holes, a thin baffle of asbestos paper which will intercept light rays but which will allow the free passage of air around it. This baffle can be held in place by three short $\frac{1}{2}'' \times \frac{1}{2}''$ strips of wood, which might be called "spreaders." If there is any possibility of energetic probing of the top ventilation holes with pencils or penknife blades wielded by curiosity-smitten individuals, these baffles had better be made of sheet metal rather than of asbestos paper, or the ventilation holes had better be covered with thin screening, on the inside surface. An idea of how the spreaders, the baffle, and the various sets of ventilation holes should be positioned in relation to each lamp compartment may be gained by reference to the series of sketches on the opposite page. It might again be pointed out that all the sketches of home-built equipment in this chapter have been carefully designed and laid out to scale, and that, in conjunction with the dimension scales on page 274 may be used not only for general information, but also as a source of definite dimensions that apply to the specific conditions which serve as their basis.

Suggestions for the remaining structural features will also be found in the sketches. The recommendations given for open-trough footlights in regard to length of units, arrangement of color circuits, and methods of wiring, internal and external, apply with equal force to the design and construction of the compartment footlight. No heavy base of 1″ wood need be used, as the double bottom and the front, back, and top shields, along with the compartment partitions at 6″ intervals, will provide more than the necessary rigidity and strength. Asbestos paper should line the entire interior of each compartment. For greater insulation and safety, the wiring channel might also be lined with asbestos, though this is not absolutely necessary. Of course, the ventilation holes in the wood must be continued through the adjoining asbestos paper — the holes in the asbestos should be sharp and clean, to permit the unrestricted passage of air.

In order to provide means for color modification, it is necessary that grooves for reception of color frames be mounted at the mouth of each compartment. These should be carefully and completely

Top view showing ventilation holes in top shield and spacing of spreaders directly below.

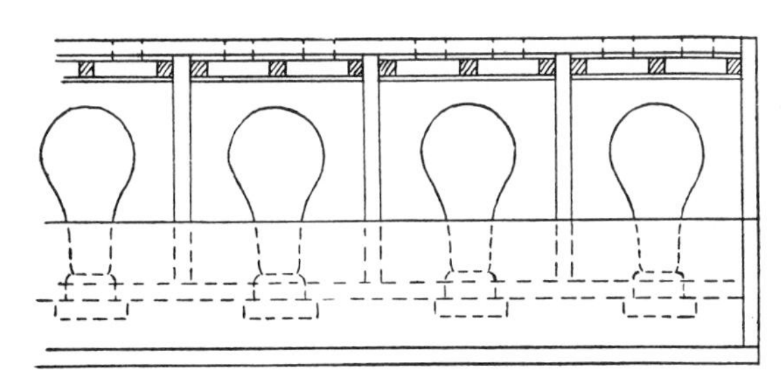

Front view showing general construction and arrangement of spreaders and baffle for ventilation. Asbestos lining on side and bottom of compartments is not shown.

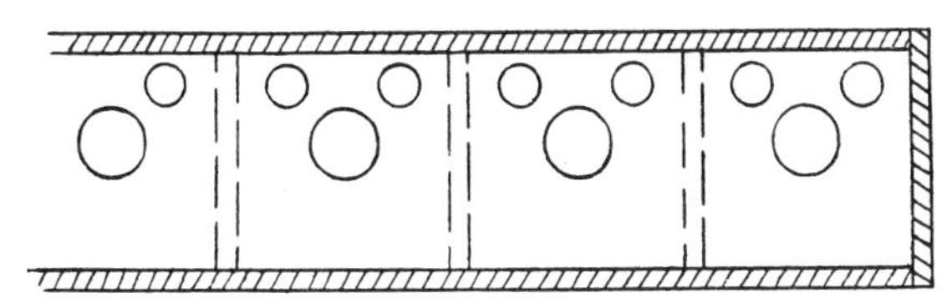

Cross-sectional view showing socket strip. The two smaller holes in each compartment space are for ventilation; the larger one for accommodation of the socket. The dashed lines indicate the position occupied by the compartment partitions when they are in place.

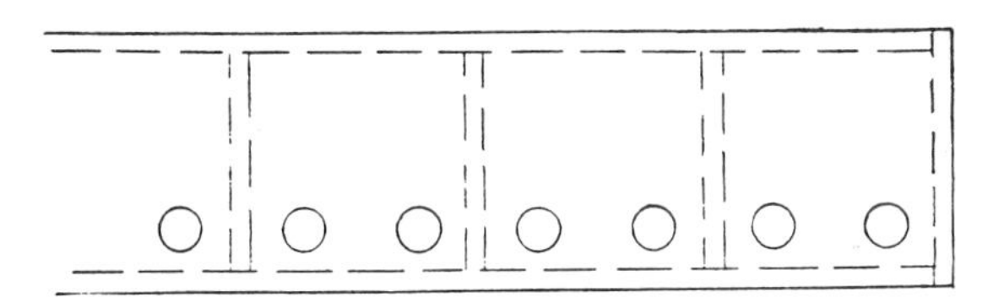

Plan view of bottom board showing ventilation holes. The dashed lines indicate the positions of the compartment partitions, the front and back shields and the end pieces when in place.

SKETCHES OF COMPARTMENT TYPE FOOTLIGHT. ONE-EIGHTH SIZE

planned for in advance of construction; otherwise numerous detailed problems of an irritating nature will arise which could have been settled with greater ease and facility with pencil and paper than with the actual materials of construction. Two methods of making the necessary color-frame grooves are illustrated in detail in the sketches, one method using strips of $\frac{1}{4}''$ wood, the other using sheet metal. The latter method will provide the more satisfactory grooves, but the former method can be used if it is not desired to attempt the fashioning of sheet metal. The wooden grooves may be applied with small "brad nails" about an inch long, and the metal grooves may be applied with $\frac{1}{2}''$ Number 2 round-head brass wood screws.

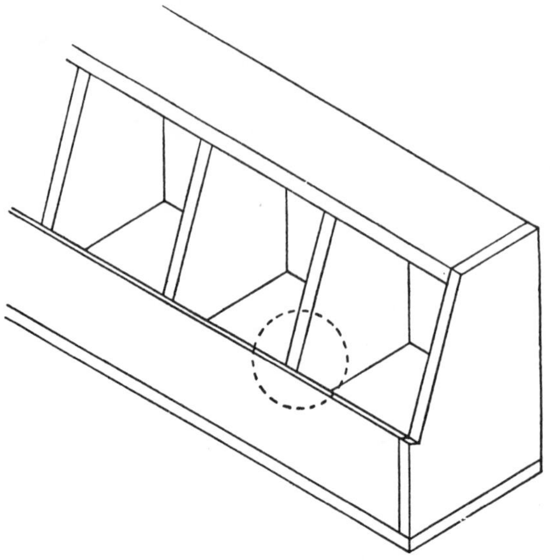

Compartment type footlight: isometric view showing principal construction features. Sockets, lamps, asbestos lining, and ventilation holes are not shown. The circle indicates that portion which is shown in the five following sketches showing details of wooden construction of color-frame slide grooves. One-eighth size.

When a satisfactory design has been arrived at, and the full-sized sketches of construction details have been prepared, and the materials have been procured, the actual construction of the footlight is not, in itself, a difficult task. Perhaps the most logical and convenient order in which the various bits of construction work should be executed would begin with the preparation of the compartment partitions and of the end pieces of each unit. The latter might be fitted either inside the top, back, and front shields, or outside them, accordingly as the design has been worked out (in the accompanying sketches it is shown on the outside of the shields). If a cardboard template of the partitions is carefully made, they can be quickly and accurately marked out on the wood, and, in addition, will assure a strict uniformity (that is, if the markings are carefully followed in cutting out and placing the partition pieces). Next, the socket strips should be prepared. The centers of the large socket holes should be carefully laid out on the wood, as should be also the centers of the ventilation holes (each 1″ in diameter) and the positions which the compartment partitions will occupy. The socket holes can then be bored with a bit brace and an expansion bit (adjustable, for large holes) and the ventilation holes with a regular 1″ bit. It is well to remember that clean-cut holes can be bored in thin wood (and especially with the expansion bit) only if another piece of wood, with a smooth surface (a trimmed-off piece of waste wood will do) is laid under the part to be bored, and the bore hole

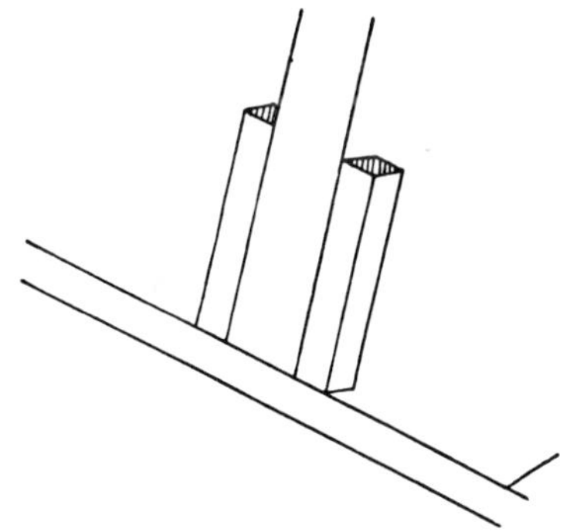

Method of applying wooden color-frame slide grooves: first step, showing strips (¼″ square in cross section) applied to the sides of the compartment partition. These strips will prevent the color frames from falling into the compartment. Half size.

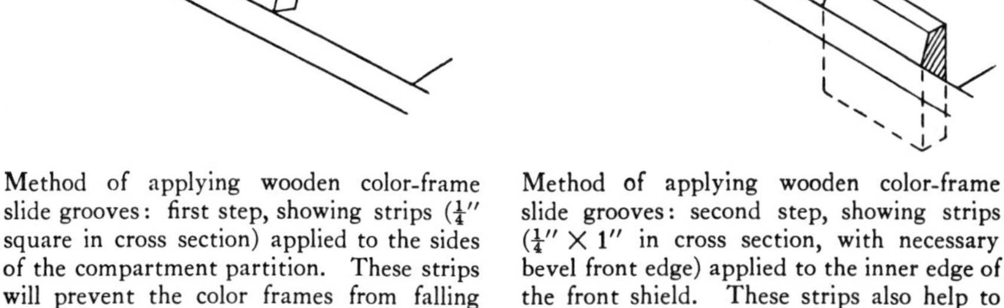

Method of applying wooden color-frame slide grooves: second step, showing strips (¼″ × 1″ in cross section, with necessary bevel front edge) applied to the inner edge of the front shield. These strips also help to prevent the color frames from falling into the compartment. Half size.

carried completely through the main piece of wood and continued for a short distance (about ⅛″) into the piece lying beneath. This little trick will result in clean, sharp holes instead of ragged ones with splintered wood on the under side where the bit has broken through. Next, the top shield should be prepared, with the positions of the partitions marked out, and the ventilation holes bored, and the front edge planed to the correct angle (if the design calls for one). Then the spreaders themselves, the requisite number of them, should be prepared. Next, the back shield, with the partition positions marked. Then, the front shield, with the upper edge planed at the angle (if any) indicated on the design. The use of an adjustable try-square will facilitate planing any angled edges to the exact angles desired. Then, the bottom strip, with the ventilation holes bored. With this work finished, the various important parts of the footlight will be ready for assembly. For fastening together the pieces of wood, 1¼″ Number 6 flat-head wood screws should be used, except for attaching the spreaders to the top shields, which will require the $\frac{3}{4}''$ Number 6 size.

First, pieces of asbestos paper should be tacked to the upper side of the socket strip in the spaces which will constitute the compartments (leaving space between the pieces of asbestos paper for the bottom edges of the partitions, where marked) and the socket and ventilation holes cut through the asbestos with a sharp, narrow-bladed knife. If the wiring channel is to be lined with asbestos, or if

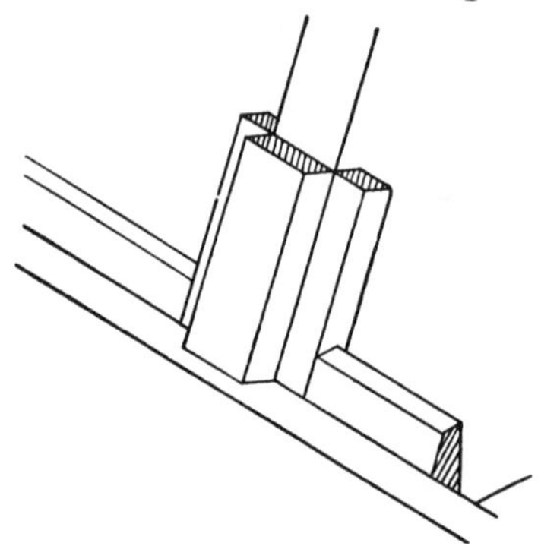

Method of applying wooden color-frame slide grooves: third step, showing strips ($\frac{1}{2}'' \times \frac{1}{4}''$ in cross section) applied to the front edge of the compartment partition. This strip acts as a spreader and provides the slide space for the color frames. Half size.

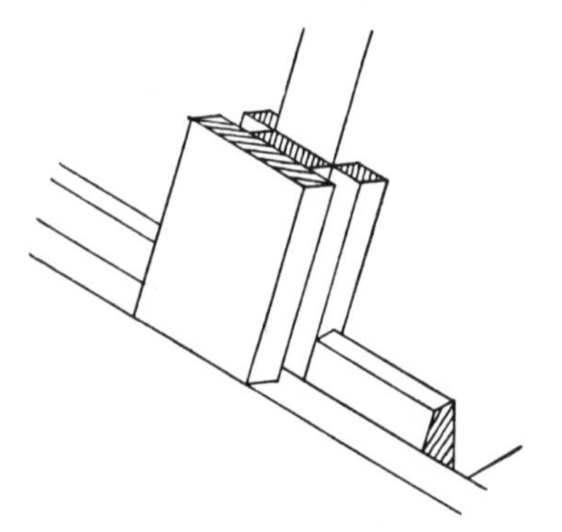

Method of applying wooden color-frame slide grooves: fourth step, showing strips ($\frac{1}{4}'' \times 1''$ in cross section) applied to the front edge of each compartment partition to serve as an outer retaining strip for holding the color frame in place. Half size.

the regular cleat sockets are used instead of the wooden-sign sockets, asbestos should also be applied to the underside of the socket strip in one long piece. Then the sockets should be mounted and wired (or, with the cleat sockets, *vice versa*). Next, the partitions should be screwed to the socket strip, from beneath. Then, the front and back shields should be screwed in place, screws being inserted through the shields into the edges of both the socket strip and the partitions. Then asbestos should be applied to the under side of the top shield (again leaving space for the top edges of the partitions, where marked), and the spreaders screwed in their proper places. The spreaders and the asbestos between them (on the under side of the top shield) and the insides of the ventilation holes, should be painted flat black. The upper side of the asbestos (or sheet metal) baffle should also be painted flat black, and the baffle then tacked in place across the spreaders. Asbestos should be applied to the interior of each partition, and then the top shield screwed down. If the wiring channel is to be lined with asbestos, this should next be done, and the end pieces screwed on and the wiring brought through holes in them, the same as with the open-trough footlight. When the wiring and splicing (if any) have been finished, the inside surface of the wiring channel, and the wires, asbestos, and sockets in it, and also the upper side of the bottom strip, and the insides of the ventilation holes, should all be painted a flat black, to prevent any slight diffusion of light through the ventilation holes. The bottom strip should then be screwed on. Except for painting, inside and outside, and the application of the color-frame grooves, the compartment footlight is then complete.

The exact method of fashioning and applying the color-frame grooves is largely a matter of individual inclination. The principal requirements are that the grooves be placed at the sides and bottom of the compartment opening, to hold the color frames in place and permit their convenient insertion and removal, and that the grooves be so made that no escape of clear, unmodified light can take place. Perhaps the two simplest methods (one in wood, the other in sheet metal) of making and applying the color-frame grooves are indicated in the accompanying sketches, which have been arranged in progressive detail so as to be virtually self-explanatory. The grooves should, of course, extend completely along the sides and bottom of the reflector. They are shown in abbreviated form in the sketches only to simplify and aid in the illustration.

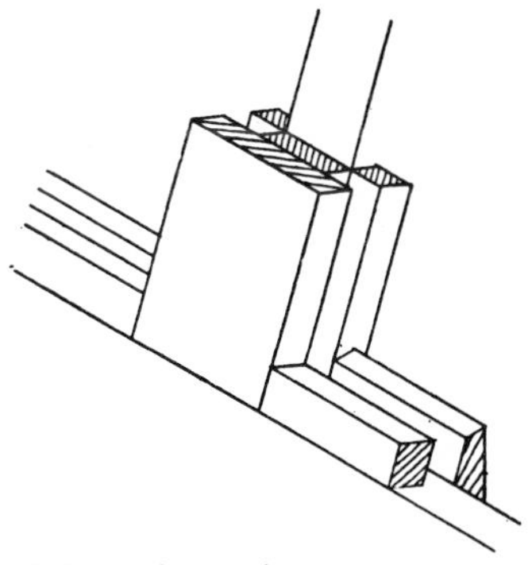

Method of applying wooden color-frame slide grooves: fifth step, showing the outer retaining strip ($\frac{1}{4}''$ square in cross section) applied to the upper edge of the front shield for holding the color frame in place. Half size.

After the color-frame grooves have been applied, the interior of each compartment should be given a coat or two of flat white diffusely reflecting paint. Mounting hooks, similar to those recommended for the open-trough footlight units, should then be made and applied. Then, the outside of the unit can be painted with a coat of flat black, or given any special finish, and the home-built compartment footlight is ready for use. If, when the units are in place, they seem too heavy for the mounting hooks (a very unlikely condition, however), they can be further supported by black, enameled-iron shelf brackets screwed to the front face of the stage.

An infinite number of modifications and variations and elaborations of these two methods, just described, for the amateur construction of stage-lighting equipment may be devised. The basic principles for all, however, will be found in the paragraphs just above.

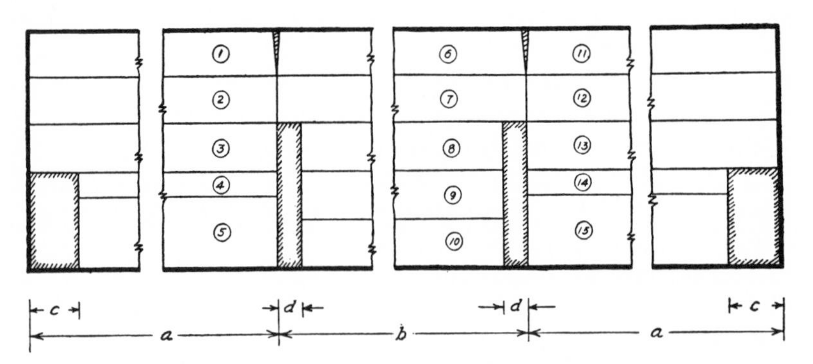

Developed view showing bending and cutting lines which should be scribed on the metal. Areas with shaded edges as well as small wedge-shaped pieces between areas 1 and 6 and 6 and 11, to be cut out completely. Unshaded lines indicate edges to be bent. Length indicated by "a" equals the distance from upper edge of front shield to upper edge of top shield. Length indicated by "b" equals the width of the compartment plus the thickness of one compartment partition. Length indicated by "c" equals the thickness of the top shield. Length indicated by "d" is arbitrary and equals about one half the width of area 3. Areas 1, 2, 3, 4, and 5, when properly bent will form one side of the groove, areas 11, 12, 13, 14, and 15 will form the other side, and areas 6, 7, 8, 9, and 10 will form the bottom.

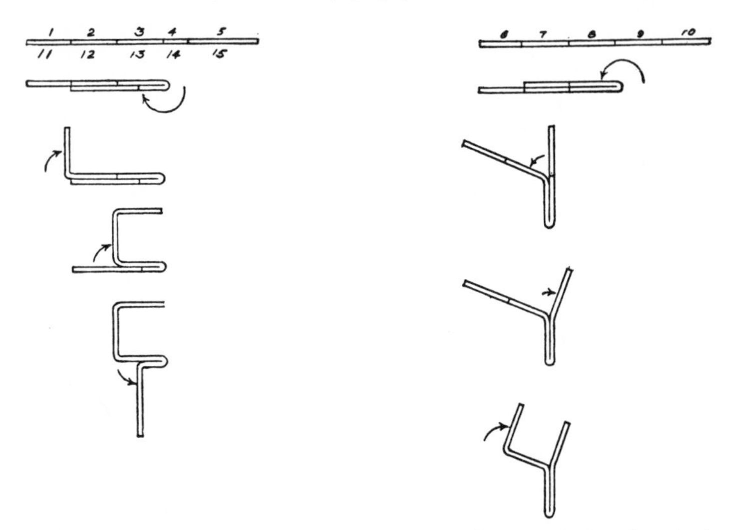

Progressive steps in bending the side grooves.

Progressive steps in bending the bottom groove.

Method of Applying Metal Color-Frame Slide Grooves to Compartment Type Footlight. Half Size.

For instance, the footlights may be made entirely of metal, instead of wood; they may be permanently installed in one complete length, instead of in unit lengths; the division into color and section circuits may be arranged differently; another method of ventilation may be adopted; and so forth. But the underlying principles of design will be alike for all. Attention should be called, again, to the possibility of using regular, commercially available reflectors, especially if the larger lamps are used. These reflectors may be mounted within wooden or metal housings, for protection—each reflector will correspond to a single compartment. Methods of holding the reflectors in place, of providing color-frame grooves, and of solving other inherent problems of design and construction will become apparent as the design is gradually worked out.

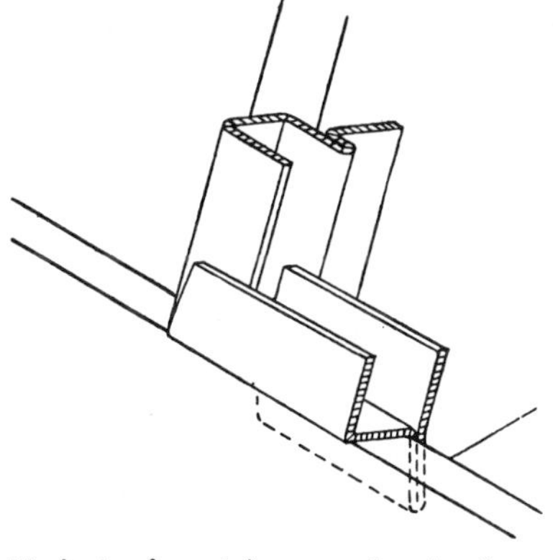

Method of applying metal color-frame slide grooves, showing a corner between the side and bottom grooves in place. The unit set of grooves made according to the sketches on the opposite page is applied to each compartment. Half size.

The indirect type of footlight undoubtedly gives the best results, as it provides what the theoretical, ideal footlight should provide; namely, a continuous, narrow strip of diffused light. Although indirect footlights have only recently been introduced, at least in this country, they are rapidly gaining in favor as their advantageous features reveal themselves. For the benefit of amateur stage workers who might care to experiment with the indirect type of footlight, the accompanying sketch is presented. This shows a suggested cross-section of unit. Details are omitted, but can be readily supplied by readers who have carefully "followed through" the previous descriptions of the open-trough and compartment footlight. Internal supports and bracing cleats must be used in order to provide the necessary strength and rigidity. The sketch is based on the use of 40-watt A–21 lamps, which may either be color dipped or have natural-colored glass bulbs on the color circuits. However, as the advantage of the indirect footlight can only be obtained at the sacrifice of light intensity, it may be thought desirable to use larger lamps. Then (unless lamps with natural-colored glass bulbs are used) it will be necessary to mount each lamp in a compartment or in a reflector, and provide grooves for the insertion of color frames. The lamps should be tilted at a slight angle in order that the maximum light emission from the lamp may fall on to the upper half of the reflecting surface. That the diffusely reflecting surface (which, in the case of the indirect footlight becomes the "secondary illuminant" that projects the light on to the stage) may be lighted as brightly as possible, polished metal sheets, or thin glass mirrors should be mounted behind the lamps. If large lamps and compartments are used, the polished reflecting metal should line the compartment sides. Provision for relamping the compartment type of indirect footlight will constitute perhaps the most difficult problem — for the open-trough type a hinged lid, such as is shown on the sketch, will render the lamps and sockets easily accessible.

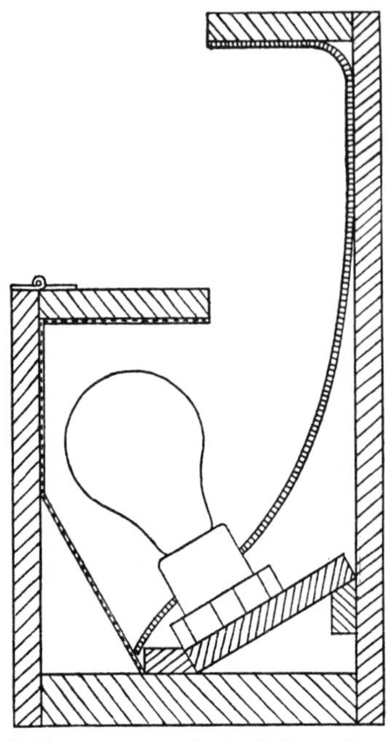

Indirect type of footlight. Suggesting a possible method of construction (omitting angle-irons and wooden cleats, which are necessary for rigidity and strength). This type of footlight can be applied to the front edge of the stage, the stage floor being level with the hinged shield. The thin strip shown at the left side of and above the lamp is of polished reflecting metal. The thicker strip shown at the right side is an asbestos lining which serves as a protective covering and also as a diffusely reflecting surface. The socket is the ordinary cleat type and the lamp is of the 40-watt A-21 size. Quarter size.

IV. Borderlights

As borderlights are virtually inverted footlights, designs such as have just been presented in the preceding paragraphs may be used, almost unchanged, for borderlights, with the necessary modifications, of course, in the mounting. In the case of the compartment footlight, slight changes must also be made in the design of the color-frame grooves and in the positioning of the ventilation holes and baffles. All the descriptions and instructions and recommendations that have been given in relation to home-built footlights apply equally to home-built borderlights.

The problem of mounting borderlights is more than inherent in the borderlights themselves — it also involves the structural features of the stage. If a stage is equipped with the standard system of rigging — which includes a fly loft, a gridiron, battens which can be raised and lowered, with their sets of lines, and an automatic counterweight system (or the older fly gallery and pin rail) — the borderlights can be mounted by suspending them from a conveniently placed batten. But these conveniences are usually denied the amateur — at any rate, the amateur who builds his own lighting equipment (*ipso facto*). But whatever the physical characteristic of the stage may be, it is a comparatively simple matter to provide a batten for mounting the borderlights. For amateur use, standard iron pipe (such as is used for water supply and for heating purposes) of the size designated as 1″, will serve excellently. It is easily available in lengths up to 22 feet, and may be obtained from the local plumber or hardware dealer. The batten should be at least as long as the proscenium opening is wide, and preferably a few feet longer. It is desirable that the batten be so mounted that it can be raised or lowered. The batten should be supported by $\frac{1}{2}$″ hemp rope lines, or $\frac{3}{16}$″ flexible steel cables. As a general rule, three lines should be used if the batten is less than thirty feet long (one line at the center of the batten, the other two lines a sixth of the batten's length from each of its ends); and four lines if it is more than thirty feet long (two lines each an eighth of the batten's length from the center, the other two lines an eighth of its length from each of its ends). The first batten should be suspended as closely as possible behind the main, or act, curtain, directly in back of the limiting curtain valance, or "teaser", sufficiently far away so that equipment, when mounted on the batten, will not interfere with the free movement of the curtain or teaser. Each of the lines supporting the batten should be run through a single-sheave pulley of the necessary size and strength that is securely fixed to the ceiling of the stage. From these pulleys the lines are brought over horizontally to either of the side walls of the stage, from which point, by means of several single-sheave pulleys, or of one multiple-sheave pulley (three or four sheaves, as the case may be), they are brought down to within reaching distance of the stage floor. They can then be fastened, or "tied off", at a cleat that is firmly secured to the wall. It is

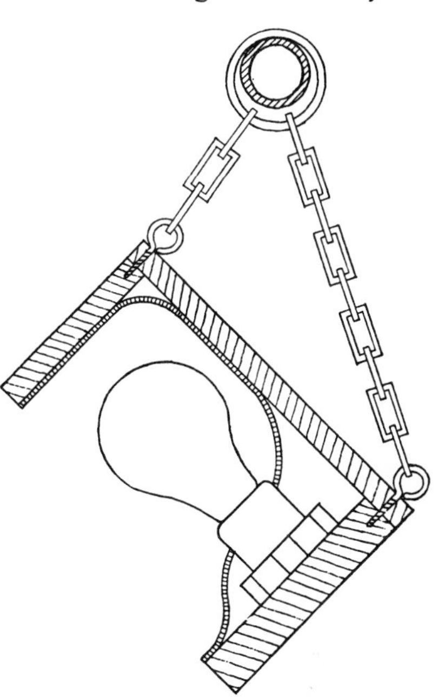

Open-trough borderlight, showing open-trough footlight adapted for use as borderlight, showing method of mounting on pipe batten. Quarter size.

highly desirable to provide a means for counterweighting each batten so installed. This can be accomplished by joining the lines (either by knotting them together or by the use of a "trimming block"), after they have passed through the second set of pulleys, and attaching them, as a unit, to sandbags or iron weights. Counterweight systems such as are used for "dumb-waiters", employing iron weights sliding up and down in a wooden runway, or guide, have been successfully used on amateur stages. They are relatively inexpensive (compared to the standard counterweight systems used on professional stages), and may be obtained through a local builder or contractor. Counterweights should be adjustable, that is, so arranged that weight may be readily added or removed in accordance with the weight of the equipment mounted on the batten. Hanging equipment should always be over-counterweighted; that is, the counterweight should be heavier than the batten and the equipment on it. This will assure ease of manipulation as well as safety. If it is not desirable or possible to provide means for raising or lowering the borderlight batten, it should be suspended at a height about two feet above the lower edge of the teaser, so that the borderlight, when it is in place, will be just out of sight of the spectators seated farthest front in the auditorium. If the stage ceiling is very low, the batten may be rigidly fastened directly to the ceiling by means of pipe fittings and short vertical pieces of pipe. What-

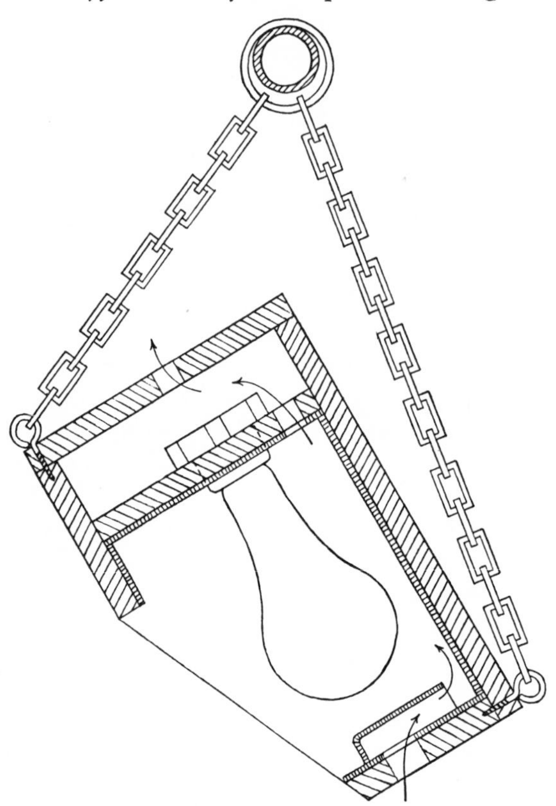

Compartment type borderlight, showing compartment type footlight adapted, with several necessary minor changes for use as borderlight, and showing method of mounting on pipe batten. Quarter size.

ever type of overhead mounting is adopted, the most important factors in its design and construction are strength and safety. It is really surprising to learn how great is the total weight of a batten loaded with borderlights and other pieces of lighting equipment. The weight can easily run into many hundreds of pounds. Every precaution, therefore, should be taken to make all installations of overhead mounting and counterweight systems safe to more than a reasonable degree. By these several general methods, then, provision can be made for mounting borderlights and other equipment, such as spotlights and olivettes, as well.

The open-trough footlight, as described previously, requires almost no changes in order to serve as a borderlight. The most convenient way to mount it to a 1″ pipe batten is as shown in the sketch on page 251. A large, solid, welded ring should be slipped over the batten (before the suspension lines have been fastened in place). To this ring can be fastened two short lengths of chain, which support the borderlight by means of the screw eyes screwed into the wood housing of the borderlight unit. These screw eyes and the chains should be sturdy enough safely to support the weight of the equipment. A set of chains should be used for each three feet of borderlight. Brace cleats, such as are used as hardware fittings on scenery "flats", may be screwed to the borderlight unit and used in place of the screw eyes. The most satisfactory angle of suspension of the borderlights can be determined by trial. If it is desired to leave the angle adjustable, the supporting chains may be left longer than necessary and an "S"-hook placed in the large ring on the batten. By hooking various links of the chain into the "S"-hook, it will be possible easily to adjust the angle of suspension of the borderlight unit.

But, except for very small stages, it will be necessary to provide an intensity of light from the borderlights of a higher possible maximum than the small lamps in the open-trough borderlight can supply. The compartment footlight, using lamps of larger sizes, can then be adapted to use as a borderlight in a manner similar to that described in the preceding paragraph. But several changes in design will have to be made. Because of the inverted position of the unit the direction of air flow will be reversed. Heated air rises and collects at the highest point of a confined space, such as the compartments in the borderlight unit. The ventilation holes, therefore, should be positioned with this fact taken into consideration. The sketch on the opposite page shows how this may be accomplished. Because of the inverted position, the color-frame grooves will have to be designed so that the color frame does not fall out, which obviously it would do if the same sort of grooves were used as were described for the compartment footlight. It should be carefully noted that, in the sketches, the outline of the front edge of the compartment partitions has been changed slightly to adapt itself to the changed conditions. The edge of the front shield is square instead of being at an angle, and the partition

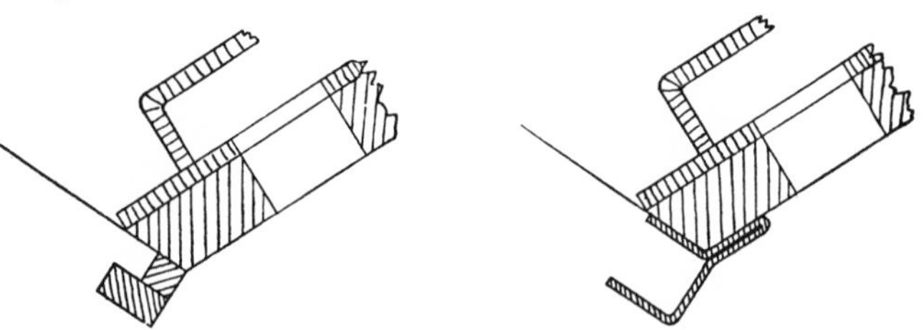

Showing details of bottom strip of color-frame slide grooves for compartment type borderlight in wood and in metal. Half size.

extends to the outer surface of the front shield instead of stopping at its inner surface. The above sketches show in detail how the bottom grooves of each compartment should be fashioned for the borderlight. The side grooves of each compartment can remain the same as in the footlight.

Just as in the case of the footlights, many modifications of these simple designs are possible — sheet metal as the construction material, different circuit arrangements, and so forth. Reflectors of the silvered metal or mirrored glass types as well as those of spun aluminum or porcelain-enameled steel are more to be recommended for use in borderlights than for use in footlights, as it is highly desirable that borderlights be subject to a fair degree of control of light direction and distribution. The control of light direction from borderlights can be adjusted by changing the angle of suspension as described above. Another way of making the suspension angle easily adjustable is to mount a stud screw in the end pieces of each borderlight unit, and mount the unit from those, using washers and wing nuts (as described for spotlights, see page 265). This will result in a sort of "rotating borderlight", whose light direction can be easily adjusted and controlled.

V. Striplights

Striplights should present no difficulties in either design or construction. They can be made very simple: a row of sockets mounted on a strip of wood will serve admirably. If desired, a back shield and end pieces may be added. Asbestos paper should be used, as with the footlights and borderlights. Striplights may be made in any lengths (2, 4, 6, or 8 feet are handy sizes) and may be provided with cable connectors for wiring purposes. Usually it is not necessary to provide more than two color circuits in striplights, as they are used mainly to supply some specific limited lighting effect

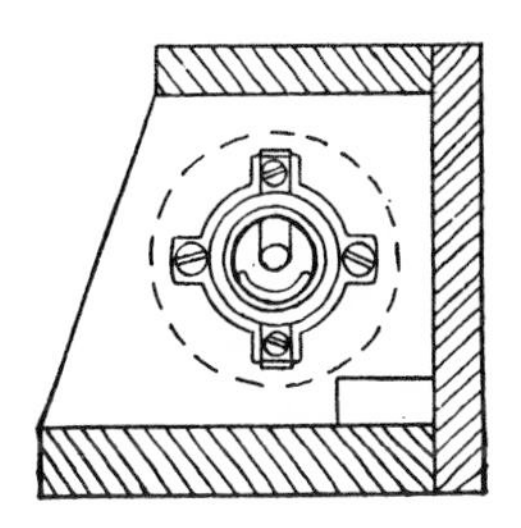

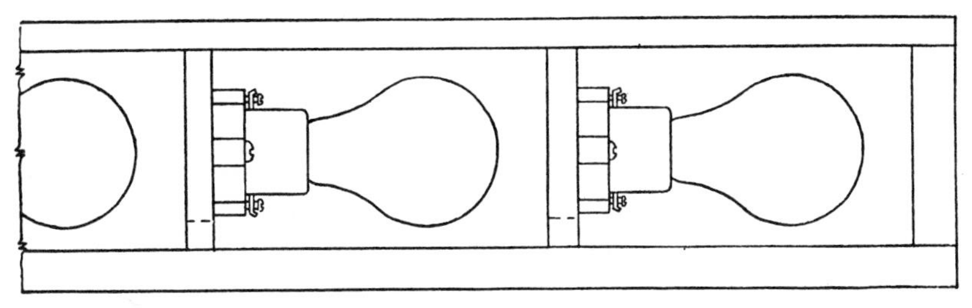

Portable striplight. Above: cross sectional view shows position of socket on compartment partition, and also the small open space in the lower right corner of the partition which allows the wiring to pass from compartment to compartment. Below: front view showing lamps and sockets in position. Asbestos lining is not shown. Quarter size.

for which the proper colored lamps (or, in the case of compartment striplights, the proper color frames) may be chosen and inserted in advance. However, if it is desired to make all the lighting equipment on any stage uniform in its color-circuit wiring, the striplights should be wired in conformity with the wiring of the footlights and borderlights.

Only one form of striplight need be specially commented on. This is the type shown in the above sketch. Its particular virtue lies in the narrow dimensions of its cross-section. This makes it possible to use it in a very restricted space, as, for example, vertically behind the narrow trunk of a tree, or, in a short length, for local lighting from behind a row of books on a desk, or from behind the front edge of a bed, or from behind the upper narrow wall of an alcove. It is also useful as a sort of portable footlight, which may simply be laid on the stage floor. Its design and construction should be carried out in the same general manner as those of the footlight and borderlight. Mounted vertically, by means of strap hinges, all forms of striplights can be used as adjustable proscenium striplights; mounted horizontally, they can serve as emergency borderlights.

VI. Spotlights

The design and construction of home-built spotlights involve a number of new basic considerations in addition to those that have already been touched upon in connection with the footlights and borderlights. Several new problems are introduced: in addition to ventilation and color modification there are the problems of designing an optical system of mounting the lens (and mirror, also, if desired), of providing a means for adjustable focus of the lamp, of designing a mounting for the entire spotlight, that will provide the universal movement so essential to the positioning of the spotlight and the aiming of its beam, as well as a host of minor problems.

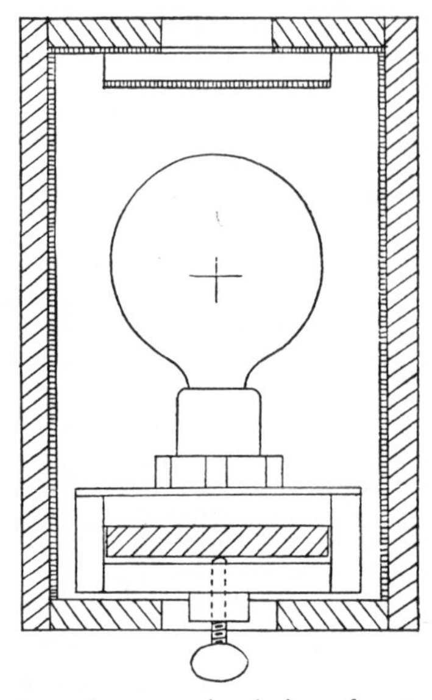

Lateral cross sectional view of spotlight showing lamp and socket mounting on lamp platform which is free to slide along the combination slide and ventilation baffle, the ventilation slot in the bottom and top and the top ventilation baffle. Asbestos lining is shown on the sides and top of the inner surface. Quarter size.

As with the design of any other equipment, the design of the spotlight should begin with the making of the lamp and lamp-in-socket templates, but including also, on the templates, the *exact* position of the light center of the lamp (this light-center length and other dimensions of the lamp can be obtained from the table on page 157). The design of the spotlight depends on both the light-center length and the external dimensions of the lamp chosen (which should be, of course, one of the regular concentrated filament spotlight lamps). The spotlight lamps can be classed in several major groups, according to their light-center length. It is wise, in designing a spotlight, to design its optical features for one of these standard light-center lengths, and simultaneously to design its other physical characteristics so that it can accommodate the largest lamp of any one group of lamps all having this same light-center length. In the accompanying sketches, for example, the design is based upon the use of the largest of the 3″-light-center-length group of lamps — the 400-watt

G–30 spotlight lamp. This design results in the so-called baby spotlight, which can accommodate the 100-watt P–25 and the 250-watt G–30 spotlight lamps as well as the 400-watt G–30 size. A smaller size of spotlight can be made for special purposes, accommodating only the 100-watt P–25 lamp. But the baby spotlight is the most useful size of spotlight for the amateur stage. Larger sizes, of course, may be necessary for long throws, from the balcony front, or from a ceiling beam, in the auditorium. The larger sizes

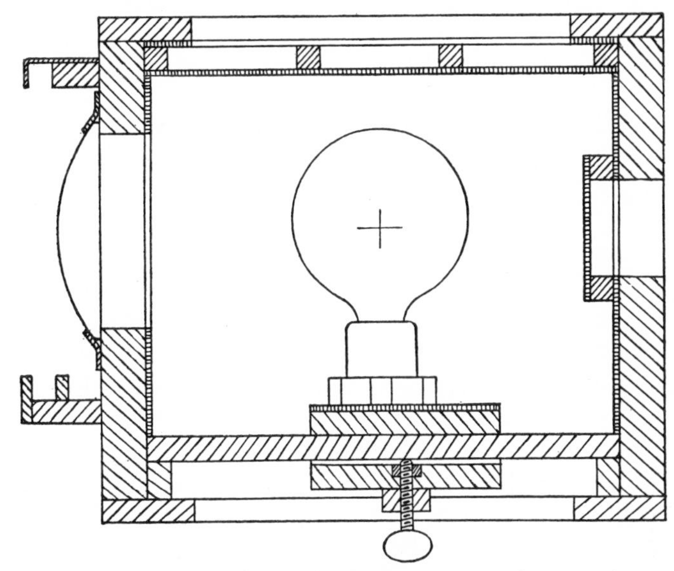

Longitudinal cross sectional view of spotlight showing spreaders for top and rear ventilation baffles and cleats for supporting combination slide and bottom ventilation baffle, also the method of using thumb screw for holding lamp platform in place. The lens opening is also shown with the lens held in position by small clamps. Two types of color frame slide grooves are shown. Quarter size.

of spotlight can be made just as easily as the baby size described below — it is only necessary to increase the dimensions sufficiently to accommodate the larger lamp and the longer light-center length.

The size of the lamp to be used determines the cross-sectional dimensions of the spotlight. The side walls of the spotlight should always be about 1″ or 1½″ distant from the lamp bulb, to provide space for air circulation. The focal length of the condenser lens to be used determines the length of the spotlight housing. If a spotlight is being designed for some special purpose — for a long projection distance, or perhaps to produce a particularly wide-angled beam — the proper condenser lens should be chosen with the help of the lens and beam angle tables on page 186. Perhaps the most useful size of lens for each of the principal sizes of spotlights is as follows:

Size of Spotlight	Size of Lens	
	Diameter	Focal Length
Footlight Baby	3½″ or 4½″	8″
Baby	4½″ or 5″	7″
Standard Small	5″ or 6″	10″
Standard Large	6″ or 8″	12″

Since a condenser lens produces its narrowest beam when the light source is at the focus of the lens, there is no virtue in making the housing of a spotlight any longer than is necessary to allow the lamp to slide back just far enough so that its filament reaches the lens focus, or slightly beyond. For all practical purposes, such as the present, this focus of the lens may be considered to lie along the optical axis of the lens (see discussion of lenses in Chapter IV) at a distance equal to the focal length, measured from the flat or "inside" surface of the lens. After the lens has been chosen it should be purchased before the design of the spotlight has been begun, as several important dimensions on the spotlight depend upon the exact thickness and diameter of the lens to be used. As pointed out in a previous paragraph, the lenses may be obtained from either an optical supply dealer or the larger dealers in stage-lighting equipment.

Wood 1″ thick should be used for the front and back face of the spotlight, and the top, sides, and bottom (of ½″ wood) should be screwed on to the edges of these faces. Thus the front and back faces will maintain the proper shape of the spotlight and also provide rigidity and strength. It is necessary that the socket be able to slide smoothly back and forth, with the lamp filament always on the optical axis of the lens, within the lamp housing. The socket, therefore, must be mounted on some sort of movable platform that can travel smoothly along the length of the spotlight and be fastened (from outside the spotlight) at any desired point in its traverse. The problem of projecting this fastening handle through a long open slot in the spotlight housing, without permitting the escape of light, is usually considered a difficult one. But, by employing a simple but ingenious "dodge", the problem can be easily solved, and half the ventilation problem solved at the same time. The accompanying sketches of the transverse and longitudinal sections of the spotlight show clearly how this can be accomplished. The lamp platform (with a thumbscrew for fastening) surrounds, and travels to and fro on, a wooden slide which simultaneously serves as a double wall, or baffle, for ventilation. The ventilation slot in the bottom of the housing also serves as the open space through which the

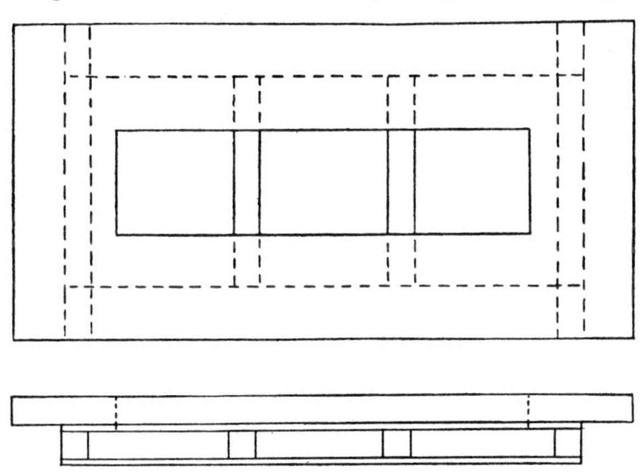

Plan and side views of top of spotlight showing ventilation slot, and positions of ventilation baffle and four spreaders to hold it in place. Quarter size.

fastening thumbscrew can project beyond the housing and in which it can slide back and forth with the lamp platform. And, in addition, light leakage is effectively eliminated.

A ventilation slot in the top of the spotlight, protected from light leakage by a baffle and spreaders, will make possible a free circulation of air from bottom to top of the spotlight when it is in a horizontal position. In order to provide for air circulation when the spotlight is aimed directly downwards, a square ventilation opening should be cut in the back face of the spotlight, centered directly behind the lamp, and equipped with a baffle and spreaders.

No elaborate mounting device for the lens is necessary. The circular lens opening in the front face of the spotlight should be slightly less (about $\frac{1}{4}''$) in diameter than the lens itself. The lens can then be held in place against the front face of the spotlight by means of three or four small, bent metal strips. As the lens opening will be slightly larger than the widest diameter of the lamp bulb, the spotlight can be relamped through the lens opening, merely by removing one of the lens clips and sliding the lens out of position. This is the simplest method of relamping, and allows the entire spotlight to be screwed tightly together, ensuring strength and rigidity. Unless there is no alternative, it is not wise for amateurs to attempt to provide their home-built equipment with access doors, as this will complicate the design unnecessarily, especially if wood is the construction material. If, however, a spherical backing mirror is to be used for the lamp, provision for adjusting it must be made. Perhaps the best way to do this is to leave the top piece of the spotlight entirely free and unattached, and held in place by several small hooks, or to hinge it to one side and provide a fastening hook on the other side. Color-frame grooves (that project far enough beyond the face of the spotlight to enable the color frame to clear the lens by about $\frac{1}{4}''$) can then be mounted on the front spotlight face.

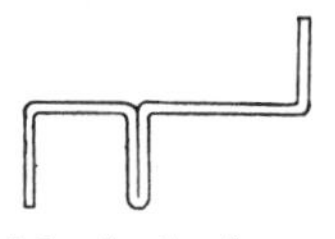

Metal color-frame groove for spotlight. Half size.

When the design has been completed, with all the details carefully worked out, construction can be begun by preparing the front face of the spotlight. The center of the lens opening should be carefully laid out — it should be on the optical axis, on a level with the lamp filament and its path of travel, and on the center line of the front face. The lens opening should then be marked out — it should be a bit smaller than the lens, in order to provide a narrow bearing surface against which the rim edge of the lens can be held in place. The opening can be cut with a narrow "keyhole saw", the cut being started by first boring a $\frac{3}{4}''$ hole inside the marked circle. The lens opening should be cut out very carefully, the cut being kept as closely to the inside of the marked circle as possible, and smoothed off first with a large half-round file and then with sandpaper. Then the back face should be prepared, with its ventilation opening.

Next, the combination slide and bottom ventilation baffle should be prepared, and also the two cleats upon which it rests at the front and back of the spotlight. These cleats (which should be equal in length to the width of the front and back faces of the spotlight) should then be screwed in place. Next, the lamp platform should be prepared. This, as is shown in the sketch, consists simply of four pieces of wood — upper, lower, and two sides — screwed together and equipped with a thumbscrew and nut. When the thumbscrew is tightened, the entire lamp platform will be held firmly in position on the combination "slide baffle." The thumbscrew should be $\frac{1}{4}''$ in diameter and $1\frac{1}{2}''$ long. The lamp platform should be carefully fitted to the slide baffle, and enough "play" allowed so that the platform can slide easily and smoothly, but without shifting from side to side (and hence throwing the lamp filament out of optical alignment). At the center point of the upper side of the lower piece, the thumbscrew nut should be embedded. This should be done by first boring a hole (equal in diameter to the diagonal of the nut) just deep enough to sink the nut level with the surface. Then, in the center of this wide hole, a small hole (equal in diameter to that of the thumbscrew) should be continued down through the remainder of the bottom piece and also through the small holding piece that has been previously screwed in place. The thumbscrew nut should be placed in the wide shallow hole and held in place and prevented from turning by the insertion of two $\frac{3}{4}''$ Number 6 flat-head wood screws close beside it (or, if desired, a square space to fit the nut exactly may be gouged with a chisel, instead of a round hole being bored to receive it). After the thumb-screw has been inserted from the bottom and found to work satisfactorily, the four pieces comprising the lamp platform may be screwed together, the top covered with asbestos, and the socket mounted exactly in place.

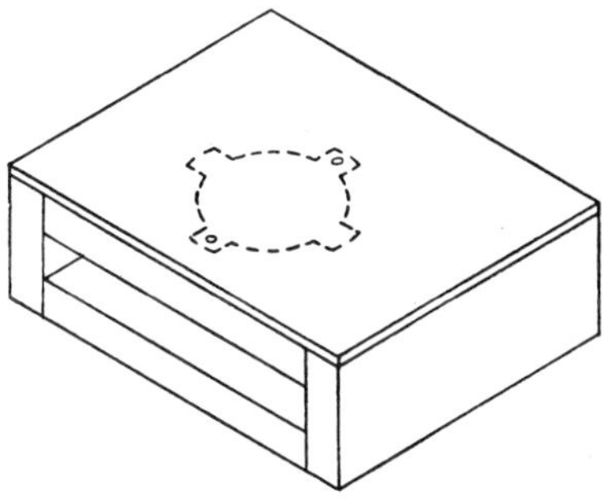

Isometric view of lamp platform with the position of the cleat socket, for holding the projection lamp, indicated by dotted outline. Quarter size.

At this point in the construction of the spotlight, the mounting of the mirror (if one is to be used) should be prepared. This mounting will require the use of metal strips, which must be bent and drilled. The mounting should be so designed that the spherical center of the mirror is coincident with the light center of the lamp. As it will be difficult for the amateur to construct any mounting that will maintain the mirror exactly in this desired position, a reasonable amount of adjustment must be allowed for. The use of a spherical backing mirror is, of course, very desirable, but unless the amateur is capable of building a mounting for it that will allow of such adjustment of position, the mirror had best be omitted. A spherical mirror out of optical alignment is a decided disadvantage, as it will act as a secondary light source and produce an overshadowed or distorted "spot" of light. The mirror, of course, should be mounted on the lamp platform, as its position in relation to the lamp must always remain constant. The mirror will, most likely, have to be obtained from a regular dealer in stage-lighting equipment. These spherical mirrors are available with an aluminum mounting.[1] This requires only a simple, bent, drilled strip of brass for fastening to the lamp platform. If an unmounted mirror is

[1] Perhaps the most convenient mirror for this purpose is that listed by the Universal Electric Stage Lighting Company in their catalogue as Number 926 (mounted) or 929 (unmounted). This is the $3\frac{3}{4}''$ size, suitable for baby spotlights. Two other sizes for use with larger lamps are also available in both mounted and unmounted forms.

used, it will be necessary to devise a more elaborate and intricate mounting. Both these conditions of mounting are illustrated and described in the two accompanying sketches. The homemade mounting occupies the greater space. This must be taken into consideration in planning the length of the spotlight. The lamp platform should also be long enough to reach the extreme limit of

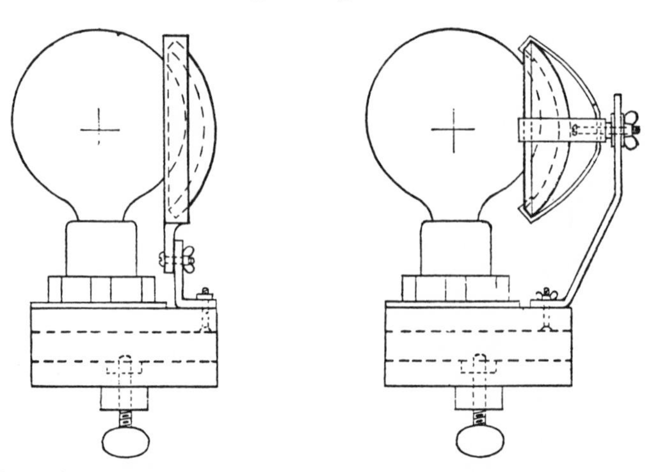

Left: method of mounting spherical mirror, with aluminum holder on lamp platform. Right: method of mounting spherical mirror, without aluminum holder on lamp platform by means of mirror holder prepared from bent copper strips, a machine screw washer and wing-nut. Quarter size.

its traverse (limited by the lower cleat on the back face) without allowing the mirror mounting to strike the back ventilation baffle and thus bend itself out of focus.

When the lamp platform with its mirror mounting (if any) has been completed, it should be slipped over the slide baffle, and the latter screwed to the front and back cleats on the face of the spotlight. It is highly important that the centers of the socket, of the lamp platform, of the front and back faces of the spotlight, and of the lens opening, be in exact alignment. To assure this, center lines should be marked on all the necessary wooden pieces when they are being prepared, and carefully matched when the pieces are screwed together.

Next, the bottom piece of the spotlight should be prepared and screwed in place. Then the asbestos lining should be applied to the front face, and also to the back face, along with the spreaders and the ventilation baffle. Then, the top piece, with its asbestos lining, spreaders, and baffle, as indicated in the separate sketch, should be prepared and screwed in place. If it is to be removable or hinged, it should be put in place only after the sides of the spotlight have been fastened on.

At this point in the construction, the exact method of mounting the spotlight must be decided upon. As previously stated, mounting accessories may be procured from the larger dealers in stage-lighting equipment. Thus, gooseneck studs (for bottom mounting)

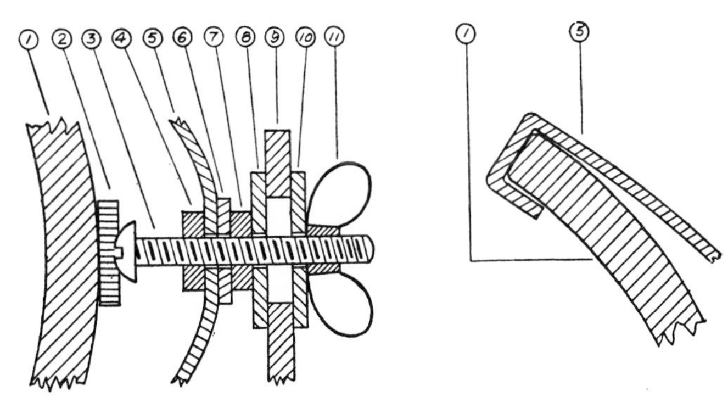

Detailed view of spherical-mirror holder. (1) is an abbreviated section of spherical mirror; (2) is a small piece of asbestos paper which prevents the mirror backing from becoming scratched; (3) is a round head machine screw; (4) and (7) are nuts to fit (3); (5) and (6) are the bent metal strips for clamping the mirror; (8) and (10) are metal washers; (9) is the upright, heavy metal strip which holds the entire mirror firmly to the lamp platform; and (11) is a wing nut for (3). After the parts have been procured and properly bent and drilled, they are assembled as follows: (4) is screwed all the way up on (3) which is then inserted through the center holes of (5) and (6). (5) and (6) are hooked over the edges of the mirror as shown by the sketch on the right. (2) is placed in position and (4) screwed forward on (3) until (5) and (6) become rigid and the mirror held firmly. (7) is then screwed up tightly against (6). (9) has previously been drilled with a hole (as shown) large enough to permit reasonable adjustment of the mirror position, and has been properly bent and firmly placed in position on the lamp platform. (8) is slipped over (3) and the combination (1 to 8) inserted through the adjustment hole of (9). (10) is slipped in place over (3) and (11) screwed down on (3) until the mirror and its improvised holder are held rigidly in position. Full size.

or straight studs (for side mounting) may be used in conjunction with wing nuts, leather washers, and swivel joints tapped for $\frac{1}{2}''$ pipe, for mounting the spotlight just described. But there is no reason why the amateur builder should not continue and complete his work himself, with his own improvised devices and by his own methods. This he can do perhaps most conveniently with a sort of "yoke" mounting, which can be made of wood (or, if desired, of a length of iron $\frac{1}{4}''$ thick and $1\frac{1}{2}''$ wide). The sketches explain its construction. The arms of the yoke should be of wood 2″ wide and $\frac{3}{4}''$ thick. The upper ends of these arms should be screwed into a crossbar 2″ wide and 1″ thick, and each joint strengthened with a heavy bent angle iron (3″ × 1″ is a good size). The lower ends of the arms should each be bored with a $\frac{1}{2}''$ hole through which a stud screw on each side of the spotlight can pass. Just how these stud screws (3″ × $\frac{3}{8}$″ bolts, with nut, wing out and four washers) can be attached to the side pieces of the spotlight is shown on the detailed full-sized, cross-sectional sketch. The point on the side pieces at which these stud screws are mounted should be about in the center of the spotlight, equidistant from the extreme corners of the spotlight (including the color-frame grooves). The entire yoke mount-

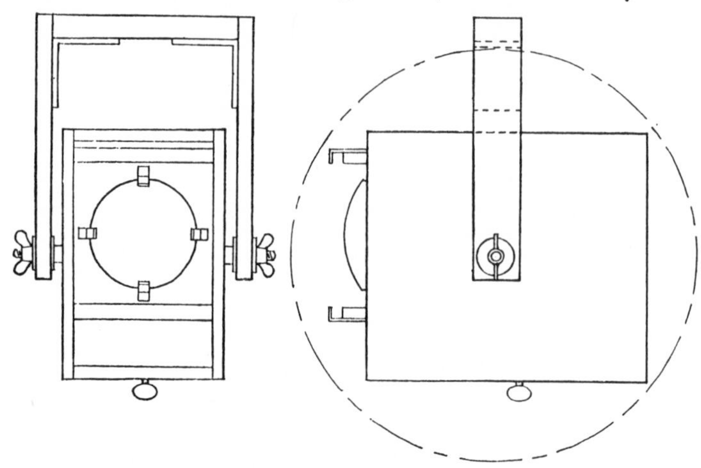

Left: front view of spotlight mounting in yoke. Right: side view of same showing the circle of swing described by the rotation of extreme corners of the spotlight and the necessity for making the yoke of proper size, if universal aiming of the spotlight is desired. One-eighth size.

ing must be so designed that (with its pipe mounting, discussed in a following paragraph) it will allow a complete revolution of the spotlight within its arms and crossbar.

When the side pieces of the spotlight have been prepared, with their asbestos linings and stud screws, the entire inside surface of the spotlight, except the mirror, of course (if there is one), should be given a coat or two of flat black paint. This is necessary because any white or unpainted space, inside the spotlight, would act as a secondary light source, to the detriment of the spotlight beam, and render difficult the proper control of the spotlight. Incidentally, the several ventilation baffles and their spreaders, the bottom combination slide baffle, and the lamp platform and socket, might well have been painted black before they were installed. Then the wiring should be done with *flexible* wire (untwisted heater cord is perhaps the most satisfactory). The wires may be brought out through holes in the rear face (allowance must be made for the extreme forward position of the lamp platform), or, loosely, through the back ventilation opening, and terminated in a male cable connector. The portion of the wires inside the spotlight should be painted black also. It is best that the wires be soldered to the socket terminals; then their twisting and turning, as the lamp platform moves back and forth, cannot loosen the screws and allow the wires to become disengaged.

When the wiring and painting have been completed, the sides of the spotlight (with the stud screws tightly in place) should be

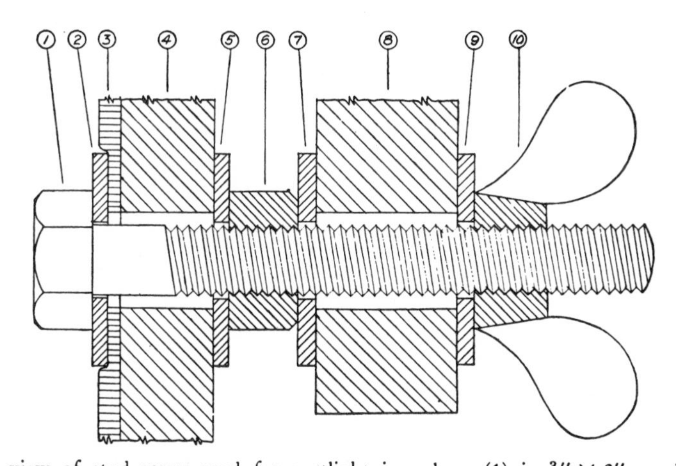

Detailed view of stud screw used for spotlight in yoke. (1) is $\frac{3}{8}'' \times 3''$ machine bolt. (2), (5), (7) and (9) are washers to slip loosely over (1). (3) is the asbestos lining of the spotlight. (4) is the side wall of the spotlight with a hole drilled, through which (1) passes. (6) is a nut to fit (1). (8) is the lower end of one of the side arms of the yoke, also drilled with a hole through which (1) passes. (10) is a wing nut to fit (1). The stud screw and yoke are fastened to the side of the spotlight in the following manner: After the hole has been drilled through (3) and (4) at the proper point, (2) is slipped over (1) and (1) inserted through the hole in (4). (5) is slipped over (1) and (6) screwed down until (1) is held firmly against (4). (7), (8) and (9) are then slipped over (1) and (10) screwed down on (1) until it is just tight enough to cause the spotlight to be held at the proper angle in the yoke and just loose enough so that the spotlight may be moved without loosening (10). Full size.

screwed in place, and the color grooves attached. These are shown in the sketch as being made of wood, or of wood and metal (the latter form is perhaps the most convenient). Or, if desired, the grooves may be made entirely of metal, as pictured on page 260.

Then the outside of the spotlight should be given a coat of black paint, the lamp screwed in the socket, and the lens carefully fastened in place by means of the small clips previously described. One $\frac{3}{4}''$ Number 5 round-head brass wood screw should be used for fastening each lens clip to the front face of the spotlight. The spotlight is then complete, except for its mounting.

If there is a special backing mirror in the spotlight, it should be properly focused. This can be most quickly and conveniently done in the following manner. The spotlight beam should be directed on to a white flat surface, at its minimum focus (that is, with the lamp farthest back in the housing, or with its filament at the focal point of the lens). At this position of the lamp, a crude, greatly enlarged image of the incandescent lamp filament will appear on the white surface. The spherical mirror should then be adjusted by moving it about until the position is found at which the "spot" appears brightest and sharpest and smallest. The adjusting screws should then be tightened to hold the mirror in exactly this position.

The yoke should then be attached to the spotlight. Obviously, the yoke cannot be fastened, in one piece, and at the same time, over both stud screws. This can be done only by *first* fastening one arm to the crossbar, and slipping it and the (unattached) remaining arm over the stud screws, and holding both arms in place with the washers and wing nuts, and *then* fastening the unattached arm to the crossbar. The yoke should also be given a coat of black paint.

With the yoke so mounted, the spotlight is ready for permanent mounting on any horizontal surface, such as the under side of a ceiling or beam, or on a shelf projecting from a wall or balcony front. It may be thus mounted simply by screwing, bolting, or clamping the crossbar firmly to the surface. The yoke itself should never be fastened in a horizontal position (unless it is made of strip iron, as suggested, or unless the joints between the crossbar and the two arms are heavily reinforced). But, although such a permanent mounting is useful and often necessary, it is essential that some sort of temporary or portable mounting be devised.

Again, for devising a portable mounting, it is possible to employ mounting accessories that may be obtained from dealers in stage-lighting equipment. Thus, pipe clamps, extension arms, swivel joints, and a variety of other fittings may be used for several different forms of portable mounting. But, again, it is also possible for the amateur to devise a fairly satisfactory means of portable mounting simply by using an arrangement of readily available material — short lengths of pipe, and various fittings for them, such as floor flanges, tees, elbows, bushings, and couplings. A type of mounting such as is discussed below is meant to be used with the pipe battens described on page 251.

The first requirement of all mounting equipment is, of course, absolute safety; beyond that, ease of positioning and aiming of the instrument. For use with pipe battens, it is necessary to provide any mounting device with some sort of clamp that will grip the pipe firmly and support the lighting unit. Several very good clamps are available which are very convenient, but a simple, though of course less convenient one may be devised by using a pipe tee large enough to slip over the pipe batten that is used. This tee can be held in place with a $\frac{1}{4}''$ thumbscrew, for which the tee has been drilled and tapped, as shown on page 268. The outlet of the tee can be used for inserting a length of pipe that, in turn, is fastened to the yoke mounting. For a 1″ pipe batten, a $1\frac{1}{4}''$ tee must be used. To accommodate the $\frac{1}{4}''$ thumbscrew, a hole $\frac{3}{16}''$ in diameter must be drilled through the wall of the tee, and threaded with a $\frac{1}{4}'' \times 20$ tap.[1]

For providing a connection between the tee (or regular pipe clamp, if one is used) and the yoke that holds the spotlight, $\frac{1}{2}''$ iron pipe is the most convenient size. It is necessary, then, that the outlet of the tee be threaded for this $\frac{1}{2}''$ pipe. If it is not possible to obtain such a tee ($1\frac{1}{4}'' \times \frac{1}{2}''$ is the trade designation) it will be necessary to use a "reducing bushing" that will give the correct reduction to $\frac{1}{2}''$ pipe thread. (A reducing bushing in use is drawn in the sketches). The $\frac{1}{2}''$ pipe can then be inserted and screwed into the tee.

It is more difficult to devise a suitable means of fastening the crossbar of the yoke to the other end of the $\frac{1}{2}''$ pipe. If the crossbar is to remain rigidly fixed to the pipe, it is an easy matter to screw or bolt a $\frac{1}{2}''$ floor flange to the crossbar and screw the pipe tightly into the flange. But the yoke should be free to revolve on the axis of the pipe. This could be accomplished by leaving the pipe connections loose, but this practice should be avoided; it is very unsafe (the yoke can easily turn off the pipe and fall from the batten to the stage), and it does not allow the yoke to be fastened at the desired position. However, a method such as is represented on the sketch will prove quite satisfactory. A hole ($\frac{7}{8}''$ in diameter) should be bored at the center of the yoke crossbar, just large enough to let the $\frac{1}{2}''$ pipe pass through. The end of this pipe should be threaded for a distance of about $2\frac{1}{4}''$ and a small hole (about $\frac{1}{8}''$) should be drilled through one wall of the pipe, close to the end. A $\frac{1}{2}''$ floor flange should then be turned up on the pipe (flat surface *down*) as far as the thread will allow, then the yoke crossbar slipped over the pipe, and then another $\frac{1}{2}''$ floor flange, screwed on the pipe (flat surface *up*) until it has passed the small hole previously drilled. In this small hole should be inserted a cotter pin, or bent nail, or several loops of wire — anything that will effectively prevent the lower flange from turning off the pipe and allowing the spotlight and yoke to fall to the ground. The lower flange should then be turned back until it is tight against this cotter pin or other obstruc-

[1] A tap is a tool for cutting screw threads in metal, to accommodate a machine screw or bolt. The "$\frac{1}{4}''$" denotes the diameter of the screw to be used; the "20" denotes the number of threads per inch.

tion. The $\frac{1}{2}''$ pipe may be very short (as short as 3″ if necessary) if it is desired to mount the spotlight as closely as possible under the batten, or it may be of any length desired. It should be screwed very tightly (with a Stillson wrench) into the tee that serves as the pipe clamp, so that it cannot be jarred loose. Then the spotlight can be turned to any position, and fastened there, simply by turning

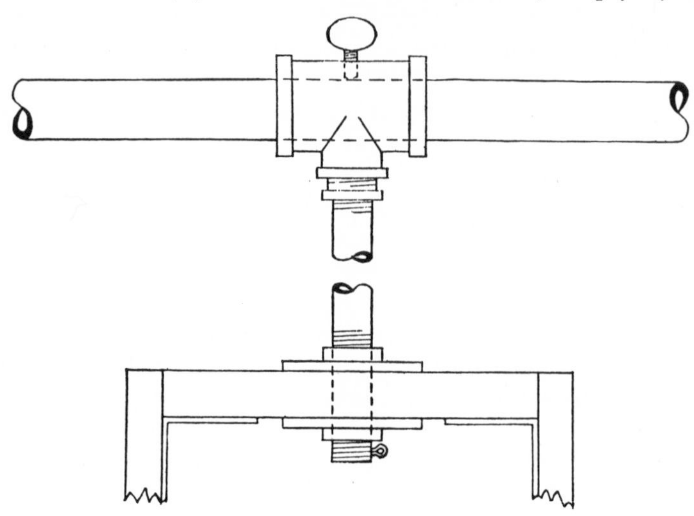

Suspension mounting for spotlight yoke, using ordinarily available pipe fittings in the manner described in the text. Quarter size.

down the upper flange until it bears tightly against the crossbar. Thus, with the yoke and the double-flange arrangement and the tee clamp, a mounting has been devised for the spotlight that provides the desirable, and, in fact, essential, universal action for aiming. And the entire mounting has been fashioned from materials and fittings that are available anywhere and that require but limited facilities for assembling them. The very small amount of absolutely necessary drilling and tapping, and pipe-cutting and threading, can be done by the local plumber or pipe fitter who supplies the pipe and fittings.

Of course, there is one obvious disadvantage in the use of the $1\frac{1}{4}''$ tee as a pipe clamp, and that is, it cannot be removed from the pipe batten without being slipped off the end. And this is manifestly impossible with pipe battens supported by lines, unless the clamp be mounted on the extreme end of the batten, beyond the end line. If the spotlight is to be removed from the batten, it is necessary, then, to unscrew the $\frac{1}{2}''$ pipe at the tee, or bushing. In order to provide for mounting spotlights and other lighting equipment on the batten, between the supporting lines, it will be necessary to keep several of these tees always on the batten, between each pair of lines. Thus they can be used whenever necessary. However, it is a question, in view of these disadvantages, whether it will not be more economical in the end (it will certainly be much more convenient) to purchase the regular pipe clamps for this purpose. They are available tapped for several sizes of pipe — for use as described above the $\frac{1}{2}''$ size should be ordered.[1]

The use of spotlights directly behind the edge of the tormentor is rapidly increasing as the advantages of directional lighting from this location are being realized. For this service, lighting units are mounted one above the other on a vertical pipe secured to the tormentor. The same size of pipe as is used for the battens (1″ pipe) will serve for the vertical tormentor mounting pipe. The wooden yokes should not be mounted in a horizontal position — the weight of the spotlight will likely prove too great for the joint between the crossbar and the arms of the yoke. Hence it will be necessary to interpose a $\frac{1}{2}''$ "ell" between the pipe clamp and the yoke, in order that the yoke may be suspended vertically. The sketch above shows how this is accomplished.

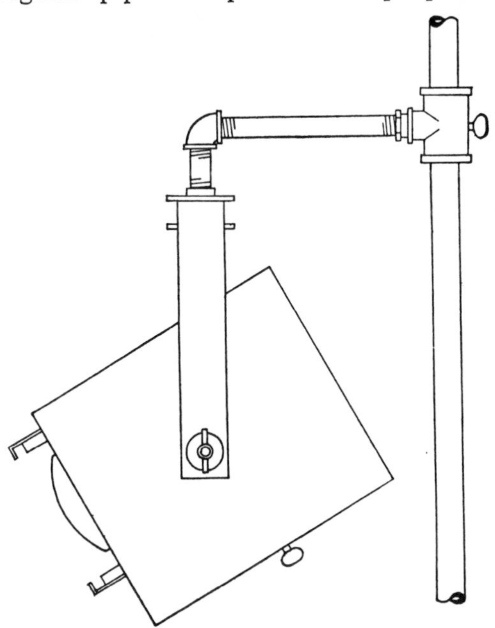

Method of mounting spotlight on vertical pipe for use in tormentor position, using ordinarily available pipe fittings in the manner described in the text. One-eighth size.

The type of mounting that still remains to be discussed is the pedestal mounting, for use of lighting equipment directly on the stage floor. The regular yoke mounting for the spotlight can be used, but the $\frac{1}{2}''$ pipe to which the yoke is fastened should be about three feet long. A base for the pedestal, about 14″ or 16″ square should be made of 1″ wood (or even thicker), and a hole just large

[1] Perhaps the least expensive and most convenient clamp to use for this purpose is that listed by the Display Stage Lighting Company in their catalogue as Number 3012.

enough to allow a 1″ pipe to pass through should be bored through its center. This hole should be about $1\frac{3}{8}$″ in diameter; an expansion bit should be used. A three-foot length of 1″ pipe should be threaded at both ends (for the usual distance at one end, and for about 3″ at the other end) and fastened to the base by means of two extra heavy 1″ floor flanges, in the manner indicated on the accom-

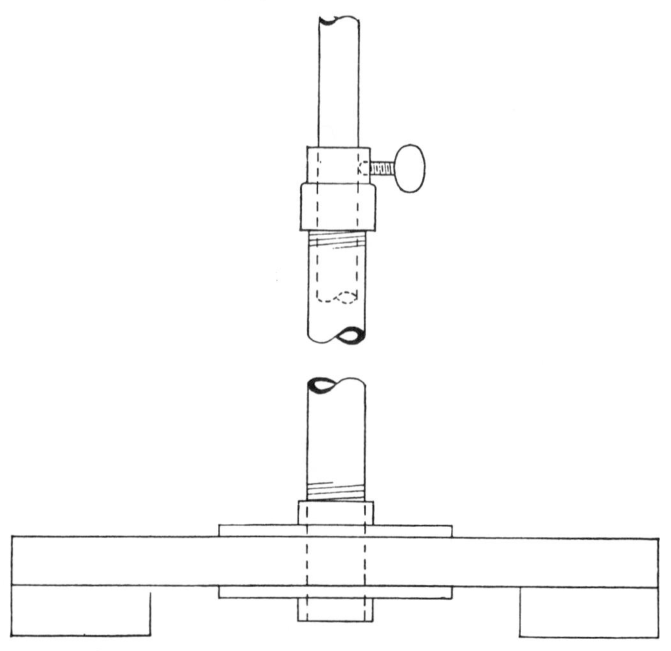

Pedestal mounting for portable equipment made from ordinarily available iron pipe and pipe fittings as described in the text. Quarter size.

panying sketch. The upper flange should first be fastened with wood screws to the base, then the long-threaded end of the 1″ pipe should be screwed into the flange until the pipe protrudes beneath the under side of the base a distance equal to the depth of the flange; then the lower flange should be screwed tight (with a Stillson wrench) against the base (while the main portion of the pipe, above the base, is prevented from turning with a second Stillson wrench). When the lower flange has been screwed in place as tightly as possible, it should be screwed to the base with wood screws. A 1″ × $\frac{3}{4}$″ "reducing coupling" (which has been drilled and tapped and equipped with a $\frac{1}{4}$″ thumbscrew as indicated on the sketch) should next be screwed tightly on to the upper end of the 1″ pipe. The $\frac{1}{2}$″ pipe, with the yoke and spotlight attached, may then be inserted within the 1″ pipe, and held in place at the desired height by tightening the thumbscrew in the reducing coupling. If the spotlight is to be used for "following" a character about the stage, a plain $\frac{3}{4}''$ coupling should be drilled and tapped and equipped with a $\frac{1}{4}''$ thumbscrew and slipped over the $\frac{1}{2}''$ pipe before the latter is inserted in the 1″ pipe on the base. This coupling will serve as a collar which may be tightened against the $\frac{1}{2}''$ pipe at the desired position. Thus the spotlight can be held at the desired height while it can be revolved about the axis of the pipe (with the thumbscrew on the reducing coupling loosened to allow the $\frac{1}{2}''$ pipe to turn freely). By equipping the wooden base with one or two bent foot irons or brace cleats (such as are used on scenery "flats") the entire spotlight and mounting may be fastened firmly to the stage floor with the regular stage screws. If the pedestal mounting seems a bit light, or top-heavy (especially when the spotlight is extended to its maximum height), heavy pieces of lead or iron may be fastened to the base in order to weight it down. Thus may a practicable telescoping pedestal mounting be easily constructed from simple, readily available materials.

With the foregoing fundamental suggestions on various types of mounting in mind, the amateur builder of stage-lighting equipment can devise many different combinations of clamps, fittings, yokes, and so forth, to achieve almost any kind of mounting necessary. The several methods of mounting described above can be applied, of course, to many types of equipment other than spotlights.

It must be borne in mind that the nominal size of iron pipe, as quoted above, is for convenience as a size designation only, and bears no relation to the actual dimensions of the pipe diameter, either inside or outside. As this erratic system of size designation almost always proves confusing to the amateur, the following table of dimensions and composite diagram of sizes are presented:

DIMENSIONS OF IRON PIPE

Nominal Size Designation	Actual Diameter (in inches)	
	Inside	Outside
$\frac{1}{2}''$	.623	.840
$\frac{3}{4}''$	.824	1.050
1″	1.048	1.315
$1\frac{1}{4}''$	1.380	1.660

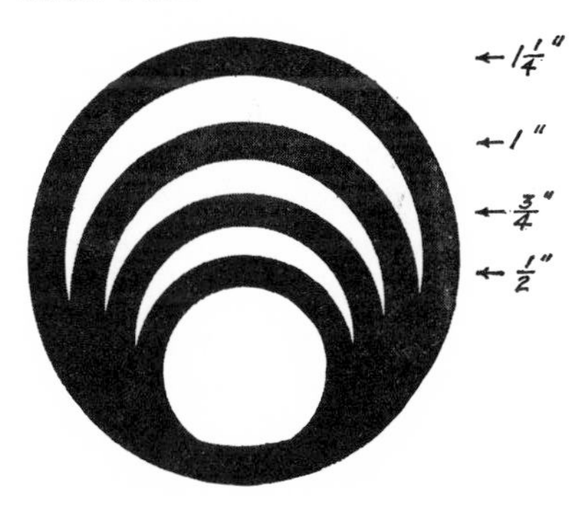

VII. Olivettes

Contrasted with the detailed and somewhat involved design and construction of home-built spotlights and mounting devices, the method of planning and building an olivette is a relatively simple and easy matter. An olivette is essentially an open box with a lamp in it. But even so, proper attention must be given to details of ventilation and mounting. An olivette may be of any size

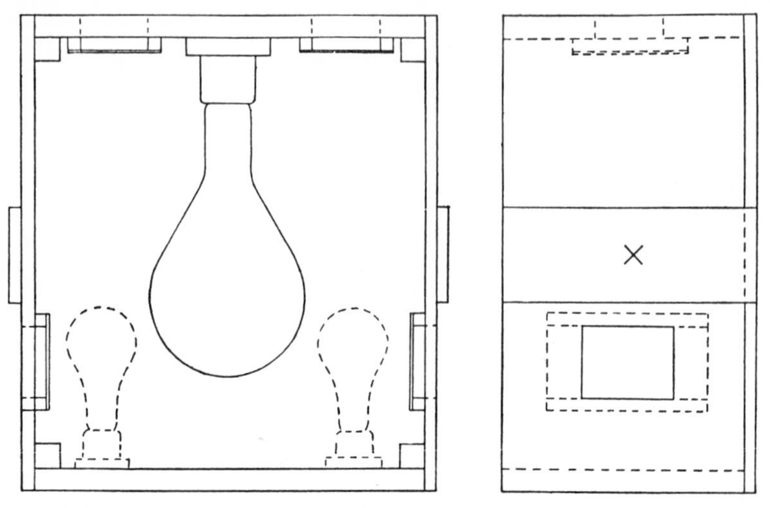

Front and side views of olivette, showing mogul cleat sockets and 1000-watt PS–52 incandescent lamp, various ventilation openings with spreaders and baffles and inside corner cleats and outer side cleats for rigidity. Asbestos lining and color-frame slide grooves not shown. The cross indicates the center of the side stud screw for properly balanced yoke mounting. The dotted outlines in the front view show positions of supplementary 100-watt A–23 lamps which make a "combination" olivette. One-eighth size.

desired, depending principally upon the size of lamp to be used (or, if in the form of the old type of bunch light, upon the size and number of lamps to be used). But it should never exceed 18″ × 20″ in its outside front dimensions, as this is the size of the color frame that accommodates the largest available sheet of gelatin color media. Olivettes (using a single large lamp) should be deep enough to keep the lamp at least two inches from the gelatin color media, as many grades of gelatin will fade and discolor rapidly from the heat of the lamp (in a spot directly opposite the lamp filament) if they are placed too close to the lamp bulb. This fading of gelatin can be avoided to a large extent if sufficient ventilation is provided in the olivette housing — at least a square inch (both for the inlet and for the outlet for the cooling air current) for every 100 watts consumed by the lamp or lamps within the housing. Ventilation openings, similar to those described for the spotlight, with baffles and spreaders, should be cut in the olivette housing at such points that a free passage of air will be assured for all the usual positions in which the olivette will be placed when in use. The sketch shows two ventilation openings in the top, and two on each side. In addition to these, another opening had better be cut in the back wall (similar to those in the sides, and positioned directly opposite the lamp filament), especially if the olivette is to be used much in the face-down position.

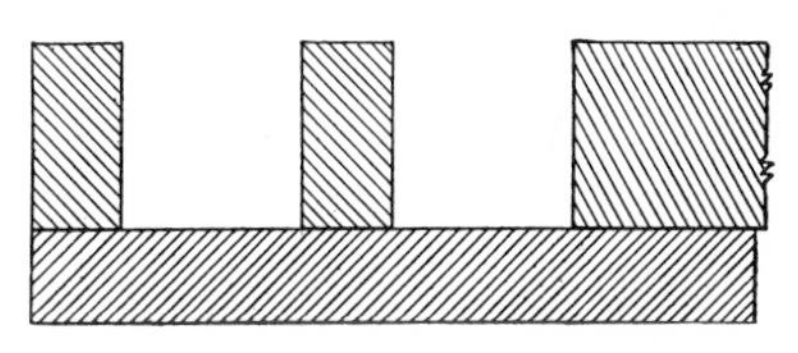

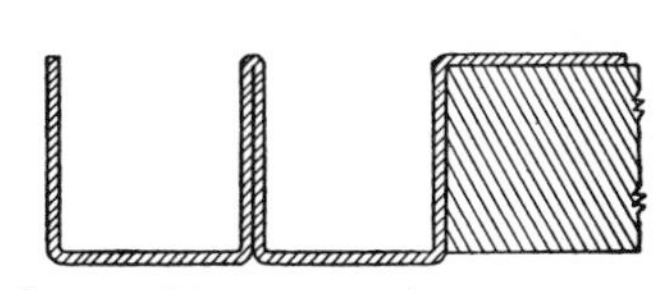

Color-frame slide grooves in wood and metal for use at top and bottom front edges of olivette. Half size.

Wood ½″ thick can be used for the sides and back of the olivette, and 1″ thick for the top and bottom, and 1″ × 1″ cleats used in each corner to strengthen the joints. For mounting the olivette, a yoke can be used similar in all respects to that described for the spotlight, but, of course, correspondingly larger. For a 1000-watt olivette the arms and crossbar of the yoke should be 3″ wide instead of 2″. The stud screws should be mounted through the walls of the olivette, and the points of support strengthened by screwing a ½″ piece of wood (several inches wide) tightly against each side of the olivette. The same methods of mounting—on horizontal battens, on vertical tormentor pipes, and on telescoping pedestal standards — as were described in previous paragraphs are equally applicable to olivettes.

Color grooves can be easily fashioned and applied to the upper and lower edges of the olivette openings. They may be made of either wood or metal, as shown in the above sketches. The grooves should be an inch wide, as the wood color frames such as are commonly used with the larger olivettes are about ¾″ thick. It is well to provide double grooves, in order that two color frames may be used simultaneously.

As with the footlights, the borderlights, and the spotlight previously described, the olivette should be lined with asbestos paper. This should be given a coat or two of flat white diffusely reflecting paint.

The wiring is very simple. For lamps 300 watts and over in size, mogul sockets will have to be used. These are also available in several types, similar to those in the medium size. If the sockets used have exposed contacts, these contacts should be covered with a layer of asbestos or other insulating material. Flexible asbestos-covered wire of the proper size should be used, and brought through the top of the olivette and terminated in a male cable connector. Each wire should be left a little slack, inside the olivette, and knotted just before it is brought through the housing. This will prevent any strain on the wires from tearing the wires loose from the contact screws of the socket.

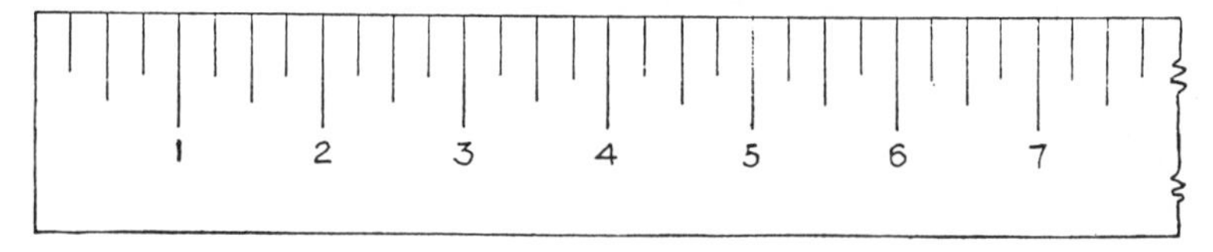

Half size scale.

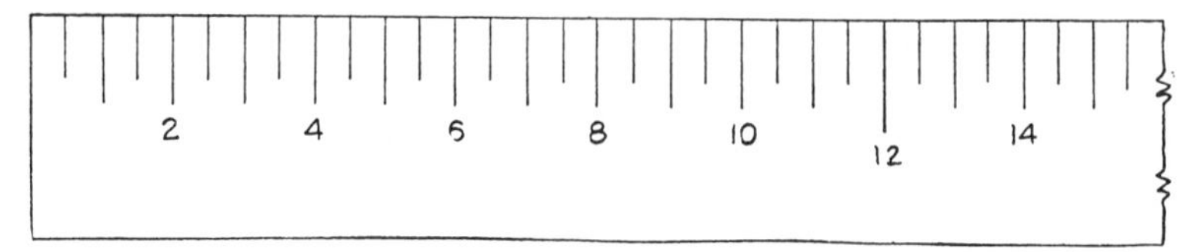

Quarter size scale.

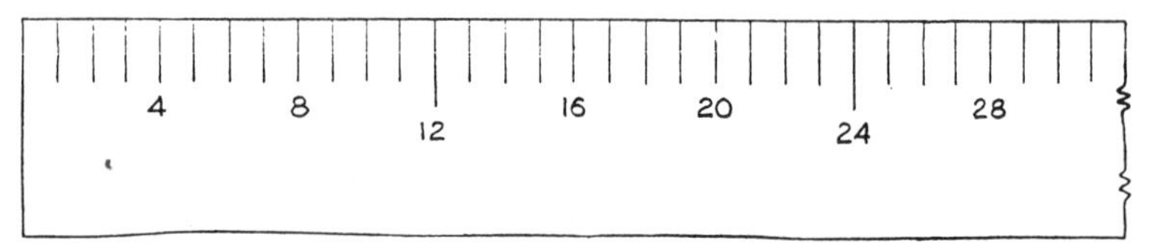

One-eighth size scale.

Three scales by which exact dimensions may be read directly from the sketches in this chapter. The numbers represent inch values.

As indicated by dotted lines on the sketch, a sort of combination olivette may be made simply by mounting two medium base sockets on the bottom of the olivette and wiring them on a separate circuit, with a separate male cable connector. These can be used, instead of the large lamp on a dimmer, if a low intensity of light is wanted. A *bunch light* may be made by mounting five medium sockets on each side wall of the olivette instead of the single mogul socket at the top. This will permit the use of lamps up to 100 watts in size in each socket. The ten sockets should be wired together on one circuit (or, if the olivette is to be used on a small stage, and color-dipped or natural-colored glass bulb lamps are to be used in place of gelatin color media, the German practice of wiring bunch lights for several color circuits may be adopted). Instead of the sockets being mounted on the side walls, they may be mounted on both sides of a $\frac{1}{2}'' \times 3''$ strip of wood placed vertically within the housing, extending from top to bottom.

With the above descriptions and sketches and recommendations (both positive and negative) as a basis, it should not be a difficult task for the amateur stage worker to design and construct a fairly complete and satisfactory set of stage-lighting equipment for his stage. Of course, it is not to be expected that his product will have the ruggedness, or the ease and flexibility of manipulation, or the compactness and the finished, professional appearance of the better grade of commercially available equipment. But, on the other hand, unless his work has been badly done, his home-built equipment should compare *not unfavorably* with professional equipment in the matter of accomplishment — of actual results produced. And, what is perhaps most significant to the amateur with a limited budget for stage-lighting work, it will compare *very favorably* in the matter of expense.

CHAPTER VIII · STAGE-LIGHTING CONTROL

The meaning of control; classification of control systems – permanent, flexible, portable; wiring; switchboard – switches, dimmers, magazine panel, assembly, some desirable features of switchboard design and construction, brief descriptions of several of the outstanding makes of stage switchboards; European control equipment; design and construction of home-built control equipment for amateur use — wiring, dimmers, switchboards.

IN order to achieve effective stage lighting, the mechanism for the *control* of a set of stage-lighting instruments is at least equally as important as the instruments themselves. Without some fairly adequate means of control, the effectiveness and range of usefulness of even the most complete and most modern and carefully designed set of lighting instruments will be very greatly restricted. The physical nature of lighting instruments is such as to allow the use of several means of control over the results that the instruments can produce. Thus, mechanical means, optical means, and electrical means are usually used in conjunction with each other for controlling, directly, the light emitted by each instrument, and hence, indirectly, the resultant effect that this emitted light produces. In previous chapters, the possibilities of some phases of each of these means of light control have been indicated. The present chapter will be devoted to a short discussion of the ultimate possibilities, and the ideal, the most desirable, characteristics of control; a description of available control devices and present control practice; and an indication of the extent to which existing control equipment has succeeded in making ideal control conditions a reality.

I. The Meaning of Control

Before the practical phases of control are dealt with, it will be necessary to inquire just what is meant by "control", especially in its broader sense. The several factors that enter into control, and the results which an ideal control would achieve, must first be pointed out in order to establish a standard, by comparison with which existing control devices and systems can be properly evaluated. *Intensity*, *quality*, and *color* of light are undoubtedly the more obvious and important attributes of projected, or emitted, light which must be under control. In addition, the attributes of the resultant of projected light (from a single stage-lighting instrument, or from a group of instruments operating as a unit), principally *distribution* (or form, or pattern, as it might be called) and *position*, also require control. A thorough control of light for the purposes of stage lighting would include the control not only of the intensity of the projected light (which, in many discussions of stage-lighting control, is often considered alone, to the exclusion of the other important attributes of light), but also its quality and color, and the distribution and position of the resultant light-area. By *intensity* is meant, of course, the degree of brightness (see page 88); by *quality*, the degree of diffusion; by *color*, the dominant hue and the degree of saturation (see page 133). By *distribution* is meant the shape, the outline of the lighted area projected by the instrument, and the pattern, the arrangement (if any) of light intensity, of light and shade, as well as of color, within this outline. By *position* is meant simply the location of the lighted area in relation to the spectator's (fixed) field of view. All these factors of control apply to each individual lighting instrument, or to each unit group of lighting instruments, used to light a production. A complete, though very awkward, definition of stage-lighting control, as applied to each lighting instrument or unit group of lighting instruments, might be as follows: the power of directing, at will, individually and collectively, and within the limits necessitated by the conditions of stagecraft, the five attributes of the light — of directing their changes and variations and the method and sequence and rate of change — projected by each instrument or unit group of instruments.

A few examples of the present rather limited means available for each of the five separate factors of stage-lighting control will serve to clarify somewhat this rather broad, inclusive idea of control. For example, the desired *intensity* of light from any instrument may be achieved mechanically by the proper choice of size and number of incandescent lamps, or optically by the use of shutters or masks that absorb part of the emitted light, or electrically by the proper arrangement of wiring, switches, and dimmers. Although the first two methods afford only a crude control of intensity, more than once on the stage has a scene been darkened or brightened by an operator removing or inserting lamps in lighting equipment, and still more often are special shutters and opaque screens placed or moved across the mouths of lighting equipment in order to control light intensity. The "soft-edge" spotlight, for example, lends itself admirably to such a manual control method. But the third method of intensity control, that of wiring, switches, and dimmers, is by far the most suitable of all and, in fact, has been developed to such a degree that it is infinitely advanced over the control methods yet devised for the four other controllable attributes of light. The *electrical method of intensity control* constitutes the greatest proportion of what is to-day commonly known as "stage-lighting control."

The desired *quality* of light from any instrument may be achieved by a proper choice of lamp, of reflecting surface, and of diffusing media. Light from frosted lamps will, of course, be more diffused in quality than that from clear lamps. The effect of various reflecting surfaces on light quality is best shown by the pictures on page 78. Frosted gelatin as a diffusing medium is commonly used in the color-frame slide grooves of stage-lighting equipment for providing a "softer" quality of light. Some lighting instruments lend themselves more readily than others to the control of light quality. For example, the "soft-edge" tormentor hood (page 191) gives a slightly more diffused beam of light when the beam is adjusted for narrow focus than when it is adjusted for wide focus, and the combination direct and indirect footlight (page 169) can be adjusted to provide light of any desired quality.

The desired *color* of light from any instrument may be achieved by methods that are discussed in detail in the following chapter — by the choice of proper color media (glass, gelatin, and so forth), which "modify" the light from the instrument. Devices such as the color wheel and color boomerang are accessories that might be regarded as the first step in the simplification of color control. A practical and fairly satisfactory method of color control is that which involves graded mixtures of light of several colors (in the better systems the three primary colors of light — red, green, and blue — in conjunction with clear, unmodified light are used), each from an individual light source or instrument, or from a group of light sources or instruments operating as a unit. Footlights, borderlights, and cyclorama lighting instruments, that are wired in several color circuits, furnish convenient examples of the *graded-mixture method of color control.* Of course, in order to achieve the desired color mixture, some method of intensity control (preferably the electrical method), for the light sources of each constituent color must be used.

The problem of achieving the desired *distribution* of light (bearing in mind the definition of distribution given in a previous paragraph) from a single instrument is a most difficult and involved one. This is evidenced by the fact that, for any production, an appreciable number of instruments is usually necessary to achieve the desired distribution of light over the stage space. By means of accessories such as opaque masks, mats, shutters, flippers, blinders, iris diaphragms, and louvers (page 206), it is possible to achieve some small degree of control over the distribution of light emitted by various types of instruments. Little or no control is possible over the distribution of indirect, or diffused, light. The reflectors, or lenses, or both, used in any stage-lighting instrument, are responsible for the inherent distribution characteristics of the instrument. By altering the reflectors or lenses, or replacing them with others, the desired distribution of light from the instrument can sometimes be achieved. For this purpose, black paint is often applied to portions of the reflecting surfaces of various types used in stage-lighting instruments. The relative positions of light source, reflector, lens, and other appurtenances also affect light distribution — for example, the focussing adjustment possible with spotlights, tormentor hoods, and similar equipment. By means of several special devices, it is possible to achieve a predetermined, *fixed* distribution of light from a single instrument. For example, the Linnebach lantern (page 198), with its painted glass slide, and the stereopticon, with its photographed or painted "lantern slide", can both produce a lighted area of any size and shape, and of any composition or arrangement of light, shade, and color within the outlines of this area. The sciopticon (page 192), with its painted or photographed revolving effect-disc, and other appurtenances, is an extension of the stereopticon principle, and makes possible a predetermined, *changing* distribution of light, and introduces the element of *movement within* the lighted area. Although mention of it may seem incongruous in connection with stage lighting, yet the fact is that the motion-picture machine is the most highly specialized and developed instrument for providing a changing, or moving, light distribution that is subject to predetermined control, and should find a wider field of use for legitimate purposes of stage lighting than it occupies at present. The motion-picture machine has been used, in a few rare instances, for the purposes of stage lighting, with varying degrees of success. Unfortunately, however, its use has been restricted to the achievement of ultra-realistic effects, which constitutes only the most primitive of its vast possibilities in the service of stage lighting.

To achieve the *position* of the lighted area produced by any instrument is a comparatively simple problem, almost wholly mechanical in nature. Its solution depends upon the location of the instrument in relation to the stage, and the mounting device employed. Of course, in all this discussion of control, it is assumed that the instruments remain in fixed locations. With a universal-direction mounting device, the instrument can be aimed in any direction, and the position of the lighted area produced by the instrument changed at will by the operator. Such change of position constitutes *movement of* the lighted area (or, from the point of view of the *entire stage space*, if a number of instruments are employed, *movement within* the stage space — change of light distribution within the stage space). Thus, two types of *movement* are possible: *movement of* the lighted area produced by an instrument, and *movement within* the area. The latter consists of change of distribution and was discussed in the previous paragraph.

These several attributes of light, and the available means for exercising some degree of control over them, have been discussed chiefly to indicate the fine extent to which light can and should be controlled for the purposes of stage lighting, and also to point out how comparatively limited are the means now available for so controlling it. In the case of each of the attributes of light, some degree of control is possible, but, except for what have been termed the "electrical method of intensity control", and "the graded-mixture method of color control", this control is a greatly restricted one. *Predetermined* control is nearly always possible: lighting equipment may be so adjusted, *in advance*, as to produce light of the desired quality; or a Linnebach lantern or a sciopticon may be equipped with the proper slides, effect-discs, or other accessories that will provide the desired distribution; or a lighting instrument may be carefully adjusted, in advance, to provide light in the desired position. But true control would allow the adjustment of instruments, in any desired manner, during the course of their operation: this might be termed *improvised control*, in contrast to the restricted *predetermined control*. Improvised control of intensity and color is possible, to an appreciable extent, by the electrical method, and by the graded-mixture method, respectively. But improvised control of quality and distribution is, except to a slight extent, virtually impossible. Improvised control of position is possible, of course, by providing each instrument with a suitable universal mounting device and a separate operator. But such a method is awkward and expensive. Incidentally, it gives rise to the important question of centralization of control.

Whatever control is possible, over the intensity, color, quality, distribution, and position of the light projected by any instrument, can only be carried out by an operator stationed at the instrument, except in the two cases noted before, namely, the electrical method of intensity control, and the graded-mixture method of color control. By means of these two methods, the intensity and color of the light from all the instruments (or unit groups of instruments) used to light a production may be controlled from a central point, and — if the apparatus, the machinery of control is well arranged — by a single operator. This sort of control is known as *centralized control.* Control that is achieved by stationing an operator at each instrument might be termed *isolated*, or *decentralized*, *control.* The latter was extensively used during the period when the limelight flourished in the theatre, and must still be used to-day where electric-arc lighting equipment is used. Existing conditions in regard to the theatre in general, and stage-lighting practice in particular, make centralized control of stage lighting by far the more satisfactory. Centralized control of intensity and color has been shown to be possible to an appreciable and fairly satisfactory extent. But centralized control of quality, distribution, and position is virtually impossible, and should be the ultimate objective toward which future improvements and developments in stage-lighting control are directed.

The apparatus, the machinery, by which centralized control is made possible is often, and not illogically, compared to the delicate system of motor nerves in the human body, which, emanating from the brain as a central point of control, directs, and unifies, and synchronizes the actions of the component parts of the entire body. Centralized control of stage lighting is also often compared to the control system of a large organ, which places the direct control of the entire huge instrument in the organist seated at the console or keyboard — the delicate, centralized mechanism which gives the organist complete control over each of the organ's multitudinous parts and which is so arranged as to enable him to blend and unify and synchronize (in any manner he may choose) the sounds produced by these constituent parts, all of which are comparatively remote from the keyboard or "control board." This comparison between the control of light and the control of sound may be extended: despite the fact that light is a wave motion of the *ether*, and sound a wave motion of the *air*, several analogies may be found between the attributes of both. Thus, intensity of light may be compared to *loudness* of sound, color of light to *pitch* of sound, and quality of light to *timbre* of sound. For distribution and position of light there seem to be no analogous attributes of sound, unless a blending, or combination of sounds — a chord, perhaps — from a musical instrument, can be considered analogous to the distribution of light.

Perhaps a more just and logical comparison between the control of stage lighting and the control of musical sounds would use as its object of comparison not the organ (which, after all, is only a single instrument, with its own peculiar properties and limitations), but rather the symphony orchestra. Here the analogy to stage lighting is closer: a comparatively large number of separate instruments of various types and capabilities are used, just as with stage lighting. But instead of all these instruments being under the *direct*, *centralized* control of one individual (as seems to have proved the better method with stage lighting), each of the instruments is under the *direct* control of a musician, its own "operator", and, through him, under the *centralized* control of the orchestral conductor. Perhaps the present tendency toward centralized *one-man* control of stage lighting, which seems to be leading to increasingly elaborate and involved and complicated control machinery that bids fair to defeat its own purposes, will prove no more logical or successful than would an attempt to eliminate the individual musicians and to place direct control of all the instruments of a symphony orchestra directly in the hands of the conductor. Perhaps the future will see stage lighting carried out by an appreciable corps of "light-musicians", each of whom is thoroughly familiar with, and a highly expert operator of, his own particular lighting instrument, or limited unit-group of lighting instruments, and all of whom serve as intelligent, artistic (not merely mechanical) media through which the unifying, coördinating, *centralized* control of the "lighting conductor" is exercised. The most notable of the recent advances in this direction was the method of control used for lighting the huge spectacle produced by Max Reinhardt — "The Miracle." For this production an appreciable number of lighting operators was used. Each had one or more lighting instruments under his direct control, which he operated in accordance with a carefully planned cue sheet, or "light score", under the centralized control of the "lighting conductor" in the person of the chief electrician. The chief electrician seated at a desk with the master cue sheets and script before him, conducted the entire lighting of the production by keeping in constant telephonic communication with his operators. Several of these operators, however, operated control apparatus from a remote point, in a room hidden from the action of the play; unaware of the effects they were creating, they followed exactly, though blindly, the instructions transmitted to them by the chief electrician. Thus, they functioned in a purely mechanical manner, and not as individual artists contributing to the ensemble effect. Nevertheless, the system of stage-lighting control used in "The Miracle" represented an interesting and significant forward step in control methods.

For the present, however, conditions of even the most advanced stage-lighting practice do not require light control as intricate or as elaborate as the highly coördinated and organized sound control exercised by the conductor of an orchestra. Unfortunately, most operators are primarily mechanicians, not artists; in comparison to music, the art of light is in a disorganized state and still awaits that influence of conventionalization which makes for universal understanding and acceptance of its principles and methods, and affords a basis for the appreciation and comparison of results; stage-lighting instruments are still in a state of comparative crudity; and play production costs, and hence the number of stage-lighting operators, must be kept at a minimum. For these and other reasons, it is perhaps most desirable, from all points of view, that the control of stage lighting, at least for the usual type of play production, be centralized, and centralized *directly* in one person, in so far as possible. Present conditions do not make feasible a type of control analogous to that of a symphony orchestra. Perhaps this may prove a development of the future.

It has been shown that, of the control of the five attributes of light — intensity, quality, color, distribution, and position — only the electrical method of intensity control and the graded-mixture method of color control are susceptible to the all-important feature of centralization. Upon closer examination, as explained previously, even the latter of these two methods resolves itself, fundamentally, into the former. Of all the factors of control, then, there is available to the stage artist, fundamentally but one, at least in centralized form; namely, intensity control, by the electrical method. So as far as the actual equipment — the machinery — for control is concerned, intensity control is fundamental: color control is more or less incidental.

A definition of stage-lighting control — the true meaning of the ideal, ultimate control — was advanced in a previous paragraph. How much, or rather, how little of this definition applies to present-day stage-lighting "control" (so-called) has been shown. All of this discussion of the ideal, ultimate control has accomplished its purpose if it has given the reader a fuller comprehension of stage-lighting control, and acquainted him with its extensive scope and with its vital importance to the art of stage lighting, and revealed to him the fact that as far as real, complete control of light is concerned, the present available machinery of control has only scratched the surface.

But while he is waiting for the advent of the ideal control facilities, the stage worker must press into service what facilities are available; in other words, he must make the most of practical, existing conditions. The practical equipment available for the centralized control of light intensity is the switchboard with its attendant electrical wiring. The meaning of control, then, for the remainder of this chapter, from this point on, will be greatly modified: it will be restricted to include simply the control of light intensity by the electrical method — by means of wiring and switchboards.

First, a rough classification of control systems into several types will be attempted. Then will follow, in order, discussions of the wiring and the switchboards for these several types of control systems; a short description of foreign control practice, which will afford an interesting comparison with current American practice; and, finally, a discussion of home-built control equipment for amateur use.

II. Classification of Control Systems

An attempt at a classification of stage-lighting equipment — the actual lighting instruments — was made in Chapter VI, and proved not altogether a success, for the principal reason that methods and practice of stage lighting seem to be passing through a stage of transition from the set, traditional methods of the past to what will probably prove to be the set, traditional methods of the future. If the classification of lighting equipment is vague, and indefinite, and arbitrary, the classification of control equipment is still more so (because to the present changing practices in regard to lighting equipment are added those peculiar to control equipment). This is true because, obviously, the characteristics of control equipment must, to an appreciable extent, be dependent on, must be a function of, the lighting equipment which is controlled. Almost each individual set of control requirements and conditions constitutes its own separate classification, and only with the greatest difficulty can it be forced into a general classification, for purposes of comparison and discussion. The classification of control systems, then, is directly dependent upon the methods, the practice, that governs the use of the lighting equipment itself.

Since the characteristics of the principal component parts of a control system — the wiring and the switchboard — form the basis for such a classification, brief descriptions of these component parts are necessary before a classification can be attempted. A *switchboard* is essentially a device for distributing the main supply of electric current to each of the various lighting instruments, or to each of the unit groups of lighting instruments, at the desired intensity or voltage. As pointed out in Chapter III, the principal component parts of a switchboard are the switches, the dimmers, and the fuses. The switches simply open and close the circuits which conduct the electric current to the various lighting instruments on the stage. Dimmers are, fundamentally, variable resistances which, when placed in series with the equipment lamp "loads" on the circuits they control, regulate the voltage of the electric current supplied to the lamps, and hence dim or brighten the lamps accordingly as the resistance is increased or decreased. The fuses provide protection for the circuits and for the dimmers and other devices on them, against the dangers of short circuit, or overload. The *wiring* for stage-lighting control consists of the conductors that convey, first, the main supply of current from the source of supply to the switchboard and, second (and more important, from the standpoint of stage-lighting control), the subdivided electric current from the switchboard to the various lighting instruments. Devices such as plugs, pockets, and connectors, which simplify and make convenient the work of connecting lighting equipment with the switchboard, are considered as part of the wiring. Of course, there is also the wiring of the switchboard itself, the electrical interconnection and grouping of the switches and dimmers and fuses, but the term "control wiring" does not ordinarily include the switchboard wiring: the latter is considered as a fundamental part of the switchboard. The arrangement of the switchboard and of the wiring is the only feature of a control system that affords a convenient and not too arbitrary basis for classification.

Perhaps the best and most logical though still unsatisfactory classification of control systems is one that would divide them into three general groups: (1) the permanent, (2) the flexible, and (3) the portable type of control.

The *permanent type of control system*, quite naturally, is the concomitant of a permanent, fixed system of stage-lighting equipment. The latter consists of the conventional arrangement of footlights, several borderlights, proscenium striplights, perhaps, and a number of plugging pockets for the accommodation of portable olivettes, spotlights, and so forth. The *wiring* that connects the footlights, borderlights, proscenium striplights, and plugging pockets is permanent in nature; that is, it is susceptible to no variations of circuit arrangement, grouping, or subdivision, or of other important mechanical and electrical features (unless, of course, it is entirely disrupted and rewired). This wiring terminates at the switchboard, the arrangement of which, both electrical and mechanical, is also fixed. In the *switchboard*, the wiring circuits that supply the stage-lighting instruments are permanently connected to the switchboard circuits (the switches, dimmers, and fuses), the arrangement and grouping of which, in relation to the equipment wiring circuits, are not susceptible to variation. The schematic diagram of a stage switchboard on page 62 is quite typical of the sort of switchboard that is used with the permanent type of control system. As dimmers are of fixed capacity (usable only for loads for which they have been designed), it can readily be seen that, with a permanent control system, it is not possible to arrange or group lighting equipment in any but the predetermined manner in which it was originally laid out and permanently installed, without impairing the usefulness of the dimmer installation. Even the plugging pockets, situated at various points on and about the stage, which seem to offer some degree of liberty in this direction, are permanently connected to dimmers of fixed capacities, and hence are almost equally restricted. In other words, a permanent control offers little or no degree of flexibility — the characteristic of stage-lighting equipment that is absolutely essential to the newer stage-lighting practice.

Nevertheless, in spite of its unsuitability as regards the more modern ideas and methods of stage lighting, the permanent type of control system is still being installed in newly constructed theatres designed for professional, non-experimental play production. The principal reasons for this are that such theatres are built and owned by real estate interests rather than by play-producing interests, and that such theatres are used for a great variety of purposes, and under the great variety of play production conditions that abound in the professional theatre, many of which, as has been pointed out before, are anything but conducive to good stage lighting. In such theatres, the control system and the stock units of lighting equipment (the footlights, borderlights, and so forth) are permanently installed and "go with the house", as "permanent fixtures", to whatever individual or organization leases the theatre or otherwise uses it temporarily for play production. It is a notable fact that, if the stage lighting of any production housed in such a theatre has received any serious attention at all, and possesses any merit, in nine cases out of ten it has been achieved by disregarding most of the permanent stage lighting and control equipment of the theatre and substituting in its place portable equipment that has been selected and assembled to satisfy the special needs of that particular production.

The *flexible type of control system* is a natural development brought about by the necessity of meeting the control needs of the newer stage-lighting practice. Its very flexibility and the wide variations in specific installations of it make difficult even so elementary a description as was accorded permanent control in the paragraphs immediately above. The *wiring* for flexible control is never permanent, that is, *electrically* permanent. However, it is usually *mechanically* permanent — installed in rigid conduit, or having the wires and wiring accessories otherwise fixed in place (in contrast to the use of flexible stage cable for connecting the lighting equipment directly with the switchboard, as is the case with the portable type of control, described below). But instead of the wiring circuits being connected directly and permanently to any units of lighting equipment such as the footlights or borderlights, they all terminate in wiring accessories, such as plugging pockets, plugging boxes, and female cable connectors. These plugging receptacles, each terminating a wiring circuit, are located in sufficient or even liberal number at various convenient points about the stage (and also in the auditorium, to supply, for example, balcony-front and ceiling-beam spotlights) at which lighting equipment is likely to be placed. By means of these plugging receptacles, any unit of lighting equipment, either permanent (mechanically) or portable, can be readily connected at will with lengths of stage cable and corresponding wiring accessories such as plugs, and male cable connectors, to a convenient wiring circuit. Just as the instrument ends of the wiring circuits are not connected permanently to any lighting equipment, so are the switchboard ends of the wiring circuits not connected permanently to the switchboard. Instead, all the wiring circuits are brought to a central point, adjacent to the switchboard, and each is terminated in a male cable connector or other type of plug. The *switchboard* for flexible control consists of a number of circuits, each of which is wired with a switch and dimmer and fuse, just as is the switchboard for permanent control. But instead of these switchboard circuits being permanently connected to the wiring circuits that supply the lighting instruments, they terminate in plugging receptacles mounted either on the face of the board or on an auxiliary "plugging panel." Thus any wiring circuit may be readily connected to any switchboard circuit by means of the plugs and receptacles in which each, respectively, terminates. Of course, each of the switchboard circuits is connected permanently to the electrical supply mains — the "feeders" — that are brought to the switchboard from the point within the building at which the electric service enters. The dimmers on the switchboard circuits are of various capacities, a sufficient number of each capacity being provided to meet the estimated needs of the average stage-lighting activities to be carried on. Incidentally, several switchboard circuits may have the dimmer omitted from them; these are so-called "constant circuits" for the accommodation of wiring circuits supplying equipment that need not be dimmed in the course of a performance. Distribution plugging blocks, or panels, are sometimes provided to make possible the combination of several wiring circuits to be controlled as a unit group by a single switchboard circuit.

The advantage of the flexible type of control system is obvious: lighting instruments may be used in any number, in any size, and in any location; and they may be controlled singly or in any desired grouping. In fact, with a well-planned flexible control system, with sufficient and adequate switchboard and wiring circuits, it is possible to achieve any reasonable set-up of lighting equipment, and to control it in any reasonable manner. It is this element of flexibility that makes it particularly suited for use with the newer methods of stage lighting. Its one drawback is the fact that some degree of caution must be observed in connecting the wiring circuits to the switchboard circuits: unless the total wattage load of each wiring circuit is carefully calculated and the wiring circuit is connected to a switchboard circuit having a dimmer of the correct capacity, it is very easy either to underload the dimmers, with resultant unsatisfactory dimming, or, on the other hand, to overload the dimmers and cause them to "burn out" and become altogether useless. The latter condition, of course, is an expensive and serious one, and until some type of self-protected dimmer, or perhaps a multi-capacity dimmer, is developed, can be avoided only by the exercise of care on the part of the switchboard operator. This is probably the chief reason why the older permanent type of control system is still used so extensively in the rented theatre building; there is less opportunity for transient users of the theatre to damage the lighting and control equipment. The full flexible type of control system, as described above, has, up to the present, been installed in but few theatres except those which are used exclusively by permanent producing organizations or in those in which the newer and more experimental forms of stagecraft prevail. Milder, modified forms of flexible control are, however, gradually being adopted for use in the so-called "commercial" theatre. Flexible control is also to be recommended for use in amateur playhouses, for the added reason of lower costs. Generally speaking, a moderate equipment for flexible control will require fewer dimmers than will one for permanent control having equal control facilities. The flexible type of control system is finding increasing favor, and there seems to be every indication that in the future it will be used almost to the exclusion of the two other types of control.

The *portable type of control system* has already been mentioned briefly. This is far from being the most desirable type of control, but the fixed, inefficient, inflexible lighting and control equipment in rented theatres has made necessary its use in instances where the lighting of a production has been given more than casual attention. As these instances have become more and more numerous, the portable type of control is now widely used. The *wiring* for portable control is temporary only and consists of a stage cable extending directly from the switchboard to the lighting equipment, being connected temporarily to each by means of the usual plugging receptacles, connectors, and plugs. The *switchboard* for portable control is somewhat similar to that used for flexible control. The same principle of switchboard circuits (each with its switch, dimmer, and fuse), to which can be temporarily connected the wiring circuits, prevails, except that fewer circuits are provided — their number is usually limited to that necessary for a specific production. The switchboard circuits are not connected permanently to the electrical supply mains. Instead, a heavy-capacity, flexible stage cable serves temporarily to connect the switchboard mains with a convenient source of current supply — usually the "company switch", a high-capacity current outlet located on the stage for just this purpose. The switchboards are built into heavy boxes and are conveniently arranged for transportation. Because of this necessity for portability, these switchboards lack the mechanical refinements that are possible in the switchboards used for permanent and flexible types of control. Although the better type of portable switchboard possesses a fair degree of flexibility, the average type, because it is selected to serve the specific control needs of a particular production, is almost as inflexible as the ordinary type of permanent switchboard.

The conditions under which the portable type of control system is used have already been outlined. The old type of fixed "house equipment" is being used less and less. The permanent switchboards in many professional theatres are seldom used, except those portions of them that control the auditorium lighting. Portable equipment, for both lighting and control, is now widely used instead of the permanent. For productions on tour, and particularly for those having lighting effects above the ordinary, the portable control and lighting equipment is especially valuable, as it assures the exact duplication of the lighting for the production, regardless of the generally unsatisfactory conditions of the "house" equipment which are sure to be encountered in the various theatres into which the production is booked while on the road.

Such, then, is a rough and perhaps somewhat arbitrary classification of the many stage-lighting control systems in use. There is no sharp division between the three types — the permanent, the flexible, and the portable; in fact, modifications of each in greater or less degree far outnumber the simon-pure examples of each. Not infrequently, for a single production, two types of control are used; in most such cases, permanent and portable are used together. These conditions make classification difficult. In spite of its deficiencies, the above classification is a very useful and convenient one and serves well as a basis for discussion.

III. Wiring

The term "wiring", as used ordinarily, would include the switchboard, but as defined previously for the purposes of this chapter, the switchboard is considered as a unit, apart from the wiring that connects it with the source of supply, and from that which connects it with the lighting instruments. The fundamentals of electricity and wiring were discussed in Chapter III; the application of these fundamentals to stage-lighting practice was indicated, and the more common types of wiring accessories were described. It is the purpose of this section to discuss somewhat more in detail the several wiring methods, and particularly their use in the service of each of the types of stage-lighting control systems enumerated above.

But first it is desirable to touch upon the wiring *up to* the switchboard, namely, the supply mains that connect the switchboard with the electric service installed by the central station. In order to guard against possible failure, it is highly desirable that the central station connect its *general lighting service* to more than one street main. This can be done by the "network" or "duplicate service" systems of current distribution that are being so generally adopted. The *emergency lighting service* (supplying exit lights and public passageways and corridors in the entire theatre) should always be connected to a street main other than the one that supplies the general wiring service, or, if this is not possible, to the "street side" of the main lighting service switch for the theatre. In addition, a *general power service* is usually installed in large theatres to supply the current for ventilation-fan motors, motor-generator sets, and so forth. The general lighting service is usually divided into two parts: one set of feeders supplies the lighting for such parts of the theatre as the lobby, foyer, offices, and general public areas (not including the auditorium), and the other set leads directly to the stage switchboard, and thus supplies the auditorium lighting and the stage lighting, and, in addition, various odd backstage lighting needs such as the stage worklights and lights for the dressing rooms, orchestra pit, workshops, storage rooms and so forth. These backstage utility lights are sometimes controlled from a separate small lighting "panel board" which is located in the vicinity of the stage switchboard, and which is supplied by a sub-feeder from the latter, and sometimes directly from the stage switchboard, being supplied by "constant" (non-dimming) circuits. The feeder for the stage switchboard is installed in the usual approved manner, the conductors being enclosed in a continuous run of rigid iron conduit, "pull boxes" and other accessories. The stage switchboard feeder terminates directly at the switchboard. In planning an installation of stage lighting it is of the utmost importance that the capacity of the stage switchboard feeder be large enough to supply the maximum total current that the complete set of stage-lighting instruments and auditorium and backstage utility circuits will require. In addition, it should still have an appreciable reserve capacity to accommodate any increase in load caused by additions to and enlargements of the stage-lighting equipment, or by the unusual lighting requirements of a particular production, both of which conditions are bound to occur at some future time. A feeder of insufficient capacity places an immediate restriction on the usefulness of the entire installation of lighting equipment and control equipment, regardless of the individual merits of either of the latter. Installing originally a feeder of more than ample capacity will prove to be a vastly more convenient and less expensive matter than replacing subsequently one that has been found inadequate. If there is any likelihood of a portable switchboard being used, another feeder from the general lighting service, or a sub-feeder from the stage switchboard, should supply a "company switch." The latter is simply a fused knife switch (terminating the feeder), enclosed in a cabinet and mounted on the wall, to which temporary connections can be made for supplying current to the portable switchboard.

Wiring for permanent control, from the switchboard to the lighting instruments, is usually carried out in rigid conduit and accessory fittings. The branch circuits are carried from the magazine panel of the switchboard to a large splicing box (which is also a part of the switchboard) by the switchboard wiring. In the splicing box the conductors of each of the switchboard circuits are permanently joined, or "spliced", to the conductors of the corresponding wiring circuits. From the splicing box the wiring circuits extend, in rigid conduit, to the instrument locations at various points on the stage. The manner in which the color circuits and section circuits of the footlights, borderlights, and proscenium striplights are connected to the wiring circuits from the switchboard has already been described in Chapter VI (pages 165, 173, and 178). The wiring circuits supplying the plugging receptacles for the accommodation of portable equipment are brought directly (also in rigid conduit) to the stage pockets, or wall pockets, and the conductors are attached to the screw terminals on the receptacles within the outer casing of the pocket. By means of plugs, plugging boxes, stage cable, and cable connectors, the units of portable lighting equipment can be connected temporarily with the wiring circuits from the switchboard.

Wiring for flexible control is also usually carried out in rigid conduit and fittings. As explained in a previous section, the switchboard ends of the wiring circuits all terminate, at a central point, in male cable connectors. The various runs of conduit enclosing the wiring circuits from various instrument locations terminate at a splicing box placed adjacent to the switchboard. In this splicing box each pair of conductors of the various wiring circuits is spliced to a length of stage cable that passes through the side of the splicing box and terminates in a male connector (or other special type of plug that corresponds to the receptacle used on the switchboard). Such a plug on each length of flexible stage cable serves to complete the flexible, temporary connection between the wiring circuits and the switchboard circuits in any desired combination. The equipment ends of the wiring circuits terminate in stage pockets or other type of plugging receptacle. Where the plugging receptacle is permanently mounted, as in the stage floor, or on a wall, the rigid conduit enclosing a wiring circuit can be extended directly to the sheet-metal housing of the receptacle, and the conductors connected directly to the receptacle. If the plugging receptacle is mounted on a movable batten, however, it will be necessary to follow the method by which borderlights are permanently connected, in order to connect the wiring circuits to the receptacles and still allow for vertical movement of the batten.

A special type of plugging box has proved especially useful with the flexible type of control system. It consists simply of a heavy sheet-steel splicing box to which the conduit is attached. The cover of the box is pierced with holes, which are equipped with cable grips. As many wiring circuits as are desired are brought into the box by way of the conduit, and the pair of conductors from each is spliced to one end of a short length (about 12 inches) of stage cable. The stage cable passes through one of the holes in the box cover, and to the other end is attached a female cable connector which serves as a plugging receptacle for the accommodation of a lighting instrument. This device may serve for one or any number of circuits: four, however, is a convenient number of plugging receptacles to group together in such flexible control, as it lends itself readily to color control by the graded-mixture method. Such a plugging box, equipped with 15-ampere female connectors, is more convenient for a flexible wiring system than one equipped with the regular heavy porcelain plugging receptacles, because it eliminates the necessity of using stage plugs, and makes possible the universal, standardized use of 15-ampere cable connectors on all equipment and cable. By recessing them in the stage floor, at convenient points about the

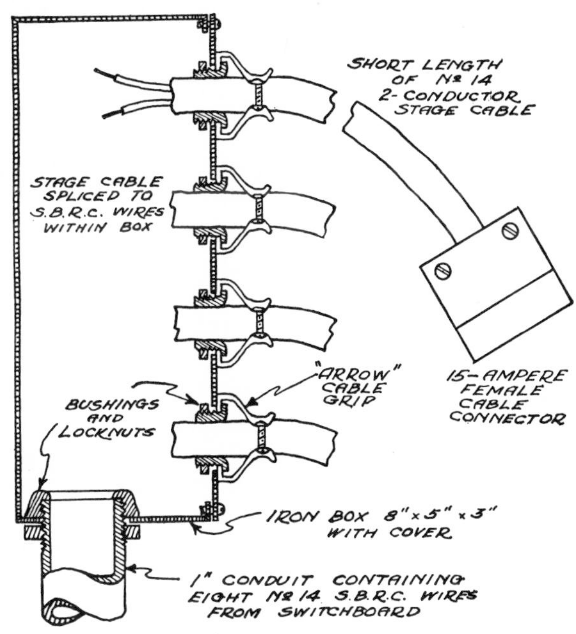

Special plugging box for use with stage wiring for flexible control.

acting area, and covering each with a hinged, self-closing lid provided with notches along its edge for passing the cables, such plugging boxes can be used in place of the regular heavy floor pockets. They can also be used at other vantage points at which lighting instruments may have to be connected. If instead of the conduit, the plugging box be equipped with a length of stage cable (about 5 or 6 feet) that terminates in a male connector, with the several female connectors spliced in parallel to this supplying cable, the plugging box can be used to connect several instruments to a single plugging receptacle. In this form it is similar to the portable plugging box described on page 69.

The plugging receptacles are placed in sufficient number at all the vantage points at which lighting instruments will possibly be located. Thus, they are placed in the space reserved for footlights; along the balcony face; in a false ceiling beam; on the inner proscenium wall; in the stage floor at intervals, along the edge of the acting area;

on the movable battens; and so forth. In order to identify the switchboard plugs of the wiring circuits, the plugs at both ends of each of the wiring circuits are marked with the same identifying location designation arranged according to a systematic scheme of notation. A tabulated list of the instrument locations represented by the designations on the plugs is posted near the switchboard for the convenience of the operator. In order to facilitate the grouping of several wiring circuits on one switchboard circuit, several distribution blocks, or distribution panels, similar in principle to the portable plugging box described above, are provided.

Wiring for portable control is effected simply by means of stage cable, lengths of which serve as wiring circuits for connecting the lighting instruments to the switchboard circuits. Wiring devices, such as plugs, plugging receptacles, plugging boxes, connectors, and "multiple-circuit" and "branch-off" connectors, are used to make the temporary connections. The portable control wiring for elaborate productions often requires the use of many thousands of feet of stage cable and a large number of wiring devices. The lengths of stage cable, or "leads" as they are sometimes called, that supply the various units of portable lighting equipment, are plugged directly into receptacles on the portable switchboard, and are thus connected to the desired switchboard circuits.

All installations of wiring for stage lighting for any type of control system should be planned from the multiple standpoint of safety, capacity, durability, and convenience. *Safety* is undoubtedly the principal factor. All wiring should be carried out in accordance with the best approved wiring practice that locally prevails, and should conform rigidly to the requirements of the National Electrical Code and to any municipal regulations that apply. The proper municipal authorities and underwriters' representatives should inspect the wiring installation and issue certificates of approval. It is especially important that any temporary alterations or changes in the wiring, to meet the needs of a particular production, be made with the same high regard for safety that should characterize the original installation. The needs for sufficient *capacity* of the feeder supplying the stage switchboard and wiring has already been stressed. The equipment circuits, from the switchboard to the equipment or plugging receptacles, should also be of ample capacity, and an ample number of them supplied, so that the wiring facilities need not be overtaxed in order to accommodate more than the usual amount of equipment. A "company switch", for the accommodation of portable switchboards and equipment, will often also be found useful for helping to supply any unusually heavy demand for electric current created by an elaborate temporary set-up of lighting equipment. A fair degree of *durability* is, of course, guaranteed by adherence to Code requirements, but the rather hard treatment accorded stage-lighting and control equipment makes highly desirable the use of materials and devices whose ability to withstand hard service is in excess of that required by the Code. *Convenience* is an important factor, especially for the flexible and portable types of wiring, and can be achieved by careful lay-out of the entire wiring system, especially of the location of plugging receptacles and the number of them at each location, and by the use of standardized, interchangeable plugs, plugging devices, connectors, and so forth.

The principle factor governing the design of wiring for stage lighting is the exact type of control system — permanent, flexible, or portable, or a modification of any one — that has been decided upon. The desirable features and the field of usefulness of each type of control systems for stage lighting have been indicated above, but a final, definite choice of the exact method of control depends upon the numerous conditions that apply to each individual case — for what purpose is the theatre to be used, who will control it, who will use it, and so forth. The only general recommendation that can be stressed is the adoption of the most flexible type of control that conditions make at all feasible.

IV. Switchboard

The switchboard has already been defined as that part of a stage-lighting control system which divides the main supply of electric current and distributes it, by means of the wiring discussed above, to the various lighting instruments at the desired intensity or voltage. It has been shown to consist of several parts, — the switches, the dimmers, and the fuses. In ordinary wiring practice, the term "switchboard" denotes only a suitably mounted group of switches. This was originally also the case with stage switchboards: the dimmers were mounted separately, apart from the switches, in a "dimmer bank", and the branch circuit fuses were also mounted separately, apart from the switchboard, in a "magazine panel." The best modern practice combines switchboard, dimmer bank, and magazine panel into a single, self-contained unit piece of apparatus to which the term "switchboard" is generally applied. Perhaps "control board" would be a better term, but since even the best stage switchboards fall so far short of providing really complete or ideal "control" of stage lighting, "switchboard" remains as perhaps the more correct term. Besides, in practice, only rarely is a stage switchboard referred to as a "control board."

The stage switchboard is often, and rightly, considered the most important part, the "nerve center", of the control system. It should be so arranged that it affords centralized control of all of the instruments used to light the stage — both separate control of individual instruments, and unit control of desired groupings and combinations of instruments. The latter function, that of group control of lighting instruments, is achieved by arranging the switches and dimmers so that they will be susceptible to mechanical "interlocking" and electrical group and master control. But such flexibility as these arrangements for interlocking and group controls provide should not be achieved (or need it be) at the expense of simplicity, which is no unimportant factor in switchboard design. Some types of switchboards are rapidly becoming larger in size and more intricate and "tricky" in design, and seem to be passing the point where flexibility and convenience of manipulation are just balanced against simplicity, and beyond which point improvements intended to increase flexibility and convenience will defeat their own purpose. Inasmuch as the graded-mixture method of color control depends primarily on the electrical method of intensity control, the provisions for interlocking and group control on stage switchboards are usually arranged from the standpoint of color control. Just how this is achieved is explained in following paragraphs, after the component parts of switchboards have been discussed.

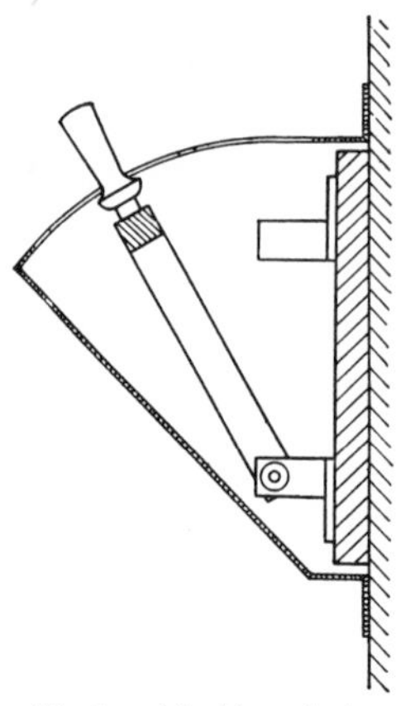

Enclosed knife switch.

A. SWITCHES

The simple, common, fundamental types of switches, namely, *open-knife switches*, have been described and pictured in Chapter III. Many modifications of these are available, each suitable for some special conditions. Nevertheless, they all serve the same purpose — to "make" and "break" electrical connections, to "close" and "open" electrical circuits — whatever their mechanical arrangements for fulfilling it may be. Formerly these open-knife switches were mounted directly on the front of the stage switchboards (many interesting examples of this old type of construction still exist), but because of the great danger presented by the many exposed "live", or current-carrying, parts, these so-called "open-face" stage switchboards have been outlawed by the Code and by almost all local municipal regulations. Where knife switches are used on stage switchboards they must be mounted so that no live parts are exposed, and provision must be made for operating them when they are so mounted. Several methods of complying with these regulations which require "dead-face" or "dead-front" switchboards for stage service have been developed.

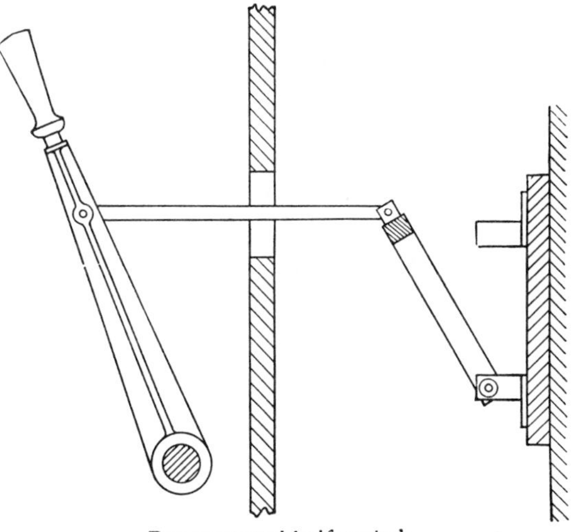

Bar-connected knife switch.

The simplest of all is that used for portable switchboards, where the ordinary type of knife switch is enclosed in a housing of sheet metal. This arrangement might be termed simply an *enclosed knife switch.* The housing is shaped so as to allow sufficient movement of the blades for opening and closing, and has a narrow slot through which the switch handle protrudes for operating the switch.

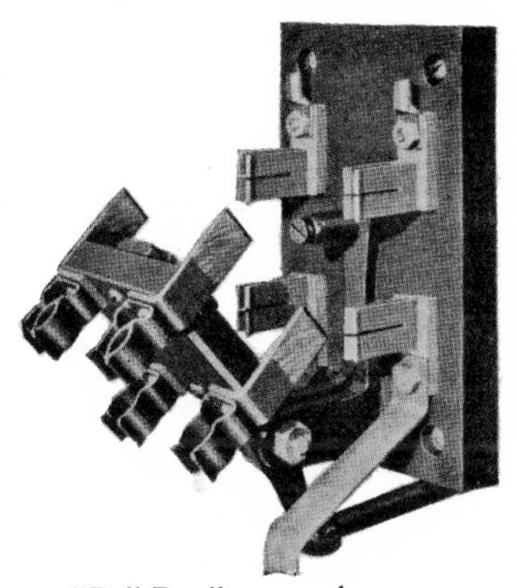

"Bull-Dog" reverse bar-connected knife switch.

For permanent switchboards a more finished appearance is necessary. Several types of *bar-connected knife switches* are commonly used. For these, a separate operating lever is mounted on the front face of the switchboard, and the actual switch mechanism — blades, insulating crossbar, and hinge-and-jaw clips — is mounted on a second board directly in back of the operating lever or handle. The operating handle is connected to the insulating bar of the switch mechanism, and passes through a small opening in the front face of the switchboard. Thus, no live parts are exposed on the face of the board, and the switch may be operated readily. The "Bull-Dog" type of bar-connected switch that is especially adapted to dead-front service on stage switchboards is what might be termed a *reverse bar-connected switch.* This switch has no blades, in the ordinary sense, and instead of but one set of jaws, it has two sets of jaws. As shown in the illustration, an insulating slab has the fuse clips for the switch mounted on its back side. From these fuse clips extend copper strips which make contact with the switch jaws. The insulating block is hinged and is actuated by the operating handle (on the front of the board), to which it is connected by the short connecting bar. Thus the copper strips, the fuse clips, and the fuses together serve as the switch blades, and each side of the circuit is broken simultaneously in two places when the switch is opened. Inasmuch as the several types

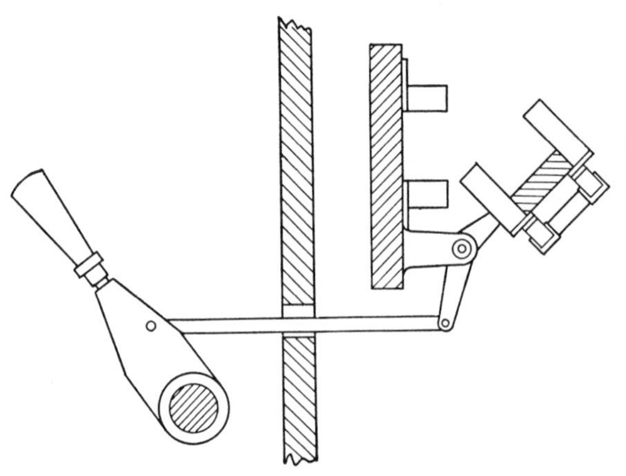

"Bull-Dog" reverse bar-connected switch.

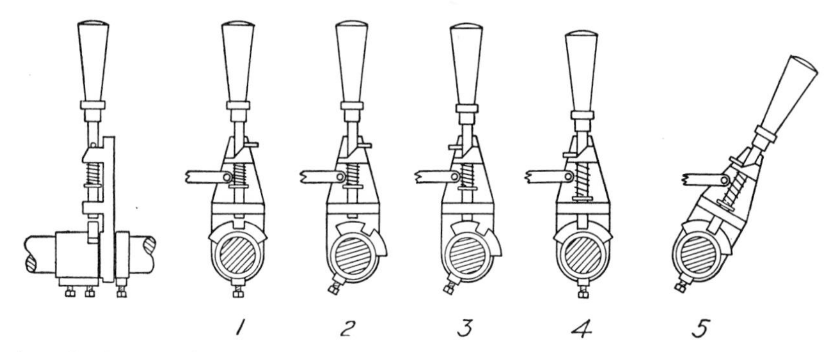

Schematic diagram of typical interlocking mechanism used for switches and dimmers. At the left is a front view of the switch handle showing the spring latching-pin, the special slotted collar, the shaft, and another collar for holding the switch handle in place on the shaft. Position 1 shows the spring latching-pin of the switch handle set for independent operation. In Position 2 the shaft and the slotted collar have been revolved in a clockwise direction by the master handle attached to the shaft. The individual switch handle, however, has remained in its original position because the latch pin could not be engaged by the slotted collar. In Position 3 the switch handle has been twisted a half turn and the latch pin thereby set for interlock. In Position 4 the shaft and slotted collar have been moved back to the original position by the master handle. The spring latching pin has engaged the slot in the collar. In Position 5 the shaft and slotted collar have been turned in a clockwise direction by the master handle, and, as the individual switch handle was set for interlock, the latter has also been moved in the same direction, thus being under the interlocking control of the master handle.

of bar-connected knife switches have separate operating handles, mechanical interlocking may be conveniently applied to them.

For the simplest type of mechanical switch interlocking, the operating handles which are to be subject to interlock, instead of rotating upon individual hinges, rotate upon a cylindrical steel shaft that runs horizontally on the front face of the board. Alongside each switch handle, a slotted collar is firmly fixed to the shaft, and each switch handle is equipped with a spring pin. By twisting the operating handle, this spring pin may be set so as to allow the

Operating handles of "Bull-Dog" reverse bar-connected knife switches as mounted on the front face of a switchboard, showing the master handle at the right end of the shaft, and the pre-set levers on the individual handles at various positions.

switch handle to rotate freely about the shaft, or it may be set so as to latch into the slot on the collar. In the latter condition, the handle and the shaft can only move simultaneously, as a unit. If a "master handle" is permanently fixed to the shaft, obviously it will serve to actuate all the individual switch handles that are "latched" to the shaft by means of the spring pin. The "Bull-Dog" type of switch handle (generally used with the "Bull-Dog" switch described above) has a more elaborate latching mechanism, which, in addition to the regular interlocking feature, makes possible a mechanical presetting, a "pre-set", as it is usually termed, of the individual switch handles on the switchboard. The spring latching pin has a beveled end, instead of a blunt one, and can be set in any one of four positions. When in the "Off" position, the individual switch handle will latch only when the master handle and shaft are rotated in the "off" direction; when the pin is in the "Positive" position, the individual handle will latch regardless of the direction of rotation of the shaft, and thus be subject to straight interlock; when the pin is in the "On" position, the individual handle will latch only when the shaft is rotated in the "on" direction; and when the pin is in the "Independent" position, the individual handle will not latch at all, and is subject to independent control. The sketches explain how this is carried out. A small auxiliary handle on each individual switch handle controls the position of the latching pin, and is termed the pre-set lever. The interlocking and pre-set are accomplished by the "Bull-Dog" switch lever in the following

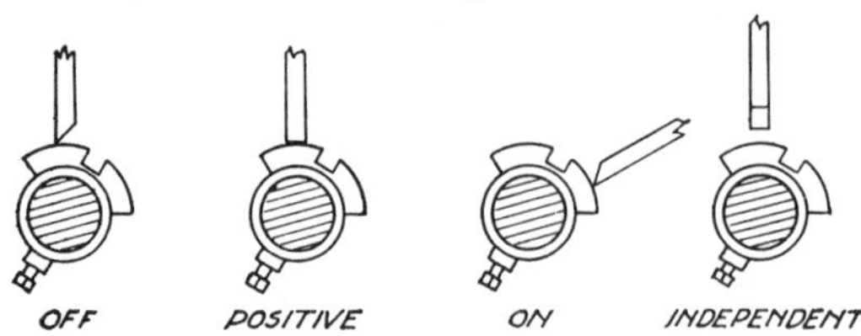

This sketch illustrates the working principle of the "Bull-Dog" pre-set switch handle. Only the shaft, the slotted collar and the lower end of the spring latching pin are represented. In the "Off" position, the individual switch handle can be moved only in a clockwise direction by the master handle, as the bevel at the end of the spring latching pin will cause the pin to disengage from the slot when the master handle is turned in a counter-clockwise direction. In the "Positive" position the spring latching pin has been twisted so that its beveled end has no effect, and the individual switch handle is therefore set for positive interlock control, in both directions, by the master handle. In the "On" position, the spring latching pin has been twisted so that its bevel faces in a direction opposite to that in the "Off" position, thereby engaging with the slotted collar only when the master handle is turned in a counter-clockwise direction. In the "Independent" position, the spring latching pin has been lifted above the periphery of the slotted collar, thus setting the individual switch handle for independent control.

manner: The pre-set levers of those switches which are to retain their present status, either on or off, are placed in the "Independent" position; those of the switches which are off but which are to be on, are set in the "On" position; and similarly, those of the switches which are on but which are to be off are set in the "Off" position. A double movement of the master handle, first in the "Off" and then in the "On" direction, will open those switches whose pre-set levers are in the "Off" position, close those whose pre-set levers are in the "On" position, and not change those whose pre-set levers are in the "Independent" position. Thus the switches controlling the lighting circuits used in a scene can be "set up" in advance without affecting the lighting of the previous scene, and the change can be made almost instantaneously. It must be remembered, however, that this element of preset, or pre-selection, does *not* apply to the *dimmers*, but only to the switches.

All the switches discussed above are of the "single-throw" variety. Often, however, it is necessary to use a "double-throw" switch on a stage switchboard. Obviously, it is not convenient to adapt the ordinary type of double-throw knife switches with straight blades (see page 67) for dead-front mounting with connecting bars, as the complete angle of blade rotation is too great. Instead, switches with angle blades are used, as pictured on page 365.

A modified type of knife switch — the so-called "*rotor-movement*", or "*R. M.*" *switch* — is being adopted for use on stage switchboards, for which purpose its design makes it particularly suitable. The switch is equipped with a double set of jaws, and the blades (which connect the two sets of jaws when the switch is closed) are mounted transversely in a cylinder made of insulating material. This cylinder rotates within an angle of 45 degrees, and its longitudinal line of rotation lies midway between the two sets of jaws. When the cylinder is at one extreme of rotation, the blades bridge the two sets of jaws and the circuit is closed; when the cylinder is at the other extreme of rotation, the blades are at right angles to their former position and the circuit between the switch jaws is broken. The switch mechanism is enclosed by a molded-insulation base and cover, and is mounted directly on the back of the front face of the switchboard. The switch is actuated by an insulated operating lever that protrudes through the face of the board, as shown in the illustration above and in the sketches on the following page. This type of switch is available in the 30 and 60 ampere sizes.

A "rotor movement" switch mounted at the rear of a unit switchboard panel, with the operating handle protruding beyond the front face. The circuit pilot-light is shown directly below the switch.

The descriptions above cover practically all the various types of knife switches used on stage switchboards. Another type of switch sometimes used for stage switchboards, especially for the pilot board in remote-controlled switchboard installations, is the tumbler switch. This type of switch is now commonly used for residential electric wiring, for which it is rapidly supplanting the older "push-button" switch. The actual mechanism of the tumbler switch, or toggle switch as it is sometimes called, is similar to that of the push-button switch. Two sets of jaws are bridged over by revolving blades when the switch is closed (somewhat like the rotor-movement switch). The mechanism is operated by a short handle of molded insulating material that projects slightly beyond the enclosed body of the switch. The mechanism is of the "quick-make" and "quick-break" type — the operating handle does not directly rotate the switch blades; instead, it trips a spring, which, in turn, rotates the blades with a quick, sharp movement. This "quick-make" and "quick-break" feature, while it minimizes the destructive arcing caused by heavy currents, militates against the use of tumbler

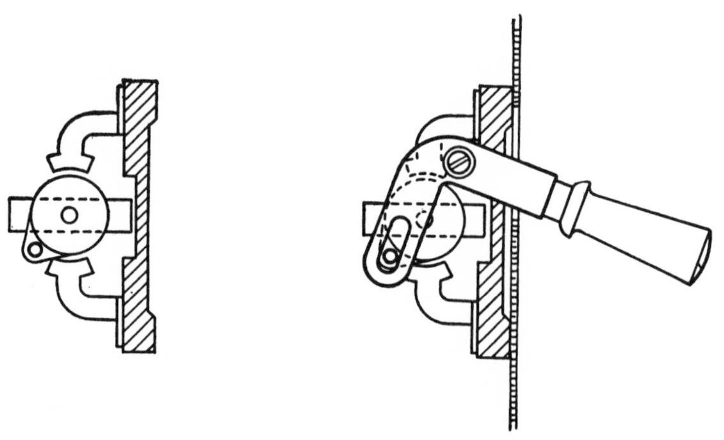

The "rotor-movement" switch. The left view shows the two switch jaws between which is the cylinder containing the switch blade. At the edge of the cylinder is shown the offset stud by which the cylinder is rotated. This stud fits in a slot in the operating handle of the switch, as shown in the view on the right. This view also shows the switch mounted behind a sheet metal face of a switchboard.

switches on stage switchboards, as the spring mechanism is audible in its operation: a resounding "click" takes place whenever the switch is opened or closed. The large, 30-ampere tumbler switch, which is often used to control the constant circuits (supplying back-stage utility lights) from the stage switchboard, is especially noisy. The chief advantage of tumbler switches is their compactness; the miniature size, rated for 5 amperes, and used to a great extent on the pilot boards of elaborate installations of multi-pre-set remote-control stage switchboards, occupies a mounting space only $\frac{3}{4}''$ wide and $1\frac{1}{2}''$ long. Because of their noisy operation, tumbler switches (and, in fact, all switches with any sort of "quick-make" and "quick-break" mechanism) are undesirable for use on stage switch-boards, especially on comparatively small stages.

Special types of switches have been developed to meet special requirements, particularly the requirements of remote-control pre-set switchboard installations. Thus there are multi-pole and multi-throw switches, and momentary contact switches. A commonly used type of pilot switch is pictured on the next page, in elemental form. The operating handle pivots at its center, and the small metal block at its lower end bridges the pair of spring contacts between which it is placed, and closes the circuit to which the particular pair of contacts is connected. Such a type of switch can be used for many purposes, depending upon the number of sets of contacts, and upon the method of connecting the contacts to the various circuits the switch is to control.

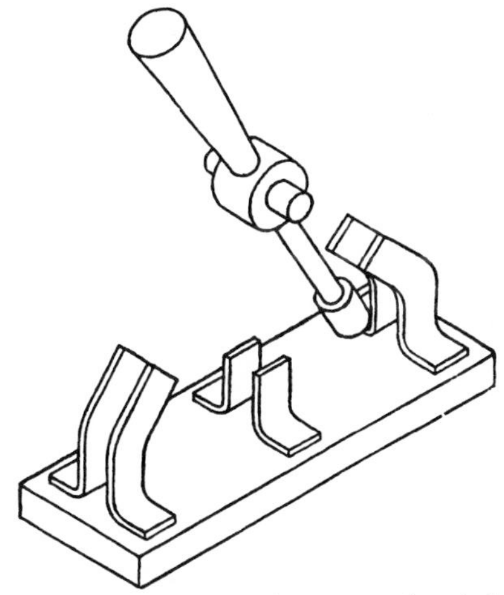

Schematic diagram of a type of switch sometimes used as a pilot switch on remote-control switchboards. Each circuit to be closed is connected to a pair of contacts which are bridged by the metal end of the operating handle as it is wedged between the contacts.

Still another type of switch used on stage switchboards is the "*flipper switch*." Inasmuch as this type of switch is mounted on, and forms an integral part of, certain types of dimmers, it will be described in connection with the latter, in the following section.

Because they make possible the convenient control of heavy current loads, and because they are adaptable to elaborate electrical pre-set switchboard arrangements, *remote-controlled switches* are being used to a greater and greater extent for stage-lighting control. Besides the actual electrical circuit, which a remote-controlled switch "makes" and "breaks", called usually the "load circuit", a second, separate circuit, called the *pilot circuit*, is necessary to provide the electric current that actuates the mechanism of the remote-controlled switch. The pilot circuit, in turn, is controlled by a small "pilot switch", of a type described above, which is placed on the "pilot switchboard" and controlled manually by the operator. The mechanism of a remote-controlled switch is actuated by an electromagnet or solenoid which is energized by the pilot circuit. When the pilot switch is closed, current flows through the electromagnet, which, by virtue of the magnetic field created, exerts a powerful attraction upon the hinged contact fingers of the remote-controlled switch (corresponding to the blades of an open-knife switch) and draws them sharply against their respective contacts, thus closing the load circuit. This complete operation takes place so rapidly that, for all practical purposes, the lighting of lamps on the load circuit may be considered coincident with the closing of the pilot switch. In principle, remote-controlled switches are the same as knife switches, except that the latter are actuated manually, and the former electrically. Remote-controlled switches are available in single-pole single-throw, double-pole single-throw, and three-pole single-throw types, and also in double-throw types, though the latter are not commonly used for stage-lighting control.

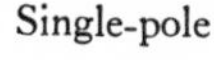

Single-pole Double-pole

Remote-Controlled Magnet Switches, or "Contactors."

The principal parts of a remote-controlled switch are the electromagnet, the stationary contacts, the contact fingers, and the movable contacts. The electromagnet is simply a coil of fine wire wound about an iron core. The current required by the electromagnet to actuate the switch is usually not more than two or three amperes, and does not vary; that is, it is independent of the actual circuit load it controls. The electromagnet coil is protected against overload by fuses. The stationary contacts, which are usually small replaceable blocks of copper, or of carbon, are mounted directly on the base of the switch, and to them, by means of terminal screws, is connected the "line" or "feed" side of the circuit. The contact fingers are pivoted at their lower end. In double-pole and three-pole switches the contact fingers are locked together by an insulating crossbar and move as a unit, actuated by a single electromagnet. The movable contacts are usually small replaceable copper blocks, mounted at the upper ends of the contact fingers, and by means of short, flexible, copper ribbons, are connected to the terminals that supply the "load" side of the circuit. Remote-controlled switches are available in various sizes, ranging in rated capacity from 30 amperes upwards to practically unlimited capacity. They are very noisy in operation, and cannot be used directly on the stage, but must be placed in a sound-proof cellar or vault, although the pilot switches that control them are mounted directly on the stage switchboard.

Two principal types of remote-controlled switches used for stage-lighting control are the mechanically-held-closed type, and the electrically-held-closed type. The *mechanically-held-closed* type is

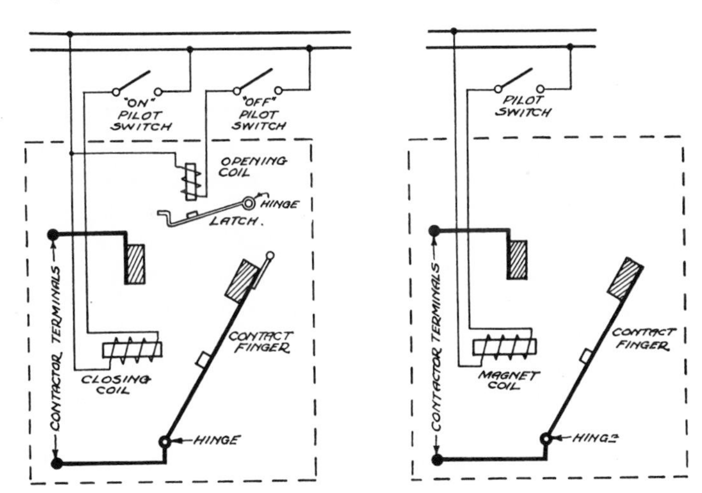

Illustrating the operating principle of remote-controlled switches. The sketch at the left represents the mechanically-held-closed, or "latched-in" type; that at the right represents the electrically-held-closed, or "magnet" type, of remote-controlled switch. Only a single pole on each switch is shown.

equipped with two electromagnets, one of which is known as the "closing coil", and the other as the "opening coil." When the switch is closed by the closing coil, the contact fingers are held in place by a latch mechanism. When the opening coil is energized, it trips the latch mechanism holding the contact fingers, and they swing open by gravity, or are pushed open by a spring, and the load circuit is opened. Thus two pilot circuits are necessary, one for closing and the other for opening the switch, although the actuating current in each need only be momentary. In fact, most mechanically-held-closed remote-controlled switches (which are sometimes called *latched-in switches*) are equipped with a set of auxiliary contacts that open the closing pilot circuit immediately after the switch has been closed, and open the opening pilot circuit immediately after the switch has been opened. Thus current cannot accidentally be allowed to flow continuously through the coils. *Momentary contact* pilot switches are usually used for the pilot circuits. Each of these is equipped with a spring that allows it to remain in the closed position only while the operator is actually holding the operating handle in the closed position. The *electrically-held-closed* type of remote-controlled switch, which is used to a far greater extent for stage-lighting control than is the mechanically-held-closed type, has but one electromagnet and requires but one pilot circuit. When the pilot switch is closed, the coil becomes energized, the contact fingers are drawn up, and the load circuit is closed. The switch is held closed by the coil as long as the pilot current is allowed to flow through the coil. When the pilot switch (which is *not* of the momentary contact type) is opened, the attractive force of the coil ceases, and the contact fingers swing open by gravity, or are pushed open by a spring, and the load circuit is opened. The pilot current must flow all during the time that the load circuit is closed. For certain classes of electrically pre-set stage switchboard installations, these electrically-held-closed remote-controlled switches, or *magnet switches*, as they are often called, are provided with duplicate coils, each of which is controlled by a separate pilot circuit, and either of which can be used to close the switch. The use of each of these three types of remote-controlled switches — the latched-in type, the magnet type, and the double-coil magnet type — is discussed in detail further on in this chapter.

B. DIMMERS

A dimmer has been defined as being fundamentally a variable resistance which, when placed in series with the lamps on the circuit it controls, regulates the voltage of the current supplied to the lamps, and hence dims or brightens them accordingly as the resistance is increased or decreased. Fundamentally, then, a dimmer is a voltage regulator. At this point, a discussion of those characteristics of tungsten-filament incandescent lamps that affect dimmer design will perhaps prove of interest.

If an incandescent lamp is operating under normal conditions, at its designed, rated voltage, it is emitting its normal amount of light, which is usually expressed in lumens. That is, it is operating at 100% normal voltage, 100% normal lumen output, and also, incidentally, at 100% normal resistance, and 100% normal amperage. If, however, external resistance (in contrast to the normal internal resistance of the lamp itself), such as is provided by a dimmer, is introduced into, or "cut into", the lamp circuit, the voltage of the current supplied to the lamp is reduced. This reduction in voltage will cause a reduction in the operating temperature of the lamp filament. As the operating temperature of the filament is reduced, the filament will glow less brightly — it will emit less light — and the lamp is then said to have been "dimmed."

But the lumen output of the lamp does not decrease at the same rate as that at which the operating voltage is reduced. For example, at 75% normal voltage, the lamp will emit not 75% normal lumen output, as might be supposed, but only about 36%; at 50% normal voltage, the lumen output is about 10% of normal; and at 25% normal voltage, the lumen output is practically zero — the lamp is "out", except, perhaps for a very dull red filament glow. This relation is shown in the first of the accompanying curves.

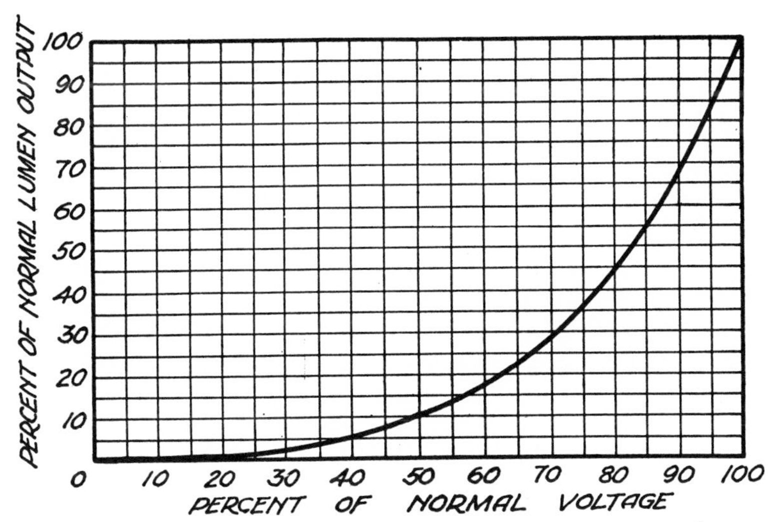

Curve depicting the relation between operating voltage and lumen output of tungsten filament incandescent lamps.

The exact per cent of normal voltage at which a lamp is "black out" is a moot question. A dull red filament glow, such as is produced by 20% normal voltage, can usually be safely considered as practically "black out", especially on a large stage. Although the lamp filament itself may be visible by direct vision, it will not produce light enough to make objects visible by reflection. When the lamp is used in conjunction with blue and green color media of high purity, even the much brighter red glow produced by as high as 35% or 40% normal voltage can be considered as "black out", because these color media will effectively absorb the red rays to which the light output of a lamp operating at such voltages is virtually restricted. However, in order to make certain that an indisputable "black-out" condition can be reached with a dimmer, a "black-out" voltage of approximately 10% of normal operating voltage is usually assumed as a basis in dimmer design. At 10% normal voltage, an incandescent lamp has an internal resistance equal to 38% of its normal internal resistance at 100% normal voltage. By applying this value in conjunction with Ohm's Law (see page 55), the reader can easily calculate that approximately three and one-half times the normal resistance of a lamp (or, three and one-half times the total normal resistance of a group of lamps) must be placed in series with the lamp (or, the group of lamps) in order to reduce the operating voltage to 10% of normal, at which voltage the lamp is considered to be "black out" as far as useful light output is concerned. To dim a 100-watt lamp to "black out" on a 115-volt circuit will require a total external resistance of 462 ohms in series with it; for a 200-watt lamp, 231 ohms; for a 500-watt lamp, 92 ohms; and so on. This relationship is depicted by the curve on page 309. This also explains why a dimmer that has been designed to dim properly a lamp load of certain wattage (termed the "rated capacity" of the dimmer), does not function properly when used to dim a lamp load appreciably greater or less than its rated capacity. Thus a 500-watt dimmer cannot dim completely to "black out" a lamp load of 200 watts, or 100 watts, because it does not contain enough resistance; its maximum resistance is 92 ohms, whereas a lamp load of 200 watts requires 231 ohms of resistance, and one of 100 watts requires 462 ohms. On the other hand, a 100-watt dimmer contains enough resistance to dim a 200-watt lamp, or a 500-watt lamp, but its rated capacity will be greatly exceeded in so doing. Such a condition is highly unsatisfactory: first, because the lamp will be dimmed to "black out" after the dimmer handle has covered only a portion of its full traverse distance — the dimming will be sharp and jerky, and will flicker, and will be difficult to synchronize with dimming done by properly loaded dimmers; and, second, because the resistance wires in a dimmer are of a size to accommodate safely only a lamp wattage equal to the rated capacity of the dimmer; if this capacity be exceeded by an appreciable amount, the dimmer will be overloaded, and its resistance wires will be in danger of burning out. Lack of synchronization in dimming may be illustrated as follows: if three dimmers, one underloaded, the second properly loaded, and the third overloaded, be interlocked and "brought down" simultaneously with a master handle, the lamps controlled by each will not dim at the same rate, will not reach "black out" simultaneously: instead, those connected to the first *will never reach* "black out" even with the dimmer at its maximum limit of traverse; those connected to the second will reach "black out" *just at* the maximum limit of dimmer traverse (the proper condition); and those connected to the third will reach "black out" *before* the maximum limit of dimmer traverse has been reached. The results of such uneven dimming can be nothing but unsatisfactory, even at best, and will usually prove ruinous to the smooth lighting effects of a production. It is necessary, therefore, in order to achieve satisfactory dimming results, that, in so far as possible, the light output of the lamps be 100% normal when the dimmer, or dimmer handle, is at the beginning of its traverse distance, at the "full-up" position, and just

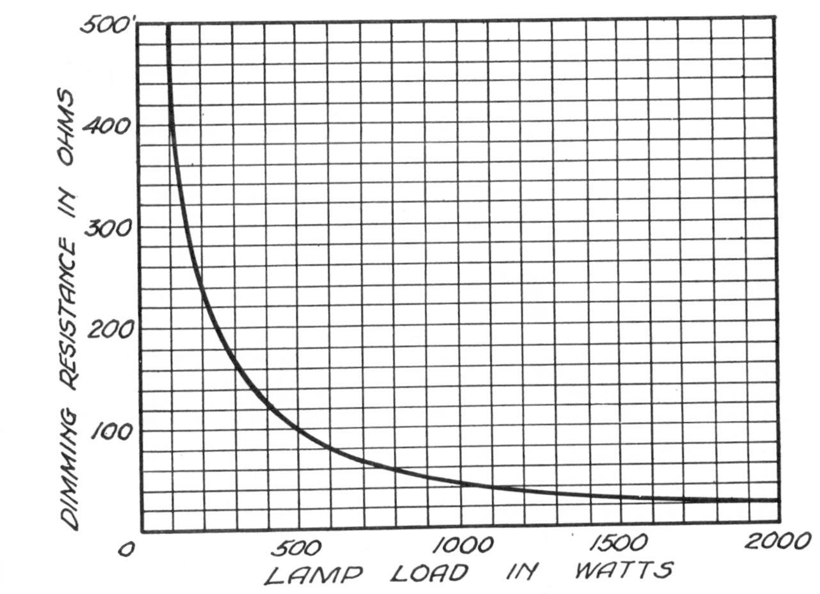

Curve depicting the resistance necessary to dim tungsten incandescent lamps to "black out."

reach zero per cent when the dimmer reaches the end of its traverse distance, at the "black out" position. In other words, the range of dimmer traverse should be just coincident with the range of light output of the lamps controlled by the dimmer. This condition can only be achieved when a properly designed dimmer is used to control a lamp load that is just equal to its rated capacity. Under practical operating conditions, underloads and overloads to an extent perhaps as great as 20% under or over the rated dimmer capacity can be tolerated. Several methods of reconciling the rated capacity of an available dimmer with a widely differing lamp load are used. For instance, if a 250-watt lamp must be carefully dimmed, and only a 500-watt dimmer is available, a "phantom load" of 250 watts can be used to "build up" the load to the full rated capacity of the dimmer. That is, if a lamp, or bank of lamps, whose total wattage equals the difference between the rated dimmer capacity and the wattage of the lamp to be dimmed, is connected to the dimmer circuit, and placed backstage so that its light is not visible on the stage, the principal lamp on the stage will be smoothly dimmed to complete "black out", as the dimmer will really be functioning at its rated capacity. The phantom load will, of course, also be dimmed at the same rate. As dimmers are available only in standard sizes, this practice of using "phantom load" often proves a great convenience, especially when smooth, careful dimming is required. On the other hand, if a 500-watt lamp must be dimmed, and there happen to be two 250-watt dimmers available (or any other dimmers whose rated capacities total 500 watts), these dimmers may be wired in parallel to each other (but, together, in series with the lamp), and the lamp may be effectively dimmed by operating the dimmers jointly, each covering its own traverse distance at the same rate. If the total rated capacities of any available dimmers exceed the wattage of the lamp load to be dimmed, phantom load can be used in addition. This practice of wiring dimmers in parallel must be carried out with the utmost care — the dimmer handles should be operated simultaneously, at the same rate of traverse (preferably they should be interlocked) — otherwise the loads impressed on each dimmer might become proportionally unbalanced, with the result that first one, and then the other, dimmer will burn out with dispatch. Wiring dimmers in parallel is never a safe practice if the lamp load to be dimmed is much greater than a thousand watts.

Another important characteristic of dimmer design is dependent upon lamp characteristics. It has been stated that approximately three and one-half times the normal resistance of a lamp load must be placed in series with the lamp load in order to dim it just to black out, and that zero per cent lumen output (black out), and one hundred per cent lumen output (full up), should be achieved with the dimmer handle respectively at opposite ends of its traverse. But it has also been pointed out that when a lamp is being dimmed, its lumen output does not decrease at the same rate as does its operating voltage, which, in turn, is a direct function of the external, or dimming, resistance. If the total amount of dimming resistance be spaced evenly over the traverse of the dimmer handle, and the dimmer handle be moved at a constant rate, the lamp will dim unevenly — that is, it will dim very rapidly at the "on" end of the dimmer traverse, and very slowly at the "off" end of the dimmer traverse. This condition, of course, is highly undesirable, and is avoided by spacing the resistance *unevenly* over the range of dimmer traverse in just the correct proportions to allow of even dimming when the dimmer handle is moved at a constant rate. Thus, a dimmer that has been designed for incandescent lamps will have its initial resistance at the "on" end of its traverse of thick, heavy wire having low resistance, and its final resistance at the "off" end of its traverse of fine, thin wire having high resistance, with the proper gradations intervening. Thus with the dimmer handle at one fourth its traverse, the lamps will be approximately one fourth dimmed; at one half its traverse, approximately one half dimmed;

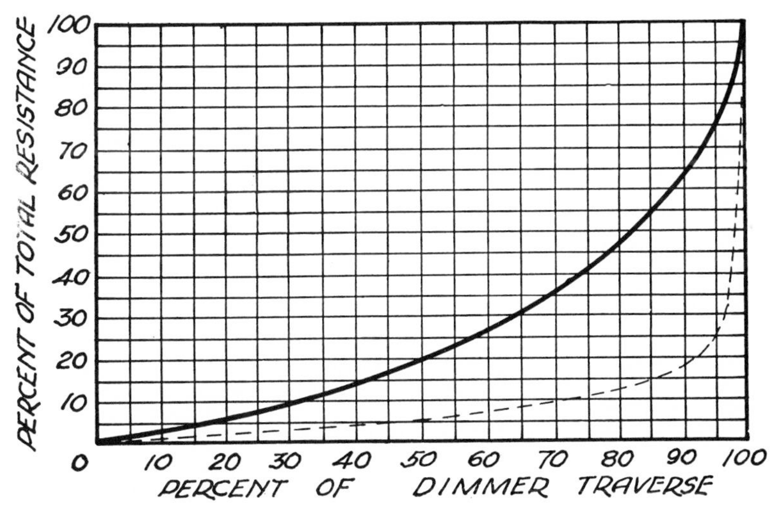

Curve depicting the distribution of the total resistance of a dimmer over its traverse. The light dotted curve shows the true, exact relationship between per cent of dimmer traverse and per cent of total resistance; the heavy, solid curve shows a modified relationship that is not quite exact but that is more adapted to practical working conditions of dimmer design and construction and of lamp operation.

and so forth. In other words, the position of the dimmer handle affords the operator a convenient and reasonably accurate gauge of the amount of dimming. Because of practical considerations, this requirement — that degree of dimming be directly proportional to dimmer traverse — is seldom perfectly fulfilled; but the ideal condition is achieved closely enough for all practical purposes. Perhaps, after all, it is well that this ideal condition is not perfectly achieved, because of the fact that the subjective, or physiological, values of light-intensity intervals vary widely at opposite ends of the range of practical operating light intensities. The above curve depicts the relationship between dimmer traverse and spacing of dimming resistance that must be maintained in order to assure smooth, even dimming. Incidentally, the characteristics of tungsten-filament incandescent lamps are favorable to dimmer design; they allow the use of heavy, high-capacity wire at the initial stages of dimming, when the current flow (in amperes) is heaviest, and allow the use of fine, low-capacity wire at the final stages of dimming when the current flow is lightest. In the case of the old carbon incandescent lamps, conditions were exactly reversed, and consequently made dimmer design a much more difficult problem than it is for tungsten-filament lamps.

At "black out", approximately one fourth of the normal wattage of the lamp load controlled by a dimmer must be absorbed by the resistance windings in the dimmer. This absorption gives rise to heat — the greater the lamp load dimmed, the greater the amount of heat liberated. Dimmers must be so designed that this liberated heat is easily dissipated into the surrounding air. This explains why overloaded dimmers "burn out", and why the physical size of dimmers increases in proportion to their rated capacities. Resistance dimmers of almost unlimited rated capacity could be constructed. However, practicability imposes specific limits on rated capacities of each type of dimmer. In order to dim lamp loads in excess of this maximum rated capacity, it is necessary to split the total lamp load into two or more parts, each of which can be handled by a single dimmer of correct capacity, and to operate these several dimmers simultaneously, as a unit. Lamp loads can easily be thus split, since loads on all lighting branch circuits are never allowed to exceed 1320 watts, which is well below the practicable maximum capacity for single dimmers of any type. Such ganged combinations of individual dimmers, for dimming large lamp loads, are usually called multiple-plate dimmers.

Slider-type dimmers, or spotlight dimmers, as they are sometimes known, constitute perhaps the simplest type of dimmer available. They consist essentially of two parallel strips of heat-resisting insulating material, about each of which half the total dimming resistance, in the form of special "resistance wire", is closely wound. These two resistor strips are mounted separately, a short distance apart, and one end of the resistance wire on each terminates in a heavy binding screw. To these two binding screws are fastened the external wires for connecting the dimmer in series with a lamp circuit. A slider equipped with a multiple leaf bronze spring, slides between the resistor strips, bridges the space between them, and makes contact between the wire windings on each, connecting them in series. When the slider contact is at the terminal binding screws, it simply connects them (electrically), and no dimming resistance is in the circuit. As the slider is moved away from the terminal binding screws, an increasing amount of resistance is "cut into" the circuit, and lamps on the circuit are dimmed. In some grades of slider-type dimmers the sliding contact rubs directly on the resistance wire, and the resistance wire is covered with an insulating cement for protection (except for the strip where the slider makes contact); in the better grades, however, the resistance wire is embedded in vitreous enamel, the slider making contact not with the wire itself, but with a row of heavy brass stud contacts, which are firmly joined to the wire at proper intervals, and which protrude through the layer of vitreous enamel. The slider moves to and fro on a thin rod between the resistors and is operated by means of a short fiber handle attached to it. The resistors and slider are inclosed in a casing of heavy sheet steel, through a longitudinal slot in which the dimmer handle projects. At both ends of the back of the casing are provisions such as clamp and set-screws for fastening the dimmer either on a flat surface or on a pipe. Thus the dimmer may be mounted on a wall, on a switchboard, or on the pipe standard of a spotlight or an olivette. Slider-type dimmers are comparatively inexpensive and are obtainable in a limited number of wattage capacities, ranging from 150 watts to 2000 watts. Their operation is not refined in nature, they are not susceptible to interlock, and hence they are not generally used on switchboards of any appreciable size, except perhaps in a supplementary or auxiliary form. However, they are light in weight, very simple in construction, and are useful for small, inexpensive switchboards, for portable switchboards, and, mounted on pipe standards, for the local control of small units of lighting equipment.

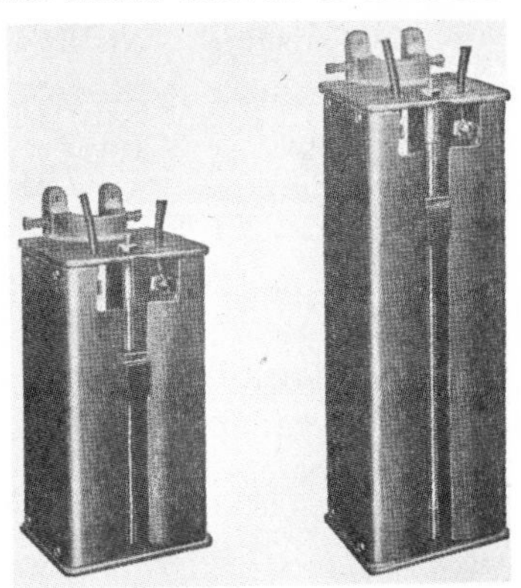

Two sizes of slider type dimmers.

Rectangular plate dimmers are also used, though not to a very great extent, for stage-lighting control. They are flat, compared to slider-type dimmers, and consist essentially of a rectangular cast-iron frame plate, with the resistance wire, embedded in vitreous enamel, mounted on one side of the plate. The wire is connected at various points to heavy brass stud contacts which protrude through the enamel. These stationary contacts are arranged close together, in an arc, and are swept by the sliding contact on a swinging arm that is pivoted at the center of the plate. At one end of the swinging contact arm is a handle by which the dimmer is operated. As in the slider type dimmer, there are two individual resistance elements, or resistors, one on each half of the plate, which are joined in series by the swinging contact arm and which together are connected to the lamp circuits by leads which terminate in screw binding posts mounted on, but insulated from, the iron frame. Rectangular plate dimmers are obtainable in various wattage capacities ranging from 1500 to 5000 watts. They find their greatest use in dimming particularly heavy loads. Because of the space-saving advantage of their rectangular shape, they are sometimes used for large portable switchboards and dimmer banks. In special forms they are susceptible to interlock, though the majority are of the non-interlocking type. Smaller sizes of rectangular plate dimmers, each having but a single resistor, are also available in capacities ranging from 100 to 2750 watts. Rectangular plate dimmers are equipped with offset mounting lugs for flat wall mounting, or if several are used in a group, for "built-up" mounting in banks.

Small, round-plate, non-interlocking dimmers constitute perhaps the most suitable type of dimmer for use by the average amateur producing group. They are also used extensively in the service of regular professional play production. They are comparatively inexpensive (in fact, the least expensive of the several types), and possess almost all the advantages of the standard type of interlocking dimmer described in the following paragraphs. The principal differences are that they are somewhat lighter in construction, and that they are not susceptible to interlock. They are similar to the rectangular plate dimmers, and consist of a cast-iron frame plate, circular in shape, on one side of which the two resistance elements are embedded in vitreous enamel. Thin concentric fins on the reverse side of the plate help radiate the heat generated by the dimmer. The resistance wire of each of the two resistors is distributed around half the circle — each resistor is diametrically opposite the other. A swinging contact arm, pivoted at its center and revolving about a shaft through the center of the dimmer plate, sweeps through an arc of 150° and connects the corresponding stud contacts (protruding through the enamel and arranged closely in circular form) of both the embedded resistors to which the contacts are joined at various points. The dimmer is operated by a handle on the reverse side of the plate. This handle is fastened by a set-screw to the same shaft on which is mounted the contact arm, and hence also sweeps through an arc of 150°. The "leads" from the resistors terminate at screw binding posts that are mounted on the edge of the frame plate, and insulated from it. Round-plate dimmers are available in capacities ranging from 60 to 2750 watts. They vary in size, according to their capacity, from 8″ to 17″ in diameter. They are equipped with offset mounting lugs along the edge for flat-surface mounting; angle holders are also available for mounting the dimmers perpendicularly to a flat surface, in compact banks. Because of the rather large arc through which the dimmer handle must sweep, the dimmers cannot be "built up" into a group (one of the mounting lugs of each dimmer would obstruct the handle of the adjoining dimmer), but must be mounted individually. Another form of round plate dimmer is also available. This employs a different method of mounting the resistance wire: instead of the latter being embedded in vitreous enamel, on a cast-iron plate, in the manner just described, it is contained in a special molded resistor plate. The resistor plate is protected by a ventilated sheet-steel casing.

Small, round-plate, non-interlocking type dimmer.

Large, round-plate, interlocking dimmers constitute the type of dimmers most widely used for stage lighting control, and are universally considered as standard equipment for stage switchboards in regular professional theatres. A dimmer of this type consists principally of the cast-iron frame plate, upon one side of which the resistors and their stud contacts are mounted, embedded in vitreous enamel; the contact arm that bridges the two resistors; the dimmer handle; and the contact-arm drive.

The cast-iron frame plate is circular in form, and bears about its edge the four lugs which are used to mount the dimmer, and the insulating block to which are attached the double buffer stop (to check the contact arm at opposite ends of its traverse) and the two terminal binding screws by which the dimmer is connected to the lighting circuit. One side of the plate is cast with a set of concentric ribs or fins, which provide a larger radiating surface for dissipating the heat generated in the resistance windings of the dimmer. The other side of the plate has a low rim about its edge, and the shallow circular space thus formed serves to keep the vitreous enamel within the limits of the plate during the firing process. The inner surface of the plate is first fired with a thin coating of the enamel. The two resistors, with their brass stud contacts, are mounted on this initial coating of enamel, and the resistance wire and the base of the stud contacts are covered with a second coating of enamel through which the contacts protrude. This is fused with the initial coating by a second firing process, thus uniting the frame plate, the resistance wire, the contacts, and the enamel into an integral structure.

The vitreous enamel supports the resistors, protects them from the deteriorating effects of moisture and air, and insulates them from the frame plate and the remainder of the dimmer mechanism. The firing process subjects the dimmer plates to a much higher temperature than they can possibly be later subjected to in actual use — a fact which assures satisfactory operation under continuous duty at rated capacity loads. The two resistors, each consisting of its crimped resistance wire of various sizes and its set of stud contacts, are each arranged in the form of a circle, one being mounted within the other, instead of diametrically opposite the other, as with the small round-plate dimmers. The two concentric sets of brass stud contacts are bridged by the contact arm, which rotates about a short shaft at the center of the dimmer plate. Self-adjusting contact shoes made of special self-lubricating copper, at each extremity of the contact arm, make a "wipe" contact against the brass stud contacts. The brass stud contacts are usually known as the dimmer "steps." The greater the number of steps a dimmer has, the more smoothly will it control the dimming and brightening of the lamp load to which it is connected. The small plate dimmers discussed previously have from 58 to 110 steps, depending upon their rated capacity. All of the interlocking plate dimmers, however, have 110 steps. This number of steps is sufficient to insure smooth, flickerless dimming. As each set of stud contacts is spaced about a full circle, it is necessary that the contact arm make practically a complete revolution. If the operating handle of the dimmer were mounted on the same shaft as the contact arm, the handle would also have to rotate through a full circle. The flexible contact-arm drive eliminates this obvious inconvenience. By means of a brass-link chain wrapped once about the contact-arm hub, and engaged positively to it by a steel pin, and attached to a bowlike arrangement at one end of the drive rod, the motion of the dimmer handle is multiplied severalfold. The operating handle of the dimmer is never mounted directly on the dimmer plate (as with the several

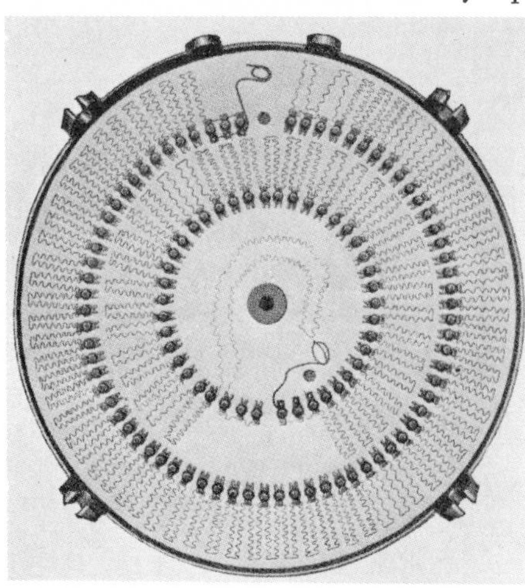

Round-plate interlocking type dimmer before the second application of vitreous enamel, showing the two resistors and their concentric rows of stud contacts.

types of dimmers already described) but, instead, is mounted on a separate shaft, and its motion imparted to the contact arm by means of the contact-arm drive. By virtue of the contact-arm drive, the operating handle need be rotated through an arc of only about 90° in order to rotate the contact arm through a full circle of 360°.

A numbered indicator scale is usually mounted on the hub of the dimmer handle. This scale, which is used in conjunction with a stationary pointer, divides the dimmer-handle traverse into an equal number of parts, usually ten, and provides the operator with a convenient means of gauging the comparative lamp brightness of the various lighting instruments and of quickly duplicating the set-up for a particular effect which had been previously determined by trial, the exact dimmer settings having been noted on the lighting cue sheet. Further conveniences in regard to dimmer operation are the two circuit-indicating tabs mounted on each dimmer handle. These indicate at a glance the exact lighting circuit, and its particular color, controlled by the dimmer.

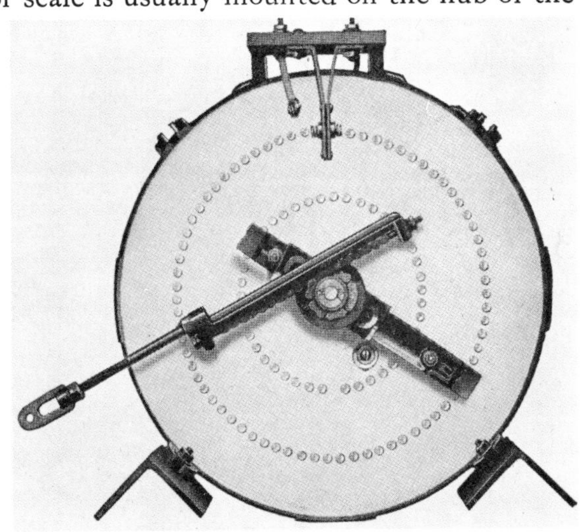

Round-plate interlocking type dimmer mounted on inverted angle-iron strips, showing the stud contacts, contact arm, contact-arm drive, and double buffer stop.

Interlocking dimmers are available in various capacities up to 3600 watts. The fifteen-inch size is available in wattage ratings of 200, 350, 500, 700, 900, 1100, 1300, 1550, and 1800; the seventeen-inch size in wattage ratings of 2100, 2400, 2700, and 3000; and the nineteen-inch size in two wattage ratings, 3300 and 3600. For dimming lamp loads in excess of 3600 watts, multiple-plate dimmers, ganged together and controlled as a unit by a single operating handle, are used. Besides the regular type of interlocking dimmers, with definite wattage ratings, there is also the recently developed type known as the "variable rating" dimmer, which can be used for dimming any lamp load within a limited range (not, however, with equal dimmer-handle traverse, to "black out", for all loads within the range). A variable rating dimmer has resistance enough for the minimum wattage for which it is designed and capacity enough (large enough resistance wire) for the maximum wattage for which it is designed. These are especially suitable for use in the flexible type of stage-lighting control, where dimmers are not permanently connected to unvarying lamp loads. Variable rating dimmers are available in four sizes: 500 to 1000 watts (15-inch size); 750 to 1500 watts (17-inch size); 1000 to 2000 watts (17-inch size); and 1500 to 3000 watts (19-inch size).

A bank of interlocking plate dimmers as arranged for open-bank mounting.

By means of the four lugs on the rim of the frame plate, the dimmer can be mounted in virtually any desired manner. When grouped in banks, large plate dimmers are usually bolted on to two parallel, horizontal, inverted strips of angle iron. Completed frames, for mounting one or more rows of dimmers, are also constructed of angle-iron strips, bolted and braced.

The important interlocking feature of the standard type of theatre dimmer is made possible by virtue of the fact that the control handle is mounted apart from the dimmer plate — on a separate shaft. At each individual dimmer handle, on the shaft, there is also mounted, rigidly (instead of rotatively, as is the dimmer handle itself), a narrow, slotted collar. Each individual dimmer handle on the shaft is equipped with a spring latching pin. This pin engages with the slot in the narrow collar, thus locking the dimmer handle to the shaft. This method is similar to the interlocking method already described for switches, on page 298. Thus the basic, fundamental operation of the several types of interlocking dimmer control is achieved. A master handle attached to the interlocking shaft makes it possible to operate simultaneously, as a unit, all the dimmers locked to the shaft. Most stage switchboards have the dimmer equipment divided into several groups, or banks — one for each color main. The master handle for each color group of dimmers is also equipped with a latching device, by means of which the master handle can be locked to a link-and-lever mechanism operated by a "grand master handle." Thus the several master handles in turn are subject to interlocking control by a grand master handle. Since considerable force must be applied to the

A bank of interlocking plate dimmers as arranged for dead-front mounting.

grand master handle in order to operate as a unit all the interlocked dimmers of a large dimmer installation, the grand master handle on such an installation is usually replaced, or supplemented, by a "slow-motion wheel." This slow-motion wheel, operating through a reduction gear ratio, makes it possible to dim simultaneously a large number of interlocked dimmers both very easily and very smoothly.

Pre-set dimmers, somewhat analogous in interlocking arrangements to mechanically pre-set switches, are gradually coming into use. The master handle of a bank of dimmers will "pick up" any individual dimmer whose latch is set for interlock; that is, set to engage its corresponding slotted collar on the shaft, as the master handle passes the position of the individual handle. For example, should it be desired to "bring down", with the master handle, four dimmers that are set respectively at points 2, 4, 6, and 8 (on a zero to ten indicator scale), the master handle is first moved to the 10, or "on", position, and the latch on each of the four dimmers set for interlock. When the master handle is moved toward the "off", or "dim", position, it will pick up and bring down with it first the dimmer positioned at 8, next the one at 6, next the one at 4, and finally the one at 2. Thus the master handle can automatically pick up individual dimmers at any predetermined position. But with the ordinary type of interlocking mechanism the reverse process cannot be achieved; that is, individual handles cannot be automatically "dropped off" the master handle at predetermined positions. Instead, each must be unlatched manually when it reaches the proper position. This automatic drop-off has been embodied in only a very few dimmer installations, which are necessarily elaborate in construction and operation. They constitute what might be called full "pre-set" dimmer installations, as, with only two quick movements of the grand master handle (one to "pick up" all the dimmers used in the previous scene, and the other to "drop off", at predetermined, or pre-set, positions, all the dimmers to be used for the following scene), the entire dimmer set-up for any predetermined arrangement of lighting equipment may be accomplished in a moment if the dimmers have been pre-set during the course of the previous scene.

By means of double latching pins on each of the master handles, and a double link-and-lever mechanism (each unit of which operates simultaneously in a direction opposite to that of the other), "cross control" by the grand master handle, or slow-motion wheel, is made possible. With an interlocking cross-control mechanism, the groups of dimmers locked to one master handle can be "brought up" at the same time, and with the same movement of the slow-motion wheel, that the group of dimmers locked to another is "brought down", and vice-versa. This is effected by locking one of the two latching pins on each master handle to the proper unit of the double link-and-lever mechanism which interconnects the several master handles and is operated by the slow-motion wheel. The usual type of interlocking cross control cannot be applied to indiscriminate groups of individual dimmers; it is restricted to groups of dimmers that are locked to master handles. This is not a particular disadvantage, however, because most dimmer installations are divided into color groups (each of which is controlled by an interlocking master handle), to which cross control is principally applied, as, for example, for dawn and sunset effects. However, some special designs of interlocking cross control employ double shafts for the individual dimmers, and are thus able to provide "adjoining cross control", which is applicable to individual dimmers within color banks.

Thus are apparent the several possibilities of mechanical interlocking systems for dimmer control. These interlocking systems are constantly being refined and elaborated, although the actual dimming unit — the dimmer plate — remains substantially the same in design and construction. Sometimes, unfortunately, interlocking devices are elaborated to an extent, and in a direction, that renders practical switchboard manipulation so cumbersome and involved that they defeat their own purpose. In spite of their many advantages and refinements, mechanical interlocking systems still fall far short of providing a fundamentally satisfactory control of dimmer installations. Perhaps their most important shortcoming is their inability to achieve what might be termed "proportional simultaneous dimming." A typical example of "proportional simultaneous dimming" — a problem that arises constantly — might be as follows: Four dimmers are positioned respectively at points 2, 4, 6, and 8 on a zero-to-ten indicator scale. It is desired to dim these simultaneously, starting together, and reaching "black out" together. This means that each dimmer must be manipulated at a different rate, as the first dimmer must traverse two scale-units, the second must traverse four, the third six, and the fourth eight, all in the same space of time. Normally, one switchboard operator unassisted could not manipulate four individual handles to carry this out smoothly. If these four dimmers were interlocked and brought down with a master handle, the proportionality of the dimming — the ratio of the four light intensities (represented by the scale positions of the dimmers) to each other — would not be preserved. Instead, the fourth dimmer would be the first to latch in and begin to dim and would be three-fourths dimmed before the third dimmer would latch in and begin to dim. The fourth dimmer would already be half dimmed, and the third dimmer two-thirds dimmed, before the second dimmer would latch in and begin to dim. And so on, until all the dimmers had been picked up in turn by the master handle and brought down to "black out", or to zero on the indicator scale. The handicap imposed by this shortcoming is an obvious one and is most keenly felt where the graded-mixture method of color control is used. Here light of the three primary hues and clear light (each, of course, under individual dimmer control) are mixed in the proper proportions to attain light of a desired resultant color. If this resultant light color be dimmed by mechanical interlocking as described above, the proportions of the constituent colored and clear light will be unbalanced and the resultant color will undergo a series of violent changes from the original before "black out" is reached. This illustrates the necessity of proportional simultaneous dimming, which has not yet been achieved by mechanical interlocking and which usually requires the synchronized efforts of several trained switchboard operators in order to be carried out smoothly. An electrical method of achieving proportional simultaneous dimming is described in a following section on page 359.

A recent development that is sometimes applied to interlocking plate dimmers, especially for use on certain types of composite switchboards, is the "flipper switch." This serves simply to open the circuit when the contact arm of the dimmer has reached the "black-out" position. It is mounted on the rim of the dimmer frame plate and consists of a "quick-make" and "quick-break" mechanism that is connected electrically to the final stud contact on the outer circular resistor. As the contact arm approaches the "black-out" end of its traverse, it engages the actuating lever of the flipper switch, and, just as the contact shoe leaves the final "live" stud contact, the electrical circuit connecting the two resistors is automatically opened, thereby disconnecting all current from the lamp circuits controlled by the dimmer. The flipper switch thus makes unnecessary the opening of the regular circuit switch on the switchboard, and avoids the waste of current (about one fourth of the normal lamp load) that flows through the dimmer even though the lamps are "black out."

Flipper switch mounted on the edge of an interlocking plate dimmer.

The dimmers described above, of all types, employing vitreous enamel resistor plates, are known as "Vitrohm" dimmers, and are a product of the Ward Leonard Electric Company.

Interlocking plate dimmers of another type of construction are also available. These are similar in principle to those described immediately above, but differ in several features of construction. Instead of the resistors being embedded in vitreous enamel on an iron plate, they are mounted on a soapstone base and covered with a protective coating of special cement. The two resistors are each arranged in semicircular form, and are placed diametrically opposite each other, their stud contacts forming an interrupted circle near the edge of the plate. The contact arm thus traverses a semicircle rather than a full circle. Instead of the flexible link contact-arm drive, a rack-and-pinion system is employed. All the various types of mechanical interlocking previously described are also applicable to dimmers of this type of construction. These dimmers are available in double-faced form; that is, two dimmers can be placed on reverse sides of the same soapstone plate. The combined rated capacities of both sides, however, cannot exceed 3600 watts, as this seems to be the practicable maximum capacity for all single plates, regardless of construction. These double-faced dimmers are useful for reducing somewhat the space occupied by large banks of dimmers. Dimmers of this type of construction are known as "Simplicity" dimmers, and are a product of the Cutler-Hammer Manufacturing Company.

Interlocking multiple switch and dimmer unit, showing the switch and dimmer handles protruding through the unit switchboard panel; the circuit fuses below, and the circuit cable-connector above.

A special form of the vitreous enameled plate dimmer, termed the "interlocking multiple switch and dimmer unit", has been developed by Munroe Pevear for use on portable or wall-type switchboards. The dimmer plate itself is fan-shaped, and the contact arm and dimmer handle form a rigid unit, pivoted on a self contained shaft at the converging end of the dimmer plate. The dimmer plate is mounted perpendicularly, on the front of which is placed a narrow panel through which the dimmer indicator handle protrudes. Branch circuit fuses, as well as a switch, are also mounted on the dimmer plate, and the interlocking switch handle also protrudes through the panel. Dimmer plate, contact arm, interlocking indicator handle, fuses, interlocking switch, and panel, together with interchangeable load outlets, constitute a dimmer unit. Any single unit is easily removed, from the front, and a bank of them may readily be added to or subtracted from to build up any desired grouping of dimmers for some particular service. By means of ingenious and rugged mechanical devices, both the dimmers and switches can be interlocked, despite the self-contained character and interchangeability of each dimmer unit. These dimmer units are available in three rated capacities: 500 watts, 1000 watts, and 1500 watts.

All the dimmers so far discussed are of the resistance type, for direct control. Another class of dimmers consists of those for remote control. Of course, the direct-control resistance type of dimmer can be equipped with tracker wires and controlled at a distance. This has been done in a number of installations, notably in the Metropolitan Opera House, where a large bank of dimmers in a sub-basement is conveniently controlled, through an intricate system of tracker wires, from the switchboard, the dimmer control handles being placed adjacent to the corresponding switch handles. In fact, the control of resistance-type dimmers at a distance, by means of wires, is "standard practice" in German theatres, direct-control dimmers being regarded as almost a curiosity. Standard resistance dimmers are often actuated by small electric motors and thus controlled from a distance.

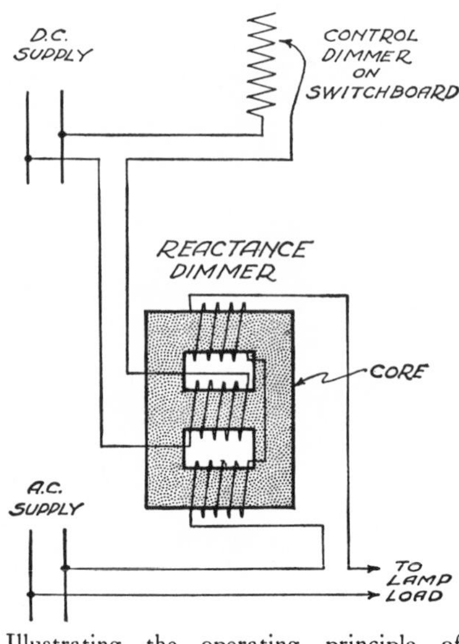

Illustrating the operating principle of a remote-controlled, or reactance type, dimmer.

But the true "remote-controlled" dimmer, analogous to the remote-controlled switches described previously, is the "reactance dimmer." This does not cause the dimming of incandescent lamps by virtue of the resistance offered to the flow of electric current by coils of fine wire, but depends for its operation on a more involved principle of alternating-current electricity. The reactance dimmer consists of three coils wound on an 8-shaped iron core. The two outer coils are wired in series with the lamp-load circuit, conducting alternating current. The middle coil is wired in series with the control circuit, conducting direct current, which is regulated by a resistance-type dimmer at the stage switchboard. When no direct current is flowing through the middle coil, the alternating current of the lamp circuit, flowing through the outer coils, is opposed by the impedance set up by virtue of the voltage self-induced by the alternating current in its two coils. The lamps are then "black out." When direct current is admitted to the middle coil, the magnetic flux it creates in the iron core reduces the impedance that opposes the passage of the alternating current in the lamp circuit, and the lamps brighten. When the direct current is at a maximum, the impedance of the lamp circuit is at a minimum, and the lamps are "full up", or bright. Thus, by regulating the amount of direct current flowing through the middle coil, by means of the resistance dimmer at the stage switchboard, the impedance of the lamp circuit, and hence the brightness of the lamps themselves, is easily controlled. The use of reactance dimmers is invariably confined to the control of lamp loads in excess of the maximum rated capacity of a single-plate interlocking dimmer of the resistance type. A single reactance dimmer, operated by a single interlocking plate dimmer, can be used to control as great a load as 30,000 watts — a load that would require a 10-plate dimmer of the resistance type. For large installations, the space-saving advantage of reactance dimmers is apparent — the single-plate control dimmers being placed directly at the stage switchboard, where space is limited and valuable, and the reactance dimmers proper being placed wherever space may be available, usually in a sub-basement or other remote location.

A remote-controlled reactance type dimmer.

The several types of resistance and reactance dimmers discussed above are universally used in this country, practically to the exclusion of all other types. Brief mention of several other miscellaneous types might prove of interest. The "water-barrel dimmer" which was perhaps the earliest form of dimmer developed, has been discarded in America but is still used to some extent in England and France despite its many disadvantages. Its principal advantage lies in its low cost. It depends for its dimming action on the low electrical conductivity of water and of water solutions of certain chemical salts. It consists principally of a non-metallic container of appreciable capacity filled with an electrolyte (usually brine, a water solution of common salt) and two metallic plates. One of the plates is stationary, lying at the bottom of the container and the other plate is free to move in a vertical direction from the bottom of the container to the level of the electrolyte in it. Each plate is connected to one of the series leads from the lamp load circuit. When the movable plate rests upon the stationary plate, direct contact is made between the two, hence no resistance is in the circuit, and the lamps are bright. When the movable plate is slowly lifted off the stationary plate, the current must travel through a portion of the electrolyte: this introduces resistance into the circuit and the lamps dim. As the distance between the plates increases, the resistance increases, until at a certain point (depending upon the area of the plates and the strength of the electrolyte) the lamps are "black-out." The water-barrel dimmer is low in cost, and, when properly maintained and operated, produces smooth, very satisfactory dimming results. But its form is bulky and inconvenient, it requires constant attention and care, and it is likely to emit noxious fumes when it is overloaded. "Carbon pile dimmers" were at one time used to an appreciable extent, and occasionally may still be found in old installations. A carbon pile dimmer consists of a number of thin carbon discs piled one on the other in a viselike arrangement for applying pressure to the pile. By varying the pressure on the carbon discs the resistance of the carbon pile can be controlled: under high pressure the resistance is very low, and the lamps connected in series with the carbon pile are bright; under low pressure, the resistance is high, and the lamps are dimmed. Several inconvenient features, principally the low maximum capacities and the impossibility of achieving rapid dimming (the pressure mechanism being operated through a fine-pitch screw which required many turns of the operating handle) resulted in the abandonment of this type of dimmer. Besides these types of dimmers, experiments have at various times been conducted to determine the adaptability of other electrical phenomena to the problem of stage dimming. Among these may be mentioned photo-electric cells in conjunction with auxiliary circuits having miniature lamps and dimmers operating on the principal that the conductivity of selenium and similar materials depends upon the amount of light falling upon them; special transformers with multiple-tapped secondary windings; large vacuum tubes, for amplification of miniature control circuits, such as are used in radio work; and small, variable-speed generators. However, no satisfactory results of practicable value have been obtained with these experimental dimmers, and the resistance-type dimmer, with metallic resistor elements, still remains the standard for stage-control work, with the reactance dimmer for exceptionally large lamp-circuit loads.

C. MAGAZINE PANEL

The two principal components of a stage switchboard, from the standpoint of operation, namely, the switches and the dimmers, have just been described. A third component, which is of importance chiefly from the standpoint of safety, is the magazine panel. A magazine panel may be briefly described as consisting of the groups of fuses that protect the various switchboard circuits. The elements of circuit arrangement and subdivision, and of the fusing of circuits — main circuits, sub-main circuits, and branch circuits — have been discussed in the third chapter.

The gradual adoption, in recent years, of the wiring practice known as the "grounded neutral" — a practice that already is virtually universal in extent — involves a modification of the fundamental method of fusing described in Chapter III. The latter method is that used with the older wiring practice of the ungrounded neutral, or the completely insulated circuit. After years of experimentation, the grounded neutral has been adopted as a safety measure (in many cases the Code makes it compulsory). The practice of using the grounded neutral consists principally of intentionally grounding (electrically connecting with the earth, which serves as a common conductor) the neutral wire of the usual three-wire system of electrical circuits, whether direct current or single-phase alternating current. In the event of an accidental ground, or a short circuit, or a leakage, from a high voltage outside electric-service wire on to the regular interior circuit wires (conditions which may be caused by improper outside wiring connections, or by contacts between outside high and low voltage systems, or by leakage between these systems in wet weather, wind, and so forth) no harm can befall the interior wiring system, which has a well-grounded neutral, for the following reason. If the contact or leakage be either to an outside wire or to the neutral of a three-wire grounded-neutral system, the high-voltage system reduces its potential, at the point of contact or leakage, to the potential — 115 volts or zero — of the wire of the low-voltage system. Or, if the high-voltage system is intentionally or accidentally grounded at another point, the current flow in the high-voltage system becomes enough to open a high-voltage system fuse and remove the source of danger.

More recently the practice of grounding equipment frames has grown up. This involves all metallic parts (the conduit enclosing the circuit wires, switch boxes, plugging receptacles, footlight troughs, borderlights, the frame and front face and operating handles of switchboards, dimmer frame plates and so forth — all normally non-conducting, that is, not part of the electrical circuit) of the electrical installation, which operators of the equipment, or other persons, touch or otherwise come into direct physical contact with. In the event of a high-voltage contact or leakage to the interior wiring system, the grounded neutral affords the proper protection, as explained in the preceding paragraph. In the event, however, of a breakdown of the insulating covering of wires or windings contained in the equipment, the grounding of the equipment frame will establish a circuit between this ground and that of the grounded neutral circuit, and this will open fuses if it is an outside wire or could in any way raise the potential of the equipment frame above the potential of the "ground" (for example, the floor the operator walks upon, or the pipes and steel building girders he cannot avoid coming in contact with). Since the operator and other persons must handle these frames of equipment in the course of ordinary duties, it is essential that the frames be reliably kept at ground potential; namely, zero potential.

Thus there are two different and separate means of protection. The circuit neutral is grounded, to avoid *abnormal* high-voltage dangers, and to assure that the highest voltage on inside wires shall be not more than half that which might exist if one outside wire became and continued accidentally grounded, as might often occur were the neutral not grounded intentionally (and did often occur before protective grounding became general). The equipment frame is grounded to prevent the *normal* low voltage dangers which would occur if insulation within these frames broke down and these frames were not well grounded. The neutral is never attached to the equipment frame, since an accident to the ground connection and several other types of accident or carelessness of workmen, inside buildings and outside, would then *make* equipment frames alive. When the neutral and equipment frames are kept unconnected, the worst which can occur is the loss of the protection by loss of ground connection — but no active hazard is imposed.

The neutral wire, being grounded, needs no protection against accidental loss of insulation between it and grounded surfaces, although such an insulation is maintained to prevent leakage of current through parts of buildings other than the wires which are designed to carry such currents safely. Also, the opening of fuses in a neutral wire might tend to impose too great voltage on a few appliances or lights on one side when a large number of appliances or lights are feeding from the other side, as explained on page 59. Furthermore, by omitting fuses in the neutral, the whole installation can be made simpler, of less first cost, and with few parts to cause trouble and bad service. Therefore good practice to-day calls for omission of all neutral fuses.

Even on branch 2-wire circuits most of the reasoning and experienced advantage lies with omitting fuses from the grounded wire. To permit and facilitate safety and simplification of such 3-wire and 2-wire grounded circuits, an identified wire and a polarized system of wires and fittings have been developed and should be used.

For these reasons it has become standard, and even compulsory, practice to omit the fuse from the neutral wire, even on the neutral-wire extension of 2-wire branch circuits, on grounded neutral-wiring systems. Only a single fuse, placed in the outside wire, is used to protect branch circuits or grounded systems. This practice of single fusing on grounded systems has materially simplified the wiring of stage switchboards, and the magazine panels that form a part of them. Only half the former number of branch fuses are required, and, in addition, all the wiring to switches and dimmers is accomplished by only one wire (the outside wire of the 3-wire system) for each circuit, the second wire (the neutral) joining it, from the grounded neutral-bar common to all branch circuits, as it leaves the switchboard on its way to supply a lighting instrument or a plugging receptacle. In order to derive the full benefit of the grounded neutral, the neutral wire must be identified, and its integrity — its continuity — maintained, throughout the entire wiring system: fuses and switches (except multi-pole switches that simultaneously open all the conductors of a circuit) and other interrupting devices must not be placed on it. Dimmers, however (except those equipped with automatic disconnect flipper switches), may be placed in a neutral wire, since they are a fixed equipment, extremely unlikely to be removed or to open the circuit completely, and since their use in this manner simplifies and makes compact the whole switchboard design, thus adding to instead of detracting from safety. Where conditions render possible the accidental transposition of the grounded neutral wire and the outside wire of a 2-wire tap circuit, a fuse must be placed in each conductor of the branch circuits into which the original circuit is subdivided. The latter condition would prevail in the case of a 2-wire plugging box connected, by means of a reversible plug, to a stage pocket: double fusing would be required on the branch circuits in the plugging box.

The arrangement of magazine panels depends entirely upon the characteristics of the stage switchboards of which they form a part. Fuses are usually grouped in a logical, systematic manner, and are so identified that necessary replacements can be readily effected. Any special or unusual features of fusing and of magazine panels will be pointed out in the discussion of the particular types of switchboards with which they are employed.

D. ASSEMBLY

There are several general methods of arranging, or mounting, the switches, the dimmers, and the fuses to form a switchboard, or control board, for the control of stage lighting. The earliest method was perhaps the simplest, at least from the standpoint of construction. Open-knife switches mounted directly on the front face of a vertical slab of slate constituted the switchboard proper. The dimmers (when there were any) were mounted in an iron frame and placed in a horizontal row across the top edge of the switchboard. The magazine panel containing the fuses was sometimes self-contained, and mounted adjacent to, though apart from, the switchboard and dimmer bank; sometimes it was merged with the switchboard, the fuses being mounted adjacent to their corresponding circuit switches. Such switchboard assemblies were nothing more or less than electrical devices for circuit subdivision, primitive in nature — in their design, no thought seems to have been devoted to convenience of manipulation or to any other characteristics of control-board design that are considered so essential to-day. The first improvements on this early type of switchboard were made from the standpoint of safety. Because of the nature of backstage conditions, the "live" circuits exposed by the open-knife switches and their connections constituted an ever-present hazard, both as to fire and as to personal safety. To obviate this dangerous condition the switches were mounted behind an insulating cover, and their operating handles extended beyond it by insulated connecting bars. No live parts were exposed, hence the name "dead-front" board. Some attention was also paid to ease of manipulation — the switches were arranged in a logical grouping, according to color and location of lighting instruments. Next, the principle of mounting dimmer handles adjacent to their corresponding circuit switch handles was adopted and developed. Interlocking systems for both dimmers and switches were devised and elaborated. The adoption of remote-control magnet switches made possible elaborate provisions for pre-set. Stage switchboards were built as a single piece of equipment embodying the switches, the dimmers, and the magazine panel, in a composite unit. At the present time, practice in switchboard design and construction varies extensively — from the most primitive to the most modern and elaborate. In many instances, the tendency of the latter practice seems to be ultimately towards the use of intricate electrical and mechanical devices which do not help greatly to solve the fundamental problems of stage-lighting control — many of the modern improvements in switchboard design seem to be superficial in nature. However, in the future development of switchboards, it is probable that most of the superficialities will gradually effect their own abandonment, while the advances of a more fundamental and substantial nature will be permanently retained and will help to create an increasingly satisfactory mechanism of stage-lighting control. Because of the wide variations in design and in methods of construction (it may truly be said that there are no two stage switchboards exactly alike in all respects) it is not feasible to give such definite descriptions of switchboards as were accorded the several types of stage-lighting instruments in a previous chapter.

Present-day switchboards may roughly be divided into two general classes: those providing direct control and those providing the so-called remote control.

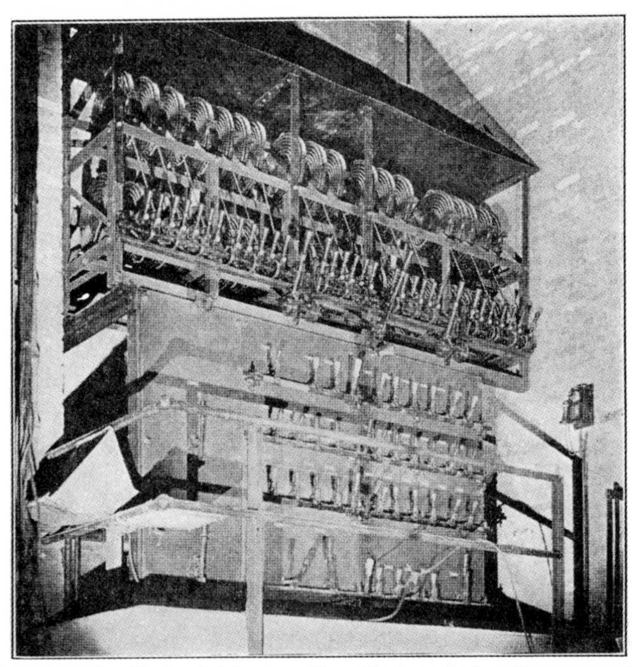

The switchboard at the National Theatre, New York: of the direct control, elemental type, with the dimmer bank mounted above the switchboard proper. This switchboard is elevated on a platform above the stage floor at the right side of the proscenium opening.

Direct-control switchboards may be further divided into two types: the elemental — in which the switchboard proper and the dimmer bank and the magazine panel are mounted separately; and the composite — in which these elements are merged into a single structure — in which the dimmer and switch handles are adjacent. Obsolete as they are, examples of the *elemental* type of direct-control switchboards — those in which the dimmer bank and switchboard proper are separate elements — are still being installed. The switchboard proper is, of course, always of the dead-front type, the switch handles being grouped according to color and instrument location. The dimmers are usually mounted in one or more horizontal rows on the top edge of the switchboard, the operating handles being brought within reach of the operator by means of extended contact-arm drives. In some cases, the dimmers are mounted in horizontal rows alongside the switchboard rather than above it. Either method of dimmer mounting, however, is inconvenient and confusing from the standpoint of manipulation, as the dimmer controls are widely separated from, and usually not even in a corresponding position to, the circuit switch controls. This type of switchboard is used principally with the permanent type of stage-lighting control, the switchboard circuits being permanently connected to the instrument wiring circuits. Such switchboards are usually limited, in circuit capacity and circuit arrangement and other accommodations, to the conditions for which they were initially designed — that is, they are quite permanent in all their features. Examples of the second type of direct control switchboards — the *composite* type — are being installed in increasing number as their advantages are becoming more fully realized. The basis of this type of switchboard is the dimmer bank, consisting of several horizontal rows of interlocking dimmer plates mounted in a rigid angle-iron framework. The switches are mounted directly behind the front panel, which is mounted on the front of the dimmer-bank frame. By thus mounting the circuit switches and their corresponding dimmers adjacent to each other, it is possible to have both controlling handles of each circuit adjoin each other on the face of the switchboard. This practice eliminates much of the confusion and uncertainty and many of the embarrassingly impromptu lighting effects that are attendant upon the earlier practice of separating the switches and dimmers. The magazine panel containing the various circuit fuses is usually mounted at one end of the switchboard. Thus the three elements of a stage switchboard are brought together in composite form, which makes switchboard manipulation immeasurably more certain and simple. The reverse bar-connected knife switches, the rotor-movement switches, and the flipper switches mounted on dimmer plates, all of which have been previously described, are among the special types of switches that have been adopted for use on the composite-type switchboard. Many composite switchboards are built on the "unit construction" principle, which allots exactly the same space, on the face of the switchboard, to each stage circuit up to 3600 watts capacity (maximum single-plate dimmer capacity). This allows for the convenient replacements of circuit dimmers in the event of future changes in circuit loads, and besides, by leaving blank spaces in the switchboard construction, provides for the incorporation of additional circuits in the future. When the composite type of switchboard is used in conjunction with the permanent type of stage-lighting control, the double sets of control handles are arranged in accordance with the usual layout, which is in intersecting horizontal and vertical rows, the horizontal rows representing the colors, and the vertical rows the various lighting instruments. But when designed for use with the flexible type of control, the composite switchboard has its switch and dimmer handles arranged differently — classification in

The switchboard at the Guild Theatre, New York: of the direct control, composite type, the dimmer handles being adjacent to the corresponding switch handles. 121 interlocking plate dimmers are mounted behind the face of the switchboard, and 24 slider type dimmers, for supplementary split-circuit service, are mounted at the bottom of the switchboard. This switchboard is on the stage floor level at the left side of the proscenium opening.

this case being usually according to the dimmer capacities. Dimmers of like capacities are grouped together, and the several groups positioned in regular order, ranging from the lowest to the highest dimmer capacities. Of course, it is a cardinal principle of switchboard design to include the auditorium lighting control on the stage switchboard; this portion is always permanent in nature, even on "flexible" switchboards. Interlocking is also used on composite switchboards; it is always applied, in more or less elaborate form, to the dimmers, and in some cases also to the switches. *Portable switchboards*, used exclusively with the portable type of stage-lighting control, also belong in the present category of direct-controlled switchboards. Since they are compactly built and altogether self-contained, most portable switchboards may be regarded as being virtually composite in nature, although in many cases the form of construction and the layout of control handles is so illogical and inconvenient as to emulate the most obsolete of the elemental type of switchboards. However, excellent portable switchboards of the strictly composite type, of interchangeable "unit" construction,

A multi-pre-set remote-controlled switchboard: the pilot board at the Farnum Theatre, Omaha.

and with interlocking features, are now available. For those portable switchboards that are "made up" to meet the special set of control needs of one particular production, the advantage of unit construction is apparent — it will allow the easy rearrangement and assembly of dimmers of various capacities, as demanded by subsequent productions, without necessitating the complete disorganization and reconstruction of the switchboard.

Remote-control switchboards are a comparatively recent development. Although remote-controlled switches or "magnet switches", or "contactors", as they are variously termed, were at first used to control large current loads, and thus eliminate heavy, and cumbersome, space-consuming control devices from the stage switchboard, they are now used principally to provide elaborate, and sometimes superficial, refinements of control, especially in the direction of "pre-set." Magnet switches are used on direct-control boards to a limited extent; as a matter of fact, there are few direct-control switchboards built at present that do not utilize at least several remote-control switches for controlling the heavier current loads, especially the larger and principal circuit subdivisions. A remote-control switchboard, then, is one that employs remote switching exclusively, and rather for achieving elaborate control arrangements than for conveniently handling heavy current loads. As a general rule, reactance dimmers (the counterpart of magnet switches) are not used extensively even on remote-control switchboards, except to dim current loads in excess of the maximum single-plate dimmer capacity (3600 watts), and then only when the switchboard installation is abnormally large or the available space abnormally small. Remote-control switchboards consist of two principal parts — the pilot board and the contactor board. The *pilot board* consists of the actual mechanism of control, and is located directly on the stage. The layout of the switch handles and dimmer handles on its front face is essentially the same as on a direct-control switchboard. The switches on the pilot board are known as the pilot switches, since they control the operation of the magnet switches, or contactors. These contactors are mounted, similarly, in relative layout, to that of their respective pilot switches on the pilot board, on the *contactor board*, which is situated apart from the pilot board, usually in a basement or other location where space is not at a premium. The fuses protecting the lighting circuits controlled by the contactors are sometimes mounted in a separate magazine panel adjacent to the contactor board, but usually they are mounted directly on the contactor board itself, adjoining the corresponding contactors whose branch circuits they protect. In addition to the usual lighting circuit fuses, a fuse is inserted in each of the pilot circuits. Where reactance dimmers are used, they are mounted in close proximity to the contactor board, in order to simplify the wiring. With a remote-controlled switchboard, the main supply of current is brought not to the pilot board on the stage, but to the contactor board, where it is divided into individual circuits which are then brought to the dimmers. With the reactance dimmers, the circuits travel directly from the basement room to the lighting equipment; with

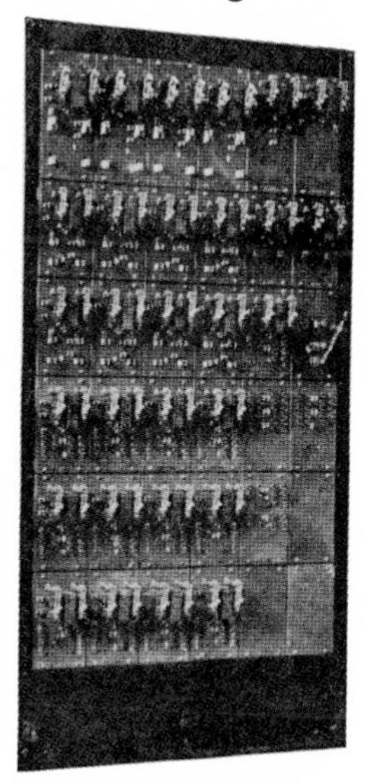

A typical contactor board, as used with a remote-controlled switch board installation, containing the magnet switches that are remotely operated from the pilot board on the stage.

regular resistance dimmers, the circuits must first travel to the pilot board and thence to the lighting equipment. The dimmer plates on the pilot board, be they direct-control resistance plates, or pilot plates operating reactance dimmers (on many pilot boards they are side by side, depending on the current loads of the various circuits), are subject to the usual ramifications of interlocking. The pilot switches, however, are never of the interlocking type, as their characteristics lend themselves to what might be termed "electrical interconnection." Usually two or more pilot switches, in complex wiring combinations, are applied to each circuit in order to achieve this electrical interconnection. The pilot switches and dimmers used on each circuit constitute an interchangeable construction-unit. The usual type of remote-control switchboard is virtually confined to use with the permanent type of stage-lighting control.

A representative *switchboard for permanent control* has already been sketchily outlined in Chapter III. A distinguishing characteristic of a switchboard for permanent control, be it of the direct-control or remote-control type, lies in its manner of circuit subdivision. The supply of electric current from the general lighting service of the theatre to the stage switchboard is first divided into two parts — that for the auditorium and that for the stage. For obvious reasons, both the auditorium and the stage lights are controlled from the stage switchboard, the controls for each being grouped and placed on separate portions of the switchboard face. The stage main circuit is subdivided into several color sub-main circuits, and each of these in turn is again divided into the circuits supplying the individual units of stage-lighting equipment. If the individual switches are not of the interlocking type, as is always the case in remote-control switchboards, color main and stage main switches are necessary. If the individual switches are of the interlocking type, color main and stage main switches need not be supplied, as they are supplanted in effect by the color master and grand master switch handles respectively. The individual switches that subdivide each color main are placed in horizontal rows. These are known as the "color sections." The switches in the color sections that supply the same units of equipment are placed in vertical rows. With this layout the circuit switches are virtually self-indexed and are easily found. With the composite type switchboard, this is also true of the dimmer controls. Usually, each individual circuit is provided with a dimmer whose rated capacity equals the known or estimated circuit load. The dimmers are interlocked more or less elaborately, according to the possibilities already discussed. With all remote-control switchboards, and many direct-control switchboards, a pilot light is wired into each individual switchboard circuit, and adjoins the switch and dimmer handles of its corresponding circuit. The pilot light itself is a low wattage lamp (which does not dim with the circuit) and serves to indicate whether or not its circuit is "alive" — whether or not any current is flowing through it. All the component switchboard circuits, and the electrical devices on them, are permanently wired to the source of supply — the feeders from the general lighting service — and are also permanently wired to the wiring circuits that extend to the various units of lighting equipment about the stage. The latter feature, of course, is the determining characteristic of a switchboard for permanent control. Although constructional features vary according to both the exact type of switchboard and the manufacturer, the general practices followed in constructing stage switchboards for permanent control service is fairly uniform and consistent. Thus, a bolted or riveted angle-iron frame forms the structural basis of the switchboard; electrically grounded sheet-metal panels constitute the face plate (instead of the older practice of using an insulating material such as slate); rigid copper bus bars, and asbestos-covered copper cable in sheet-metal ducts and raceways are used for the conductors of the switchboard circuits; and so forth.

A *switchboard for flexible control* is much the same in constructional features as one for permanent control. It also controls the auditorium lights in addition to the stage lights, but the portion controlling the former is permanently wired and permanently connected to the auditorium wiring circuits. In circuit subdivision, however, it is entirely different. The stage main is not divided into color mains, and the layout of control handles on the switchboard face is not according to color sections and equipment supplied. Instead, the stage main is simply divided into a number of switchboard circuits, each with a dimmer. The dimmers on the switchboard circuits are of different capacities. The number of switchboard circuits, and the number of dimmers of each capacity, vary widely from one switchboard to another, depending altogether upon the estimated demands that the switchboard will have to meet — the size of stage, the amount and type of lighting equipment, and the general type of play production work for which the switchboard will be used. The layout of the circuit controls — switch and dimmer handles — on the face of the switchboard also differs in each case. Usually it is simply an orderly, logical sequence arrangement according to the circuit-dimmer capacities — circuits of equal capacities being grouped together. Dimmer interlocking (and also switch interlocking, if there is any) is usually not as elaborate as in switchboards for permanent control. Pilot lights for each switchboard circuit are usually supplied. The switchboard circuits are all permanently wired to the incoming supply feeders from the general lighting service. But the determining characteristic of a switchboard for flexible control is the fact that the switchboard circuits are not permanently connected to the wiring circuits that extend to lighting instruments or to lighting instrument locations. Instead, each terminates in one or several plugging receptacles of convenient type. These plugging receptacles are grouped together and are usually mounted in a special panel on the switchboard, or sometimes apart from, though adjacent to, the switchboard. The switchboard circuits are usually designated by number, and their control handles so identified on the face of the board.

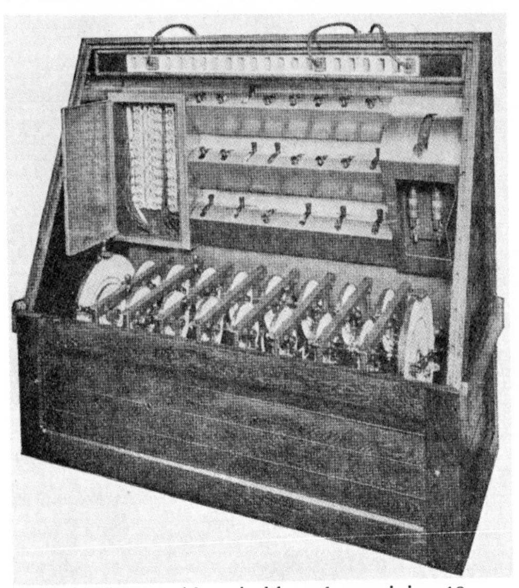

A 22-circuit portable switchboard containing 18 non-interlocking plate dimmers.

The plugging receptacles are correspondingly identified on the plugging panel, as well as being marked with the maximum circuit-dimmer capacity of the circuit which each terminates. This latter designation is necessary in order to reduce the possibility of overloading the circuit dimmers — a possibility which is the bane of flexible switchboards. The instrument wiring circuits in the form of short leads of cable terminate in the immediate vicinity of the switchboard in plugs that fit the receptacles on the circuit plugging panel. Thus it is obvious that any lighting instrument or unit group of lighting instruments, irrespective of location, can conveniently and quickly be connected to a switchboard circuit of suitable capacity, and so controlled. But it need not be permanently connected — it is connected to the switchboard only when it is being used, thus, when it is not in use, freeing the switchboard circuit facilities for other instruments. This permits a maximum of instrument wiring facilities with a minimum of switchboard facilities — all of which are instantly interchangeable and adjustable as to instrument locations, circuit loads, and so forth. Flexible switchboards are almost invariably of unit construction and of the composite type, the magazine panel usually being mounted at some convenient location on the front face or end side of the switchboard. In addition to the principal features of a typical switchboard for flexible control just pointed out, there are many minor features that are at times incorporated in the design of such switchboards in order to enhance their flexibility, such as special methods of circuit grouping, circuit transfer switches, the use of "variable rating" dimmers, and the use of special wiring hook-ups to provide for proportional simultaneous dimming. Switchboards for flexible control, as compared with those for permanent control, are a recent development, and it is reasonably certain that rapid progress will be made in their design and construction in the near future.

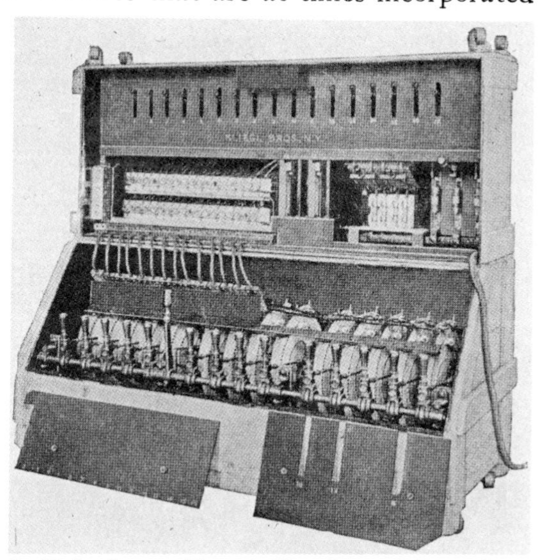

A 19-circuit portable switchboard containing a bank of 14 interlocking plate dimmers and 2 slider type dimmers. For transportation, the switchboard is packed in two parts, one of which rests upon the other, as shown, when the switchboard is set up for operation.

A *switchboard for portable control* is radically different in construction from those for permanent or flexible control, though generally it resembles the latter in circuit subdivision. It is necessarily reduced to simplest terms, and hence lacks many of the refinements that make for convenience of manipulation. A metal-lined wooden case equipped with casters, a locking cover, and otherwise designed for easy transportability, houses the switches and dimmers and fuses. Inclosed knife switches are ordinarily used, and the fuses are mounted in a sheet-metal cabinet, but the dimmers (which may be of either the interlocking or non-interlocking plate types, or the slider type) are not inclosed. These component parts are usually arranged in the most compact manner possible, little attention being given to logical layout of control handles. Either stage plugging receptacles of the usual type, or female cable connectors permanently mounted on the switchboard, terminate the switchboard circuits and provide means for ready connection with the portable stage-cable wiring circuits. Lugs and terminal bolts on the main switch are provided for readily attaching the portable feeder cable that connects the switchboard with a source of current. Portable switchboards for general use are provided with dimmers of various capacities, the number of dimmers of each capacity depending upon

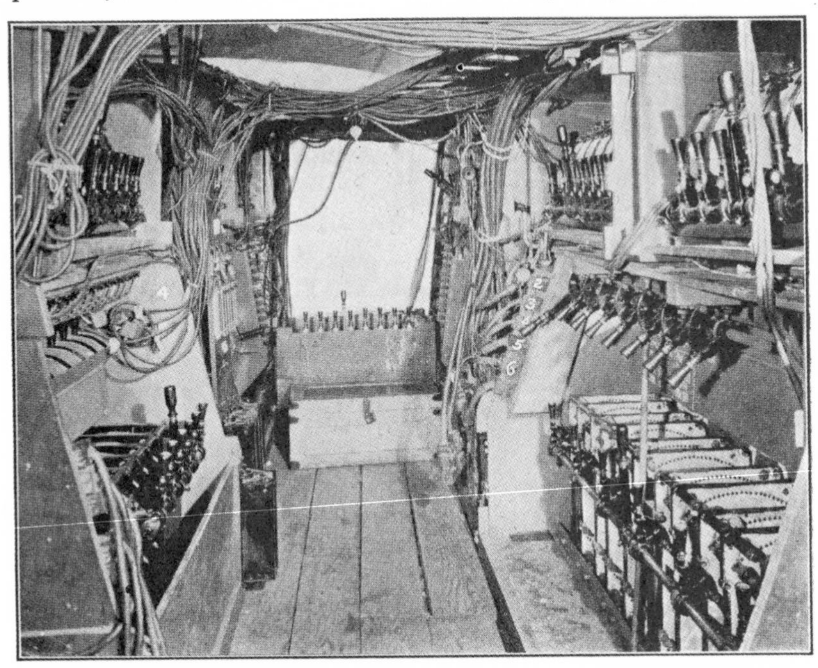

Part of the portable switchboard equipment assembled for the control of the lighting equipment used for *The Miracle*.

the anticipated use to which the switchboard will be put. In effect, such portable switchboards are appreciably flexible. On the other hand, portable switchboards that are "made up" for one particular production contain only such switches and dimmers as are required, and hence have only a very limited application.

E. SOME DESIRABLE FEATURES OF SWITCHBOARD DESIGN AND CONSTRUCTION

Although the details of design and construction of any stage switchboard are dependent principally upon the specific conditions that determined the choice of the switchboard, there are several general principles to which the design and construction of stage switchboards should basically conform.

The most important of these principles, particularly from the standpoint of efficiency of control, is what might be termed *convenience of manipulation.* As the control of a set of stage-lighting equipment is often a very complex and arduous task, the best way to assure smooth and effective lighting for a production is to facilitate this task as much as possible — to reduce the actual mechanical

Portable switchboard equipment assembled for *The World We Live In*, for the control of the special equipment pictured on page 435.

work required of the switchboard operator to a minimum, thus enabling him to divert the greater part of his attention from the mechanical requirements of mere switchboard manipulation to the artistic requirements of actual stage-lighting control. Perhaps the biggest factor in the achievement of convenience of manipulation is the logical orderly layout — the relative positional arrangement — of the control handles on the face of the switchboard. Except, of course, on portable switchboards, the control of the auditorium lighting should always be included on the stage switchboard, and, if practicable, also the control of the various backstage utility lights. Many helpful features, mechanical or electrical in nature, can be incorporated in switchboard design. There are, for example, the many different combinations of interlocking devices — each suited to some special needs — whose choice depends upon the anticipated use of the switchboard; the indicator scales on the dimmer handles, which facilitate duplication of original experimental or trial results; the proper designation of control handles (and, on flexible switchboards, the circuit receptacles and plugs) by means of suitable markings or legends on the face of the switchboard; pilot lights on each of the switchboard circuits, adjacent to the control handles; an operating light that really satisfactorily illuminates the entire switchboard without spilling light on to the acting area during dark scenes; provision for mounting a cue sheet where it may easily be consulted by the switchboard operator without handling; perhaps also a telephone for inter-communication with other operators of lighting equipment when control is decentralized, or for critical instructions from a person situated at a vantage point in the auditorium — all these facilities and many others are available to make switchboard operations more convenient. For certain types of play production it might prove of advantage to equip the switchboard with transfer switches and double fuses, or with other means of pre-setting the circuit switches for the scene ahead. All operating parts of the switchboard should be fairly accessible, especially the main and branch circuit fuses, which should preferably be grouped in a magazine panel incorporated in or at least adjacent to the switchboard, and the fuses properly designated as to the circuits they protect, for easy and rapid replacement.

More or less related to convenience of manipulation are the factors of compactness, of simplicity, and of location. *Compactness* in a switchboard is essential because it permits the close grouping and orderly arrangement of control handles, which in turn facilitate operation and strengthen centralization of control. For compactness, the operating and structural parts of the switchboard should be mounted as closely together as is consistent with safety, but without sacrificing accessibility of the parts. Often it is in the interests of compactness to employ magnet switches and reactance dimmers for controlling circuits of large loads. For portable switchboards (many of which hardly deserve the descriptive adjective) compactness is an especially necessary feature. Incidentally, it might be pointed out that *portability* is a factor that should not be unduly neglected in the design and construction of "portable" switchboards. For some conditions of use it is advantageous to keep the gross weight of portable switchboards, or of separate units, within the maximum limit allowed by railroads for personal baggage — namely 250 pounds. *Simplicity* of circuit layout and wiring connections greatly facilitates operation of the switchboard. Too often are expensive superficialities, in the guise of conveniences, included in switchboards, only to be subsequently ignored under practical operating conditions, when they are likely to prove rather a hindrance than a help. Although only indirectly related to the design and construction of switchboards, the factor of *location* is of great objective importance in facilitating switchboard operation. The ideal location of the switchboard, in relation to the stage, would be such that the operator could view the entire acting area — the entire stage scene — from his position at the control handles. He would then be able to gauge his control according to the results he produced, and would not have to depend upon an intermediary for his lighting cues. Unfortunately it is almost impossible to achieve quite this ideal location in actual practice. Stage switchboards are usually placed on the stage-floor level, against the proscenium wall, either to the right or left of the proscenium opening, whichever side happens to prove structurally most convenient, although probably the better position is on the right side, or "prompt side", of the stage. Sometimes, either to achieve better visibility for the operator, or to conserve backstage space, the switchboard is mounted on a platform about ten feet above the floor. The slight advantage in visibility that the platform location has over the floor location is more than offset by the manifest disadvantage engendered by the isolation of the operator from the coördinate activities on the stage floor. And when a conventional "box-set" interior is used, as it is in perhaps the majority of instances, the floor location has the advantage, even as regards visibility. Occasionally, the switchboard is located beneath the extreme down center of the stage, so positioned that the operator can view the entire scene, from the more desirable viewpoint of the spectator, through an opening in the footlights similar to the prompter's station at the opera. This location has an immense advantage in visibility over the backstage locations, but only during the course of the performance. The operator cannot conveniently "set the lighting" prior to the raising of the curtain. He is also out of touch with the vital, coördinated activities that prevail backstage during a performance, and so cannot well participate in that undefinable spirit that pervades the back stage workers and makes for a performance unified in its elements. And also, switchboard controls cannot be grouped closely enough to enable the operator to reach the furthermost control handles while he is viewing the scene from his allotted station. Switchboard manipulation, because present-day control equipment cannot be sufficiently condensed, unfortunately requires some freedom of movement. Switchboard location, then, is seen to be an important factor of stage-lighting control. As switchboard location and structural characteristics of the stage are interdependent, it is obvious that both must be determined simultaneously, and well in advance of actual construction.

After convenience of manipulation, the next important characteristic which stage switchboards should possess is *flexibility*, which may be broadly defined as a ready adaptability to the many widely varying demands of stage-lighting control. The design characteristics of switchboards for flexible-control systems have already been outlined. But the feature of flexibility should be applied to all switchboards, to as great an extent as is possible with the specific type of control used. The judicious use of the variable-rating type of dimmers, especially on the flexible and portable types of switchboards and also on the stage pocket circuits on the permanent type of switchboard; and the use of appropriate interlocking devices, and perhaps also of preset systems, appropriate to the anticipated use of the switchboard, all greatly enhance switchboard flexibility. Unit construction, to allow for interchangeability, replacement, and subsequent additions of unit circuit control equipment, is applicable to all types of switchboards and is a very important factor in increasing what might be termed the "flexibility of construction" of switchboards. In connection with the flexible and portable types of control, the circuit flexibility of the switchboards can sometimes be increased, if necessary, by the use of an auxiliary plugging panel, or plugging blocks, for grouping several instrument wiring circuits for control by a single switchboard circuit.

Closely related to switchboard flexibility is the factor of *capacity*. A stage switchboard should have ample capacity both as to the number of switchboard circuits and as to the electrical capacity of each of them. A sufficient number of switchboard circuits, of the most useful load capacities, should be provided so that special auxiliary control equipment need not be set up every time it is necessary to use slightly more than the average amount of lighting equipment. The wiring and other current-carrying parts of the switchboard (except the dimmers, of course) should be of a size sufficient to prevent overheating when operating at rated capacity loads. And the need for sufficient capacity of the feeder supplying the stage switchboard cannot be overstressed. *Durability* is another essential factor. The stage switchboard should have its component parts of ample strength, and only the highest quality of materials and workmanship should be used throughout its construction so as to withstand the heavy usage to which it will be subjected. Stage switchboards cannot afford to break down in operation.

Safety, of course, has been presumed to take precedence over all the desirable switchboard characteristics that have just been listed. Needless to say, stage switchboards should comply with all the provisions of the Code and to any local regulations that apply. No current carrying parts should be exposed to physical contact; the face of the switchboard should be dead: that is, it should either

Two views of a "Controlite" switchboard unit: the side view shows the dimmer, with the automatic flipper switch, the "R. M." circuit switch, the pilot light and the dimmer handle; the front view of the unit panel shows, in addition to the latter three devices mentioned, the circuit designation marker.

be totally insulated or, safer still, it should be of metal and should be grounded to carry off any accidental leakage of current. All other metallic structural parts of the switchboard should also be grounded. Because of the heat liberated by the dimmers in operation, it is necessary to provide suitable ventilation. Open grille work at the top and bottom of the switchboard will allow a current of air to circulate through and carry off the heat liberated by the dimmers. Because of the heat of the dimmers, all wires used to connect the component parts of the switchboard should have asbestos-covered insulation. In connection with the flexible and portable switchboards, there is a distinct need for some simple method or device for protecting the circuit dimmers against overloading. In the final analysis, the regular circuit fusing does not adequately protect the dimmers, as it will permit the dimmers to be greatly overloaded when near the "black-out" end of their traverse. This is due to the fact that the safe operating amperage for the "black-out" end of a dimmer is much less than the amperage-rating of the circuit fuses — these being intended to carry the higher amperage that prevails when a normally loaded dimmer is at the "full-up" end of its traverse. The only safe protection would seem to consist of mounting several small thermoelectric relay cut-outs on the frame plate of each dimmer, which would open the circuit as soon as the temperature of any part of the dimmer exceeded a safe maximum.

A "Controlite" switchboard of the direct-control composite type, installed at the Capitol Theatre, Worcester, Mass.

F. BRIEF DESCRIPTIONS OF SEVERAL OF THE OUTSTANDING MAKES OF STAGE SWITCHBOARDS

Within recent years the construction of stage switchboards has become somewhat more standardized. In the early days of electric stage lighting, each stage switchboard was simply a collection of electrical control devices that might have been applied to any lighting problem in general. Since that time, however, a number of standard switchboard mechanisms and wiring systems have been evolved and perfected expressly to achieve a better control of stage lighting. These are assembled in various manners into a number of distinctive trade types of stage switchboards. Brief descriptions of several of the more important of these are given below and, along with pictures and diagrams that show the general aspects of both these and some other switchboards, will give the reader a fairly comprehensive idea of the standard equipment now available for stage-lighting control.

The switchboard shown on the opposite page, before the addition of the front panels, showing dimmer mounting and other details of construction.

The "Controlite" make of stage switchboard is of the direct-control, composite type, and is of unit construction. Its basic feature is the use of "Vitrohm" dimmers equipped with flipper switches. The flipper switch automatically opens the circuit when the dimmer is at the "black-out" position. Thus the actual circuit switch is of minor importance (though one is usually provided, so that the lamps may be flashed on or off without dimming, as is occasionally necessary) and the dimmer handle itself becomes the principal external means of circuit control. The dimmers, as on all the other switchboards mentioned in this section, are subject to the usual combinations of interlocking. As the front face of a Controlite switchboard is built several inches forward of the steel dimmer-bank frame, the dimmer shafts are neatly concealed, and only the actual control handles appear on the face of the board. Controlite switchboards have been built for use with all three types of stage-lighting control — permanent, flexible, and portable — although, as is also the case with other switchboards, principally for the permanent type of control. The unit construction employed greatly facilitates the fabrication of the switchboards to meet each individual set of requirements, as well as provides an easy means of accommodating future circuit additions and changes in circuit loads. Although stage switchboards of the Controlite type are built by several makers of electrical control equipment, one manufacturer, the Trumbull Electric Manufacturing Company, has been particularly active in developing this type of control board. Its product, known as "Trumbull Controlite", is one of the best of recent achievements in the design and construction of stage switchboards, and its intelligent and sympathetic work on the special switchboard for the Yale University Theatre (discussed on a following page), betrays a real understanding and appreciation of some of the more fundamental problems of stage-lighting control. On standard Trumbull Controlite switchboards, "R.M." switches are used for the circuit switches, and bar-connected knife switches for the color main and stage main circuits. Remote control switches are sometimes used on the main circuits. Pilot lights on each circuit are used on the larger switchboards, and, where provision for advance set-up of circuit switches is desired, a double-throw transfer switch is provided for each circuit, in conjunction with a double set of fuses. Magazine panels containing the main, group, and branch circuit fuses and the neutral bar, are built as an integral part of the switchboard and are usually mounted on either the right-end or left-end side. The accompanying pictures of Controlite switchboards are of those of Trumbull manufacture.

Right end view of a "Controlite" switchboard, showing dimmers, wiring channels, "R. M." switch, dimmer shaft, and switch and dimmer handles.

Another make of direct control, composite type, stage switchboard is manufactured by the Bull-Dog Electric Products Company.

The basic feature of this make of switchboard is the "Bull-Dog" reverse-bar-connected knife switch and its mechanical interlocking and pre-set features (see page 297). Besides the interlocking of the circuit switches, the dimmers also are subject to the usual possibilities of interlock, depending upon the needs of the individual installation. The shafts for the dimmers and switches, and the interlocking mechanism, are mounted on the face of the board. The magazine panel of a "Bull-Dog" stage switchboard is usually placed at the back of the switchboard. The switchboard at the Guild Theatre, New York, pictured on page 333, is of Bull-Dog manufacture.

Left end view of a "Controlite" switchboard, showing magazine panel: in the center are the group and branch-circuit fuses, arranged for the single-fusing system; at the bottom are the two outside "legs", with sub-main fuses, of the incoming 3-wire feeder; and at the top is the neutral "leg" with the "neutral bar" providing unfused taps for the grounded side of the branch circuits.

Munroe Pevear uses his compact multiple-type dimmer unit (see page 323) in building small portable or wall mounted switchboards, for use in small theatres and schools and for traveling productions. As previously explained, these dimmer units are self-contained, embodying not only the dimmer and the load outlets for interchanging circuits, but also the circuit switch and fuses. Being of unit character, they can easily be assembled into switchboards, and their assembly easily added to or subtracted from, or they can be interchanged as to rated dimmer capacities, according to the prevailing control requirements for which they are used. Six such dimmer units mounted in a suitable "trouping box" constitute a standard form of small portable switchboard. Master interlocking control of both switches and dimmers is provided.

There are several different makes of remote-control switchboards available, their principal distinguishing characteristics depending upon the exact method by which is achieved their electrical pre-set and electrical master control of the circuit switches. According to these wiring methods, remote-control switchboards may be divided into three general classes, which might be named as follows: preselective; single pre-set; and multi-pre-set. The wiring systems employed in each of these types are ingenious, and descriptions of them, in conjunction with the accompanying elemental schematic diagrams, may prove of interest at this point.

The *preselective* remote control switchboard uses mechanically-held-closed, or "latched-in" contactors (see page 305) for each circuit. The unit-control panel for each circuit on the pilot board consists of two pilot switches (similar to the special type described on page 303), a pilot light, and a dimmer. Each pilot switch has two sets of contacts, the upper momentary, the lower fixed, and, in addition to the momentary and fixed positions, has also a neutral, or "dead", position. The upper pilot switch on each panel closes the respective contactor, and is called the "on" switch, the lower opens the contactor, and is called the "off" switch. The color-main and stage-main control panels each consist of only the "on" and "off" pilot switches. Independent control of each individual circuit is achieved by holding the pilot switches in the upper position, thus making momentary contact with the "hot bus." [1] This operation either closes or opens the contactor, depending upon whether the "on" or "off" pilot switch is operated. By placing an individual circuit pilot switch in the lower, or fixed position, its control is extended to the respective color-main pilot switch. The latter, in turn, either may be momentarily connected to the "hot bus," thus controlling all the individual-circuit contactors whose pilot switches have been set up in the lower, or fixed position; or its control (and hence also the control of all the individual pilot switches that have been set up in the fixed position) may be further extended (by its being also set up in the fixed position) to the stage main pilot switch. This extension of control applies, of course, separately to each complete set of "on" and to each complete set of "off" pilot switches on the switchboard. When the stage main "on" pilot switch makes contact with the "hot bus" (in the upper position), it will

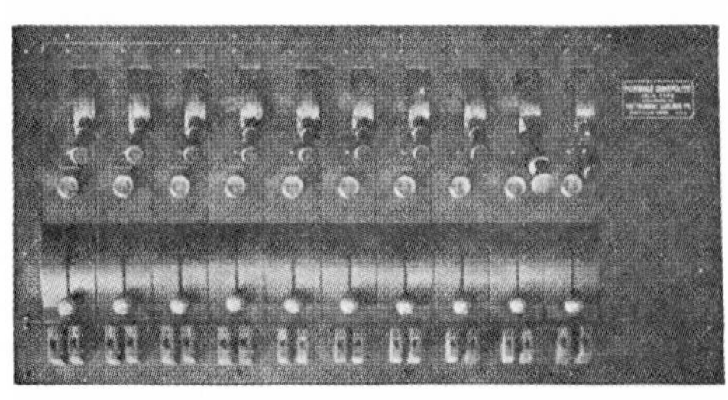

A 10-circuit portable switchboard of the "Controlite" type, with dimmer handle, pilot light, double-pole transfer switch, and double circuit receptacles on each panel.

[1] The "hot bus" on remote-control switchboards is simply a single wire, or "bus," which is always energized (except when the lock switch is open) regardless of the settings of the color-main and stage-main pilot switches, and which extends to all the pilot switches on the switchboard.

energize the closing coil of each individual contactor whose respective "on" pilot switch and color-main "on" switch have been set up in the fixed position. The stage main "off" pilot switch exercises a similar control. If both stage main pilot switches are placed in the fixed, or lower, position, the "on" or "off" control can be extended, by means of a 3-conductor cable, to a single-pole,

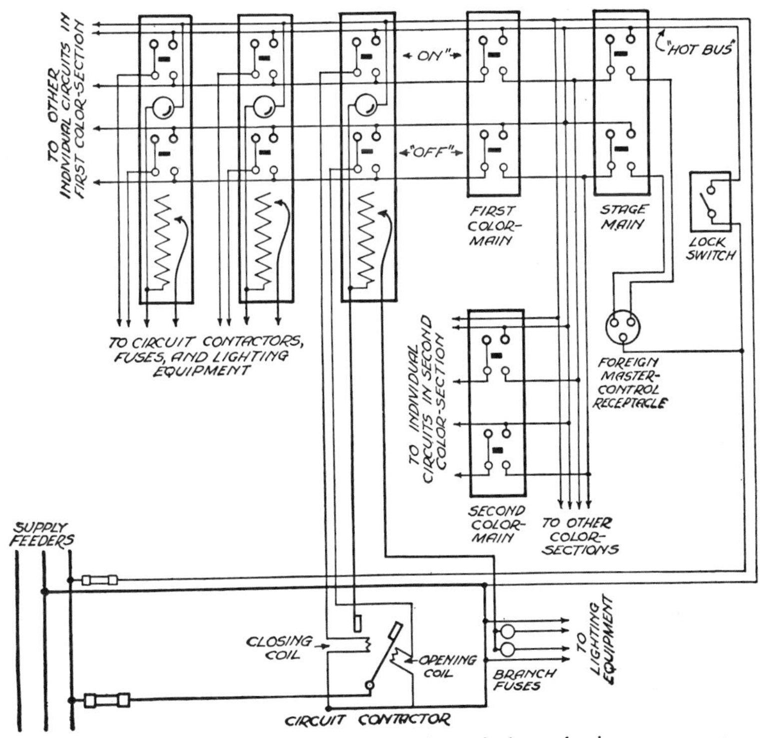

Schematic diagram showing principle of operation of a typical preselective type remote-control switchboard. Each pilot switch is diagrammatically represented as having two sets of contacts (the upper momentary, the lower fixed) with the movable contact bar, between the two sets, in the neutral position. The circuit pilot-lamp is represented between the "off" and the "on" pilot switches, and the circuit dimmer beneath the "off" pilot switch, on each unit panel.

double-throw, momentary-contact, push-button switch located at a point foreign to the stage switchboard, such as the wall switch in an interior setting on the stage. This feature, known as "extended master control", or "foreign master control", is useful, especially for plays that have intricate cues for room lighting that is switched on and off by a character on the stage — all "on" and "off" pilot switches of circuits supplying equipment that provides the ostensible room lighting, as well as color-main and stage main pilot switches, being set up for extended master control, and pilot switches for other lighting, such as cyclorama, moonlight, and firelight, being left in the neutral, or dead, position. This system of extended master control thus puts the room lighting under the direct control of the character operating the wall switch on the stage, and eliminates difficult light cues and the possibility of lack of coördination. The preselective feature of this type of remote control switchboard operates as follows: After a scene has been lighted, all the pilot switches can be returned to the neutral position. It is then possible to *preselect* the lighting for the following scene by (1) putting in the fixed position (*a*) the "on" pilot switches of circuits then open but required to be closed for the following scene and (*b*) the "off" pilot switches of circuits then closed, but required to be open for the following scene; and (2) leaving in the neutral position the pilot switches of circuits which remain the same (either "on" or "off") for the following scene. The color-main pilot switches that are involved in such an operation must also be properly set up in the fixed position. After all the pilot switches have been properly set up, it is necessary, in order to supply current to the proper stage-lighting equipment as required for the following scene, only to connect the stage main "on" and "off" pilot switches, by momentary contact, to the "hot bus", thus energizing the proper coils of the preselected contactors. Then the pilot switches can be set up for the next scene, and so on. However, it must be remembered that, except for unused circuits, whose dimmers can naturally be set at the position required for the following scene (an operation that is equally possible on direct-control switchboards), this feature of preselection, and indeed all electrical pre-set methods, apply *only* to switching operations and *not* to dimming operations. And, as dimmer control is of much greater importance than mere switch control, this restriction denies to remote control switchboards the position of great value, in the field of stage-lighting control, that is so often claimed for them.

The *single pre-set* remote-control switchboard uses electrically-held-closed contactors, or "magnet switches" (see page 305). Each contactor has two coils, called, for convenience, the "A" coil and the "B" coil, either of which can be used to hold the contactor closed. The unit control panel for each circuit, on the pilot board, consists of two pilot switches (similar to the special type described on page 303), a pilot light, and a dimmer. Each pilot switch has two sets of contacts, both fixed, the upper for "hot bus" connection, the lower for extended control, and, in addition, a neutral or dead position. The upper and lower pilot switches on each panel are termed respectively the "A" pilot and "B" pilot and are connected respectively to the "A" coil and "B" coil on the circuit contactor. The color-main and stage-main control panels each consists of only the "A" and "B" pilot switches. The single degree of pre-set is made possible by the fact that two separate, complete parallel control circuits, "A" and "B", are provided, each with its own individual, color-main, and stage-main pilot switches

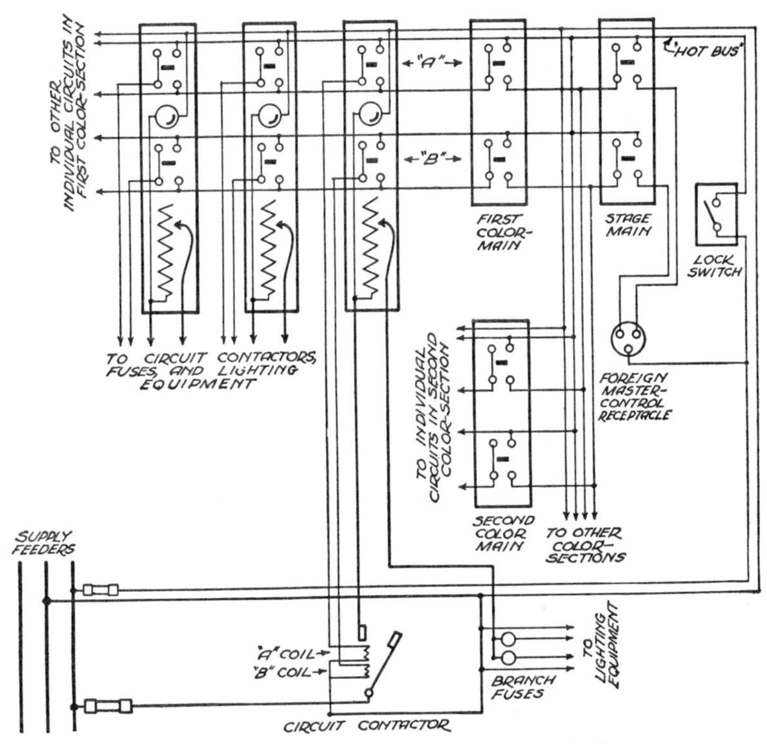

Schematic diagram showing principle of operation of a typical single pre-set type remote-control switchboard. Each pilot switch is diagrammatically represented as having two sets of contacts (both the upper and the lower sets fixed) with the movable contact bar, between the two sets, in the neutral position. The circuit pilot lamp is represented between the "A" and the "B" pilot switches, and the circuit dimmer beneath the "B" pilot switch, on each unit panel.

and its own contactor coil. Independent control of each individual circuit is achieved by placing either pilot switch in the upper position, thus making contact with the "hot bus" and energizing one of the contactor holding coils. By placing the pilot switches in the lower position, control is extended to the color-main pilot switches, and thence, similarly, to the stage-main pilot switches. By properly setting up the individual and color-main pilot switches on the "A" circuit, the lighting for a scene may be switched on by placing the main pilot switch in the upper position, thus energizing the "A" holding coils of the contactors. It is then possible to pre-set the lighting for the following scenes by setting up the proper pilot switches on the "B" circuit. It is then necessary, in order to supply current to the proper stage-lighting equipment as required by the following scene, only to return stage main "A" pilot switch to the neutral, or dead position, and place the stage main "B" pilot switch in the upper, or "hot-bus," position. Then the lighting for the third scene can be pre-set on the "A" circuit, and so on. Foreign master control can be provided by placing the stage-main pilot switch, of the control circuit in use, in the lower position, and the stage-main pilot switch of the control circuit not in use, in the neutral position.

The *multi-pre-set*, remote-control switchboard also uses electrically-held-closed contactors, but each contactor has only a single holding coil. The unit control panel for each circuit, on the pilot board, consists of several pre-set switches, a pilot light, a pilot switch, and a dimmer. The number of pre-set switches depends upon the degree of pre-set provided, some switchboards having as many as twenty. The pre-set switches are miniature single-pole, single-throw tumbler switches (see page 301). The individual pilot switches are similar to the special type used on the preselective and double pre-set switchboards just described, but have three sets of contacts, all fixed: the upper (extended-control position) making connection with the color main pilot switch; the middle (pre-set position) making connection, through a common feed, with one side of each of the pre-set switches; and the lower (independent position) making direct connection with the "hot bus." The pilot switches have no neutral, or dead, position. The pre-set switches are connected to their respective scene-main switches; that is, all Number 1 pre-set switches are under the control of Number 1 scene-main switch, all Number 2 pre-set switches are under the control of Number 2 scene-main switch, and so forth. Any number of scenes (up to the total the switchboard can handle) can be pre-set. In order to pre-set a scene, all the pilot switches are placed in the middle, or pre-set, position, and all the Number 1 pre-set switches are set "on" or "off", accordingly as their respective individual circuits must be "on" or "off" to light the scene. The next scene can be pre-set by similarly manipulating the Number 2 pre-set switches, a third scene by similarly manipulating the Number 3 pre-set switches, and so on. The switching for each scene can then be instantly accomplished by closing the particular scene-main switch involved. Closing the Number 1 scene-main switch, for example, will energize those individual-circuit contactors whose corresponding Number 1 pre-set switches have been closed, or have been set in the "on" position. The second scene can be lighted by opening scene-main switch Number 1 and closing scene-main switch Number 2, and so on. The usual type of color-main and stage-main control can be used, when desired, in place of the pre-set control, by placing the individual pilot switches in the upper position, which places them

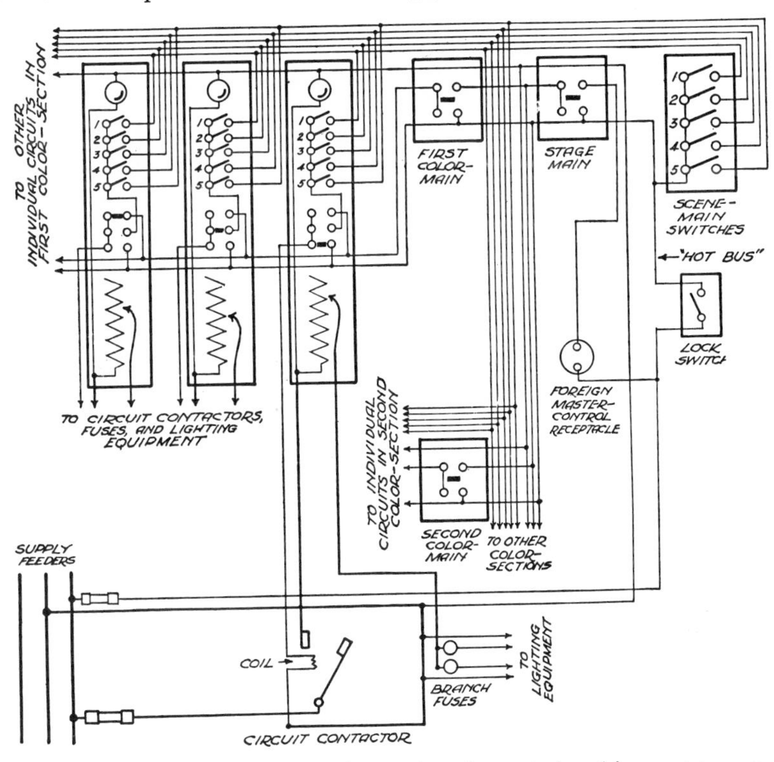

Schematic diagram showing principle of operation of a typical multi-pre-set type remote-control switchboard. Each unit panel is shown with a group of five pre-set switches, and a three-position pilot switch. The pilot switch in the first panel (at the left) is shown with its contact in the "extended-control" position; that in the second panel in the "pre-set" position; and that in the third panel in the "independent," or "hot-bus," position. The circuit pilot lamp is represented above the pre-set switches, and the circuit dimmer beneath the pilot switch, on each unit panel.

under the control of the color-main pilot switches, which, in turn, can either be operated independently, by "hot-bus" contact in the lower position, or be placed under control of the stage-main pilot switch. Foreign master control, by means of a single-pole, single-throw, push-button or tumbler switch, can be provided by placing the stage-main pilot switch in the upper position. Independent control of individual circuits, regardless of the settings of the pre-set switches or master pilot switches, may be achieved by placing the individual pilot switches in the lower position, for "hot-bus" connection.

Such, then, are the characteristics of the three general classes of remote-control stage switchboards. It must be understood that the above descriptions and diagrams are elemental and are simply typical of the general classes. As actually manufactured under various patents, the several classes of remote-control switchboards embody detailed modifications and elaborations of the simple wiring designs that have just been discussed. The preselective type was the earliest type in use, and was developed by R. E. Major and manufactured by the Frank Adam Electric Company. Because of certain limitations as compared with the other classes of remote-control switchboard, the preselective type is now seldom in demand. The double pre-set type of switchboard, developed by the Hub Electric Company, is a rational, not too elaborate, type of remote-control switchboard which has a possible application to the problems of stage-lighting control for "legitimate" dramatic production. The Frank Adam Electric Company now specializes in the multi-pre-set type of switchboard, which finds its principal application in vaudeville theatres and in motion-picture theatres, where stage-lighting practice, of necessity, differs widely from that of regular play production. The Westinghouse Electric and Manufacturing Company also manufactures the various types of remote-control switchboards.

However, as fascinating as are the analyses of remote-control switchboards, a description of a special stage switchboard which will most likely be of particular interest to the reader is that of the one in use at the Yale University Theatre at New Haven. This switchboard, which is of the direct-control, composite type, is used with a completely flexible system of control, and embodies several unique features of design and construction that may be considered as concrete, fundamentally significant advances in the field of stage-lighting control. This switchboard was planned by Stanley R. McCandless, instructor of stage lighting at the University and in charge of the stage-lighting work at the Theatre, and, as previously mentioned, was built by the Trumbull Electric Manufacturing Company. As may be seen from the layout on page 358, the switchboard is divided into three principal sections: the magazine panels at the top, the actual control section in the center, and the plugging panels at the bottom.

The plugging panel is divided into two sections — upper and lower. One hundred thirty-six wiring circuits, leading from plugs, plugging boxes, and pockets at various instrument locations about the stage and auditorium, are brought to the switchboard, where the outside, or non-neutral, wire of each terminates in a countersunk male plug, more conveniently termed a "load receptacle", on the lower section of the plugging panel. The load receptacles are arranged in a logical and orderly formation, depending upon the instrument location each supplies. Most plugging boxes have four plugs; hence the corresponding load receptacles are arranged in vertical rows of four each — an arrangement that lends itself particularly well to the graded-mixture method of color control. The twelve load receptacles grouped at the extreme lower left corner of the plugging panel supply the cyclorama lighting equipment — in this case the three vertical rows each represent a color (three colors, rather than four, are used in the cyclorama lights). The outside, or non-neutral wires of the switchboard circuits, of which there are sixty-four (exclusive of the circuits supplying the auditorium lighting and the arc pockets) each terminate in two female receptacles, or "circuit receptacles", except circuits 40, 41, 42, "G", and "H", which, being of high capacity, have four circuit receptacles each. These pairs of circuit receptacles occupy positions on the upper section of the plugging panel that correspond to the positions occupied by the unit control panels, of their respective circuits, on the control section of the switchboard. Both the load receptacles and the circuit receptacles are properly labeled: the former with location and number, the latter with number and circuit capacity, as determined by the rating of the circuit dimmers.

The actual control section of the switchboard is divided into six sections: Sections "I", "II", "III", and "IV", which divide among them the sixty-four stage circuits; the "House" section, comprising the five circuits that supply the auditorium lighting; and the "Arc Pocket" section, comprising the six constant (undimming) high-capacity circuits that supply direct current to arc pockets located at various points about the stage and auditorium. The unit control panel of each of the sixty-four stage circuits measures two inches wide by twenty inches high, and consists of a dimmer, a pilot light, and a transfer switch. The dimmer is of the standard round-plate, interlocking Vitrohm type, equipped with a flipper switch; the pilot light is of the usual type — a small lamp mounted behind a colored bull's-eye lens, and protected by a miniature fuse; and the transfer switch is an enclosed single-pole, double-throw knife switch whose insulated operating handle projects through a narrow slot in the face of the switchboard panel unit. The dimmers are mounted closely in four horizontal banks, but, in order to conserve space on the front of the switchboard, the control handles are mounted in two horizontal rows, as closely as possible — on two-inch centers. The unit control panel of each of the five "house" circuits consists of a dimmer, a pilot light, and an "R.M." switch. No dimmer handle is provided for circuit Number 65, as the dimmer for this circuit is ganged with that of circuit Number 64, both dimmer plates constituting a double-plate dimmer (with a split load),

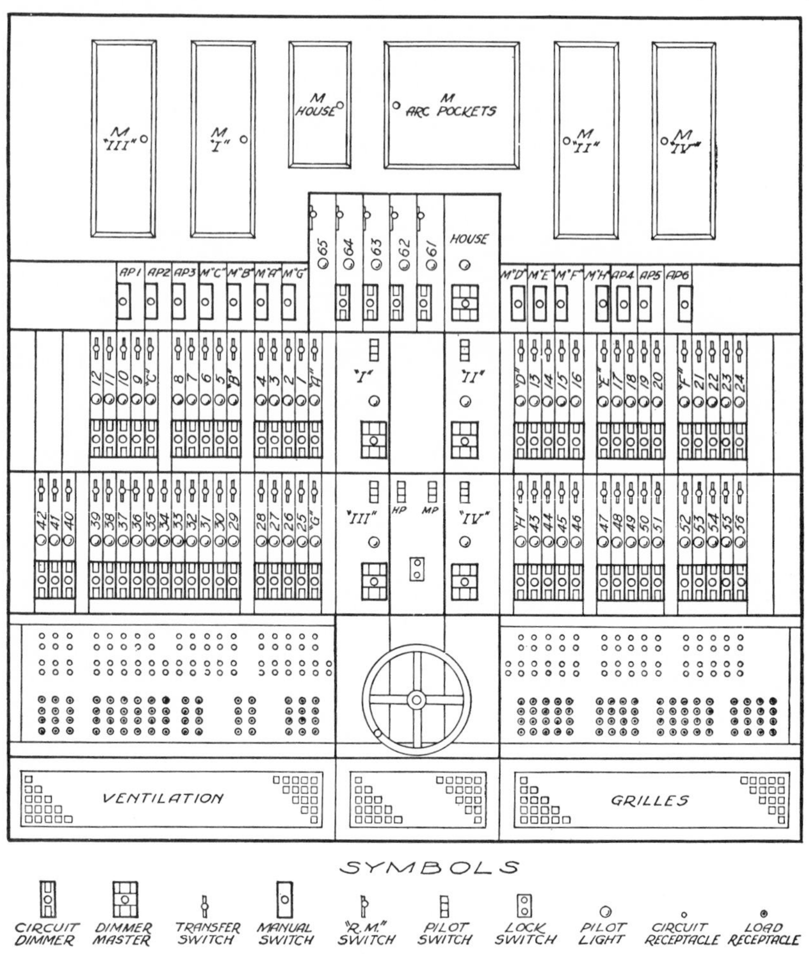

Diagrammatic representation of the layout of the Yale switchboard.

operated by the handle in panel Number 64. Each of the six unit control panels for the direct-current "arc pocket" circuits consists of a bar-connected double-pole, single-throw knife switch. This leaves the eight group master switches, designated on the accompanying diagram as M "A" to M "H", unexplained, thereby calling attention to the unique feature of this switchboard, namely, the provision for achieving proportional simultaneous dimming — an operation so important in connection with the graded-mixture method of color control — by means of group master dimmers.

The switchboard at the Yale University Theatre, New Haven, Connecticut.

The difficulty of achieving proportional simultaneous dimming with mechanical interlocking devices has been pointed out in a previous section of this chapter (see page 321), and a typical example has been given. But if four individual dimmers as cited in that example were wired in series with a fifth, or master, dimmer (though remaining wired in parallel with each other) whose rated capacity equaled the total of the rated capacities of the four individual dimmers, it would be possible to dim simultaneously the lamp loads connected to each of the four individual dimmers, and maintain the original proportionality of light intensities, simply by bringing down

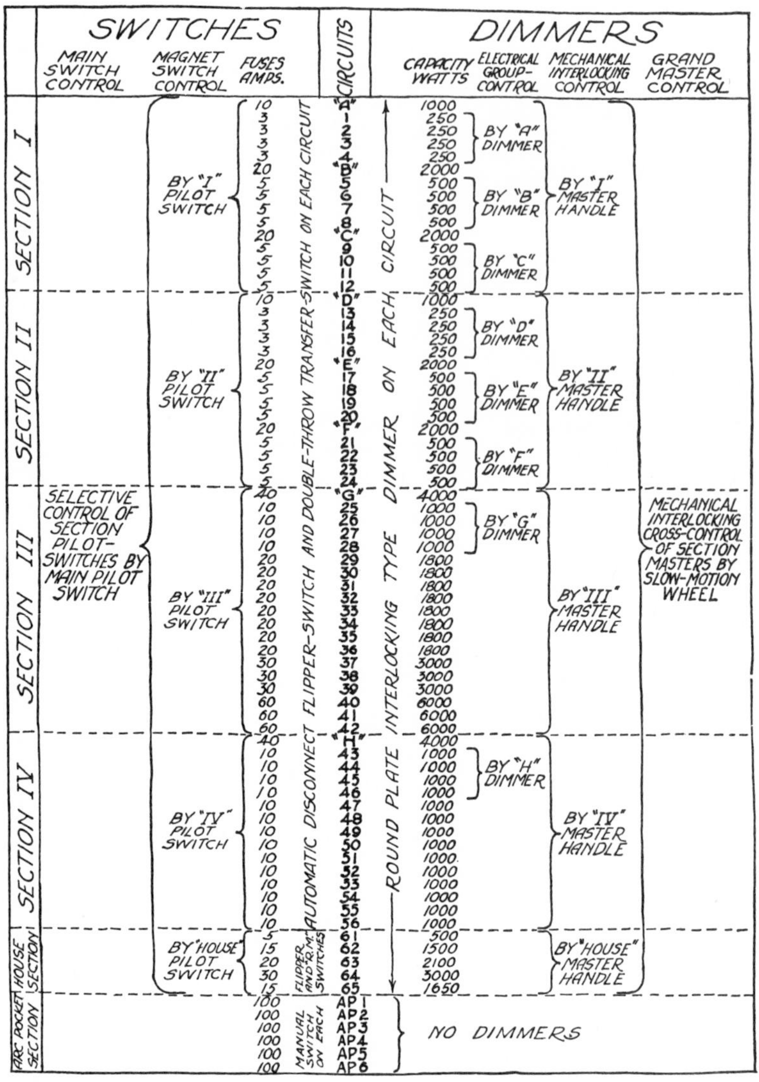

Chart showing circuit capacities and control characteristics of the switchboard at the Yale University Theatre.

the group master dimmer from "full up" to "black out", the four individual dimmers remaining constant at their original settings. Eight such master-dimmer control groups are provided on the Yale switchboard. The parallel-series wiring of a group of individual dimmers with a master dimmer, which is depicted in the following diagram, is basically very simple.

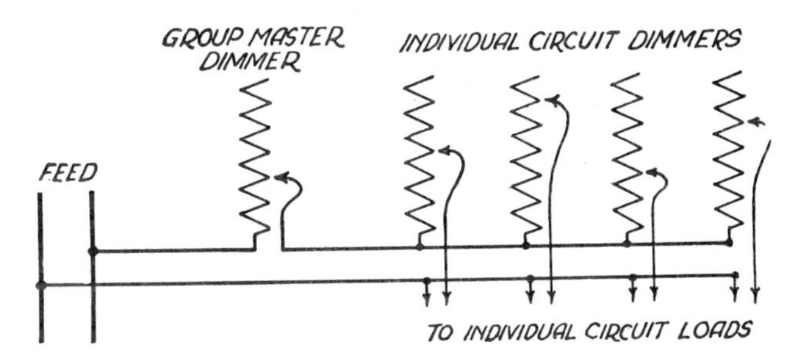

But to have forty dimmers on a stage switchboard permanently wired so that they can be used only for proportional simultaneous dimming is obviously highly uneconomical. This problem is solved on the Yale switchboard by a most ingenious system of wiring, whereby a double-pole, double-throw knife switch, called the group master switch, is used to provide the parallel-series wiring when set in one position, and to provide plain parallel wiring (releasing the five dimmers for independent service on five individual stage circuits) when set in the other position. The exact method by which this is accomplished is shown on the elemental schematic wiring diagram of this switchboard, presented on the following page.

The wiring of the "D" group, in section "II", comprising circuits "D", 13, 14, 15, and 16, has been represented in this diagram. It may be considered as being typical of that of all the other groups and circuits. When the "D" contactor has been closed by the "II" pilot switch (the section-master pilot switching is described in a later paragraph), current, from a "live" (non-neutral) side of the 3-wire grounded neutral feeder supplying the switchboard, flows to the "II" magazine panel where it passes first through three group fuses, one for each of the groups "D", "E", and "F." From the "D" group fuse it flows to the center left contact of M"D", the double-pole, double-throw group master switch.

When this switch is in the *lower* position, the five dimmers are connected in parallel, for independent service. With M"D" in the lower position, the current passes next down the lower left blade of M"D" and energizes the "D" group bus in the "II" magazine panel. From this point the passage of the current can easily be traced as it passes first through the individual circuit fuses in the magazine panel, through the dimmers of circuits 13, 14, 15, and 16, and then to the center contact of the single-pole, double-throw transfer switches of each circuit. But the passage of the current to the transfer switch of circuit "D" is not as direct. From the "D" group bus in the "II", magazine panel, it passes first through the fuse "D" 1, thence through the "D" dimmer, back through the fuse "D" 2, then to the center right contact of M"D", down the lower right blade, and thence to the center contact of the "D"

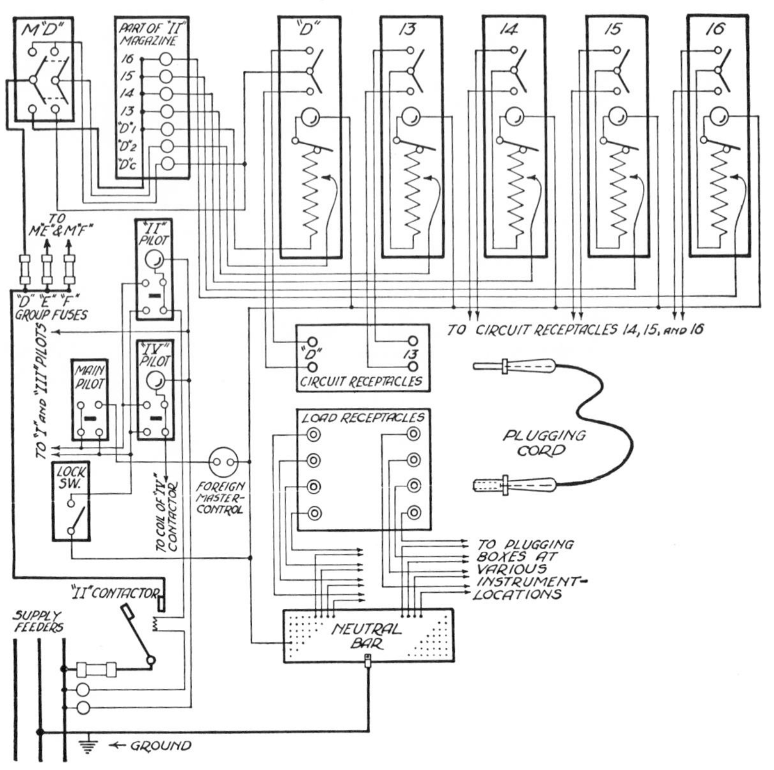

Schematic diagram showing principle of operation of a typical master control group of the Yale switchboard.

transfer switch (it will not pass through fuse "D"c, as that passage is "dead-ended" when M"D" is in the lower position). From the center contacts of the transfer switches of each circuit, the current can be directed to either the upper or lower circuit receptacles of the respective circuits. Thus each of the five circuits — "D", 13, 14, 15, and 16 — can be used independently.

When the group master switch M"D" is in the *upper* position, the dimmers of circuits 13, 14, 15, and 16 are connected in parallel, but together are connected in series with the dimmer of circuit "D", thus being placed under the master dimmer control of the latter. With M"D" in the upper position the current from the "D" group fuse passes from the center left contact of M"D" through the upper left blade, from which it flows in two directions: (1) to fuse "D"c and thence to the transfer switch and circuit receptacles on the "D" circuit (alternative path dead-ended), without passing through a dimmer, thus freeing circuit "D" for use as a

A portion of the plugging panel of the Yale switchboard, showing circuit receptacles in the upper group, and load receptacles in the lower group, with a plugging cord connecting one of each.

constant, undimming circuit while its dimmer is used for group master control; and (2) down the upper right blade of M"D" through fuse "D"2, through the "D" dimmer, thence back through fuse "D"1 to the "D" group bus in the "D" magazine panel (alternative path dead-ended), from which point it passes through the individual fuses, the dimmers, and the transfer switches to the circuit receptacles of circuits 13, 14, 15, and 16, which are connected in parallel, as before. Thus the five circuits of any of the eight master control groups on the Yale switchboard can be connected in parallel for independent control, or in series-parallel for group master control, simply by placing the proper group master switches in either the lower or upper positions, respectively. And, of course, by placing any group master switch in the neutral position, its five circuits can be completely disconnected, or "killed", simultaneously. The group wiring as just traced out applies in a similar manner to circuits "A" to "H", 1 to 28, and 43 to 46. Circuits 29 to 42, and 47 to 56 are permanently wired in parallel, and hence are not subject to any group master control as described above. Circuits 40, 41, and 42, of 6000 watts capacity each, are used almost exclusively for controlling the cyclorama lighting equipment.

Thus far, then, the wiring of all the stage circuits has been traced to the respective pair of circuit receptacles on the upper section of the plugging panel. As previously explained, the "live" or non-neutral wire of each stage wiring circuit (leading to various plugging boxes) terminates in a load receptacle on the lower section of the plugging panel. This makes it convenient to control any stage wiring circuit by any switchboard circuit simply by connecting the circuit receptacle of the former with the load receptacle of the latter by means of a flexible plugging cord equipped with a suitable plug at each end. Thus the current flow can be further traced from any "live" circuit receptacle (one that is energized with current), along a plugging cord, to any load receptacle. From the load receptacle it passes along one of a twin pair of conductors to a plugging box, thence to the lighting instrument, returns from the lighting instrument to the plugging box (along the other of the twin conductors) to the neutral bar (which is common to all load circuits) on the switchboard, and from there to the neutral wire of the supply feeders. Thus the current has been traced through a complete circuit. The transfer switch in each circuit, by means of which the current can be directed to either of the pair of circuit receptacles, enables the operator to make tentative connection between a load receptacle and a circuit receptacle, while the circuit is otherwise in use. Thus, if an upper circuit receptacle is connected with a load receptacle for use in one scene, another load receptacle may be "pre-connected" to the same stage circuit by cord connection with the lower circuit receptacle for use in a following scene, and the actual connection made at the right time by changing the transfer switch from the upper to the lower position. And by placing the transfer switch in the neutral position, the circuit may be disconnected entirely without having to move the dimmer to the "black-out" position. An accessory of great convenience in manipulating the switchboard is the "plugging block." This is a small device containing four circuit receptacles and one load receptacle, all wired together. By using the usual plugging cords, as many as four load receptacles on the switchboard plugging panel may be connected through the medium of this plugging block, to one circuit receptacle. This device greatly increases the circuit capacity and flexibility of the entire switchboard. The use of the various plugging cords for connecting load receptacles to circuit receptacles gives the switchboard, during operation, an appearance somewhat similar to that of a jack-cord type central telephone switchboard.

The pilot lights on the individual circuits are connected to the flipper switch on each dimmer. As shown in the diagram on page 362, the flipper switch is simply an automatic disconnect switch which breaks the circuit when the dimmer is in the "black-out" position, and is actuated by the dimmer contact arm as the latter reaches the "black-out" position (actually, the flipper switch breaks the connection between the inner and outer resistors of the dimmers, but the effect is the same as though it were wired as shown in the diagram, which is simply a more convenient representation).

Close-up view of a section of the Yale switchboard with some of the front panels removed, showing a group of the single-pole double-throw angle type transfer switches and one of the wiring channels.

The current supply to each of the four stage sections of the switchboard, and to the "House" section, is controlled by five contactors which are operated by the section pilot switches on the switchboard. These section pilot switches are of the type described on page 303 and have two sets of contacts, as well as a neutral, or "dead" position. For independent control of any section, the pilot switch of that section is placed in the lower position, thus making contact with a "hot bus" (direct from the single-pole, single-throw lock switch) and energizing the holding coil of the section contactor and thereby closing the supply to that section. If a section pilot switch is placed in the upper position, its control is extended to the main pilot switch. When the latter is in the lower position, it makes direct contact with the "hot bus" and energizes the holding coils of the section contactors whose pilot switches have been set in the upper position. When the main pilot switch is placed in the upper position, its control is extended to a single-pole, single-throw foreign master control switch. The lock switch can be locked in either the closed or open position, and when in the latter, completely locks the switchboard and prevents unauthorized use. Pilot lights, connected as shown in the diagram, are provided for each section pilot switch.

The five circuits in the "house section", being permanently wired to the auditorium lighting fixtures, have no transfer switches, but have "R.M." switches for opening and closing each circuit independently when necessary. Each of the six "arc pocket" circuits has simply a manually operated, double-pole, single-throw switch, and is connected permanently to a special 3-wire system supplying direct current for arc lights (all the remainder of the switchboard is supplied with alternating current).

The main fuses for the four stage sections, and for the house section, are located adjacent to the corresponding contactors on the contactor board. The various group fuses and individual branch circuit fuses, however, are contained in magazine panels mounted in the upper section of the switchboard. A separate magazine panel is provided for the fuses in each section, and all are conveniently arranged and labeled for ready inspection and replacement. One branch fuse is provided for each individual circuit, but for each of the group master circuits ("A", "B", "C", "D", "E", "F", "G", and "H") three fuses are provided, two for protection of the dimming circuit (because the current flows in either direction, depending upon whether the dimmer is used independently or as a group master) and the third for protection of the constant circuit that exists when the dimmer is used as a group master.

The dimmers in each section are subject to mechanical interlocking master control by a section master handle. Each of the latter are connected to a double link-and-lever mechanism and are thus subject to interlocking cross-control by a slow-motion master wheel.

The many advantages of the switchboard at the Yale University Theatre are apparent from the above description and the accompanying circuit schedule, switchboard layout, and wiring diagrams. It is seen to be a switchboard of the fully flexible type. It is, of course, mainly for experimental use, and hence contains perhaps a few more circuits and dimmers and provides perhaps greater operating facilities than would be necessary on a switchboard given over to the more routine activities of regular play production. But, nevertheless, there is hardly a single feature of this switchboard that could not be advantageously adapted to the design and construction of stage switchboards intended for use with general play production activities, either professional or amateur.

V. European Control Equipment

Just as in the case of European stage-lighting equipment, which was briefly discussed in a previous chapter, the control equipment used in Continental Europe is almost exclusively German in design and manufacture. A brief description of German control equipment will perhaps afford an interesting contrast between American and European equipment and will supplement the previous description of the various types of German stage-lighting instruments. As with the latter, German control equipment is neither commercially available in this country, nor, in the main, compatible with the conditions of current American theatre practice.

European control *practice* is not dissimilar to American control practice, even though the control *equipment*, the mechanism, differs radically from that used in this country. The stage-lighting control is usually centralized, so far as is possible. It has been pointed out that centralized control systems in America resolve themselves primarily into the electrical method of intensity control, which also embraces the graded-mixture method of color control. These two methods also form the basis of centralized stage-lighting control in Europe; in addition, however, there is often also used in Europe what might be termed a centralized "mechanical method of color control", which has no direct counterpart in this country, and for which special mechanisms have been developed. Of the three types of centralized control — the permanent, the flexible, and the portable — the permanent is the most widely used, just as in America, but perhaps to an even greater relative extent. Examples of the flexible and portable types of control are rare.

The wiring — *die Leitungsanlage* — for stage-lighting control differs but little in principle from that used in America. Strangely enough, regulations governing its installation do not seem to be as exacting as those in the American Code, and hence, in some respects, it is not characterized by quite so high a regard for safety as is wiring installation in this country. The wiring proper is carried out in metallic conduit or in metal-sheathed insulated conduit. The various wiring accessories, such as sockets (*Fassungen*), plugs (*Stecker*), pockets (*Anschlussdosen*), connectors (*Steckerkupplungen*), and stage cable (*Biegsameskabel*), generally resemble those used here, except that they are available in a multitude of forms and combinations — there seems to be no such standardization and interchangeability of wiring devices as exists in this country.

But by far the greatest contrast to American control equipment lies in the switchboard, which is virtually always of the direct-control type. Instead of the switchboard being as compact as possible, it is split up into several parts: *die Schalttafel* (the switchboard proper, containing the switches — *Ausschalten*, and fuses — *Schmelzsicherungen*); *der Bühnenregulator* (the bank of dimmer control handles); and *die Rheostaten* (the dimmers proper). The *Schalt-*

tafel and the *Bühnenregulator* are the actual instruments of control and are placed in the *Beleuchterlage* (control station) from which the *Beleuchter* (operator) can view the action on the stage; the *Rheostaten* are placed in a convenient, sometimes distant room, being actuated from the *Bühnenregulator* by means of a *Seilzugübertragung* (system of flexible tracker wires). The *Schalttafel* is usually of the old fashioned "live-front" type, long "verboten" in America, with all sizes of open-knife switches and fuse cut-outs mounted directly on a slab of marble. The *Bühnenregulator* consists of the dimmer operating handles (*Hebel*), the layout of which is the same as that used on American stage switchboards for permanent control; namely, horizontal rows representing the colors, and intersecting vertical rows representing the various units of lighting equipment and plugging pockets.

The *Hebel* in each horizontal row revolve about a single shaft to which they can be interlocked. The method of interlocking, however, is not that used in this country — the spring latching pin in a slot — but involves the use of either friction clutches or of friction rollers, by which each individual *Hebel* may be locked to the shaft at any position (in contrast to American interlocking devices, which permit an individual dimmer handle to be locked to the master shaft only at the moment that its latching pin passes over the slot on the latter). This permits the use of color-master control wheels, on each shaft, which have no limit of traverse in either direction, but at the same time requires the use of limit stops on each individual *Hebel* to unlock the latter from its shaft as it reaches either limit of its individual traverse. In many installations these limit stops are made adjustable, so that they can be set at any points on the *Hebel* traverse, thus providing what might be termed an automatic "drop off." *Der Hebelkopf* (the small handle on each *Hebel* which actuates the friction interlocking device) may be set (1) to provide independent operation of the *Hebel*, (2) to lock the *Hebel* to the shaft and *completely* unlock it as it reaches either limit stop, or (3) to lock the *Hebel* to the shaft but only *tentatively* unlock it as it reaches either limit stop, permitting it to relock itself to the shaft as soon as the latter is moved in the return direction. Thus it is readily apparent that the friction interlocking used on European *Bühnenregulatoren* provides several advantages, in regard to flexibility of dimmer control, over the latch-and-slot interlocking used on American dimmer banks. The master control wheel on each horizontal row of *Hebel* is equipped with a worm-gear mechanism and auxiliary wheel that provide slow-motion control. The several color master wheels on a *Bühnenregulator* may be interlocked to a grand master wheel having slow-motion control and, by means of double sliding sets of bevel gears, also cross control, of the several color rows of *Hebel.*

Physically, the *Rheostaten* do not even remotely resemble their American counterparts — the interlocking type plate dimmers. Each *Rheostat* consists principally of an angle-iron framework about four or five feet high and about one and a half feet broad, in which are mounted three vertical rows of electrically connected resistance units, the number of the latter usually totalling a hundred. These resistance units consist of special resistance wire, open-wound on porcelain. A sliding contact strip is mounted on the front edge of the iron frame. This contact strip is made of laminations insulated from each other, each lamination being connected to its respective resistance unit in the frame by means of an asbestos-covered conductor. A sliding contact that moves over the laminated strip is actuated through the medium of a tracker wire by its corresponding *Hebel* on the *Bühnenregulator* in the *Beleuchterlage*, and thus cuts the resistance units in and out of the lamp circuit. Each *Rheostat* has a "dead point", or automatic disconnect mechanism at its "black-out" position which corresponds to the domestic "flipper switch." Such dimmers are available in rated capacities of as high as 6000 watts. As a result of the careful design and the accurate construction, and of the nice counterweighting of the tracker wires, of the moving parts, these *Rheostaten* are remarkably smooth and precise and easy in operation, despite the fact that they are mechanically actuated from a remote point. Although the rheostaten are usually mounted in banks and operated by a *Bühnenregulator*, sometimes several of them are mounted together within a ventilated case to the outside of which the *Hebel* are attached for direct operation. *Schiebwiderstände*, small portable dimmers corresponding to the domestic slider-type dimmers, are also used, though not extensively. In very large installations of stage-lighting equipment especially of that having a five-color system, the number of dimmer-control color circuits is often one or two less than the number of equipment wiring color circuits. This necessitates the use of a *Wahltafel*, a sort of plugging-panel auxiliary to the *Schalttafel*, for connecting the desired lighting equipment circuits to available control circuits.

The mechanical method of color control referred to previously is used principally in connection with such lighting instruments as *Spielflächenlaternen* (acting-area floodlights), and *Horizontlaterne* (cyclorama lighting units) of other than the *Ovallaterne* type. These lighting instruments are often equipped with *Farbscheiben magazinen* (what would correspond in American practice to "color magazines" or "color boomerangs") which are operated by intricate systems of *Seilzüge* (tracker wires) from a central point, usually at the *Beleuchterlage*. The tracker wires from the *Farbscheiben* (color screens) of the various *Seilzuglaterne* for *Spielflache-* and *Horizontbeleuchtung* terminate at the *Hebel* of a *Seilzugstellwerk*. The latter is a mechanism that, in all its cardinal features, is virtually identical with a *Bühnenregulator* as just described. By means of the various slow-motion, cross-control mechanical interlocking mechanisms, color combinations and blendings without number can be achieved. When this mechanical method of color control is used in conjunction with regular electrical control as afforded by the *Bühnenregulator*, the various ramifications and possibilities of control become little short of enormous. It requires only an operator skillful and level-headed enough to keep from getting bewildered and lost amid the maze of control operations that he must carry out.

All that has been previously pointed out in regard to the characteristics of German stage-lighting equipment, namely, that convenience of manipulation is secondary to scientific and technical elaboration and detail, is equally applicable to the control equipment. The German mechanism for the centralized control of stage lighting is unquestionably admirable in many ways, and, when properly used, can produce lighting effects that are unquestionably of the highest artistic merit. But instead of its being physically compact and simple, in the interests of practicability and convenience under modern theatre and play-production conditions, it is bulky and expensive and elaborate, with the actual controls scattered over several individual units. An ideal stage-lighting and control equipment might be imagined as resulting from the combination of the American regard for practicability with the German regard for scientific nicety.

VI. Design and Construction of Home-Built Control Equipment for Amateur Use

For the reason that stage-lighting control equipment lacks the uniformity — the standardization — that characterizes the lighting instruments themselves, it is not possible to give, and would prove hardly helpful enough to attempt, as thorough and detailed a set of instructions for the design and construction of home-built control equipment as was given for home-built lighting equipment, in the preceding chapter. Most of the introductory discussion of the latter, incidentally, applies with equal force to the present subject of home-built control equipment. However, most of this actual work of construction will very likely be found to be more difficult, or at least to require a greater amount of specialized, practical experience, as well as to require more complete working facilities and a greater variety of tools, than the construction of the various units of home-built lighting equipment. And in addition, there is greater probability of running afoul of Code and municipal regulations. But even with these added difficulties, there is every reason why the amateur worker who has built his own lighting equipment should continue his activities and build his own control equipment.

Needless to say, control equipment should be just as carefully planned in advance, especially as to the general type it is to be. For reasons that will later become evident, the flexible and portable types of control systems are by far the most adaptable to amateur construction and use. As a matter of fact, it is highly desirable that the set of lighting instruments and the control equipment should be planned jointly, in conjunction with each other, as many of the characteristics of each are mutually interdependent. In planning his control equipment, the amateur builder should use as a general guide the discussion of standard control mechanisms and apparatus that has been presented previously in this chapter. If possible, he should also acquaint himself with the characteristics and operations of the wiring systems and switchboards in use at local theatres — not with a view to direct imitation, for such an effort would be abortive, but for the purpose of carrying away general information and specific suggestions that he can apply to his own problem. In so far as possible, home-built control equipment should conform to the general principles of safety, simplicity, capacity, flexibility, convenience of manipulation, and durability, in relative importance, as applied to home-built control apparatus, to the order in which they are named.

The following paragraphs give, in the main, fundamental rather than specific recommendations regarding the wiring, the dimmers, and the switchboard, which can be applied and adapted to the definite control requirements of individual cases.

A. WIRING

The flexible and the portable types of control have been indicated as being the most suitable for amateur use. From the standpoint of the wiring, the latter is especially suitable. Briefly stated, portable wiring for amateur use should consist of a number of separate pieces of stage cable, in several convenient standardized lengths, each equipped with a male cable connector at one end and a female cable connector at the other end. These lengths of cable can then be conveniently assembled to connect stage-lighting instruments to the switchboard. The instruments themselves should all be equipped with male connectors — few, if any, of the instruments should be permanently connected to the wiring circuits. The cable should be of the regular type used for stage service, known commercially as "type T", and should be of size Number 14. The connectors should also be of the type used for stage service, and should preferably be of the 15-ampere size, which is the size designed for use with Number 14 cable. It is important to standardize, throughout a complete set of lighting and control equipment, on one size of stage cable and on one size of connector, preferably on those sizes just recommended, so that all parts of the entire system can be conveniently interchangeable. High-capacity stage pockets and plugs, such as are used in regular professional theatres, are not desirable, as they are too heavy and awkward for average amateur use, besides being comparatively much more expensive than a standardized outfit of 15-ampere connectors. Only on very small stages, and only for very light service, should smaller size cable (Number 16 or Number 18), and smaller size connectors (such as those used for ordinary household service, rated at 6-ampere capacity) be used. It is best to use the Number 14 cable and 15-ampere connectors throughout; the extra expense they entail is more than compensated for by the greater safety and reliability they afford. As regards this portable wiring, there is nothing in particular to plan: it is only necessary to have on hand a sufficient supply of these cables, of suitable sizes. The number of cables, and the lengths of each, depend of course on the amount and location of the lighting equipment in use, on the size of the stage, and on the location of the switchboard. It is sometimes convenient to leave these portable cables, or "leads" as they are sometimes called, in place between productions, especially when they are in positions difficult to reach: on battens, for example, several leads can be taped or tied in place, so that current outlets are spaced at intervals for the ready connection of borderlights, suspension-type spotlights and olivettes, and other instruments, without having to rig up a new lead every time such equipment must be used. All such leads terminate, near the switchboard, in male connectors, and may be plugged into switchboard circuits when the instruments they supply are to be used. Such portable wiring, for amateur use, requires no official inspection certificate, and hence may be carried out by any one, providing the work, which is extremely simple, is properly done.

If the stage is used to any great extent, the necessary cables running from the lighting instruments to the switchboard may physically interfere with other backstage equipment and activities. In this event it is highly desirable to install some wiring such as is used with flexible control; namely, rigid wiring that carries circuits from a point adjacent to the switchboard to an instrument location, where each terminates in a female connector. This wiring, which is especially useful for conducting control circuits to the side of the stage opposite the switchboard, and thus for clearing the stage floor of loose cables, can be carried out either with rigid conduit, or with "BX" armored cable (other types of wiring, such as the "knob and tube", or that with non-metallic sheathed cable, are not generally safe enough for use on even amateur stages). The former is difficult, virtually impossible, for an amateur worker, who is not a regular electrician, to manage, but the latter — the "BX" cable — can easily enough be installed by a person with not too limited practical experience. All such rigid-wiring circuits should terminate in a sheet-iron splicing box of suitable size (large enough to accommodate all the rigid-wiring circuits), near the switchboard. In this splicing box, each pair of conductors of the rigid-wiring is permanently spliced (with solder and tape) to a length of Number 14 stage cable that passes through a hole in the side of the box (the hole must be equipped with a porcelain bushing to protect the insulation of the cable). At the free end of this length of stage cable (which should be long enough to loop over to the furthermost switchboard receptacle or connector) is attached a male connector; thus can the circuits be connected to the switchboards. Each of the rigid-wiring circuits leaves the splicing box in the form of "BX" and runs to its respective instrument location. These "runs" of "BX" should be carefully installed, according to Code regulations, with the proper accessories (principally "BX" connectors — devices for anchoring the armored cable to the iron boxes at each end of its run; and "BX" straps—supports for fastening the cable in place). They can be run concealed or not, as desired, the only provisions being that the runs must be continuous from box to box—splicing of armored cable conductors outside a box is not permitted); the cable must be fastened, or "strapped", firmly in place; and, where emerging into the open from beneath a floor, it must be encased in a short length (about twelve inches) of iron pipe for protection against mechanical injury. Such rigid-wiring circuits need not be fused — when they are in service, they are protected by the fuses on the switchboard circuits to which they are connected. Incidentally, the size of the conductors of rigid-wiring circuits must never be smaller than Number 14. At the instrument location, the run of "BX" terminates in a small iron box (the commonly used $3\frac{1}{4}''$ round boxes, sometimes designated as "17*a*", serve very well). In the box the "BX" conductors are spliced to those of a short length (about 12 inches) of regular stage cable, the other end of which terminates in a female connector. The short length of stage cable passes through a hole in the cover of the box, which is equipped, as at the central splicing box, with a porcelain bushing, or, better still, with a "cable grip" (such as "Arrow" Number 112) that holds the cable firmly to the box and prevents any sharp jerks from tearing apart the splice inside the box. Thus a lighting instrument can be connected to the switchboard by first connecting it to the nearest instrument-location outlet, and then connecting the respective rigid-wiring circuit (by means of the plugging cable, at the central splicing box) to the desired switchboard circuit. The plugging outlets may be placed at various instrument locations, such as near the footlights; high up on the stage side wall opposite the battens on which the borderlights and other units of equipment are mounted; and at suitable intervals around the acting area — either recessed in the stage floor, beneath a small hinged cover, or mounted, about a foot above the floor, at convenient points along the wall surrounding the stage. The simple plan outlined above may be varied in any number of ways: each rigid-wiring circuit may have several plugging outlets, wired in parallel, located about the stage, or may have several connectors at a single location, or the connectors of several circuits may either be grouped at one location, or, wired in parallel, be grouped at several locations, and so on. Of course, the greater the number of outlets and connectors, the greater the capacity and flexibility of the wiring system. All such rigid wiring requires a certificate of inspection, at least from the Underwriters, and, in many communities, from municipal authorities as well. Some municipal regulations insist upon rigid wiring being installed by licensed electricians. The nature of these various restrictions must be determined in each locality, and any necessary formalities attended to before such work is carried out.

The materials for either the portable or rigid type of wiring as outlined above can be easily obtained. Stage cable and stage connectors for portable wiring can be secured from the nearest dealer in stage-lighting equipment. "BX" armored cable and all other necessary material for rigid wiring is in common use and may be obtained from the nearest electrical supply dealer.

The wiring of the feeders from the main electrical service to the switchboard must also be given adequate attention. It is highly important that this supply feeder wiring be of sufficient capacity to accommodate the heaviest lighting load that it is estimated the various units of lighting equipment will total at one time. Over and above this estimate, a liberal excess capacity should be provided. Demand will sooner or later be found for all the current that the supply feeders are capable of carrying, and very likely there will be a cry for still more. It must be remembered that supply feeders of insufficient capacity place a serious restriction, at the very outset, on the results which any set of lighting equipment, however complete, can produce. The supply feeders should be properly fused, and the wiring should preferably be of the rigid type. They should terminate on the stage, adjacent to the switchboard, either in a knife switch that is inclosed in an iron box, or in an industrial type safety switch, both of which are capable of being locked when not in use. From this control switch, heavy flexible conductors, equipped with lugs, can be run to the switchboard. The installation of the supply feeders, in rigid wiring, is a matter of more moment and greater difficulty than the installation of the rigid-wiring stage circuits as described above, and had better be left to a qualified electrical contractor. In some instances, a switchboard or panel board for the control of the lights in the auditorium and elsewhere in the building, containing feeders of great enough capacity, is conveniently located in relation to the stage switchboard. It is then often practicable to supply the stage switchboard from it, making connection by means of a 2-conductor or 3-conductor stage cable of suitable capacity. But it is recommended that reliable advice as to the feasibility of this practice should always be first secured.

B. DIMMERS

For the amateur stage worker to construct his own dimmers is likely to prove a rather difficult undertaking, and one that might perhaps be considered as of doubtful value, especially as there are available relatively inexpensive dimmers, of either the slider type or the small, round-plate, non-interlocking type (described on pages 312 and 314). Dimmers of the latter type can particularly be recommended for amateur use: they are the least expensive of all, they are of practically the same high-grade construction as are the standard interlocking type of dimmers, and they are available in a series of rated capacities that are well suited to the more modest lamp loads that are used on amateur stages.

Nevertheless, difficult though it is, the job of building one's own dimmers is a very engaging one, and, if properly carried out, is one that will afford no small amount of the "satisfaction of achievement." The water-barrel type of dimmer, which is almost always considered as a fundamental adjunct of non-professional stage-lighting activities, should be used, if at all, only as a temporary makeshift. Its use should be discouraged, for reasons that have already been pointed out, and the far more satisfactory metallic-resistance dimmer substituted in its place. Simple forms of the latter can be constructed both easily and cheaply: for example, some common forms of resistance wire, such as thin German silver wire, can be wound upon a framework of three or four porcelain tubes (the long porcelain bushings that are used for knob-and-tube wiring serve well), or coiled around a short length of iron pipe that has been wrapped with a layer or two of asbestos paper, and the whole suitably mounted and equipped with a sliding contact that cuts the turns of resistance wire into or out of the lamp circuit, thus dimming or brightening the lamps, as it is moved to and fro over the coil of wires. For best results, however, a little more thought should be given to the design of the dimmer.

Dimmer design is based fundamentally upon certain inherent characteristics of incandescent lamps which have been discussed earlier in this chapter. It has been shown that dimmers must be built for specific wattages, as each wattage requires a definite resistance, expressed in ohms, in series with it to dim it properly. The exact number of ohms necessary to dim a lamp load of specified wattage can be determined from the curve on page 309. This resistance is supplied by so-called "resistance wire", which is available in many sizes — the thinner the wire, the greater its resistance. As the exact resistance (usually expressed in ohms per linear foot of wire) of each size of wire is definitely known, it is only necessary to determine the length of resistance wire of proper thickness that will supply the correct number of ohms required to dim to black out a lamp load of definite wattage. Dimmers can be built with the same size of resistance wire throughout, but then the dimming resistance will be spaced evenly over the range of traverse, and this condition, as previously explained, will result in uneven dimming — the lamp load will dim rapidly at the "on" end of the dimmer traverse, and very slowly at the "off" end. To offset this condition, the resistance should be distributed *unevenly* over the range of dimmer traverse, the larger portion of it being placed in the half toward the "off" end. As the resistance wire of dimmers must be evenly wound, it is necessary that several different sizes of wire be used — with the thickest wire at the "on" end, through several gradations of reducing thicknesses, to the thinnest wire at the "off" end.

The slider-type dimmer is the only type at all practicable for construction by amateurs. A general method of design and construction for a home-built slider-type dimmer is indicated in the following paragraphs.

After the rated capacity of the dimmer to be constructed has been decided upon, the first step is the choice of a suitable resistance material. Undoubtedly one of the best resistance materials for dimmers is that known as "Advance" resistance wire, a product of the Driver-Harris Company. This "Advance" resistance wire possesses physical characteristics (among the most significant of

DATA ON "ADVANCE" RESISTANCE WIRE

No. (B & S Gauge)	Diameter (inches)	Resistance (ohms per foot)	Feet Per Pound
11	.091	.035	40
12	.081	.044	50
13	.072	.056	63.7
14	.064	.071	80.6
15	.057	.090	102
16	.051	.113	128
17	.045	.145	161
18	.040	.184	204
19	.036	.226	256
20	.032	.287	323
21	.0285	.362	400
22	.0254	.460	526
23	.0226	.575	667
24	.0201	.725	833
25	.0179	.919	1031
26	.0159	1.162	1299
27	.0142	1.455	1639
28	.0126	1.85	2083
29	.0113	2.30	2632
30	.0100	2.94	3334
31	.0089	3.68	4167
32	.0080	4.60	5263
33	.0071	5.83	6667
34	.0063	7.40	8333
35	.0056	9.36	10530

Extract from Bulletin R-26, "Alloys for Electrical Resistance", published by Driver-Harris Company.

which is its remarkably constant specific resistance over a wide range of temperatures) that are responsible for its extensive use in the construction of dimmers of all types. This wire is available in sizes ranging from Number 1 to Number 40 (Browne and Sharpe Gauge) and thinner. The data pertaining to sizes Number 11 to Number 35, useful for the design of home-built dimmers, are presented in the accompanying table. After the resistance material has been chosen, a suitable base or material must be selected to wind it on, and for this purpose "Transite" asbestos wood, a Johns-Manville product, has proved useful. This material, though tough and hard, can be "worked" easily — it can be cut with a regular wood saw, and drilled and tapped just as can iron, though much more easily. Two parallel strips of this asbestos wood, each wound with half the total resistance, with a sliding contact between the two bridging the resistance windings, comprise the principal parts of a home-built dimmer. Perhaps the most useful capacity of dimmer for general amateur use is 250 watts. From the curve on page 309 the necessary total dimming resistance is seen to be 186 ohms. The most convenient size, for amateur dimmer construction, of the Transite asbestos wood strips, is 24″ × 3″ and ¼″ thick. With two inches allowed at each end for proper mounting and for terminal binding posts, the active length available for winding resistance wire on each strip of asbestos wood is 20″. The turns of resistance wire should be wound not closer than ⅛″ apart (which is equivalent to 8 turns of wire per inch), to prevent short-circuiting between the turns. In order to hold the turns of resistance wire in place, and keep them from sliding together along the smooth edge of the asbestos wood strips, small notches, ⅛″ deep and spaced eight to the inch, should be carefully cut with a thin hacksaw blade along both edges of the 20″ active length of the two asbestos wood strips of each dimmer. These notches will reduce the active width for resistance winding to 2¾ inches. The actual length of each complete turn of resistance wire will therefore equal twice the active width of the strip plus twice its thickness (2¾″ plus ¼″ plus 2¾″ plus ¼″), or six inches. The total length of resistance wire that can be wound in such a dimmer will equal twice the active length of each asbestos wood strip, multiplied by the number of turns per inch, and multiplied again by the length of each turn (2 × 20 × 8 × 6), or 1820 inches, or 160 feet. If the same size of resistance wire were used throughout the dimmer, each foot of wire would have to have a resistance of 1.162 ohms (186, the total required ohms, divided by 160, the total available winding length), which happens, by sheer coincidence, to be exactly the resistance of Number 26 Advance resistance wire. If the dimmer were wound with this size of wire, it would dim a lamp load of 250 watts to "black out", but it would dim in a very crude fashion, as already explained. In order to achieve smooth dimming, with the same dimmer dimensions, spacing, and so forth, the resistance must be unevenly distributed over the 20 inches of dimmer traverse: the traverse must be divided into several sections of equal size, and a different size of resistance wire used for each section. To determine the correct sizes of wire requires a few simple calculations. First, the curve on page 311, which depicts the relation between per cent of dimmer traverse and per cent of dimmer resistance for smooth dimming results, must be consulted. Columns A and B of the accompanying table represent the result of such consultation. The dimmer traverse has been divided into ten equal sections. The curve shows that at the end of the first tenth section the total resistance must equal $2\frac{1}{2}\%$ of the total dimmer resistance, at the end of the second,

TYPICAL DESIGN DATA FOR 250-WATT HOME-BUILT DIMMER

Dimmer Traverse Section	Calculated Resistance			Actual Resistance			
	Per Cent of Total	Ohms	Ohms Per Foot of Wire	"Advance" Wire		Ohms	Per Cent of Total
				No.	*Ohms Per Foot*		
A	B	C	D	E	F	G	H
1	3	5.6	.35	21	.362	5.8	3.1
2	3	5.6	.35	21	.362	5.8	3.1
3	5	9.3	.58	23	.575	9.2	5.0
4	5	9.3	.58	23	.575	9.2	5.0
5	7	13.0	.81	24	.725	11.6	6.3
6	7	13.0	.81	24	.725	11.6	6.3
7	10	18.6	1.16	26	1.162	18.6	10.0
8	10	18.6	1.16	26	1.162	18.6	10.0
9	20	37.2	2.32	29	2.30	36.9	19.8
10	30	55.8	3.49	31	3.68	58.9	31.6
Total	100	186.0				186.2	100.2

$5\frac{1}{2}\%$; third, 9%; fourth, 14%; fifth, 20%; sixth, 27%; seventh, 35%; eighth, 47%; ninth, 63%; and tenth, 100%. From this it is obvious, by simple successive subtraction, that the first section must contain $2\frac{1}{2}\%$ of the total resistance; the second, 3%; the third, $3\frac{1}{2}\%$; the fourth, 5%; the fifth, 6%; the sixth, 7%; the seventh, 8%; the eighth, 12%; the ninth, 16%; and the tenth, 37%. This would require the use of ten different sizes of resistance wire. The construction of the home-built dimmer can be simplified by treating alike sections 1 and 2, sections 3 and 4, sections 5 and 6, and sections 7 and 8 (the resistance percentages of each pair differing but little); and keeping sections 9 and 10 separate, as their resistance percentages differ rather widely, and hence should be more carefully adhered to in the design. A re-allocation of resistance-percentages to each traverse section which is more suitable to present purposes would then be as follows: first section, 3%; second, 3%; third, 5%; fourth, 5%; fifth, 7%; sixth, 7%; seventh, 10%; eighth, 10%; ninth, 20%; and tenth, 30%. This will require only six different wire sizes. These values have been entered in column B on the table. The resistances required in each traverse section (the respective per cent of the total — 186 ohms) are listed in column C. As each section contains 16 feet of resistance wire (a tenth of the total — 160 feet), the necessary ohms-per-foot value for the resistance wire in each section may be found by dividing each of the values in column C by 16. The results are listed in column D. Knowing the required ohms per foot, the

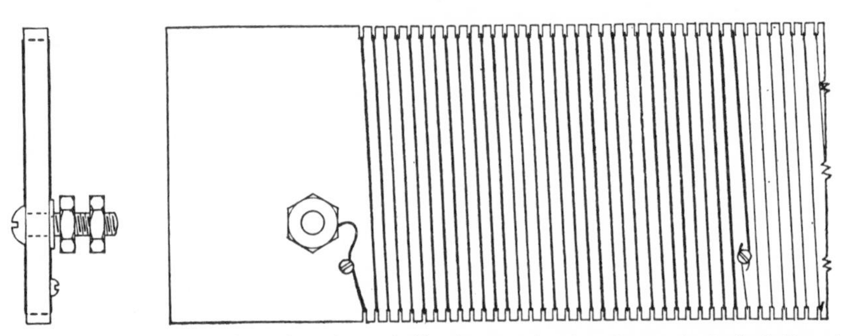

Sketch of one end of a resistor for a home-built dimmer, showing the method of winding the resistance wire in notches at the edges of the asbestos wood strip. The "anchor" screws for each length of resistance wire, as well as a terminal binding post, are also shown. Half size.

most suitable size of "Advance" resistance wire for each section can be chosen by reference to the data table on page 377. The proper size of wire for each section, and its exact resistance in ohms per foot, are listed in columns E and F respectively. Having determined the most suitable size of resistance wire for use in each traverse section, it will prove interesting to "check back" and see how closely the calculated requirements have been approximated with the actual materials available. Thus the actual amount of resistance in each section can be obtained by multiplying column F values by 16. The results listed in column G are seen to be all that could be desired — they compare very favorably with the values in column C. The sectional percentages of the total resistance are listed in column H, and "check up" most satisfactorily with the required values in column B.

When the two asbestos wood strips have been prepared as previously directed, the ten traverse sections, each 2″ long, should be marked off on the active length of each strip. For the 250-watt dimmer, the first two sections *on each strip* should be wound with Number 21 "Advance" resistance wire; the third and fourth sections with Number 23 wire; the fifth and sixth sections with Number 24 wire; the seventh and eighth sections with Number 26 wire; the ninth section with Number 29 wire; and the tenth section with Number 31 wire. The wire must be wound as tightly as possible, because loose turns of wire will short-circuit themselves and cause trouble. At the beginning of the first section, where the winding begins, the resistance wire can be initially "anchored" by looping it under the head of a $\frac{1}{4}''$ — 3 × 48 round-head brass machine screw, for which a hole has previously been drilled and tapped in the asbestos wood. Such screws can also be used to anchor the resist-

TYPICAL DESIGN DATA FOR 1000-WATT HOME-BUILT DIMMER

Dimmer Traverse Section	Calculated Resistance			Actual Resistance			
	Per Cent of Total	Ohms	Ohms Per Foot of Wire	"Advance" Wire No.	"Advance" Wire Ohms Per Foot	Ohms	Per Cent of Total
A	B	C	D	E	F	G	H
1	3	1.4	.087	15	.090	1.44	3.1
2	3	1.4	.087	15	.090	1.44	3.1
3	5	2.3	.144	17	.145	2.32	5.0
4	5	2.3	.144	17	.145	2.32	5.0
5	7	3.2	.200	18	.184	2.94	6.4
6	7	3.2	.200	18	.184	2.94	6.4
7	10	4.6	.288	20	.287	4.59	9.9
8	10	4.6	.288	20	.287	4.59	9.9
9	20	9.2	.575	23	.575	9.20	19.8
10	30	13.8	.865	25	.919	14.70	31.6
Total	100	46.0				46.48	100.2

ance wire at the "off" end of the traverse, and to anchor and join two sizes of wire between the several traverse sections. A terminal binding-post screw for connecting the dimmer to the lamp circuit should be placed on each of the two asbestos wood strips, at the beginning of the traverse, near the first anchor screw. A 1″ — $\frac{3}{16}''$ × 24 round-head brass machine screw equipped with a washer and two hexagonal nuts is best for this purpose. As shown on the sketch, the free end of the resistance wire in section 1 is brought from the initial anchor-screw and is held permanently between the washer and the first nut. The second nut is used for fastening one of the conductors of the lamp-circuit wiring, thus joining it in series with the resistance wire of the dimmer. The two strips of asbestos wood thus wound with resistance wire are commonly termed the "resistor elements" of the slider type dimmer. This description of the design and construction of the resistor elements applies specifically to a dimmer of 250-watt capacity, but the general plan can easily be followed for a dimmer of any capacity. It is only necessary to determine, from the curve on page 309, the "black out", or total dimming resistance necessary for the particular wattage, and then to proceed in the same general manner as indicated above. The data for a 1000-watt dimmer, for example, are listed in the table on page 381. Amateurs should never try to construct dimmers of higher capacity than 2000 watts, because, with greater loads than this, the problem of heat dissipation becomes a more important factor in design, and the proper distribution of resistance over the traverse range requires more detailed consideration.

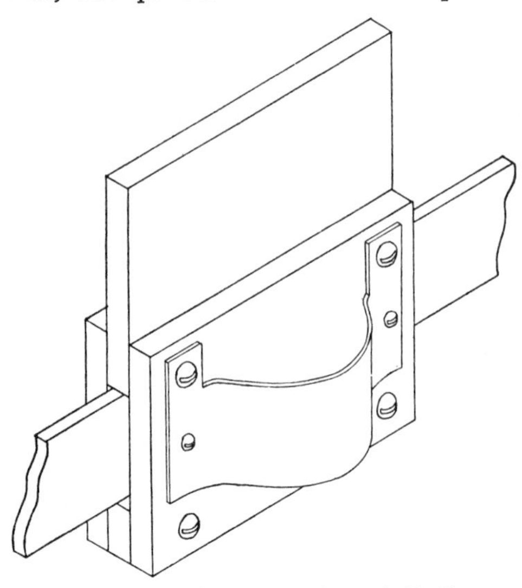

Sketch of a slider for use on a home-built dimmer, showing the spring brass contact and the slide-bar along which the slider moves. Half size.

The slider, which bridges the two resistors, can be made most simply and effectively in the manner shown in the accompanying sketch. Four pieces of $\frac{1}{4}''$ thick, Transite asbestos wood, three of them $2'' \times 3''$, the other $\frac{1}{2}'' \times 3''$, are joined as shown, with four bolts ($1'' - 8 \times 32$ round-head brass machine screws with nut) at the corners of the side pieces. This leaves an open space for the slide bar. The upper piece of asbestos wood serves as the handle for operating the dimmer. If the slider is made as shown, with a handle of generous size and with a thin flat sliding bar (about $1'' \times \frac{1}{8}''$ in cross-section), it will not develop a tendency to become tightly jammed, as do so many slider-type dimmers with closely fitting circular slide bars and short, stubby handles. The contacts that slide to and fro over the coils of resistance wire can be made of thin spring brass or spring bronze (of either five or ten thousandth of an inch thickness). Ordinary brass will not do: it must have a spring temper. To ensure adequate contact, the spring contacts should be about an inch wide. A square ear should be left at each end. These ears are drilled and are placed under two of the bolt heads, as pictured. This is important, as the two bolts make electrical connection between the spring contacts on each side of the slider, and thus serve as a link in bridging the two resistors. The spring contacts should be carefully shaped, and cut of such length and bowed to such degree that, when properly mounted and placed between the two resistors, they will be under sufficient compression to insure a good contact at all points along the dimmer traverse. Each contact spring should be held in place at each end (in addition to the two bolts mentioned above) by a $\frac{1}{4}'' - 4 \times 36$ round-head brass machine screw, for which a hole has been drilled and tapped in the asbestos wood.

The two complete resistors, with the sides containing the terminal binding posts turned outward, can be fastened together at each end as shown in the third sketch, by bolting them to the bent ears of a crossbar made from a piece of flat strip iron, the cross-section of which is $1'' \times \frac{1}{8}''$. The crossbars should separate the two resistor strips by about 2″. The slide bar for the slider should be made of the same size material as the crossbars, and can be held in place between the resistors by bolting it to the crossbars at each end, as shown in the sketch. The completed dimmer can be mounted by providing a narrow crossbar (of $\frac{1}{2}'' \times \frac{1}{8}''$ iron strip) at each end, and bolting or screwing the dimmers to a supporting surface by means of a hole in each of the various crossbars. The latter should extend about $\frac{1}{4}''$ beyond the edges of the resistors, in order to provide a space between the dimmer and its supporting surface. All joints between crossbars and resistors and slide bar should be made with two bolts each, to lend rigidity to the entire dimmer assembly. Round-head stove bolts of the $\frac{1}{8}''$ size are satisfactory, and, if equipped with "lock washers" such as are extensively used on automobiles, will provide a tight joint that will withstand vibration and handling without becoming loose or shaky. It is best to provide a stop or bumper of some sort at each end of the dimmer traverse that will prevent the spring contact from leaving the resistance wire windings. This is highly desirable, as the destructive arcing that would take place every time the contact moved beyond the final turn of resistance wire would ruin both the contact and the wires.

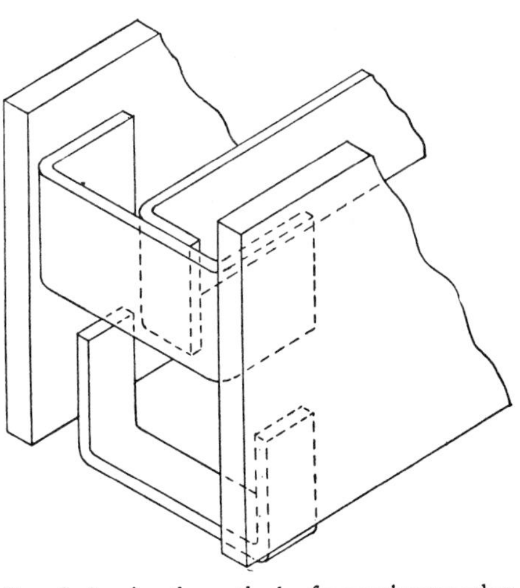

Sketch showing the methods of mounting together the two resistor strips of a home-built dimmer, of mounting the slide-bar, and also of mounting the entire dimmer to a supporting surface, by means of strip iron of various sizes. The bolt fastenings are not shown. Half size.

In mounting the dimmers, adequate provision must be made for ventilation of the resistance windings. If the dimmer is to be a unit complete in itself, it should be mounted within a protective case, or housing, of sheet metal or perhaps one of $\frac{1}{2}''$ wood carefully lined with asbestos paper. In addition to the slot through which the dimmer handle protrudes, openings should be provided for circulatory-air ventilation and for admitting and fastening the circuit wiring conductors to the terminal binding posts. If a number of dimmers are to be mounted together, they may be inclosed side by side, within a housing that consists of a frame built of firmly bolted angle irons and strip iron and covered on the back and edges with stiff $\frac{1}{4}''$ mesh wire screening and on the front by special sections of sheet metal, or asbestos-lined wood, with the proper slots for the dimmer handles. Thus a bank of 12 home-built dimmers of the type just described could be mounted within a protective housing that measured 42″ long, 26″ high, and 5″ deep. Adjoining dimmers should be spaced not less than one inch apart. An indicator scale can be painted alongside each dimmer slot, the numbers 0 to 10 being spaced at two-inch intervals along the 20″ traverse range. Such a bank of dimmers may be used either as an integral portion of a home-built stage switchboard, or, with the individual dimmers equipped with cables and plugs, in conjunction with a switchboard having a "dimmer-insertion" system, as indicated in a later paragraph.

The principal materials needed in the construction of the dimmer described above must be obtained from the manufacturers, the "Advance" resistance wire from the Driver-Harris Company, and the Transite asbestos wood from Johns-Manville. The other materials, including the machine screws, bolts and nuts, spring-temper sheet brass for the contacts, and strip iron of various sizes, can, of course, be obtained from local dealers.

C. SWITCHBOARD

A home-built stage switchboard for use with portable or flexible wiring can be easily enough constructed, simply by assembling a number of standard wiring devices in such a manner that the main current supply can most conveniently be distributed, through the wiring, to the various lighting instruments. The number of switchboard circuits to provide depends altogether upon the amount of lighting equipment used for a production of average lighting requirements. In order to accommodate the various wiring circuits, which terminate, in the vicinity of the switchboard, in male connectors, the switchboard should be either of the flexible or of the portable type, with the switchboard circuits terminating in female connectors. Ideally, each switchboard circuit would consist of a switch, a pair of fuses, a dimmer, and one or two female connectors. However, a switch is not an *absolute* necessity, for the circuits can be "made" and "broken" simply by joining and pulling apart the respective connectors. Fuses are always necessary on each circuit. Dimmers need not be connected to each circuit: if the number of dimmers is limited, either they may be connected to as many switchboard circuits as there are dimmers, and the other circuits used for "constant" circuits, or the "dimmer insertion system" may be employed, wherein dimmers can be connected to the desired circuits and interchanged as requirements dictate. Thus a bank of home-built dimmers may be used as the basis of a switchboard, each dimmer circuit being equipped with a switch, fuses, and connectors, and wired to an incoming main supply of current.

As switchboard operation, especially on small amateur stages, should be made as noiseless as possible, the common type of snap switches, push-button switches, or tumbler switches, such as are used for residential wiring, should not be used. Knife switches, of the inclosed or bar-connected dead-front type, are noiseless in operation. The switchboard should be so constructed that circuit connections can easily be made and fuses be readily replaceable. The various component parts of a switchboard should be mounted and wired with the highest regard for safety: usually it is best to inclose all the current-carrying devices in a shallow box of sheet metal (which can be made up to order by a local metal-working shop) and extend the operating handles of the switches and dimmers beyond the dead-front panels, which can be used to cover the switchboard box. Great care should always be exercised to prevent the overloading of dimmers — an expensive habit that operators of amateur switchboards must guard against forming.

It is impossible to outline any detailed instructions for planning and building home-built stage switchboards, since the determining factors, which depend entirely upon the conditions that surround each individual case, vary over too wide a range to render specific recommendations of any general use. A home-built switchboard should represent an assembly of available devices in a manner that the builder has decided is most suitable to his particular needs. Many effective arrangements and combinations can be devised by the ingenious amateur builder; the advantages of simplicity, however, should never be lost sight of. Many suggestions can be gleaned from the previous discussions of switchboards in this chapter, and also from the illustrations depicting actual installations of various types of switchboards. The three stage switchboards which are briefly described below were designed and built, and are being effectively used, for certain types of amateur play production activities. They indicate the almost unlimited degree of variation possible in both basic features of design and detailed features of construction.

The first of these three switchboards, which was designed by Bassett Jones, is of a comparatively simple nature, though highly useful and effective by virtue of this fundamental simplicity. It is meant for use only on small stages and only for productions having simple lighting requirements. It contains eight switchboard circuits, six of which are connected, in groups of two, to three slider-type dimmers, and two of which are without dimmers. Each circuit terminates, on the face of the board, in a plugging receptacle. Twelve plugging cables are provided: at one end of each is a female connector for accommodating the stage wiring circuits; at the other end of each is a plug that corresponds to the circuit receptacles on the switchboard face. A heavy-duty receptacle is provided for plugging in the current-supply cable. Fuses are provided for each circuit, but the switchboard contains no switches — the circuits are closed by inserting the plugs into the circuit receptacles, and opened by removing them. This switchboard can easily be built of materials that are obtainable at any well-stocked electrical supply dealer, except for the sheet-metal box that contains the wiring devices, which would have to be made up to order. The sheet-metal cover of this box is pierced with holes that leave the circuit fuses and receptacles permanently exposed. At the back of the box are two drilled brackets for mounting the switchboard to a wall or other flat surface, and also three pairs of slots for inserting the six drilled strips of iron to which the three slider-type dimmers are bolted. At the extreme left of the switchboard a heavy-duty receptacle (Number 59198, accommodating a Number 59197 plug; if for 3-wire supply, a Number 59193 receptacle and its corre-

An 8-circuit plugging type amateur switchboard. A slider type dimmer may be bolted to each pair of vertical rods.

sponding Number 59192 can be used) is mounted. Wires from this are led to the main fuse cut-out (Number 62965; the same also for a 3-wire supply, as the neutral should not be fused). From the main fuse cut-out, wires are led to the four double-branch fuse cut-outs (Number 62587; or for 3-wire system, Number 62199). The first branch cut-out, supplying the two constant circuits, is directly connected to the wires from the main cut-out; but at each of the three remaining branch cut-outs a female connector (Number GE716), is connected in series as shown in the illustration. The

The 8-circuit amateur switchboard with the front panel removed, showing the wiring connections.

pair of leads from each dimmer terminates in a male connector (Number GE625), and the dimmers are thus placed in the three pairs of branch switchboard circuits at the right side; that is, two switchboard circuits are connected to each dimmer. From the branch fuse cut-outs, each pair of circuit wires is connected to a switchboard receptacle (Number GE287). To the bottom of the sheet-iron switchboard box is fastened a double-strip wooden clamp for holding the twelve plugging cables, each about four feet long, in place. One end of each plugging cable terminates in a plug (Number GE554) which fits the switchboard receptacle, and the other end terminates in a female connector (Number GE716). Directly above each plugging cable a small thin piece of slate is attached to the face of the switchboard. On these slate pieces can be marked the designations of various stage wiring circuits or of the units of lighting equipment to which each plugging cable is connected (by means of the flexible or portable stage wiring). Such a switchboard has the advantages of compactness and light weight. As the dimmers are demountable, the switchboard and dimmers can be packed together in a small, easily handled wooden case for transportation. The total cost of the materials used in the construction of such a switchboard, exclusive of the dimmers, should not exceed thirty-five dollars.

A home-built stage switchboard for amateur use that lends itself particularly well to transportation and to flexibility of control, is one developed by George Junkin, and used in many cities throughout the country in connection with the amateur play-production activities of National Community Service — the Playground and Recreation Association of America. This switchboard is built into a small, sturdy trunk, and hence is ideally suited to the transportation it must undergo, as it is prepared for shipment in an instant, merely by closing down the lid of the trunk. It is a bit more elaborate than the switchboard just described, though resembling the latter somewhat in principle. It contains sixteen switchboard circuits, and four slider-type dimmers, none of which is permanently connected to a switchboard circuit. However, each circuit is equipped with a series-wired twin receptacle into which any one of the dimmers can be plugged when needed, and removed, when it is no longer needed, for possible use on another circuit during the same scene. Such a feature, which might be termed the "dimmer-insertion system", is particularly to be recommended for inclusion in amateur switchboards, as it makes possible the maximum use of the dimmer equipment, which usually constitutes the most expensive part of amateur-built control apparatus. Switchboard receptacles, plugging cables with the proper connectors, branch- and main-circuit fuses, and a heavy-duty receptacle for the current supply, are all provided. In addition, the switchboard has an operating light and a transformer outlet for 6-volt bell and signal circuits. By reference to the accompanying illustrations, the wiring of this switchboard may be traced out as follows: from the main supply receptacle and main fuse cut-out (at the top), first to the operating-light socket, then around to each of the 16 branch-circuit fuse cut-outs, and

A 16-circuit plugging type amateur switchboard built into a trunk, with four slider type dimmers attached to the lid of the trunk.

terminating at the transformer outlet in the upper left corner. From each of the branch cut-outs, the circuit wires connect in series the single switchboard receptacle (Number GE658) and the twin dimmer-insertion receptacle, both of the ordinary type used for residential wiring. The dimmers are bolted to the trunk lid and are each equipped with a three-foot plugging cord that terminates in a male connector that fits the twin dimmer-insertion receptacles. Each of the latter consists of two receptacles wired in parallel, one receptacle for accommodating the dimmer plug, and the other for accommodating a plug (with a white porcelain handle, as shown) whose prongs have been short-circuited, for the purpose of keeping the lights at "full up" when no dimmer is in the circuit, or when the lamps have been brought to "full up" and the dimmer must be removed for use on another circuit. Thus the short-circuit plug acts as a "by-pass", and "shunts" the current past the dimmer. When a "full-up" circuit (with the short-circuit plug in one of the twin receptacles) is to be dimmed, the dimmer is plugged into the other twin receptacle, its handle set at "full up", and the short-circuit plug removed. The current must then pass through the dimmer, whence it can be dimmed down as ordinarily. Obviously, then, the dimmer will have no effect on the circuit while the short-circuit plug is in place. The plugging cables on this switchboard extend from the circuit receptacles, through a piece of insulating loom down each side of the trunk, to a wooden clamp, where they terminate in female connectors for the accommodation of the stage wiring circuits. A miniature 6-volt transformer, with push buttons for telephone bells and cue signals, is mounted beside the dimmers, on the lid of the trunk. The wiring devices of this switchboard are inclosed in an asbestos-lined sheet-metal box with a sheet-metal cover so pierced with

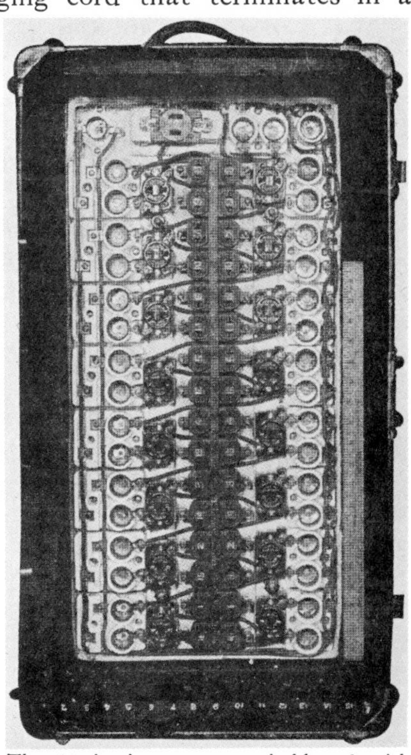
The 16-circuit amateur switchboard with the front panel removed, showing the wiring connections.

holes that the various receptacles and fuses are exposed, for operation and replacement. All these parts are logically arranged and properly labeled in order to enable the operator to pick out the various devices on the same circuit. A separate cable with several male connectors and one female connector is used to bring several switchboard circuits under the control of a single dimmer. The materials of which this switchboard are constructed (with the exception of the iron box which must be specially ordered) are in common use and can be obtained from any dealer in electrical supplies. The total cost of the material for this switchboard (exclusive of the dimmers) did not exceed seventy-five dollars.

Another home-built switchboard, somewhat more elaborate in construction than the two switchboards just described, was designed more from the standpoint of convenience of manipulation. This switchboard consists of twelve switchboard circuits, each equipped with a pair of fuses, a double-pole, single-throw, bar-connected knife switch, a dimmer-insertion receptacle, a single-pole, single-throw, bar-connected knife switch that "by-passes" the dimmer insertion receptacle, and a female connector for the accommodation of a stage wiring circuit. There are also two other circuits: one equipped with fuses, a 6-volt transformer, and push buttons and miniature female connectors for bell and buzzer circuits for telephone, cues, and other signals; the other equipped with fuses, a momentary-contact push-button switch, and a female connector, for controlling solenoid lightning flashers. There is also a main fuse cut-out, and a main switch. The switchboard is built into a specially designed sheet-iron box four feet wide, three feet high, and five inches deep, and is of the dead-front type, all "live" parts being inclosed behind an insulated front face of ebony asbestos wood.

The wiring may be traced out as follows: The main current supply is of the 3-wire system. The supply feeders enter the switchboard box at the upper right corner, where they are "lugged" to the main fuse cut-out, of 60-ampere size, which gives the switchboard a total capacity of 120 amperes. A three-pole cut-out Number 34377 is used, and a solid brass cylinder placed in the neutral fuse clips. Asbestos-covered conductors are used for all of the internal switchboard wiring. Three wires lead to the main switch (60-ampere, 3-pole, single-throw, Trumbull Number 3083), and thence to the upper five of the double-branch fuse cut-outs (Number 62199). Another set of three wires leads from the main cut-out *directly* to the lower two of the double-branch fuse cut-outs. The upper five cut-outs protect switchboard circuits one to ten, which are under the control of the main switch. The left halves of the lower two cut-outs protect switchboard circuits eleven and twelve, which are *not* under control of the main switch. The right halves of the lower two cut-outs protect the transformer circuit and the "lightning" circuit. From their respective fuse cut-outs, the wires of circuits one to twelve lead to their respective circuit switches (30-ampere, double-pole, single-throw, Trumbull Number 3042). From each circuit switch, one of the pair of wires leads directly to the bottom of the switchboard where it is spliced to a conductor of a short length of Number 14 stage cable that emerges from the box through a porcelain-bushed hole and terminates in a female connector; the other wire leads to the by-pass switch (30-amperes, single-pole, single-throw, Trumbull Number 3002), and thence to the dimmer-insertion receptacles (polarized, Hubbell Number 5621, accommodating polarized plug, Hubbell Number 5553). From the dimmer-insertion receptacle and by-pass switch, the wire joins its corresponding circuit wire, being spliced to the other conductor of the short length of stage cable. Each switchboard circuit thus terminates in a female connector: circuits one to five have two connectors each, and hence can accommodate two stage circuits. As shown in the illustration, all of the connectors are of the light, household type, Number GE716: these were temporary only, and were later changed to the regular, heavy twin-prong stage connectors when the entire set of portable stage wiring was so changed over, all at one time. The wires of the "lightning" circuit (Number thirteen) lead from the fuse cut-out to a momentary cut-out push-button switch (Diamond-H Number 091) which is used to control lightning-effect solenoids, and thence to a female connector. The wires of the transformer circuit lead from the fuse cut-out to a six-volt transformer, and thence to six miniature push-buttons mounted flush in the switchboard face, and to six miniature female connectors

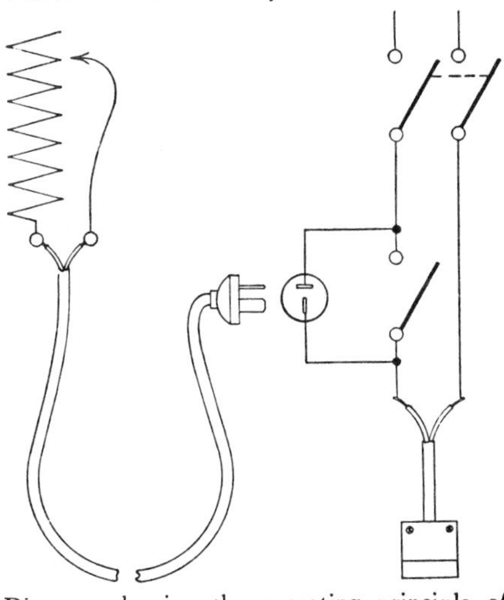

Diagram showing the operating principle of the dimmer-insertion system. The dimmer is connected into the circuit by means of the flexible lead and the polarity plug and polarity receptacle, the latter of which is mounted on the switchboard. The single-pole switch is used for "by-passing" the dimmer receptacle. The double-pole circuit switch, as well as the female connector in which the switchboard circuit terminates, is also shown.

(Number GE1347, which accommodate male connectors, GE Number 1346). The sheet-metal switchboard box is covered over by four panels of $\frac{1}{4}$-inch thick ebony asbestos wood (a Johns-Manville product somewhat similar to the Transite asbestos wood recommended for home-built dimmers); three of these panels are screwed firmly to the crossbars of the switchboard box, and the other, on the right, over the main and branch fuses, is hinged and equipped with a lock, and thus serves as a door to the magazine panel of the switchboard. This provides a dead front to the switchboard. The operating handles (and their pivot brackets) of the circuit and by-pass switches were made of $\frac{1}{2}'' \times \frac{1}{16}''$ strip copper, being bent over a template into the desired form and riveted together. The original handles on the knife switches were replaced with switch hinge clips obtained from the switch manufacturer, and transferred to the home-built operating handles on the face of the switchboard. Fiber connecting-bars (6″ long, $\frac{1}{2}''$ wide, and $\frac{1}{8}''$ thick) extend, through holes in the front panels, from the special hinge clip on each switch to its operating handle outside, and thus completely insulate the latter. The dimmer-insertion receptacles are mounted on $\frac{1}{2}'' \times \frac{3}{16}''$ iron strips suspended between the crossbars of the switchboard box, and hence come flush with the front panels. The momentary contact switch is equipped with a special button $1\frac{1}{2}''$ long, and is mounted on a saddle, in order that the button may extend the proper distance beyond the front panel. Adjacent to each circuit switch is mounted a small tab of specially-surfaced white celluloid, upon which any necessary circuit designations can be inscribed with pencil, and easily erased with a damp cloth when no longer needed. In addition, the various parts of each circuit all have proper identifying labels. On the hinged panel at the right are two spring clips for holding the lighting cue sheet.

A 12-circuit home-built amateur switchboard, in its traveling case.

No dimmers are provided on this switchboard, because it was definitely designed to be used in conjunction with dimmer equipment that had previously been acquired. The plugs on the dimmer leads, and the dimmer-insertion receptacles on the switchboard, are of the polarized type in order to prevent any dimmer from being inadvertently connected to a switchboard circuit, and thus thrown directly on the line without any lamp load in the circuit. A length of stage cable containing several polarized dimmer plugs and one polarized female connector wired in parallel is provided for combining several switchboard circuits, through the medium of the dimmer insertion receptacles, and controlling them, as a unit, with a single dimmer.

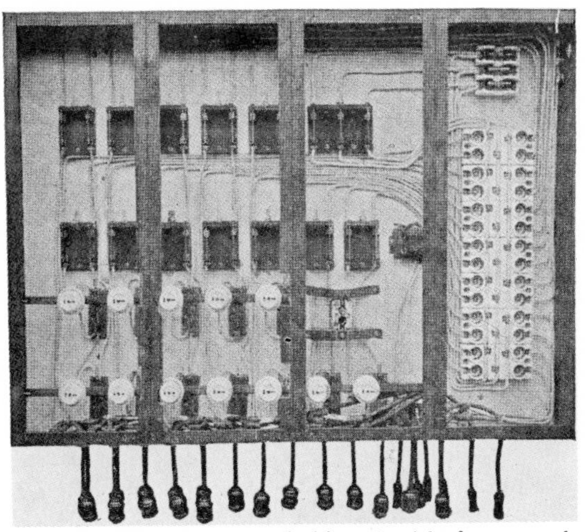

The 12-circuit amateur switchboard with front panels removed, showing the wiring connections.

A receptacle is provided at the top surface of the switchboard into which can be plugged the operating light. The latter consists of a tubular lamp in a home-built reflector which confines the light to the switchboard, allowing none to spill out into the acting area, where it would easily be noticeable in dimly lighted scenes. A miniature tumbler switch adjacent to the receptacle controls this operating light. Inside the switchboard, directly to the left of the main fuse cut-out, is mounted a small lamp controlled by a home-built spring switch. The latter is actuated by the door of the magazine panel, and is so adjusted that, as soon as the door is opened, the magazine panel is flooded with light, thus enabling the operator quickly and conveniently to detect and replace a blown fuse.

At the rear of the switchboard are two heavy steel brackets by means of which the switchboard can be mounted on a wall or other flat surface. Under usual conditions, the switchboard remains mounted within its heavy wooden case. When used on the stage, this case rests upon a set of casters; for shipment, these are removed and the front of the case locked in place. The 3-conductor Number 6 stage cable that connects the switchboard with the source of current supply is usually left in place, being connected to a 60-ampere, 3-pole, industrial-type, safety lock-switch (Trumbull Number 20322), which is mounted on the side of the wooden case.

A close-up view showing the wiring of circuit switches, dimmer by-pass switches, and dimmer insertion receptacles, and the hinge clips (which replaced the original switch handles) to which may be fixed the fiber connecting bars.

The practice of leaving one or two switchboard circuits (in this case numbers eleven and twelve) independent of the main switch often proves particularly convenient on amateur switchboards. Often all the stage circuits must be flashed out simultaneously (as, for example, when a character on the stage operates a "dummy" wall switch), except perhaps for several stage circuits, which might be supplying a fireplace light, or a moonlight flood outside a window, and so forth. If these latter stage circuits can be connected to switchboard circuits independent of the main switch, this operation would become very simple, whereas if the main switch controlled *all* the switchboard circuits, the operation would become very complicated and almost impossible to carry out smoothly.

Used in conjunction with this switchboard, a device that might be termed a "distribution panel" has often proved its worth. It consists simply of a number of female cable connectors mounted together, in groups of varying sizes, in a sheet-metal box, to form a sort of auxiliary plugging panel to the switchboard. The female connectors in each group are wired in parallel to a plugging cable that terminates in a male connector.. Thus by plugging several stage circuits into one group of connectors on the "distribution panel", they may be brought under the control of a single switchboard circuit by means of the plugging cable. The distribution panel thus makes it convenient for the switchboard operator to group any desired stage circuits and control them as a unit by one switchboard circuit. Naturally, such a distribution panel greatly increases the flexibility and the circuit capacity of the switchboard with which it is used.

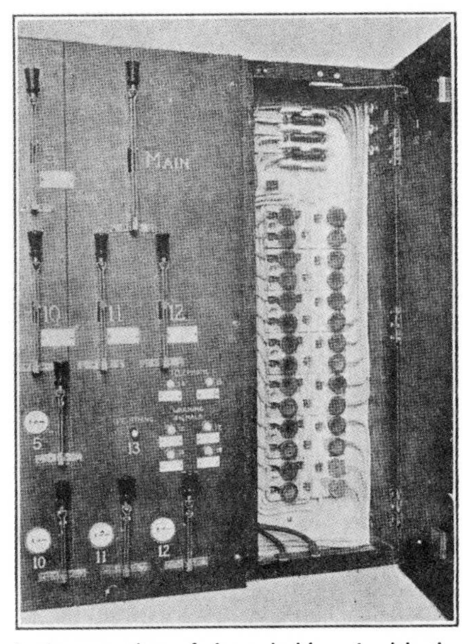

A close-up view of the switchboard with the hinged panel open, showing main and branch circuit fuses of the magazine panel.

Most of the materials used in the construction of this switchboard can be obtained from local dealers in electrical supplies. The principal exceptions are the ebony asbestos wood panels and, as in the case of the other amateur switchboards, the sheet-iron box. The total cost of the materials for this switchboard amounted to slightly less than one hundred and forty dollars.

It is quite apparent that the operation of the amateur switchboard last described is more simple and convenient than that of the two other amateur switchboards previously described. The former have the advantage as regards cost, simplicity, extreme compactness, and portability, while the latter has the advantage of the important factor of convenience of manipulation. These three switchboards may be considered as fairly representative of the design and construction and general possibilities of amateur switchboards, and amateur stage workers who contemplate building their own switchboards may derive from these brief descriptions some suggestions that they can successfully apply to their own specific problems.

CHAPTER IX · COLOR MEDIA

Selective reflection – color-sprayed lamps, opalescent dipped lamps, metal foil, fabrics, paper; selective transmission – transparent dipped lamps, natural-colored lamps, glass color caps, gelatin color sheets, glass color plates, fabrics.

THE principles governing the production of color have been discussed in a previous chapter. The present chapter is an extension of that discussion — a treatment of the practicable methods of applying these fundamental principles of color production to the requirements of stage lighting. A brief resumé of the foregoing material dealing with these principles of color production will therefore be useful as a basis of the present discussion.

The problem of producing colored light is not one of "coloring", or of "adding color to", white light, but of removing from white light, by *selective absorption*, that portion of it which is unwanted — that portion which would not form part of the dominant hue desired. This fact must be constantly borne in mind by the reader, despite the use of fundamentally faulty nomenclature (the term "colored light", for example) that would seem to indicate otherwise. The removal, the absorption of the undesired hues, is the function of *color media*. Pure "white" light, by definition, is made up of equal quantities of light of all hues, and thus serves ideally as a sort of "raw material" from which any desired hue of light can be segregated merely by removing the remaining undesired hues. Light from the incandescent lamp is almost equally as suitable as pure white light for the production of colored light, as it also is made up of light of all hues, although these hues are not present in exactly equal proportions. The principal constituent hues of white, or "unmodified", or "raw", light from the incandescent lamp may be considered to be red, orange, yellow, green, blue-green, blue, and violet. If red light is wanted, it can be obtained by absorbing the orange, yellow, green, blue-green, blue, and violet; if green light is wanted, it can be obtained by absorbing the red, orange, yellow, blue-green, blue, and violet; and similarly for each of the other hues. This method of absorbing from white light *all* hues but the desired one produces a *pure* single hue. In actual practice, however, this theoretically simple method of color production, or color selection, as it might be more truly called, does not apply in quite so simple a manner, for several reasons. In the first place, color media, or "color filters", as they are also termed, that can achieve such an absolute selection of hues are rare and expensive. Secondly, absolute selection of single hues involves a great loss of light, and requires an unduly large amount of unmodified light (with a heavy consumption of electric current) to produce even a reasonable intensity of light of the desired color. In addition, for most practical purposes of stage lighting, hues of very high spectral purity, although they are highly desirable, are not often considered absolutely necessary. Actually, the usual type of fairly good red color medium will absorb the violet, blue, blue-green, green, not quite all of the yellow, only a small part of the orange, and of course, a minimum of the red. Although the unabsorbed light contains orange and yellow, its *dominant hue* is red. Similarly, the average green color medium will absorb the violet, blue, only part of the blue-green, virtually none of the green, a small part of the yellow, most of the orange, and all but a very small portion of the red. Yet in spite of the presence of red, orange, yellow, and blue-green light, the unabsorbed light from such a green color filter will appear green to the eye — that is, its dominant hue is green. This dominant hue of green has an exact equivalent, in visual appearance, in a monochromatic hue of green of some particular single wave length. The eye is spectrally non-analytic, and cannot distinguish the component hues that make up any dominant hue, or distinguish between a dominant hue and an equivalent monochromatic hue. Thus very few of the commercially available color media provide light that can be considered spectrally monochromatic.

Color media all operate on the principle of absorption. They can, however, be divided into two general classes: (1) those operating on the principle of *selective reflection;* and, (2) those operating on the principle of *selective transmission.* Color media of each of these classes can be divided into two sub-groups: (*a*) those which form an integral part of, or are applied directly to, the light source, the incandescent lamp; and (*b*) those whose applications are extraneous to the light source, across the mouths of reflectors, for example. Color media of these several groups will be discussed in the following paragraphs from the standpoint of their suitability for stage-lighting purposes — their color purity, their color permanency, their relative efficiency, their method of manipulation, and their availability. Where accessories are necessary to apply color media to stage-lighting equipment, they also will be considered under each description. In addition, a few simple but effective methods of experimenting with the "home production" of the two more common types of color media will be described.

But before these characteristics of individual types of color media are taken up, brief descriptions of the first three are necessary. The *color purity* of a color medium is the ability of the medium to produce light whose range of wave lengths lies within the wave-length limits generally assigned to the hue by whose name the color medium is designated. This definition of color purity includes also the ability of the medium to produce a saturated color — one free from, or undiluted by, white, unmodified light. An absolutely pure blue color medium would produce no color of light other than spectral blue. An absolutely pure yellow color medium would produce no color of light other than spectral yellow. Another yellow color medium, however, might produce light of the same dominant yellow hue and yet produce little, if any, spectral yellow — it might produce only red and green, and derive its dominant yellow by additive mixture. The latter case would represent the diametrical opposite of absolute purity. Between these two extremes — absolute purity and "absolute impurity", as the latter might be called — range the purities of available color media. High color purity in a color medium is not necessarily an advantage unless it is especially sought after. In fact, many color media, especially some of the colored gelatin sheets, are deliberately made *impure*, in order to provide various gradations of tints and intermediate hues, and colors for special purposes. None the less, high purity in color media for stage lighting use is generally to be desired, especially for use with the graded-mixture method of color control, in which the three primary colors of light — red, green, and blue — are used in combination with clear light to obtain any desired color. The *color permanency* of a color medium is the ability of the coloring agent — the pigment or dye — in the medium to withstand disintegration, such as fading or discoloring, caused by the conditions of use to which it is subjected. The principal causes of pigment or dye disintegration are the effects of light and heat. Color media that are applied directly to the lamp, or form a part of it, are subject to the most rigorous disintegrating influence, as they are exposed to the entire heat and light output of the lamp. In general, mineral pigments are more stable under the disintegrating influences of light and heat than are organic dyes. The *relative efficiency* of a color medium is a measure of the ability of the medium to absorb as little light as possible over and above the amount necessarily absorbed in order to achieve its correct color selection. Relative efficiency must not be confused with absolute efficiency, the latter being simply the ratio of the amount of unabsorbed, "colored" light produced by a color medium, to the amount of incident, unmodified light originally delivered to it. Relative efficiency is a measure of the proportion of light unnecessarily wasted by a color medium; it is dependent upon the material of which the color medium is made, the dye or pigment used as the coloring agent, and its shade, or density. A color medium of high relative efficiency absorbs a minimum of light in excess of the selective absorption by which it produces colored light.

Because of several conditions, principal among which are the unequal proportions of the spectral hues in the composition of light emitted by the incandescent lamp, and the differing relative luminosity values of each of the spectral hues, the amount of light, of each color, that it is possible to obtain by selective absorption from a given amount of unmodified light is limited, even under the most favorable conditions. For example, the limiting values for the principal colors used in stage lighting are, roughly, as follows: *amber*, 60% of the incident light delivered to the color medium; *red*, 20%; *green*, 15%; and *blue*, 5%. These figures, which are for color media of average color purity and high relative efficiency, indicate that if it is desired to produce the same effective intensity as would be provided by the unmodified light from a 100-watt lamp, 165 watts would have to be used in conjunction with the amber medium, 500 watts with the red medium, 700 watts with the green medium, and 2000 watts with the blue medium. Each of the values given above is, of course, subject to rather wide variation, depending upon the type of color medium employed — its relative efficiency, its color purity — and other minor factors.

I. Selective Reflection

A color medium operating on the principle of selective reflection has the property of absorbing the undesired portion of the unmodified light and of *reflecting* the remainder. Selective reflection, in fact, is the principle involved in the visualization of colored objects. The color of the light reflected by an object under white light is commonly termed the "color" of that object. Selective reflection as a means of color production is not utilized to any great extent for stage-lighting purposes. The principal color media that are used to produce colored light by selective reflection are the following: sprayed coatings on incandescent lamps; so-called "opalescent" lamp dips; various fabrics, principally silk; and lacquered metal foil, principally silver.

Incandescent lamps of the more commonly used types and sizes are regularly available with *sprayed colored coatings.* White, inert, finely ground materials, of a mineral nature, such as chalk and barytes, form the foundation of these coatings. Suitable pigments, usually also mineral in nature, are added in the correct proportions, to serve as the coloring agents. A liquid "binder" is added to this mixture to form a very thin paste. This thin paste is sprayed uniformly, in a thin coating, over the surface of the lamp bulb, and is then baked at an appreciably high temperature, to harden the coating and to make it adhere firmly to the lamp bulb. Although it would seem that the colored light is produced by selective transmission through the colored coating, the emitted light from a color-sprayed lamp really acquires its tint through its many successive selective reflections from the minute particles of this opaque coating, on its devious passage through the interstices between these particles. It is obvious that high color purity cannot be secured with color-sprayed lamps, because the interstices between the opaque particles, which permit the passage and tinting of the emitted light, will also allow no small proportion of clear, unmodified light to pass out and dilute the color. For this reason, the colored light produced by color-sprayed lamps is invariably a tint rather than a saturated color. Furthermore, it is obvious that the multiple reflections to which the emitted light has been subjected on its passage through the coating will cause an undue amount of light absorption over and above that required by the color selection itself; hence the relative efficiency of color-sprayed lamps is rather low. But on the other hand, because of the mineral nature of the coating, and the baking it has undergone, the color permanency of color-sprayed lamps is fairly satisfactory, except in the case of the larger sizes of lamps and in the case of any lamp not cooled by sufficient ventilation. Color-sprayed lamps over 150 watts in size usually will not give satisfactory service, except under the most favorable conditions. Color-sprayed lamps should not be used where color purity or relative efficiency is desired, or where the lamps are mounted in close-fitting reflectors or housings which do not provide abundant ventilation. Although not used much on the stage proper, color-sprayed lamps are used extensively in theatres, finding their chief uses in achieving decorative lighting of the auditorium and in sign lighting. Color-sprayed incandescent lamps in the smaller sizes (up to 50 watts, in the "A" bulb) are available in five colors: red, green, blue, amber-orange, and yellow. They are also available in a light flame tint. These sizes and colors are regularly stocked by local electrical dealers. Color-sprayed lamps of other sizes and styles can be obtained on special order to the manufacturers. Incidentally, sprayed colored coatings on incandescent lamps constitute the most widely used application of the selective reflection principle of color production.

Opalescent lamp dips are occasionally used for stage-lighting purposes. In regard to their color purity, color permanency, and relative efficiency, they are very similar to the sprayed colored coatings. Like the latter, the opalescent lamp dips also consist of opaque "fillers" and, usually, mineral pigments, but, instead of being sprayed on the lamp bulb, the latter are applied, in mixture with organic solvents, in the form of a lacquer or varnish. Some types of opalescent lamp dips require several days to dry on the lamp bulb. They are available in red, green, blue, amber, and several intermediate colors, and are stocked by dealers in stage-lighting equipment, in liquid form, ready to apply. The chief advantage they offer is their high color permanency, especially their resistance to weather erosion. Hence they are used extensively on lamps that are to be employed for outdoor service.

The other applications of the selective reflection principle of color production take forms that are extraneous to the light source itself, and consist of colored fabrics and colored metal foil. *Colored fabrics* have occasionally been used for stage-lighting purposes. Perhaps the most notable instance was their use abroad, in the Fortuny system of indirect lighting. In this system, silk and velvet fabrics were used in the form of double sets of endless bands, or belts, one fitting closely inside the other, each passing over its own set of small cylindrical rollers. The several areas of the inner continuous band of fabric were each of a single, principal color. One section of the outer band of fabric was open (except for the edges), and the remaining part was black on one side of the opening, and white on the other side. Upon this double band of fabric was directed a powerful beam of clear light from an arc spotlight. By means of small electric motors connected to the rollers over which the fabric bands passed, each of the latter could be controlled as desired, from a remote point. By thus moving the fabric bands, the areas of the several colors on the inner band, and the areas of the black and white on the outer band, that were exposed to the beam of light, could be varied in any proportions. Thus could be produced light of any desired color by selective reflection from the colored fabrics. This system, which was applied to various types of stage-lighting units, provided an excellent quality of diffused light, and was used principally for lighting the cyclorama and for creating realistic lighting for exterior scenes. Colored fabrics vary greatly in color purity, color permanency, and relative efficiency, but even the best values for these characteristics are not particularly good. The principal disadvantages of the use of silk fabrics as color media are their tendency to fade under the high intensity of light that their low relative efficiency makes necessary, and their rather high cost of replacement and maintenance.

Colored foil has also been used on the stage to obtain colored light by selective reflection. The equipment that David Belasco has been using to produce indirect lighting, employing the bowed circular discs coated with pure silver leaf, has been described on page 174. For producing colored light with this equipment, a coat of colored lacquer — the so-called "French varnish" — is carefully applied to the silver leaf, and the colored light produced by selective reflection of the beam of light from the lacquered-covered silver foil. In addition to its use in this equipment, the selective reflection principle of color production was used also to achieve a realistic lighting, over the entire stage, for outdoor scenes, in a manner somewhat similar to that of the Fortuny system described above. A large, flat surface (about eight feet long and three feet wide) of veneer, or "compo-board", was entirely covered with silver leaf. This surface was divided into three equal areas, and to one was applied yellow lacquer, to the second, red lacquer, and to the third, blue lacquer. This large surface, really a flat, colored, silvered reflector, was mounted in a suitable frame and suspended over the stage at the desired angle, supported by two sets of lines from the gridiron. These lines were so arranged that the angle of tilt of the silver-leaf reflector could be adjusted, and the entire reflector raised and lowered, from the fly gallery. A bank of powerful floodlights was directed on one colored area of the reflector, and the stage was flooded with light that was diffused but that also had a predominant direction. By gradually raising and lowering the reflector, and thereby changing the relative areas of each color exposed to the beams of light from the floodlights, the color of the reflected light that covered the stage could be changed almost imperceptibly. By this means, gradations in color from the light yellow of afternoon, through the red of the sunset, to the pale blue of the evening moon, were obtained. Obviously the color purity, the color permanency, and the relative efficiency of the colored silver foil described above depends entirely upon the lacquer used. In place of the silver foil it is possible to use colored tin foil; the latter is less expensive, though not as satisfactory, as the former.

It must be pointed out that colored light produced by selective reflection is generally diffused in quality. A metal foil, however, provides a semi-diffuse reflection, and hence also, to a limited extent, a directional control of the diffused colored light. Selective reflection as a means of producing colored light can often be utilized in an emergency when other color media are not readily available. By directing white light upon a piece of colored paper or colored cloth of even the commonest type, a fairly satisfactory colored light can be secured by reflection, with a little experimentation. And not infrequently will colored light obtained by reflection be found to possess certain characteristics that make it far more suitable for certain special purposes than colored light produced by direct transmission.

II. Selective Transmission

A color medium operating on the principle of selective transmission has the property of absorbing the undesired portion of the unmodified light and of transmitting the remainder. The majority of the color media available for use on the stage operate on the principle of selective transmission. They are in much wider use for stage lighting than are those operating by selective reflection, for the reason that they possess, on the average, greater color purity, greater color permanency, and greater relative efficiency, and can be manipulated, or applied to lighting instruments, with greater convenience. The principal color media that are used to produce light by selective transmission are the following: transparent lamp dips, natural-colored glass bulbs on incandescent lamps, and glass "color caps"; and gelatin sheets, glass plates, and silk fabrics. The color media in the first group are applied directly to the lamp; those in the second group are used extraneously.

Transparent lamp dips are special colored lacquers which can be applied to the bulbs of incandescent lamps to form transparent, superficial coatings. Transparent lamp dips, in general, have three major constituents; first, the soluble, transparent dye, usually organic in nature (in contrast to the opaque mineral pigments usually used in opalescent lamp dips), which serves as the actual coloring agent; second, a clear, transparent "carrier" for the dye, which with it will form the colored film covering the lamp bulb; and third, a volatile solvent in which both the dye and the carrier are soluble. These three constituents, in the correct proportions, form the "lamp dip." In order to apply the lamp dip to the lamp bulb, the lamp is dipped, while it is lighted and hot, into the lamp dip. The heat of the lighted lamp drives off the volatile solvent from the adhering dip, and leaves the desired firm, transparent, colored film adhering to the surface of the lamp bulb. The light emitted from the lamp is "colored" by selective transmission through this film.

The color purity of the many transparent lamp dips on the market varies from good to very poor. A lamp dip of very high purity is a rarity. However, the lamp dip of average purity meets fairly well the requirements for which it is ordinarily used. The color permanency of transparent lamp dips is usually rather poor. It depends principally, of course, upon the dyes used, which are generally spirit-soluble coal-tar dyes. These, unfortunately, are not very stable to light and heat. As the lamp dip is subjected to the total amount of light and heat continually emitted by the lamp filament, the dye fades, or becomes discolored. This is especially the case if the lamp dip is used on type C (gas-filled) lamps, the bulbs of which are relatively much hotter than those of type B (vacuum) lamps. Lamp dip applied to a type C lamp fades and discolors, and even the carrier itself scorches, in a very short time. For these reasons, transparent lamp dips can be used successfully only on type B lamps. Even on these the dye fades, especially if the lamp is not cooled by proper ventilation. A new transparent lamp dip has recently been developed for use on the *smaller* sizes of type C lamps. This new dip is at present available in amber only. Under favorable conditions this color will be in fairly good condition at the end of 500 hours of use. Lamp dips are comparatively inexpensive, however, and lamps that have become faded can be cleaned in a boiling solution of caustic soda, and can readily be re-dipped. The relative efficiency of transparent lamp dips is, on the average, fairly good.

Although regular commercial lamp dips are neither expensive nor difficult to procure (being regularly obtainable from dealers in stage-lighting equipment), some stage workers, especially the experimentally inclined, may occasionally find it interesting to compound their own lamp dips, particularly if they are trying to achieve some special color which is not ordinarily available. It is a comparatively simple matter to make up, from ordinary, readily available materials, homemade lamp dips that will prove fairly effective. Spirit-soluble dyes can be obtained at most local dealers in paints and chemicals, or they may be ordered from some of the larger dyestuff manufacturers. Only dyes which are known to be "light-fast" should be used. For the carriers and solvents (this combination of both is commonly called the dye "vehicle"), any one of several different materials may be used: ordinary collodion (which is guncotton dissolved in a mixture of alcohol and ether); or celluloid (old, discarded photographic film, from which the emulsion has been removed by soaking in boiling water, serves very well) dissolved in either amyl acetate (refined banana oil) or denatured alcohol or acetone; or a high grade of bleached, wax-free shellac, dissolved in alcohol (the so-called "French varnish"). The dye should be dissolved in a small quantity of denatured alcohol and the insoluble particles, if any, filtered off. The vehicle (carrier and solvent, together) should then be prepared, and also filtered, in order to exclude any foreign matter. The dye solution should then be added to the vehicle, and both should be thoroughly mixed. If suitable proportions of each constituent — the dye, the carrier, and the solvent — have been used, the homemade lamp dip is ready for use. It is not possible to give formulæ with exact amounts or proportions for making up these lamp dips. However, no unreasonable difficulty should be experienced if the following points be kept in mind: the dye must be soluble in the solvent used (unfortunately, package dyes such as those sold at drugstores, for domestic purposes, are not generally soluble, and cannot be used for lamp dips); a sufficient quantity of dye must be used to color the vehicle to the desired shade after the vehicle has been spread out in a thin film, and dried, on the lamp bulb; and the vehicle must be of sufficient consistency to cause a reasonable amount of it to cling to the lamp bulb when the lamp is dipped. The solvents and carriers, like the dyes, can usually be obtained at a local dealer in paints and chemicals. Incidentally, it is highly probable that among the many quick-drying lacquers that in the past few years have begun to supplant oil paints, may be found some that are transparent and otherwise suitable for use as lamp dips.

If more than a very few lamps are to be dipped, the process can most conveniently be carried out as follows: A long strip of wood should be wired with ordinary cleat sockets, spaced on about six-inch centers (a length of skeleton striplights is very useful for this purpose). This strip of wood should be mounted horizontally, with the sockets pointing downward, and the sockets connected with a source of current. The lamps to be dipped should first be thoroughly cleaned, with soap and water, if necessary, in order to remove any grease and dirt on the lamp bulb. They should then be inserted in the sockets and given a final cleaning with a clean cloth dampened with alcohol, to remove finger marks. It is really important, to insure a good job of dipping, that the lamp bulbs be quite free from even traces of oil or grease. After the lamps have been lighted a minute or two, to allow them to become warm, the dip can be applied. A small cylindrical tin can, slightly larger in diameter than the lamp bulb, should be about half filled with lamp dip, and should be raised around the lamp just high enough so that the lamp dip covers the bulb completely. After a few seconds it should be withdrawn and the excess lamp dip on the bulb allowed to flow back into the container. Any air bubbles in the dip on the lamp bulb should be pricked, otherwise they will permit the passage of unmodified light. The lamp dip should be allowed to dry in a dust-free atmosphere, with the lamp remaining lighted. The lamps should not be removed from the sockets, or otherwise handled, until the dip has completely dried. A coating of lamp dip can be made denser, or deeper in color, by repeated applications of the dip after each previous coating has "set" (though not necessarily dried). By trial experimentation with the judicious mixing of lamp dips of different colors, it is sometimes possible to obtain suitable intermediate colors. By adding a "thinner" to the lamp dip (more of the original vehicle, less of the dye), tints of various degrees of saturation can be secured.

Natural-colored glass bulbs (instead of the usual clear glass bulbs) are regularly available on incandescent lamps of a limited number of types and sizes. They have all the advantages possessed by clear lamps to which superficial coatings of lamp dip have been applied. In addition, they produce light of a higher average color purity. Also, vitrifiable mineral pigments, instead of the far less stable organic dyes, are used as coloring agents. As these pigments are fused with the molten glass at a very high temperature, before the lamp bulb is blown into shape, it is quite obvious that the color permanence of natural-colored glass bulbs will be of a very high order when they are subjected to the lesser heat emitted by the lamp filament. This practically indestructable nature of the coloring agents in natural-colored glass bulbs permits their use on lamps of even the largest size now made, with very satisfactory results in regard to color permanency. The relative efficiency of natural-colored glass bulbs is almost, though usually not quite, that of dipped lamps. Lamps with natural-colored glass bulbs are available in four standard colors: ruby, green, blue, and amber. Their principal disadvantages are their comparatively high cost (lamps of some colors cost almost three times as much as a clear lamp of the same wattage) and their comparative rarity. Lamps with natural-colored glass bulbs are not commonly available. They are usually not stocked by local electrical dealers because of the relatively small demand for them, and because of the great variety in which even this small demand manifests itself. Limited stocks are carried by the larger dealers in stage-lighting equipment. The larger sizes, and the more uncommon types, must usually be obtained from the lamp manufacturers, who make them on special order. Under the heading of natural-colored glass bulbs should also be mentioned the so-called "daylight lamp." A daylight lamp has a bulb which is colored a special tint of blue. This blue-tinted bulb modifies the light from the filament so that its spectral characteristics are changed to approximately those of average daylight. A daylight lamp emits light that approaches the theoretical "white" light more closely than does light emitted by a clear-bulb lamp. Under certain special conditions, daylight lamps can be used to advantage on the stage.

A glass color cap as applied to a 150-watt incandescent lamp (approximately one-fourth size).

Glass color caps of various types have long been used on small lamps in connection with sign lighting. In the past few years, however, they have become available in larger sizes, and have been equipped with improved holding devices for mounting them firmly in place over the lamp bulbs, and, as a consequence, their use for color modification is becoming more and more widespread. Glass color caps are essentially cup-shaped, or globe-shaped, in form, and are made of natural-colored glass. They inclose the major portion of the lamp bulb to which they are fastened, and "color" the light emitted from the lamp by selective transmission. There are two general types of color caps: one is globe-shaped in form, and is fitted over the lamp bulb by means of a beaded edge on the cap snapping into spring clips which are fastened, by a special holder, directly to the lamp socket; the other is cup-shaped in form, and is fitted over the lamp bulb by means of a large, double-looped spring-wire clamp, which is screwed through the tip of the color cap and which grasps the sides of the lamp bulb and holds the cap firmly in place. Both types of color caps are equipped with circular aluminum shields that fit over the neck of the lamp bulb and prevent the escape of unmodified light. Glass color caps possess a uniformly high degree of color purity, and, as the vitrifiable pigment is applied while the glass is in molten condition (as in the case of natural-colored glass bulbs), color permanency is assured. The relative efficiency of glass color caps is usually somewhat lower that of dipped lamps or of natural-colored glass bulbs, because the color caps are of an appreciable thickness (about an eighth of an inch), and thus absorb relatively more light than do the thinner media. Glass color caps are very easily applied, being merely slipped on and off the lamp bulb. They are relatively heavy, and the holders, whatever form they take, must be able to hold the caps securely under severe conditions. This is especially the case when the caps are used in the borderlights, where accidental knocking and swaying are likely to dislodge the caps, causing perhaps personal injury or ruined stage effects. As a precaution, it may sometimes be advisable to attach a metal screen of fine wires and of about half-inch mesh, across the mouth of each borderlight reflector; or to extend it the entire length of the borderlight, if the latter is of the open-trough type. Glass color caps may be obtained from most dealers in stage-lighting equipment. They are available in three sizes, the largest of which will accommodate a 500-watt PS–40 incandescent lamp, and in six standard colors: red, green, blue, amber, moonlight (a shade of blue-green), and daylight (a light blue tint similar to that of the daylight lamp described above).

Colored gelatin sheets constitute undoubtedly the most widely used of all types of color media for stage-lighting purposes. A gelatin color medium is simply a thin sheet of dyed gelatin — the gelatin being very similar to the gelatin used for domestic purposes. A colored gelatin sheet is made by dissolving a water-soluble dye in a hot-water gelatin emulsion, and flowing the dyed emulsion on to a level sheet of polished plate glass, or a smooth, level sheet of aluminum. The thin film of dyed gelatin emulsion, which at this stage is sometimes rolled smooth, is allowed to dry hard, and the flexible, colored sheet of gelatin is then "peeled off" the level plate. Colored gelatin sheets are also sometimes made by rolling a water solution of dye into a sheet of clear, transparent gelatin. No positive statement as to the average color purity of colored gelatin sheets can be made with assurance: each grade and each color of gelatin sheet must be judged individually. The color purity of colored gelatin sheets ranges from that of the poorest quality of gelatin sheets to that of the highest quality of small, expensive sheets that are made for scientific test purposes. The color purity of gelatin sheets available for stage-lighting use varies between these extreme limits. As relatively unstable organic dyes are generally used as the coloring agents, the color permanency of colored gelatin sheets is, unfortunately, always rather poor. Colored gelatin sheets will fade very rapidly if they are mounted too close to a large lamp, or if insufficient ventilation is provided. If the gelatin sheet is subjected to excessive heat, the gelatin itself will scorch and burn. The relative efficiency of gelatin color media, because of the thinness of the sheets, is generally of a high degree.

Gelatin color media must be handled with great care, because the thin gelatin material is rather fragile, and is extremely susceptible to varying conditions of moisture and temperature. Extreme heat or cold will make the gelatin brittle and will cause it to crack easily.

Gelatin color media are best stored in a moderately cool, moist atmosphere, and stored flat rather than rolled. When used before the mouths of any but the smallest reflectors, special precautions must be taken to prevent the gelatin sheets from buckling or contracting. The larger sizes of frames for holding the gelatin sheets in position on stage-lighting equipment must be provided with an open network of thin wires on both sides of the gelatin that will

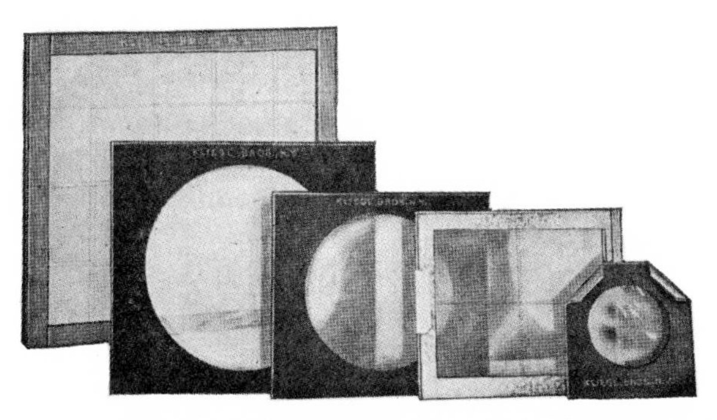

A group of color frames, of various types and sizes, by means of which gelatin color media can be applied to stage-lighting equipment.

keep it in place and will prevent it from curling or cracking. The gelatin sheets should never be fastened firmly, or rigidly, in the holding frames, but should be inserted loosely enough to allow for the comparatively large expansion and contraction that takes place when the light is turned on and off. In order to obtain light of the desired shade, or depth, it is often convenient to mount several thicknesses of gelatin sheets in a single color frame. This practice invariably causes the gelatin to fade almost immediately, especially when used before large lamps, as in a 1000-watt olivette, because it does not allow the innermost sheet of gelatin to cool rapidly enough. The air trapped in the small pockets and bulges between the several sheets of gelatin acts as a heat insulator, preventing the escape of heat through the layers of gelatin and subjecting the innermost sheet to an excessively high temperature. If it is necessary to use more than two sheets of gelatin, especially blue or purple ones, or other colors with high absorption factors, they should be mounted in separate frames, with a sufficient space between each to allow for free circulation of air between them for cooling. The drying out and cracking of gelatin sheets when in service can often be retarded somewhat by lightly rubbing into their surface, before they are first used, a thin film of either some vegetable oil or glycerine. If small cracks occur in a gelatin sheet, or if a small portion of it has faded badly, a "wet patch" can be made by moistening a small scrap piece of gelatin, of the same color, and applying it to the broken or faded part. The moisture will form a firm bond between the old and the new gelatin surfaces.

If stage-lighting equipment is properly provided with color-frame slide grooves for the reception of color frames holding the gelatin media, colored gelatin sheets can easily be applied. The holding

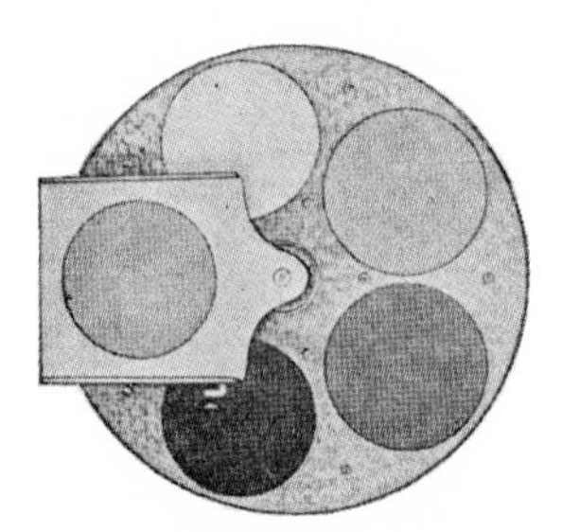

Two types of color-wheels for use with spotlights.

frames for gelatin sheets are comparatively simple. Most color frames are made of thin sheet metal, in two paired sections. The gelatin sheet fits loosely between these two parts, which slide together, or are held together with small clips. The large sizes, such as are used on olivettes, are usually made of thin wooden strips joined to form two paired sections, which are screwed together with short wood screws after the gelatin sheet has been placed loosely between them. The larger sizes of color frames have fine wires stretched across the opening, as described in the previous paragraph. It is convenient, in a complete installation of stage-lighting equipment, that color-frame slide grooves on lighting instruments be of such size that a minimum number of standard sizes of color frames need be kept on hand. These color frames, and the slide grooves on the instruments, should be so designed and constructed as to prevent the escape of unmodified light from any lighting instrument, which would mar the desired effect.

Perhaps one of the greatest advantages of using gelatin color media for stage-lighting service is the large number of hues and tints in which they may be procured. They are available in more than fifty standard colors, tints, and shades. The four standardized colors — red, green, blue, and amber — in which natural-colored glass bulbs, glass color caps, and colored glass plates are available will meet the majority of stage-lighting needs; but where delicate tints and intermediate colors are wanted, from a single light source, the gelatin sheets are of great convenience and practical service, as they are almost universally obtainable from dealers in stage-lighting equipment. They are available in the standard size — about 19″ × 21″ (some special grades of gelatin sheets are available in a slightly larger size — 20″ × 25″). They are comparatively

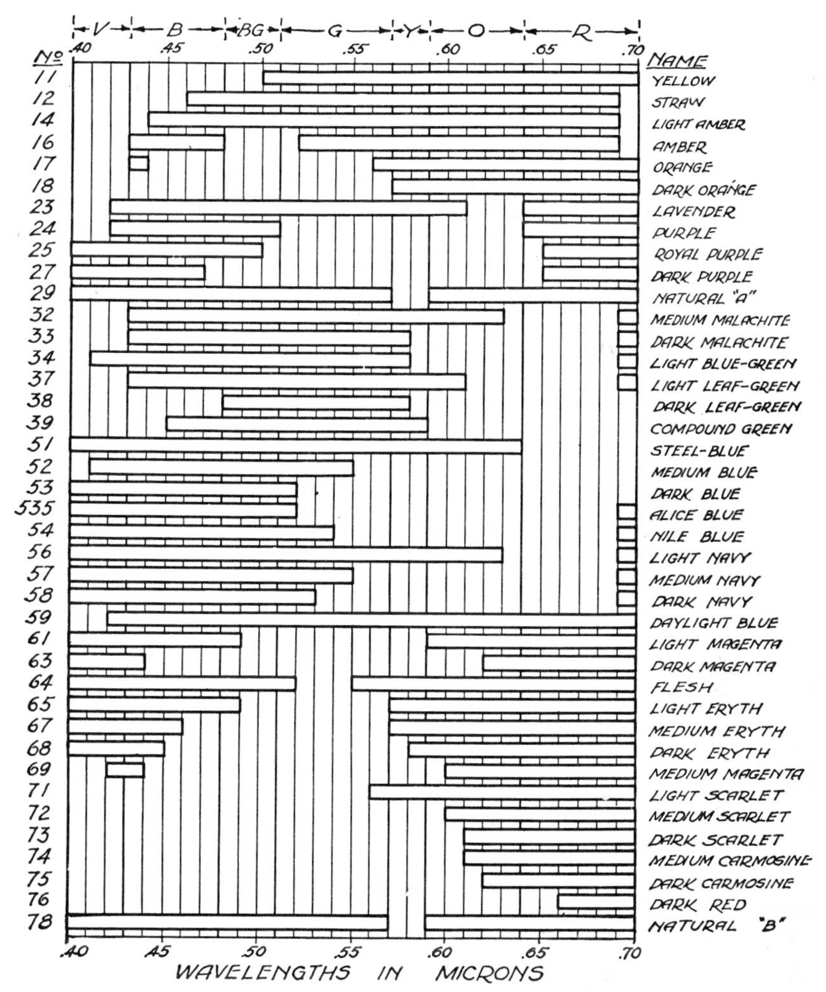

Approximate qualitative spectral analysis of Townsend gelatin color media.

inexpensive, costing, on an average, only about twenty cents a sheet. These large sheets can readily be cut up into smaller sizes for use with the smaller holding frames. Special quality gelatin media which have a higher uniform color purity than the average gelatin media, also colors of true purity and fastness, are available at a slightly higher cost.

In order to indicate the large range of colors in which gelatin media are available, and to indicate the spectral characteristics of an uniformly good grade, there appears on the previous page a diagrammatic tabulation of the approximate, qualitative spectral analyses of the principal colors of the complete set of Townsend colored gelatin sheets. These qualitative spectral analyses were made with a Zeiss comparison spectroscope, under actual noon sunlight. The horizontal lines represent the ranges of light wave lengths which each colored gelatin sheet transmits. However, as the analyses were merely qualitative, the exact proportion of light transmitted at each individual wave length is not shown. The set of standardized colors having the highest color purity would be as follows: red, Number 76; green, Number 38; blue, Number 53; and amber, Number 18. Gelatin sheets Number 29 and Number 78 are comparatively new developments in the field of color media, being known as the "surprise" colors. Their spectral composition is such that the light they transmit emphasizes the reds in the colored objects it falls upon, without perceptibly changing the appearance, or values, of the other colors. When playing in light transmitted by these color media, actors need apply only a minimum of make-up, if any at all, as the natural color qualities of their complexions are not subdued as they would be under bright, unmodified light.

It is somewhat more difficult to make colored gelatin sheets than it is to make lamp dips. Nevertheless, with a little care and experimentation, and with the proper preparation, homemade gelatin color media can be made that will serve their purpose very well. There is hardly any material advantage to be gained by a stage worker in making his own gelatin color media, as they can be regularly obtained, in virtually any color, at small cost. But for the experimentally inclined, the process will afford no small degree of interest. The necessary materials can be procured at most local dealers in paints and chemicals. The dyes used should be water-soluble and light-fast; and the gelatin should be of a fairly "hard" grade (Number 9102), and should be in ground, or flaked, form. The water and gelatin should be combined in the correct proportions to form a six per cent (by weight) gelatin emulsion. One ounce (avoirdupois) of flaked gelatin to sixteen ounces (fluid) of water (one pint) is the ratio that will achieve approximately the desired concentration of emulsion. The gelatin and water should both be carefully measured, and about a fourth of the water reserved to dissolve the dye. The remainder of the water should be poured over the gelatin, in a suitable vessel, and allowed to stand several hours. The dye, meantime, should be dissolved in the one-fourth portion of water. When the water and gelatin have formed a gelatinous mass of uniform consistency, the latter should be heated just enough to liquefy it. It should not be boiled: a small double boiler is convenient for heating the gelatin. At this stage the dye solution should be added to the gelatin emulsion, and the mixture stirred well. The heating of the dyed gelatin emulsion should continue for about ten minutes. Then the emulsion should be filtered through several layers of cloth in order to remove foreign matter. It is then ready to flow on to the level plate, which should have been previously prepared. The level plate should be slightly larger than the ultimate size of the gelatin sheet desired, and should be made of polished plate glass, or of some other perfectly flat and smooth surface. It can be mounted on a frame provided with three leveling screws, and should be leveled very carefully, in each direction, with the aid of a small, exact spirit level. A strip of narrow adhesive tape, bound around the edge of the plate and projecting slightly above its upper surface, will retain the liquid gelatin emulsion when it is first flowed on the plate. After the plate has been leveled, it should be carefully cleaned. In order to prevent the gelatin sheet from adhering firmly to the plate, the latter should be covered either with a thin film of vegetable oil or glycerine, or with a thin coat of good shellac. After the gelatin emulsion has been filtered, and while it is still hot, it should be flowed on to the plate in a thin film (the ratio of one fluid ounce of emulsion to a hundred square inches of plate surface will provide a film of about the proper thickness) and spread out evenly over the plate with the aid of a small piece of paper. It should then be allowed to stand and harden in a dust-free atmosphere. When the gelatin has thoroughly dried and hardened, it should be carefully stripped, or "peeled", from the plate. Colored gelatin sheets can also be made by swabbing a water solution of dye over the surface of a sheet of clear, transparent gelatin. The latter may be procured from dealers in stage-lighting equipment. Transparent colored lamp dip can also be used to color clear gelatin sheets. The latter method is especially useful when it is desired to match exactly the colored light produced by dipped lamps in open-trough lighting equipment with that produced by clear lamps in conjunction with gelatin color media in compartment lighting equipment.

There has recently been introduced a new material — transolene — which, because of its great durability and high degree of color permanency, promises eventually to supplant the gelatin color media. In appearance, a transolene color sheet hardly differs from a gelatin color sheet, except that the former is a trifle thinner and is more flexible. It differs entirely, however, in chemical composition. Its stability, its power of resistance to drying out, buckling, cracking, and fading of color, under extremes of heat and cold, dampness and dryness, appears almost phenomenal to any one who has grown accustomed to the use of gelatin color media. Transolene color media are available in much the same assortment as are gelatin media. Their average color purity and relative efficiency are also much the same as the average values for gelatin media. Transolene color media are available in sheets 20″ × 21″, and cost about three times as much as the average gelatin color media.

Colored glass plates, for use before the mouths of reflectors, are gradually coming into wider use. In color purity and color permanency they are equivalent in value to the natural-colored glass bulbs and the glass color caps. In relative efficiency they approximate the latter only, as they are usually of appreciable thickness (glass plates of some colors are almost a quarter of an inch thick). They are available only in comparatively small sizes, the largest being about six inches square. Besides the several small rectangular sizes, they are also available in the form of circles (usually termed "roundels"), for use with the newer type of individual-unit, spun-aluminum reflecting equipment in footlights, borderlights, and similar equipment. Compared to gelatin color media, the colored glass plates are very expensive — initially, at least. They are available in the four standardized colors: red, green, blue, and amber, as well as in a series of intermediate colors. Although used very extensively in Germany, glass color media have only recently been adopted for stage-lighting service in this country.

The use of colored glass plates in borderlights and other suspended stage-lighting equipment should be attended by due precautions for the safety of the persons on the stage. Thin wire screening, of about half-inch mesh, should surround the glass plates in order to prevent shattered pieces of glass from falling to the stage in the event of accidental breakage. Colored glass plates are easily breakable, both by mechanical shocks, and, in the thicker sizes and more absorptive colors (such as green and blue), by the heat of the lamps, especially if sufficient ventilation is not provided. Because of the small size of the largest colored glass plates available, the use of glass color media has been restricted to small reflectors. A recent development, however, in which small pieces of colored glass (about two inches square) are assembled and held in place by a thin metal latticework construction, makes possible their use with larger reflectors. In these glass color screens the glass used is thinner than the larger single plates, and each piece of glass is comparatively small and fits loosely into the latticework. Hence, unequal heating over the face of the entire color screen will not create internal stresses in the glass due to unequal expansion (as happens in the case of the thicker, larger, single glass plates), since each piece of glass is free to expand and contract at its own rate. The latticework color screens are, therefore, more safe and more practicable for stage-lighting service than are the individual glass plates. The latticework color screens are available in the four standardized colors: red, green, blue, and amber.

Colored silk is also occasionally used as a color medium, particularly arranged in special holders that fit in the slide grooves of olivettes and provide "sunset" effects. For these, a strip of silk, wide enough to cover the mouth of the olivette and several times as long as it is wide, is dyed in graded colors ranging from light yellow at one end, through amber and red, to blue at the other end. This strip of silk is mounted on two cylindrical rollers, and, by being moved slowly before the mouth of a reflector, can be used to simulate dawn or sunset effects. As explained previously, colored fabrics have comparatively low values for color purity, color permanency, and relative efficiency, and rarely prove practicable for stage-lighting service, except, perhaps, as emergency makeshifts.

CHAPTER X · METHODS AND PRACTICE

Assembly of lighting and control equipment; methods of stage-lighting treatment, general practice in planning and carrying out the lighting of a production; effects – simulated, projected, fantastic; methods of lighting outdoor productions.

THE basic physical phenomena of electricity, light, and color that are pertinent to stage lighting have been discussed and their contribution to the several functions of stage lighting have been indicated. The apparatus available for utilizing their physical phenomena in the service of stage lighting — the actual lighting instruments and control equipment, have also been described and the characteristics and the particular range of usefulness of each have been pointed out. The preceding chapters thus serve to outline the nature of the several types of stage-lighting tools, as they might be termed, and the various operations for which each can be used. It remains for the present chapter to indicate very briefly some of the general methods of utilizing these tools — of planning and carrying out the lighting of a production — and the usual procedure, or "practice", that is followed in achieving, to the greatest extent possible with available apparatus, the essential lighting effect desired for a particular production. In addition, further sections of this chapter are devoted to a discussion of so-called stage-lighting "effects", and to a description of special methods that are usually necessary for the lighting of outdoor productions, such as pageants and celebrations. But first must be taken into consideration the question of just what assortment, what *assembly*, of apparatus can be regarded as constituting a fairly complete and adequate set of lighting and control equipment for use with "legitimate" dramatic play production (as distinguished from other types of theatrical performances: vaudeville, revues, "presentations", and so forth).

I. Assembly of Equipment

The dominating principle that should govern the selection of a complete set of stage-lighting and control equipment is *flexibility*. Flexibility may be defined as ready adaptability to the greatest possible number of uses, and is achieved principally by having the component parts of the complete equipment readily interchangeable. Thus any arrangement, or "set-up", of equipment desired or necessary for any purpose can be easily and quickly affected. By this method, the maximum degree of usefulness can be obtained from the individual units of equipment. This does not mean that less equipment should be supplied for a flexible system than for the older type of inflexible, rigid system (although it is true that less equipment might suffice); it means that, with a given amount of equipment, or with a given expenditure for equipment, the flexible system offers infinitely greater possibilities for achieving effective stage-lighting results than does the rigid system. To achieve real flexibility, not only must the lighting instruments themselves be interchangeable, and adaptable to many different needs, but the control system — the wiring and switchboard — must also provide for the electrical interchangeability of circuits and the adaptability of control manipulation to the various anticipated control requirements.

One of the earliest factors that should be considered in planning a complete set of equipment is the provision for color control — the number of color circuits to be provided. The number decided upon will affect the exact choice of certain types of lighting instruments and, principally, the arrangement of the wiring circuits and the switchboard accommodations. Certainly not less than three color circuits should be provided; four, however, is the minimum consistent with convenience and good practice, and should be provided in every installation of equipment that makes any pretensions whatsoever to completeness and adequacy; and, if feasible, five color circuits should be provided, especially in footlights and borderlights. In a system of *three color circuits* it is not necessary to adhere to the patriotic red-white-and-blue combination that characterizes the permanent installations in virtually all the older theatres. Light-amber or straw can be substituted for the white ("white" being produced by clear-bulb lamps, without color media), or blue-green, or even green, substituted for the blue, in order to make up a more satisfactory and generally useful combination. But, in any event, the exact choice of colors for a three-color system is not an easy one, and, after all, will most likely depend upon the personal preference of the user of the equipment. Because of these restrictions of a three-color system, the system of *four color circuits* is recommended. As explained previously, this is the basis of the graded-mixture method of color control that is finding wider adaptation for stage lighting. Red, green, and blue, in conjunction with clear light, constitute the standard four-color combination. Occasionally, variations have included the use of light amber or straw in place of the clear, and also the use of blue-green and amber in place of the blue and green. The four-color-circuit system can provide light of virtually any hue and saturation. Amber, however, in various tints is so often required that it is sometimes separately provided in addition to the red, green, blue, and clear, thus forming the system of *five color*

Stage of the Children's Theatre of the Hecksher Foundation, New York: the footlights and borderlights are of the compartment type, with white-painted metal reflecting surfaces, and are wired in four color circuits.

circuits. The latter can thus directly provide the oft-required amber (otherwise red and green in the proper proportions would be necessary), and therefore simplify control and economize electric current.

The physical characteristics of the stage — its width, depth, and effective height — constitute an important factor in planning a set of equipment, as upon these will depend to some extent the aggregate *amount* of equipment necessary and the exact *type* and *size* of the individual lighting instruments that will prove most suitable. In so far as stage-lighting units are located at various points about the auditorium, the characteristics of the latter will also exert an influence on the choice of equipment.

For a flexible system, no lighting instruments, with the possible exception of the footlights and borderlights, should be installed *mechanically* permanent; no lighting instrument *of any kind* should be installed with permanent *electrical* connection with the switchboard. All lighting instruments, then, should be equipped with male connectors, by means of which connection can be made with the switchboard through the medium of flexible and portable wiring as described in Chapter VIII. In order to insure maximum flexi-

Stage of the National Theatre, New York: the footlights and borderlights are of the compartment type, with aluminum-finish reflectors.

bility, one standard size of cable connector, preferably the 15-ampere size (arranged at instrument locations in the form of plugging-boxes as described on page 292), should be used throughout the entire installation of equipment, even in place of the regular high-capacity floor and wall pockets that require the heavy stage plugs.

Footlights, of the proper type, should always be included in a complete installation. The ideal footlight unit would consist of a comparatively low-intensity light source in the form of a narrow strip across the front edge of the stage. Hence footlights should consist of low-wattage lamps, wired in the color circuits decided upon and spaced closely in a white reflecting trough, or preferably, they should be of the indirect type, or combination direct and indirect. In length they should be about three-fourths or four-fifths of the proscenium width, extending on each side to a point several feet within the proscenium arch. All light must be restricted to the stage side of the proscenium, none being allowed to escape on to the auditorium ceiling or proscenium frame. Footlights can be installed permanently, or they can be arranged in portable unit sections, and a suitable recess with mounting facilities provided at the front edge of the stage. In this recess can be located the several plugging boxes for connecting the footlights to the wiring circuits, as well as an extra female connector or two for accommodating small footlight spotlights when desired.

At least one set of *borderlights* should be provided. The "first" borderlight, directly behind the teaser, should always be of the *distributive* type, directing the bulk of its light equally both downward and backward; if more than one borderlight is used, the remaining ones should be of the *concentrating* type, each directing the bulk of its light principally downwards and only slightly backwards. The first borderlight is really the only one necessary, however. It should consist of 100-watt to 200-watt lamps wired in the color circuits planned, in compartments of mirrored or spun aluminum reflectors, or at least in white painted compartments. Low-wattage lamps in an open trough do not always constitute an adequate borderlight. The new type of revolving borderlight, which permits the directioning of the emitted light, is to be preferred to the stationary types. In length, the first borderlight should be the same as the footlight, as it must fit within the side walls of the usual type of interior ceilinged box set, for which it provides one of the principal sources of illumination. If more than one borderlight is used, they should be spaced about 8 to 10 feet apart and each, except the first, should extend to several feet *beyond* the acting area rather than *within* it, as does the first borderlight. Borderlights are most conveniently installed in portable unit lengths, mounted on a movable batten suspended from the gridiron. On the batten can be mounted also the several plugging boxes for connecting the borderlights, as well as a number of extra wiring circuits and female connectors for accommodating spotlights, olivettes, and similar units of lighting equipment mounted, when necessary, on the same batten as the borderlight.

The increasing use and importance of *spotlights* in stage-lighting work demand that adequate attention be given to the choice of size and type, and to the location, or positioning, of the individual units of spotlight equipment. To conform to the general feature of flexibility, all the spotlights of a complete installation, regardless of their size and type, should be equipped with the same mounting devices, in order that they may be easily interchangeable as to position. For use *backstage*, provision for mounting spotlights might be as follows: several extension pipe standards for individual use of spotlights at various points about the stage; a traveling spotlight tower (a tall, vertical pipe standard mounted on a heavy platform base equipped with casters for moving about) for group use of spotlights at various points about the stage; a movable batten directly behind the teaser and slightly above the first borderlight batten, for use of spotlights in the teaser position (for such use the spotlights can also be mounted directly on the first borderlight batten, along with the borderlights); and a vertical pipe standard directly behind each tormentor, for use of spotlights from the side tormentor positions. This tormentor pipe mounting for spotlights is best built as an integral part of the tormentor, thus allowing the spotlight mounting and the tormentor itself to be moved as a unit: narrow flippers on each tormentor will conceal the spotlights from spectators at extreme front-side positions in the auditorium. Seven feet above the stage-floor level is the best mounting height for the lowermost spotlight in the tormentor position. A most useful device for mounting spotlights and other units of lighting equipment in the teaser position is the "light-bridge", which is a narrow, well-braced platform, extending the width of the proscenium opening, suspended directly behind the teaser, and above the first borderlight batten and the teaser spotlight batten. A light-bridge thus provides not only a vantage point for mounting lighting instruments, but also an important position from which the instruments so mounted can be manually controlled by operators. In the *auditorium*, provision for mounting spotlights might be as follows: along the front face of the balcony, at the middle and at both ends, so that the light will strike the center of the stage at an angle of from ten to fifteen degrees; in one or several false ceiling beams, also at the middle and at both ends, or behind false ceiling panels, so that the light will strike the stage at an angle of from twenty to forty degrees. If these provisions for mounting spotlights in auditorium positions are taken into consideration in designing the architectural features of the theatre, the spotlights and mounting devices can be effectively concealed yet actually located at strategic positions. In theatres already built, the problems involved in mounting lighting equipment in the auditorium and making it appear reasonably unobtrusive are much more difficult. In some instances it might prove advantageous to have a small projection booth at the rear of the balcony in which lighting equipment can be placed and manually operated; in other instances it might prove feasible to incorporate stage spotlights or other instruments in the actual lighting fixtures in the auditorium; at any rate, many ingenious places can be devised for mounting stage-lighting equipment in auditorium positions, which are vitally important from the standpoint of directing light on to the stage at the most effective angles.

Standard small spotlights and baby spotlights are perhaps the most generally useful sizes for the backstage locations: in the teaser and tormentor positions, on the extension standards and traveling spotlight tower, and on the light bridge. For the auditorium locations — the balcony-front, and the ceiling-beam or ceiling-panel positions — especially in the larger theatres, the standard large spotlights will most likely be necessary, although the two smaller sizes can also be used with great effectiveness. For long projection distances, such as might be encountered in the auditorium locations, the size of the spotlight condenser lens should be carefully chosen. For very long throws, arc spotlights might be found necessary, though this condition will be only rarely met with in theatres of medium size. As with other equipment, the actual amount, the necessary number of spotlights, depends upon the individual conditions of each case. With the recommended interchangeable mountings, fewer instruments need be provided, as they may be set in position as required for each production. Of course, for the greatest convenience, for the greatest range of possibilities, for the greatest effectiveness, as many spotlights should be provided in the various backstage and auditorium locations as can be conveniently brought under *facile* centralized control by means of available control devices. The special "soft-edge" spotlights, the tormentor lens units, the teaser lens units, and the balcony-front lens units (all described in Chapter VI), although somewhat more expensive than the standard type of spotlights, offer many advantages if used instead of the latter, at the proper locations for which they have been specially designed, and should be taken into careful consideration when a flexible and interchangeable installation of stage-lighting equipment is being planned.

Olivettes, or floodlights, as they are sometimes termed, should be equipped with the same type of mounting device as the spotlights, so that the backstage mounting provisions for the latter — extension standards, traveling tower, teaser batten, tormentor standard, and light-bridge — are equally available for mounting the olivettes. The standard type of olivette is, at best, a rather crude and inefficient lighting instrument, and is rapidly being supplanted by the newer types that are equipped with a spun-aluminum reflector. Floodlights, equipped with large parabolic reflectors of mirrored glass or metal and with a set of spill rings, or louvers, designed especially for stage-lighting purposes (in contrast to the regular outdoor flood-lighting projectors) are now available and should be used where the most efficient utilization and accurate control of the light is desired. *Striplights* are always useful for many different purposes, and several of various lengths should be provided for use as required.

Part of the lighting equipment of a "little theatre" stage: teaser and tormentor lens units on the stage of the Carolina Playmakers Theatre at Chapel Hill, N. C.

The problem of choosing the proper *cyclorama lighting equipment* is perhaps the most difficult of successful solution. The few available standard types of lighting instruments especially designed for this purpose (the most outstanding of which are discussed on page 200) may prove suitable in many cases, but often a deviation from the standard design may be necessary in order to meet some particular phase of the individual problem. The choice of cyclorama lighting equipment depends primarily, of course, upon the type of cyclorama to be lighted — that is, its shape and its surface material. The type of cyclorama that seems to have been found generally most suitable for use in American theatres is, in *shape*, a curved vertical surface (being bent around the back and sides of the acting area, but not overhanging it, as does a cyclorama of the quarter-spherical or cupola type); and, in *surface material*, usually of linen or canvas fabric. Such cycloramas are usually suspended from the gridiron, and can sometimes be "flied" out of sight when not in use. For lighting a cyclorama of this type, lighting units with running parabolic reflectors, suspended along the entire front upper edge of the cyclorama, and producing what might be termed

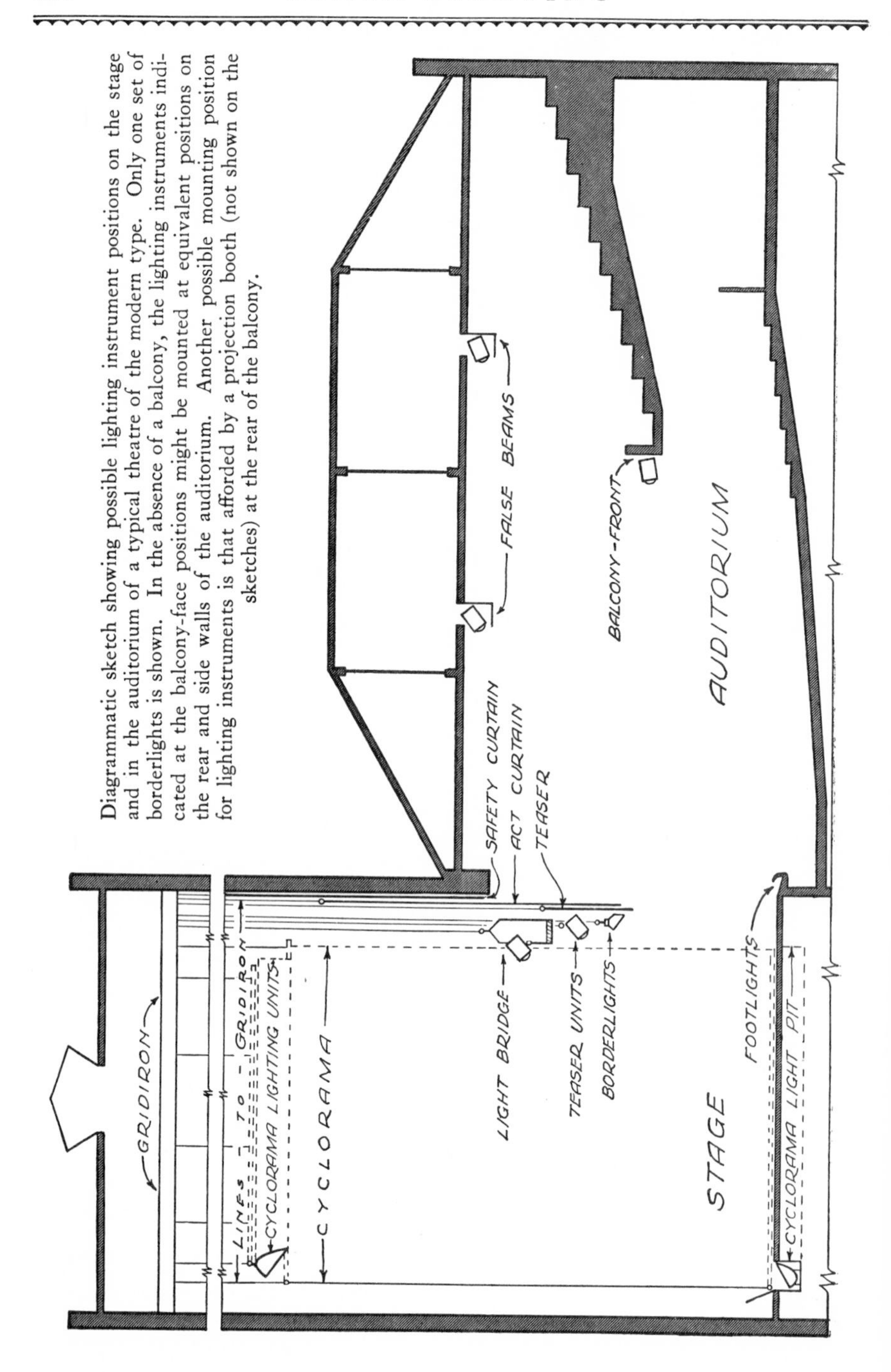

Diagrammatic sketch showing possible lighting instrument positions on the stage and in the auditorium of a typical theatre of the modern type. Only one set of borderlights is shown. In the absence of a balcony, the lighting instruments indicated at the balcony-face positions might be mounted at equivalent positions on the rear and side walls of the auditorium. Another possible mounting position for lighting instruments is that afforded by a projection booth (not shown on the sketches) at the rear of the balcony.

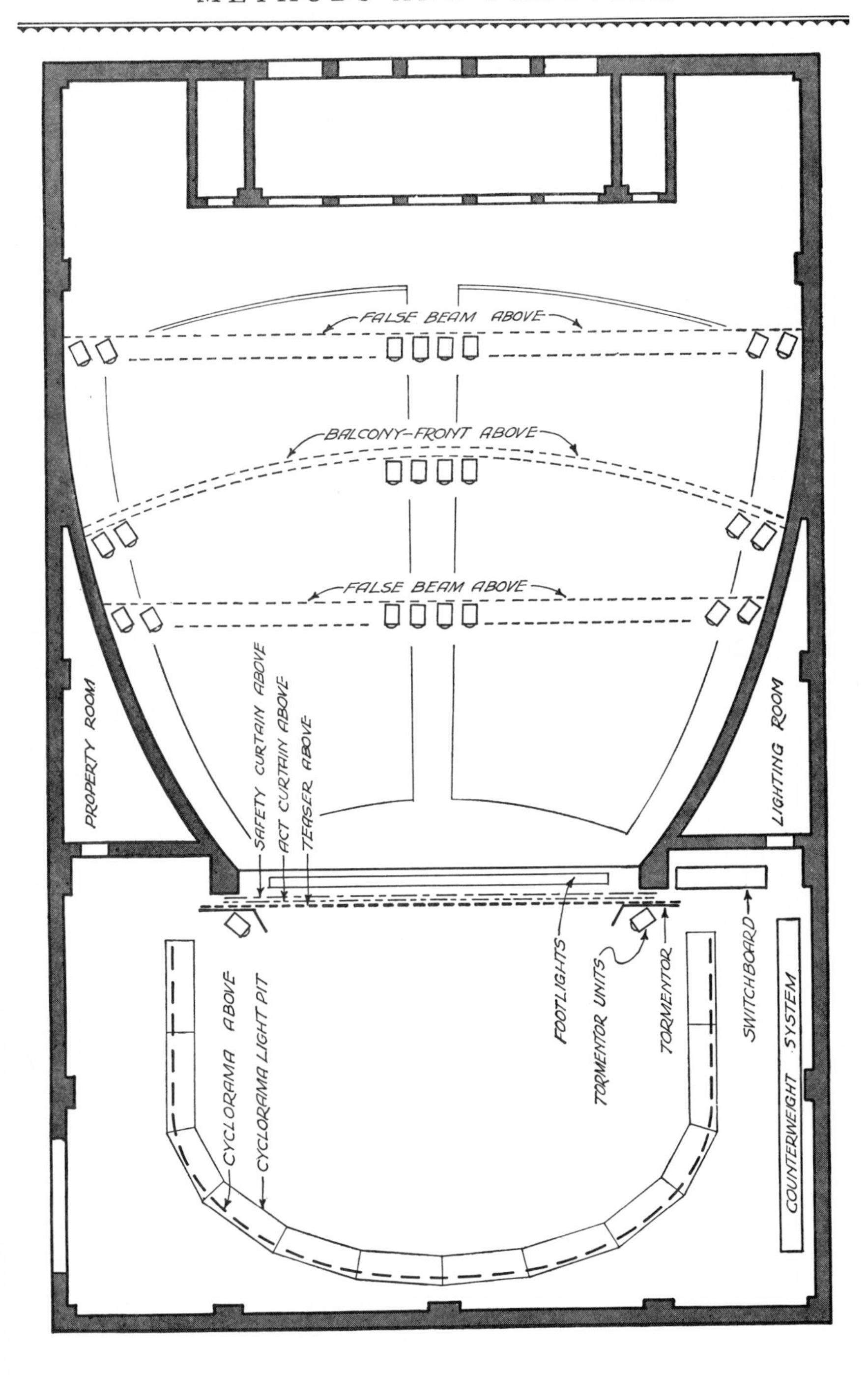
FALSE BEAM ABOVE
BALCONY-FRONT ABOVE
FALSE BEAM ABOVE
PROPERTY ROOM
SAFETY CURTAIN ABOVE
ACT CURTAIN ABOVE
TEASER ABOVE
LIGHTING ROOM
CYCLORAMA ABOVE
CYCLORAMA LIGHT PIT
FOOTLIGHTS
TORMENTOR UNITS
TORMENTOR
SWITCHBOARD
COUNTERWEIGHT SYSTEM

a "sheet" of light, prove perhaps the most suitable of all. Such lighting units, properly designed, and constructed, and properly positioned, can effectively light and evenly produce graded color mixtures on a cyclorama as much as seventy-five feet in height, without the use of any auxiliary lighting equipment. None the less, they are usually supplemented, for tinting and color-contrasting effects, by similar though much smaller units located in a "light pit" recessed in the stage floor along the entire front lower edge of the cyclorama. Cyclorama lighting equipment should confine its emitted light to the cyclorama: it should not allow any light to spill on to the acting area. One great difficulty of lighting an all-fabric cyclorama is its tendency to develop wrinkles and furrows in its surface. In very high cycloramas, these furrows are often as much as two or three feet deep, and hence are practically impossible to light satisfactorily by any known means. For this reason, cycloramas constructed of a light wooden framework covered with a smooth layer of "compo-board" and surfaced, in some cases, with fabric, are coming into greater favor. Rigid, permanent cyloramas of the quarter-spherical, dome-shaped type, having a surface of double-curvature, and surfaced with plaster or similar material, present a still more complex problem. In some instances, the equipment with running parabolic reflectors mentioned above can be adapted to meet the requirements; in others, floodlighting equipment grouped on a frame suspended above the acting area, similar to the German practice, must be provided. In any event, however, no specific type of equipment can be generally prescribed for cyclorama lighting; equipment must be chosen or perhaps even specially designed for each individual set of conditions — each problem must be solved solely on its own merits. As a matter of fact, the cyclorama had better be planned from the standpoint of the lighting equipment than the lighting equipment planned from the standpoint of the cyclorama, especially as the cyclorama, in the final analysis, is dependent upon the lighting for whatever degree of effectiveness it might achieve. The problem of cyclorama lighting is an important and difficult one, and should receive careful and adequate consideration. It is hard to conceive of a bigger "white elephant" in the theatre than a cyclorama which cannot be properly lighted.

For the accommodation of a complete set of stage-lighting equipment planned as above described, facilities for "plugging in" the equipment and connecting it with the switchboard must be provided at all the instrument locations at which provision has been made for mounting the various lighting instruments. Plugging outlets (preferably of the type described on page 292) must therefore be carefully placed at suitable intervals (1) about the edge of the acting area, recessed in the stage floor; (2) in the recess provided at the front edge of the stage for the footlights; (3) in the cyclorama light pit; (4) on the cyclorama light batten (the batten upon which the cyclorama lighting equipment is mounted); (5) on the borderlight batten; (6) on the teaser-light batten; (7) on both tor-

Stage of the Guild Theatre, New York: behind each tormentor is a group of tormentor lens units and spotlights; three spotlights are shown mounted on the light bridge (which also has plugging receptacles for the accommodation of additional equipment), directly below which are a group of teaser lens units and two sections of compartment borderlights. The cyclorama lighting equipment used on this stage is pictured on page 202. In addition to the lighting equipment on the stage, six large-size "soft edge" spotlights are mounted in a false ceiling beam in the auditorium, to provide necessary front-lighting.

mentor pipe standards; (8) on the light-bridge; (9) at the middle and both ends of the balcony front; (10) at the middle and both ends of false ceiling beams or panels in which lighting equipment is to be mounted; and (11) in the projection booth or any similar location. This list includes most of the possible locations: in many instances, some will be omitted, and in certain instances, some will be added to the list, depending upon the prevailing conditions. In many locations, principally in the footlight recess, on the borderlight batten, on the cyclorama light batten, and in the cyclorama light pit, the female connectors (or other form of plugging outlet employed) should be placed in groups of three, or four, or five — depending upon the number of color circuits planned. The number of plugging outlets provided should be judiciously planned: too few will restrict the use of lighting instruments; too many will cause an undue expenditure for installation. Enough should always be provided, however, to accommodate conveniently the anticipated maximum amount of lighting equipment required to be in place for any one production.

This maximum should also determine the capacity — both the total load capacity and the number of control circuits — of the switchboard, which should preferably be of the flexible type. When the complete set of lighting equipment and the lay-out of the wiring circuits have been planned, the design of the switchboard should receive consideration. Enough switchboard circuits, containing dimmers of a suitable assortment of rated capacities, should be provided. In this connection, the feasibility of incorporating into the switchboard design such features as variable-rating dimmers, and group master-dimmer control to achieve proportional simultaneous dimming, should be carefully studied. The various other factors involved in the design and construction of switchboards and wiring systems, as detailed in Chapter VIII, should all receive due consideration, so that the complete installation of stage-lighting and control equipment will be capable of meeting the anticipated requirements in a manner that is as effective, convenient, reliable, and safe as possible.

In addition to the equipment itself, there should also be planned, at the same time, adequate means for servicing it and maintaining it. The instrument locations, at the various points backstage and in the auditorium, should be provided with a means of access that is both convenient and safe, so that the operator will not hesitate to accord the equipment the care and attention that it deserves and requires. There is little virtue in providing instrument locations at, for example, a false ceiling beam, and then omitting a suitable means of access, so that personal safety must be jeopardized every time it is necessary to reach the equipment in order to carry out ordinary, routine tasks that are required in the course of its use or operation or maintenance. There should also be provided a lighting room, or a lighting workshop, dedicated entirely to stage-lighting activities and free from any trespass by other divisions of play production activity. In this room there should be suitable provisions for storing things incidental to stage-lighting work, such as a stock of color media; incandescent lamps; mounting devices, extra lenses, and various other necessary accessories; "leads" of stage cable used for setting up lighting equipment; cable connectors; and such electrical supplies and fittings as may be necessary for minor repairs that must be made from time to time. And, incidentally, it must be remembered that of all the backstage equipment, the lighting and control equipment is unquestionably the most delicate and the most needful of proper care and maintenance. Periodic inspections of all the lighting and control equipment should be made, and all shortcomings corrected at once. Burned-out or blackened lamps, and faded or cracked color media, should be replaced with new; all reflecting surfaces and lenses should be kept clean; lamps should be kept adjusted to proper focus; mounting and focussing devices should be kept in good working order; all wiring and plugs and connectors should be kept secure; equipment not in current use or not mounted in place should be neatly stored in the lighting room; and the switchboard should occasionally be thoroughly overhauled to insure smooth operation. Like any other mechanism, stage-lighting and control equipment must be given a reasonable amount of attention and care if it is to continue at its initial efficiency and to operate with its initial effectiveness.

In the case of non-professional play-producing organizations, the budgets of all but a very few fortunate ones will not permit the *acquisition* of a complete set of equipment at one time. But this fact should not stand in the way of *planning* a complete set of equipment. Although the financial conditions of the moment may permit the use of only home-built, or even of only makeshift, apparatus, a complete set of standard equipment, such as is ultimately desirable, should be planned with care and forethought. Then, as funds gradually become available, the equipment can be acquired piecemeal until the complete set is built up. It is recommended that whatever funds are initially available be divided into two unequal portions. The *larger* of these portions should be spent for a few standard lighting units (or perhaps even only a single unit) of unquestionable usefulness and of the highest quality — the best design and construction — that can be obtained. These standard units initially acquired should be among those called for by the complete plan. For this initial outlay, a good set of borderlights should be the first instrument secured; if a balance remains, then a few spotlights of the smaller sizes should be secured; and if some money is still left over, then a few good dimmers of suitable capacities (preferably of the small, round-plate, non-interlocking type described on page 314), which can later be incorporated in a regular switchboard, should be secured. The *smaller* portion of the initial lighting appropriation should be used for constructing home-built lighting and control equipment to make up a set complete enough to serve for the initial activities of the organization. Subsequent lighting appropriations should be used for "retiring" the original home-built equipment and substituting in its place units of standard equipment as called for by the original plan. In no event should any money be squandered on worn-out, obsolete equipment that has been cast off by the professional theatre and given a coat of paint or otherwise "reconditioned", however impressively "professional" it may be in appearance.

II. Methods and Practice

The several functions which light possesses when it is used in the service of the theatre have been fully discussed in the first chapter. While, under certain conditions, a single light can be made to achieve the purposes of all these functions (as was the case in "Tristan and Isolde", cited by Irving Pichel), in almost every case it is necessary to use light from several sources, from several directions, of various colors, of various forms, or patterns, and of various intensities. If light that is applied to achieve the purposes of any one of these functions interferes, or clashes, with that applied to achieve the purpose of any other function, obviously it will be to the detriment of all. It is therefore important that light designed to achieve the purpose of each of these functions be tempered and modified so as to produce a smooth, harmonious whole. Stage lighting, even as any other of the theatre arts, has no value whatsoever (that is, for purposes of play production) when it is used as an end in itself; its ultimate effectiveness depends wholly upon the extent to which it has been merged, or coördinated, with the several other elements that go to make up a complete, finished stage production. No result at all will be possible if the dramatist or director demands lighting, which, although it enhances the psychological or symbolic values of the play, hampers the stage designer because it does not fit in with his conception of the stage picture, and spoils his settings or costumes; or which does not render the action sufficiently visible; or which greatly distorts the features of the actors. It is necessary that a balance be maintained between the conflicting demands of the several functions of stage lighting in one production or scene. Since such a balance can best be maintained by some one individual, it is desirable, theoretically at least, that the functions of dramatist, director, and designer be combined and the authority be centralized in one person. Of all the theatre arts, stage lighting would profit most by such a centralization of authority.

The first step in securing an effective balance between the several elements entering into the lighting of a play would be the determination of the fundamental method of lighting treatment to be employed — whether the lighting will be used to achieve realism, a simulation of natural conditions, either indoor or out; or to achieve the expression of the mood and atmosphere of the play, either symbolically or psychologically; or to achieve an intrinsic beauty of design and color composition of the stage picture. The method of treatment depends to a large extent upon the type of play for which the lighting is designed — the symbolic treatment which would prove so effective with Maeterlinck's "The Blue Bird" could hardly be used for Shaw's "The Devil's Disciple", for which obviously a realistic treatment is necessary, or for Stephen Philip's "Paolo and Francesca", for which the esthetic treatment is most desirable, or for "Hamlet", which offers almost unlimited opportunities for the psychological type of lighting.

In spite of a great deal of scoffing criticism by some of the more advanced of stage workers, the *realistic* type of lighting will perhaps be found the most satisfactory for the average play, produced before an average audience, under average conditions — and much can be said in its favor. The strongest defense cited by those who wish to reproduce lighting conditions in nature is nature herself — a skillful and most effective designer and colorist. But whereas nature uses the light of the sun, modifies it with atmospheric conditions and the coloring inherent in natural objects, and applies it to her own handiwork, the stage worker not only uses such comparatively unsatisfactory substitutes as incandescent lamps, mechanical projection and dimming apparatus, and artificial dyes and color media, but applies his light to hollow, pretentious shams, which are usually made of canvas covered with pigments, and which, when he is not using them, he folds up and either hoists out of sight or stacks against the wall: he is trying to reproduce nature under conditions that do not even remotely resemble those of nature, and hence he is foredoomed to failure — that is, failure to reproduce natural lighting. But this very failure points the way to the use of light for its intrinsic value as an art medium. If the advocate of realism is satisfied with his blue-green light for moonlight, amber light for sunlight, his puffy clouds repeating themselves across a bewrinkled "blue-ey" blue sky, and his mechanical dawns and dusks — which even in the hands of the most experienced and painstaking appear as nothing more or less than what they actually are — well and good; but if so, he is unconsciously using them as tried and true conventional forms which the playgoer accepts without remonstrance only because he has learned to adjust himself to them. From this point of view, such "realistic" lighting actually becomes in effect simply *suggestive* of natural conditions, and as such leans towards a conventionalized, or stylized, treatment, which uses light primarily for esthetic purposes.

The very nature, the mechanics, of some plays demand realistic settings and lighting. Comedies and farces, for instance, will almost always require realistic treatment. Perhaps the most useful application of realistic lighting is to interior scenes that take place at night, and, to a lesser degree, to interior scenes in general. And for good reason, since stage-lighting devices are but an extension of those actually used for ordinary artificial lighting indoors; or, if for a day scene, because natural light coming through a few windows is infinitely more easy to simulate than natural lighting reflected from the entire dome of the sky; and, also, because the light, either natural or artificial, in each case (actually, and on the stage), falls upon man-made objects, instead of upon those of nature. But, even here, conditions are sufficiently different to require constant watchfulness and diligent effort on the part of the realistically inclined stage worker.

The stage worker escapes from the unsatisfactory results of realism if he takes the most obvious step, as outlined above. This is the acceptance of the fact that light itself, when not forced to imitate the inimitable, can be used, by virtue of its inherent qualities and characteristics, as an art medium, to achieve, in form, design, and color, a sheer esthetic beauty which will serve as a most effective environment for many plays. For instance, instead of trying to imitate moonlight and merely achieving a blue-green colored light, which after all does not remotely resemble moonlight, but which, in itself, happens to possess quiet, pleasing qualities, the stage worker would be more successful if he dropped all attempt at simulation and deliberately set out to achieve, to the fullest extent, the beauty of blue-green light. Plays of a romantic, or poetic, nature are likely to lend themselves most readily to this, which may be called the *esthetic*, treatment.

The next logical step away from realism is that treatment which may be called *symbolistic*. This treatment is particularly applicable to plays which, to a certain degree, are in themselves symbolic, such as fantasies and allegories, and provides an effective means of reinforcing and coördinating their symbolism. Symbolism in the content of a play will be infinitely more effective if it is expressed simultaneously by the lighting. The fundamental psychological values of color, as well as those of unmodified (clear, or "white") light, and shade, are utilized in this symbolistic treatment.

This leads quite naturally to the fourth method of lighting a play, which may be termed the *psychological.* Although this is rich in possibilities, its application is virtually restricted to plays having a deep emotional appeal, such as tragedies, and the more serious and profound of those plays rather indefinitely classed as "dramas." Here the psychological values of light, shade, and color, in all their known ramifications, are depended upon to coöperate with the dramatist and the actor to express the mood, the atmosphere, the feeling of the play, by exerting their subtle, dynamic, almost hypnotic, effects on human emotion, perhaps even through undiscovered physiological means.

Thus there are the four fundamental methods of lighting a play: the *realistic*, generally most suitable for farces and comedies — plays having little depth of emotional appeal; the *esthetic*, for plays poetic, idealistic, or romantic; the *symbolistic*, for plays allegorical, symbolic, mystic, or fantastic; and the *psychological*, for plays deepest in emotional appeal, such as dramas and tragedies. Of course, but few plays are lighted consistently throughout by any one of these methods independent of any other: how the methods merge and overlap has been indicated. Nevertheless, one form of treatment will be predominant, and this will decree the extent to which each of the five primary functions of stage lighting will contribute to the lighting, as a whole, of the play.

As to the actual planning and carrying out of the lighting of a play, no specific set of "rules" can be formulated. Notwithstanding a great deal of enthusiastic abstract discussion to the contrary, the problems of stage-lighting design and execution still remain to be solved, in the final analysis, by methods that are largely experimental, or "cut-and-try", in nature. Aside from the fundamental determination of the general method of lighting treatment to be employed — of the dominant note to be struck by the lighting — throughout a production, stage-lighting design resolves itself ultimately into a question of what range of results the available equipment is capable of producing, and what skill and experience are possessed by the persons who will operate the equipment. The designer of stage lighting must, of course, be thoroughly familiar with the characteristics of his media of expression, and these involve not only the characteristics of light and shade and color in general, but also, more specifically, the characteristics of those media as produced under prevailing physical conditions by the actual set of equipment which will be at his disposal for the particular production on which he is working. And such familiarity will come only with actual experience, coupled with intelligent experimentation with the various lighting instruments and control apparatus for the express purpose of sounding out their inherent possibilities and limitations. Of course, it is very desirable that he have at his disposal an assembly of equipment of his own choice: this will give him an infinitely greater latitude in his design. This practice of assembling special equipment for a particular production is rapidly growing; still, there are a great many cases where the person responsible for the lighting of a production must work with a fixed set of equipment. The ideal condition would be for the stage-lighting designer to have at his disposal a reasonably complete and *flexible* set of first-rate equipment.

As stage lighting is still in the initial stages of its development, no hampering traditions, no arbitrary "systems", no set methods, no "schools", no superficial standards, have yet been evolved — none, at least, that receive any serious general consideration. This is a wholesome condition, as it leaves the stage-lighting designer free from any petty restrictions. Perhaps the only restriction placed upon him (aside from those imposed by limitations of equipment) is that the effect he creates be subservient, or contributory, to the general effect created by the production in its entirety; that it exist not for its own sake — not as an end in itself — but as a unit medium of expression that, coördinated with the various other contributing media of expression, forms an integral part of dramatic expression as a whole.

In order to insure such coördination, the ideal condition would be to have the stage lighting of a production designed by a person who had complete authority over the entire production in all its various phases and detailed ramifications. But seemingly this is not practicable. The next best condition is to place the responsibility for the stage lighting with the person who is responsible for the settings and costumes, and who might be termed the "art director" of a production. These three elements — the lighting, the settings, and the costumes — are interdependent to such a degree that to specialize still further by dividing the responsibilities for them will, more often than not, prove detrimental to the production as a whole. Moreover, the stage lighting should be planned simultaneously with the settings and costumes, and in conjunction with them, and as early as possible in the course of preparations for the production.

One of the principal reasons why the lighting should be designed in conjunction with the settings and costumes is the extent to which the latter are dependent upon the former for their ultimate appear-

Some of the special equipment assembled for lighting *The World We Live In*, at the Jolson Theatre, New York: two spotlight cradles were used in place of borderlights; eight spotlights were used behind each tormentor; and a number of spotlights were also used from the auditorium. On the light bridge are shown several more spotlights; one sciopticon; and two Linnebach lanterns that projected on to the cyclorama the gigantic blades of grass amidst which the "insects" played their ironic "comedy."

ance, particularly the appearances of the colors. With the aid of a color booth (such as is described on page 131) the designer can select the exact colors of light and pigment and dye necessary to secure effects about which he is uncertain. In connection with stage designs that emphasize color to more than the average extent, it is often helpful to block out the outstanding colors of costume and scenery with colored crayon upon black paper. With this method, the necessary lighting suggests itself, as it must be constantly borne in mind that everything on the stage is lost in blackness until it is made evident by light of the proper characteristics. Scale models of settings are also helpful in planning the lighting for a production, as they enable the designer to determine roughly the relative locations and intensities of light sources necessary to achieve the desired plastic effects. The action on the stage — the general stage business — is also an important consideration that enters into lighting design; in fact, in some types of plays, it is of major importance. The several factors that determine lighting design are, then: fundamentally, the type of play; the particular method of treatment accorded it; the nature of the settings and costumes — the general scenic investiture; the stage action — the grouping and movement and positioning of the characters, especially in important scenes; and finally, the capabilities of both the lighting equipment and its operators. In addition, many plays require special lighting "effects" of some sort or another. These "effects", especially if they are of an unusual nature, must be taken into consideration: the ones most in demand are discussed in the following section of this chapter. The settings and costumes of a production can usually be completely planned, down to the last technical detail, on the designer's drafting table. But the lighting cannot be planned in any such great detail; usually only the broad, general effects desired can be planned in the abstract. Usually the lighting for the important critical moments in the play is planned first, and then the intervening transitions in the lighting are worked out. These desired lighting effects constitute what is usually termed the "light plot" of a production, and, in the majority of cases, represent the extent to which the lighting of a play can be designed, or planned in advance.

After the light plot has been prepared, the technical details of the lighting of a production must be worked out experimentally under the actual conditions that will prevail during the regular performance of the play. Just as there is no formula for designing the lighting of a play, so there is no formula, no set of rules, for executing the lighting. Questions such as which lighting instruments to use for achieving a desired effect, where to locate them, how to aim and focus them, what color media to equip them with, what intensity to operate them at — are all of the utmost importance, and each must be solved with the minutest care if the lighting of a production is to be successfully carried out. Yet every one of these details is utterly dependent upon the specific conditions that surround each individual case of play production. Without question, previous experience on the part of the stage-lighting worker is the general requisite, and actual, direct experimentation in each case is the specific requisite, for sucessfully working out these important details.

In planning the light plot for a play, the designer must constantly bear in mind what equipment he has at his disposal, and to what extent he can depend upon it and upon its operators to achieve the effects which he is prescribing. The preparation of an elaborate light plot calling for effects that are physically impossible of achievement under prevailing conditions is obviously abortive effort, however meritorious it may otherwise be. It is necessary, therefore, that the stage-lighting designer have an approximate idea of the equipment necessary to achieve the effects called for by his light plot.

The actual handling of the lighting equipment to carry out the light plot prepared by the art director of a production is entrusted to a corps of "operators" under the direction of an "electrician." These commonly used designations are unfortunate: "operators" and "electricians", if they are of the right type and have the proper qualifications, are highly important members of a production staff and are far more than their names seem to indicate. The number of such stage-lighting workers that are necessary to execute the lighting throughout a performance depends entirely upon the nature of the light plot: the more elaborate and intricate it is, the more operators will be required. For average productions, usually an electrician, assisted by an operator or two, are sufficient.

The actual assembly and setting up of equipment, preparation of special "effects", and so on, should begin well in advance of the dress rehearsal, especially if the light plot is at all involved, or if the lighting of the production is to be accorded more than casual attention. The necessary experimentation is time-consuming to a degree, and a sufficient time allowance must be provided for it. It is during the lighting preparations and experimentation and during the light rehearsals that the light plot prepared by the art director is gradually transformed into the electrician's lighting cue sheet. The latter contains all the necessary specific details pertaining to the lighting equipment and its operation, arranged, for reference, so as to parallel the action of the play. It lists, for example, the various instruments in use, their dimmer settings and color media, and gives directions for changes or transitions in the lighting that takes place as the action of the play develops: all of these instructions are carefully cued either to specific moments in the play or to specific lines spoken by the characters. Very often, for productions with simple lighting requirements, the cue sheet resolves itself into a few brief notes, but nevertheless it retains its important relation to the routine of lighting a play. Of course, after several rehearsals or performances, electricians and operators commit the gist of the cue sheet to memory, just as the actors assimilate the rôles they play. And the lighting cue sheet is of the same relative importance to the stage-lighting workers as the script of the play is to the actors. This cue sheet is usually placed at the switchboard.

In the course of the experimentation to determine the details that shall comprise the lighting cue sheet, the art director, or other person who has designed the lighting, or at least upon whom rests the responsibility for the lighting, views the various experimental results from critical points in the auditorium, in the position of the spectator, directing the electrician and operators in their experimental work and pronouncing judgment upon the results. The detailed conditions of equipment set-up and operation by which the art director's light plot are achieved are noted, and so the lighting cue sheet is built up. Often these light rehearsals are tedious and prolonged, but there is no other way of arriving at the desired results except through this system of direct experimentation. It is highly desirable that these light rehearsals be merged with the regular play rehearsals as early as possible, in order that the more subtle lighting effects can be adjusted to the characters on the stage, and, what is of great importance, to their movement and grouping about the stage. All the details of the stage lighting should have been decided upon before the final dress rehearsal, for at that time there is usually no opportunity to make any further adjustments except those of a very minor nature.

Realistic lighting undoubtedly requires the greatest concentration on details. In fact, a good job of realistic lighting is perhaps the most difficult of all to achieve, as the standard by which it is judged is a rigorous and inflexible and quite definite one, namely, complete illusion. As has been pointed out, the other types, or methods of stage-lighting treatment owe their inception in no small measure to the fact that most of the attempts at realistic lighting were so difficult, or even impossible, to achieve with complete success.

For realistic lighting, it is essential that all light on the stage have an *ostensible* source — this source need not be apparent on the stage, but it must exist, even if only in the subconscious imagination of the spectator. That is, the light on the stage, as seen by the spectator, must come *supposedly* from the sky, or through a window, or from a lighting fixture in the room, or from a fireplace, and so forth. This realistic effect can perhaps be most subtly achieved by building up the light on the stage with a number of individually controlled light areas, as produced by equipment other than the footlights and borderlights, but using the latter two units to some degree as blending media. There must be no light on the stage that is glaring to the spectators. A glaring condition may be caused either by a point of light in brilliant contrast or by a large area of even comparatively low brightness. For example, a single exposed candle flame would prove glaring if it were used in a darkened stage, but not if it were used on a well-lighted stage; and if a cyclorama is lighted a bit too brightly in contrast to the objects and actors that appear before it, the effectiveness of the latter will be reduced accordingly. An actor should never be provided with a brilliantly lighted background, unless, of course, a silhouette effect is deliberately aimed at. Generally, also, the ceilings of "box sets" should also never be brilliantly lighted: in fact, the apparent brightness of the walls of such a set should taper off gradually from its brightest part at a level just above the actor's head, to the ceiling, which should be kept rather dim. Shadows, especially in enlarged form as cast by too-bright footlights, should under no circumstances be visible on the cyclorama. In order to prevent this, it is necessary that the light used on the stage be cast in a direction that is predominantly almost horizontal, though just slightly downward. That is, although light from many different directions may actually be utilized, in its sum total, in its ultimate effect, it should appear to be coming from an overhead source that is just a bit above the horizontal. This predominant direction will also be found generally the most suitable for properly lighting the features of the actors. In order to achieve the predominant direction that is most suited to the needs of a particular case, it is necessary to secure an effective balance between the light produced by the various lighting instruments used to light the acting area. The balance can be secured by proper positioning of the instruments, and by proper control of their respective intensities with dimmers. Light from an angle of about thirty-five degrees overhead (such as would be produced by instruments placed in the ceiling beam or ceiling panel of the auditorium), is perhaps the most useful as a basis for this balance. This should be supplemented by light from the teaser and tormentor positions (and perhaps also from the first borderlight and from the light bridge), and with comparatively low intensities of light from an angle of about ten degrees overhead (such as would be produced by instruments placed at the balcony front), and perhaps also with low intensities of light from the footlights. The color of the light from these various positions must also be carefully balanced; for some purposes the careful balance of complementary tints will be found most effective. Careful control of the dimmers connected to the lighting instruments at the various locations is, of course, of the utmost importance for achieving and maintaining this balance. Incidentally, the use of individual dimmers on the lighting instruments at the various locations should be kept at a minimum, as it breaks up the centralization of control, and will often be found decidedly detrimental to the general effect. For achieving particularly delicate and subtle effects, and for controlling the intricate lighting of elaborate productions, it is often a decided convenience to centralize the lighting control in some one individual who can view the entire stage from an auditorium location, and who can transmit detailed instructions by telephone to the actual operator of the switchboard and lighting instruments. Careful dimming of the auditorium lights just before the rise of the curtain will be found to contribute decidedly to the lighting and general effectiveness of the play itself. This is purely a subjective, a psychological, and subconscious matter on the part of the audience, but its influence is often a marked one. In some cases, the brightness (and sometimes even the color) of the auditorium lighting that prevails before the performance and between the acts can be so adjusted as to enhance the effect produced by the actual lighting of the play, either by helping in mood-creation, or by providing contrasting effects.

As has been pointed out in the first chapter, stage-lighting workers in the amateur field have many advantages over those in the professional field. Principal among these advantages is the far greater opportunity for experimentation that exists in amateur activities. And as stage lighting, in the final analysis, is almost wholly dependent upon experimentation for its effects, this advantage is an important one. Amateur stage-lighting workers should realize this, and should make the most of this opportunity. They should evolve their own methods, their own routine, of stage-lighting practice, and not attempt to borrow the troubles of their professional contemporaries. Each amateur producing group differs in the detail of its organization and personnel, and hence each should study its own situation carefully and evolve its own method of placing responsibility for the stage lighting of its productions. Stage lighting, intrinsically, has no mysteries for the amateur worker to unravel, no formulas for him to learn. Assuming that he possesses an intelligent understanding of the few fundamental principles of electricity and light and color that are involved; a general comprehension of lighting instruments and control equipment; a reasonable degree of "practical ability"; a moderate amount of artistic discernment; and a little patience as well — stage lighting resolves itself principally into a matter of experimentation, which he can carry on with convenience. And his experimentation will prove all the more intriguing in view of the fact that should he conduct but a single successful experiment in stage lighting that is of *fundamental* and not merely superficial significance, he is in a position to command the respectful attention of the entire world of play production.

III. "Effects"

Although there are no specific formulæ in stage lighting, a few of the more common "effects" that often prove useful for realistic lighting are usually achieved by methods that are fairly definite and that are universally applicable. Hence brief descriptions of them can be given. By "effects" in this sense is meant not the general ensemble lighting effect — the effect as a whole — over the entire stage, but a single *unit* "effect" that constitutes a part of the *general* effect. Such "effects" are among the most important adjuncts of realism. They may be divided into two principal classes, one of which may be termed simulated effects, and the other projected effects. *Simulated* effects utilize light as an integral part of the realistic scene, as a whole, that they help to create, and include principally a representation, or rather imitation, of such things as sunlight, moonlight, the sky, fog and mist, lightning flashes, fireplaces, camp fires, torches, lighted lamps, and so forth. *Projected* effects utilize light to project a picture, or what is virtually a picture, of what they seek to simulate, and include principally such effects as clouds, the moon, stars, bolt lightning, flames, water, snow, rain, and so forth.

Most of these "effects" require special apparatus, or special combinations of apparatus. The sciopticon, for example, which is described on page 192, is the chief means available for producing projected "effects." Such apparatus, however, has only a limited usefulness, and is not ordinarily included in a regular set of stage-lighting equipment that is used for general purposes. It is obtainable from dealers in stage-lighting material, and usually it is only acquired when needed for a particular production. For the amateur stage-lighting worker, the expense of acquiring apparatus for so limited a use will most likely prove prohibitive. The following paragraphs outline a few methods by which he can achieve his own "effects."

A. SIMULATED EFFECTS

The successful simulation of *sunlight* in exterior scenes is one of the most difficult of all stage-lighting problems. The "color" of sunlight, if it may be said to have any, can be easily simulated by the use of straw or light-amber color media. But the difficulty lies in having the objects on the stage cast shadows which have the same characteristics as those cast by actual sunshine. The sun's rays being virtually parallel, all the shadows cast are unidirectional and have parallel sides — that is, they do not diverge as do those cast by a light source as close at hand as that used in stage lighting. The best approximation of this condition can be obtained on the stage by having the lighting instruments so balanced in effect that the resultant light has a strongly predominant direction, and by keeping these instruments as far away from the stage as the other factors entering into the stage lighting will allow. The position of characters and objects on the stage in relation to possible shadow-receiving surfaces should be so adjusted that no shadows are cast that are noticeably out of keeping with those that would be produced under similar conditions by actual sunlight. In interior scenes, the effect of sunlight streaming through a window, a door, or other aperture, is also difficult of simulation for the reasons noted above. The outline of the lighted area representing the aperture must be of the correct shape. If the aperture is small, a large floodlighting projector that emits a parallel beam of light will give a fairly satisfactory result; for a larger aperture, several of these could be used, or a battery of four or six spotlights could be so positioned, focussed, and aimed (most conveniently when mounted on a traveling spotlight tower) so that the edge of the aperture will intercept the several spotlight beams in such a manner that the proper shape of lighted area is cast. The conditions outlined above apply equally well to *moonlight*, except that a much lower intensity of light is used, along with light-blue, or blue-green, color media.

The use of the cyclorama as an effective means of simulating the *sky* has already been discussed in a previous chapter. Small cycloramas for amateur use can be made of linen fabric such as is commonly used for covering scenery "flats", or of ordinary *bleached* muslin (the light tan color of unbleached muslin is likely to produce an unsatisfactory resultant color when it is lighted with blue light). The material of which the cyclorama is made should be sewed very carefully in order to avoid puckering at the seams, and, for best results, the seams should run horizontally across the cyclorama. Such a cyclorama can be suspended from a straight wooden batten or pipe batten, or from a pipe batten the ends of which have been bent so as to curve around the edge of the acting area. The cyclorama should be as high and as wide as the physical conditions backstage will permit; and if its ends are curved, they should run forward as far as possible; that is, they should almost meet the proscenium arch. The elimination of folds and furrows in the surface of the cyclorama can best be achieved by providing a six-inch hem along the bottom of the cyclorama in which a heavy chain can be placed, or which can be filled with sand, for weighting the cyclorama and keeping its surface smooth and taut. A cyclorama is best painted when it is suspended in position. Small cycloramas can be often very successfully lighted by the use of several home-built borderlights, striplights, and olivettes. As with other phases of stage-lighting work, the proper choice and positioning of such lighting equipment, and the correct color media to use, is almost entirely a matter of experimentation. In conjunction with the use of the cyclorama as a device for achieving the effects of *distance* and *atmosphere* on the stage, so-called "theatrical gauze" can often be employed to great advantage. A gauze drop suspended three or four feet before the cyclorama itself will increase the effectiveness of the latter many-fold. If the acting area is divided into several zones by gauze drops and each zone lighted independently of the other, almost infinite distance can be convincingly simulated on a stage of even the most cramped proportions. An atmosphere of depth and mystery can be secured by using a black velvet drop in place of the cyclorama and zoning the acting area with several gauze drops and lighting each zone separately. The effects achieved with gauze can be heightened if to the gauze are attached forms or silhouetted representations of natural objects. The achievement of successful results with theatrical gauze is almost entirely dependent upon the lighting. Such lighting can be planned by utilizing the fact that a gauze drop illuminated entirely from in front is practically opaque from the spectators' point of view, and that it becomes practically transparent as to illuminated objects behind it when unlighted itself. By varying the ratio of the amount and color of the light falling upon the front of the gauze to the amount and color of that falling upon objects behind it, and by applying this process to each of several gauze drops used in conjunction with either a cyclorama or a black velvet back drop, the variety of effects obtainable with gauze are seen to be almost unlimited. *Fog* and *mist*, for example, can be simulated by suspending a gauze drop directly in back of the proscenium opening and lighting the gauze to a very low intensity from in front, and lighting the stage scene behind the gauze in the usual manner. This so-called "theatrical gauze" is an open-meshed material known as "bobbinette", and is woven in widths as great as thirty feet. Bobbinette is, as might be supposed, very expensive, but amateur producers can always fall back upon the "old reliable" — cheesecloth — and also upon ordinary white, plain-weave mosquito netting that has had the stiffening in it removed by soaking in water. These fabrics, if sewed together carefully with the least possible material at the seams, will provide a not unsatisfactory substitute for the true bobbinette gauze at a much lower cost. A back drop of black canton flannel is a most effective and inexpensive substitute for one of black velvet.

Lightning flashes can be simulated simply by "flashing" the white circuit in the borderlights on or off. But a far better effect can be secured if real lightning is reproduced, on a small scale, by actually drawing an arc between opposite poles of an electrical circuit. This can be done most simply and most effectively by firmly connecting one wire of a circuit to a large, coarse-tooth, flat file or rasp, and the other wire of the circuit to a short length of carbon (such as is used in carbon arc lights). A suitable resistance should be interposed in the circuit to restrict the flow of current to a safe maximum. Both the carbon and the file should be provided with well-insulated handles by which the operator may safely grasp them. When the circuit is alive, the arc may be drawn by lightly touching the file with the tip of the carbon. The arc can then be "trickled" to and fro along the file. With a little practice, lightning flashes can be most realistically simulated in this manner. The process is likely to appear a bit hazardous: the inexperienced operator should wear gloves and should keep his face behind a sheet of red gelatin, which will protect his face from flying sparks and his eyes from the blinding effect of the flash. With a little ingenuity a home-built automatic lightning flasher can be constructed. This consists of a hollow coil of wire that will act as a solenoid when it is energized with current; a hollow cylindrical iron plunger that fits the core of the solenoid, and that will be drawn up into the solenoid when the latter is energized; and a piece of carbon with a small iron plate on which it makes contact. The solenoid coil is wired in series with the carbon, and the various parts of the flasher so mounted that when the flasher is energized with current, the plunger is drawn into the solenoid, thus causing the carbon to leave its contact plate, draw an arc, and break the circuit. As soon as the circuit is thus opened, the solenoid releases the plunger and the carbon falls back upon its contact plate, thereupon re-closing the circuit and repeating the flash. Thus a regular series of flashes will result as long as current is supplied to the flasher. One such automatic lightning flasher will serve well, but if several of them are mounted at various locations above the stage, and operated in succession, a much better effect will be produced. Automatic lightning flashers should be totally inclosed in a wire screening, in order to the prevent the escape of sparks which might ignite back-stage materials.

A simulated effect often in demand is the open *fireplace*. A simple construction with most of the attention given to color and shading will prove most effective. For a log fire, the "logs" themselves can be formed of half-inch-mesh wire screening. Each such log should be covered, separately, with orange-colored silesia, or similar fabric, which can be applied to the wire mesh with a flour-and-water paste. The silesia should be wrinkled to form the "bark", and it should be lapped in order to hold it securely to the wire mesh. When the logs are covered they should be laid up in the desired arrangement, fastened together with wire, and allowed to dry. When they have dried, they should be given a coat of stiff glue sizing. When the coat of sizing has dried, a small amber-dipped lamp should be placed within each log, and lighted. The logs should then be painted, while the lamps are lighted. Ordinary distemper (the same as is used for painting scenery) can be used, and the logs should be left translucent at the proper places, especially on the under sides. When in use, the logs should rest on andirons. Part of the under sides of the logs may be left uncovered, and the escaping light allowed to reflect from some small wrinkled pieces of thin red and gold metal foil. These wrinkled pieces of foil can be pasted on the upper side of the log directly beneath the top log, and on the top of a mound of "ashes" that has been constructed in a manner similar to the logs themselves, and painted appropriately. Thin silk streamers attached to the logs, so placed that they are properly lighted by the lamps within the logs, and actuated by the gentle breeze from a miniature electric fan beneath the logs, can be used to simulate flames. The lower portion of the streamers should be colored bright amber, to represent the flame; the upper portion should be gray, to simulate smoke. The actual light cast by the fire can be simulated by a spotlight or olivette placed behind the fireplace opening. To produce a satisfactory effect, the color media should be carefully chosen (preferably amber, or orange, should be used, but never pure red), and the lamp should be dimmed to a point consistent with the comparatively low intensity of light emitted by a wood fire. A realistic flicker to this emitted light, that is often of great effectiveness in firelight scenes, can be produced by slowly moving, in the beam of light, a piece of wrinkled tissue paper in a vertical direction, and at the same time shaking the tissue paper gently. Obviously, such a flicker effect should never be pronounced enough to attract attention for its own sake. Open fires, such as camp fires, can be simulated in a manner similar to that just described. A *grate fire* can be simulated by placing, in a regular iron grate, a box-like form shaped from half-inch wire mesh, and surrounding the latter on sides and top with glass cullet, or pieces of broken condenser lenses or vault-light glasses. The glass should be colored with amber lamp dip, and touched up in places with daubs of red lamp dip and of black paint. Several small amber and red dipped lamps should be placed beneath the mesh in the grate. Wide wood shavings, when properly colored, are a good substitute for the lumps of broken glass. It must be remembered that a coal fire in a grate casts a dimmer and somewhat more reddish glow than does a wood fire.

As a general rule, lighting fixtures that are a part of the stage setting, such as chandeliers, table lamps, and wall brackets, should never be depended upon to furnish a part of the actual stage lighting. They should simply be made to appear luminous, and the light they ostensibly cast should be simulated by the use of the regular stage-lighting equipment: spotlights and other lens units in the teaser location are perhaps the most suitable for this purpose. Lighted candles on a darkened stage often produce the desired effect without supplementary lighting. A candle flame on a darkened stage, however, should *always* be shielded from the audience. The effect of a lighted candle can often be heightened by the use of a small, dimmed amber lamp, recessed in a table top or similar surface directly upstage of the candle itself. If the use of actual candles is considered hazardous, they can be simulated by the use of miniature lamps (the small amber-orange flame-shaped incandescent lamps are especially useful) in sockets that have been mounted in a suitably disguised hollow cylinder (such as a narrow cardboard mailing tube).

B. PROJECTED EFFECTS

For projected effects a regular sciopticon is most desirable, but for the amateur worker an ordinary stereopticon will prove an effective substitute. A stereopticon is almost invariably at the disposal of the amateur producer. It can usually be borrowed from a church or school in the vicinity, and can be made to achieve many of the effects for which the sciopticon is used professionally. For stationary effects, of course, it serves particularly well, but it can also be used to achieve a limited number of moving effects. And with a little ingenuity it is even possible to devise some sort of simple device by which a revolving transparent disc (of mica or glass, or of celluloid, if it is protected from overheating) may supplant the stationary lantern slide. Some of the more important effects that the amateur producer can devise with the aid of a stereopticon are the following.

Clouds, which constitute perhaps the most called-for effect of all, can easily be projected by placing in the lantern-slide carrier of the stereopticon a transparent photographic positive print, on either a celluloid film or glass plate cut to lantern-slide size — $3\frac{1}{4}'' \times 4''$. A regular lantern-slide photographic plate can be used, the positive on this being obtained most easily by contact printing from either a roll-film or a glass-plate negative. The latter is secured by photographing actual cloud formations in the sky. The positive prints should be as "contrasty" as possible; that is, the white of the cloud should be as transparent as possible, and the blue of the sky as black and opaque as possible. The use of a yellow sky-filter before the lens of the camera, along with correct exposure and proper development, should give excellent results. Many different and useful pictures of cloud formations can be "snapped" in the course of an afternoon. These can serve as a cloud-effect "library" for use as desired. This process, of course, will result only in stationary clouds. Moving clouds can be simulated by carefully matching a number of cloud pictures on celluloid film, and joining them in an endless chain with collodion or amyl acetate joining cement. This "endless chain" of cloud pictures can then be moved slowly and smoothly through the beam of light in the space ordinarily occupied by the lantern-slide holder. All the space on the film positives, except that occupied by the clouds, should be opaqued-out with India ink. When the cloud pictures, either stationary or moving, are sharply focussed on to the blue-lighted cyclorama or sky drop, the clear white light representing the clouds will "fade out" the blue light on the cyclorama in just the proper shading to simulate a bank of clouds standing out against a blue sky. The stereopticon can be placed at the rear of the auditorium, or in a projection booth, or on a balcony front, or in any position that is found most convenient and satisfactory. Care must be taken, of course, not to project the "clouds" upon the side of a building, or a tree, or an actor, or any other object upon the stage. This can conveniently be avoided by cutting a "mask" of heavy paper or thin cardboard, to keep the light off all objects in the scene except the cyclorama. Such a mask should also be placed in the lantern-slide holder of the stereopticon, along with the cloud photograph. It is not altogether necessary to take actual photographs of clouds; fairly good results can be obtained by placing in the lantern-slide holder a piece of glass or celluloid which has been smeared over with India ink and then daubed clear, in puffy, cloudlike blotches, with a tuft of absorbent cotton. Such an improvised cloud picture, however, will reveal its identity when it is projected upon the cyclorama. This can easily be avoided by throwing the objective lens of the stereopticon slightly out of focus, and thus blurring the edges of the "clouds." With skillful manipulation, stationary cloud pictures can be moved across the cyclorama simply by slowly swinging the entire stereopticon about.

Moons of various sizes and shapes can easily be projected on to a cyclorama with a stereopticon. A piece of medium-thick cardboard or heavy paper is cut to lantern-slide size — $3\frac{1}{4}'' \times 4''$. With a small compass, a moon of the desired size and shape is drawn in the center of the piece of cardboard and cut out carefully with a sharp-pointed knife or razor blade. By placing the resulting "moon slide" in the lantern-slide holder, and focussing the objective lens sharply, a fairly good moon will be projected. If the entire stereopticon be turned on its side, and the lantern-slide holder moved vertically, and the entire stereopticon swung horizontally at the same time, the moon can be made to rise in any desired manner. If a small piece of gelatin color medium — either yellow, straw, or light amber — be moistened and pasted over the cut-out moon, harvest moons or others of varying temperaments can be projected.

Bolt lightning can be achieved similarly — by cutting a jagged gash, or a sinuous, forked gash, depending upon what style of lightning is preferred, out of a cardboard "lantern slide", and focussing its projected image sharply upon the lighted cyclorama. The objective lens of the stereopticon should be covered with the hand, and, when the bolt of lightning is supposed to strike, quickly uncovered and covered, with the outstretched fingers of the hand passing rapidly before the lens to give a realistic flicker to the flash. A little practice with this hand manipulation will develop an astoundingly realistic bolt of lighting.

Stars can be projected on to the cyclorama by using in the lantern-slide holder of the stereopticon a thin sheet of metal, or of metal foil, which has been pricked with numerous tiny holes. Cardboard cannot be used, as the fibers in it are very likely to cause fuzzy "stars." With heavy lead foil, or tin foil (such as tea comes wrapped in) the small holes can be cleanly and sharply pricked with a needle or pin. If desired, the pin pricks may be arranged so as to represent the various constellations. The metal foil should be mounted in a frame of heavy cardboard, or, better still, glued to a clear piece of glass. The stars can easily be made to twinkle by placing in the lantern-slide holder, in addition to the pricked foil, a piece of fine-mesh wire screen (such as is used for window screens), slightly smaller than lantern-slide size, and moving it slowly about in a vertical plane. Of course, stars can also be directly simulated on larger stages by studding the cyclorama with miniature incandescent lamps such as are used in pocket flashlights.

A *rainbow* may be projected from a stereopticon by carefully striping the rainbow colors in a narrow arc in the proper position across a clear glass lantern slide, and opaquing out the remainder of the slide with dense black. Transparent lantern-slide colors, or regular lamp dips, should be used, with a fine-pointed brush, for the colored stripes. The latter can be just sufficiently blended, and the appearance of too great a regularity avoided, by throwing the objective lens very slightly out of focus, or by placing a piece of frosted diffusing gelatin close to the painted slide in the lantern-slide holder.

The above-listed effects obtainable with an ordinary stereopticon are essentially stationary in nature. Two moving effects that can easily be obtained with a stereopticon are the flame and the water ripple. Both require a revolving, small, circular glass disc placed with its center on the rim of the objective lens, so that one side of the glass disc revolves through the projected beam of light. In diameter, the glass disc should be about three times the diameter of the objective lens, and should have a quarter-inch hole drilled at its center. A copper band about a half-inch wide should encircle the outer rim of the objective lens, and should be fastened in place with a screw and wing-nut combination. To the outside of the copper band is soldered a small brass pin (projecting a half-inch beyond the edge of the band), so positioned that the glass disc may revolve about it in a plane perpendicular to the projected beam of light, and close to the front face of the objective lens. The arrangement of the glass disc may be as simple or as elaborate as facilities permit. The glass disc itself is inexpensive, and may be obtained from the nearest glazier. The same glazier will also be able to supply another requisite so necessary for projected moving effects, namely, sheets of pressed glass in various designs. Small pieces of pressed glass, of lantern-slide size, are used to distort the rays in the projected light beam in the manner necessary to achieve a certain effect.

For *flames*, there is placed in the lantern-slide holder of the stereopticon a piece of glass pressed with crude heavy furrows, or striations, that run in a predominantly vertical direction, that is, parallel to the narrow ($3\frac{1}{4}''$) side of the rectangular lantern-slide opening. The revolving glass disc on the front of the objective lens is streaked with alternate stripes (about a half-inch wide) of red and amber lamp dip that radiate from the center of the disc. When the glass disc is revolved in the proper direction (so that the red and amber stripes pass upward through the beam of light), a very good semblance of rising flames will be projected by the stereopticon. Experience will enable the user to determine the most suitable design of pressed glass, as well as the most suitable arrangement of colored stripes on the revolving glass disc, for his particular purpose. Of course, "masks" cut out of cardboard can be placed in the lantern-slide holder in order to restrict the flame effect to a certain area of the scene.

The *water ripple* is similarly produced, except that in the lantern-slide holder is placed a piece of pressed glass with comparatively narrow furrows, which run horizontally. The revolving glass disc is streaked with blue and blue-green stripes, with narrow stripes of clear glass left unpainted between the colored stripes. This combination will provide a very realistic water ripple. Masks can also be used to restrict the area covered by the "water"; for a "moonlight water ripple" a wide, sharply jagged, V-shaped notch is cut out of cardboard, and the mask thus formed placed in the lantern-slide holder. The colored glass disc is best revolved vertically, and rather slowly, through the light beam. A waterfall effect can be secured by using a pressed-glass plate with vertical instead of horizontal furrows, along with a suitable mask. It is easy to see how several stereopticons, equipped with various appropriate water effects such as have just been described, can be used in conjunction with one another to stage effectively plays such as Dunsany's thriller, "The Queen's Enemies", which always present knotty problems to the amateur producer.

Moving projected effects, such as clouds, rain, and snow, usually require a regular sciopticon with a revolving painted or photographed disc in place of the stationary lantern slide (the revolving color-striped disc used before the objective lens for the flame and water ripple effects should not be confused with the revolving mica disc that forms part of the professional sciopticon effect head).

For *moving clouds*, several carefully matched photographic positives of cloud pictures are mounted in succession about the edge of the mica disc. For *falling snow*, the mica disc is blackened, and the numerous "snowflakes" scratched off with a sharp-pointed knife, or the holes are pricked in a disc of suitable thin, stiff material. For *falling rain*, the mica disc is also blackened, and a series of short, parallel, fine scratches are made rather close to each other. A blackened glass plate, which bears a set of long parallel scratches, is mounted permanently in the effect-head casing. The light that escapes through the two intersecting sets of fine scratches, one stationary, the other moving, is such that a continuous stream of descending "raindrops" deluges the stage. Incidentally, a swivel joint in the effect-head casing allows adjustment of the direction in which the revolving effect-disc intercepts the projected beam of light. Hence the raindrops or snowflakes can descend at any desired angle, and, by virtue of the adjustable-speed clockwork or motor, can be made to descend rapidly or slowly.

For projecting clouds, the stereopticon or sciopticon is most conveniently positioned on a "light-bridge" directly over and behind the proscenium opening, and the cloud pictures projected directly on to the cyclorama. Because of the necessary short throw, the objective lens must be of the short-focus, wide-angle type. For projecting rain and snow, the sciopticon is most conveniently positioned "out front", either on a balcony front, or auditorium rear wall, or in the projection booth, if there is one. Best results will be obtained if the effect image is projected, not directly on to the objects on the stage, but on to a large piece of theatrical gauze, or some effective substitute, that completely fills the proscenium opening. Raindrops and snowflakes projected upon gauze in this position will seemingly cover the entire stage, but will not effect the visibility of the scene behind the gauze, or the invisibility of the gauze itself.

C. FANTASTIC

Besides the simulated and projected effects discussed above, there is a third class of effects which may be termed "fantastic." These are of interest principally as novelties or diversions, except in a few instances when they may be found of service in regular dramatic production. Among such fantastic effects may be included those which utilize the phenomena of phosphorescence and fluorescence. *Phosphorescence* can be conveniently achieved by the use of so-called "luminous paint", which consists of some such material as special impure grades of calcium sulphide or barium sulphide mixed with a quick-drying liquid "vehicle." Such paint can easily be applied to wood, metal, and fabrics, and thus may be used on scenery, draperies, properties, and costumes on the stage. This paint is capable of being energized by strong light rays, and of being de-energized in the dark with the gradual feeble emission of light rays, usually phosphorescent in appearance. If the paint is exposed to a bright white light for even a very short time, in the dark it will give off an appreciable glow of light for about five to fifteen minutes immediately afterward. This luminous paint is available in several different colors. Its many diverse possibilities in achieving fantastic and novel effects are obvious. *Fluorescence* involves the action of invisible ultra-violet rays on fluorescent material. The latter can be applied to objects on the stage, just as can the luminous paint. When invisible ultra-violet rays fall upon fluorescent material, their wave lengths are increased and they are reflected as visible light. Thus, on a darkened stage a beam of ultra-violet rays is invisible but where it strikes fluorescent material it will be reflected as visible light. Fluorescence takes place only while ultra-violet rays are actually striking fluorescent material: that is, there is no after-luminescence as with the luminous paint. Ultra-violet rays can be produced by arc spotlights (and also with regular incandescent spotlights, but to a much lesser extent) that are equipped with color filters and lenses made of special glass. Among other purely novel lighting effects are the so-called "chameleon" color effects, which involve the use of pigments, dyes, and color media of special spectral characteristics; and the "shadowgraph", which produces an interesting stereoscopic effect through the use of enlarged double shadows that are cast from behind on to a white translucent drop by two adjoining light sources equipped with complementary color media, and that are viewed through a pair of eyeglasses equipped with the same color media in reverse position.

IV. Outdoor Productions

The usual methods of stage lighting must, of necessity, be greatly modified for lighting outdoor productions, especially the larger and more elaborate ones such as pageants, masques, and celebrations. The principal differences are necessitated by the much greater quantity of light needed, by the absence of a regular proscenium behind which stage equipment can be conveniently mounted out of sight of the spectators, and also by the fact that out-door stage-lighting installations are usually only of a temporary nature.

A much greater quantity of light is needed because of the high light-absorption characteristic of the natural background and also because of the prevailing physical dimensions — the comparatively vast acting area and the great distance between it and the furthermost spectator. Because of the dark natural background it is desirable that settings and costumes be as light colored as is consistent with the decorative scheme as a whole. Still pools of water should be avoided if possible, as they are practically impossible to light satisfactorily (except when they are positioned between the

A scene from the community pageant produced at Newark, New Jersey.

spectators and the acting area, when they possess distinct advantages). The general vastness of an outdoor production makes any subtle and delicate lighting effects virtually impossible of achievement. As with the several other production factors, the lighting must be conceived and carried out on a large scale; it must be clear-cut, bold, and pronounced in effect. Delicate shades of colored lighting fail to make the impression that they would make in a regular theatre production; colored lighting must be applied in bold, broad, sure strokes. And as a general rule, visibility takes precedence over effect.

The absence of a proscenium wall renders difficult the proper positioning of the lighting equipment. Although regular stage-lighting instruments can be used to some extent for outdoor productions, those units of equipment described on page 203 have been especially designed for such service and are far more satisfactory. The choice and location of such equipment depends on the manner in which the production is presented. If the action is confined to the same small area throughout the entire performance, it is a comparatively simple matter to mount a number of floodlights at the front edge of the acting area. These can be mounted on short poles at each side of the acting area, and also directly on the ground. But if the action takes place successively at various sections of a large field, the problem of lighting is much more difficult. For such

Some of the outdoor floodlighting projectors used for lighting the Newark pageant, mounted behind a permanent unit of scenery.

large outdoor productions perhaps the best method is to "cover" the entire acting area by one or more "banks", or groups, of floodlighting projectors mounted on towers located at the rear of the spectators, behind the seating stands. Each of the projectors is so mounted, aimed, and focussed that it illuminates a definite unit area of the entire acting area. The floodlighting projectors are under individual control from some central point. The switch for each is designated as to the unit area it illuminates, and hence any portion of the entire acting area can be lighted for a particular scene by closing the switches of the projectors whose unit illumination areas together constitute the space to be lighted for the scene. The

A scene from the Massachusetts Tercentenary Pageant, *The Pilgrim Spirit*, produced at Plymouth, Massachusetts.

exact number and type of floodlighting projectors can best be determined graphically. The entire site of the production (including both the acting area and the space for the spectators) should be drawn to scale both in plan and in several strategic section profiles. The plans should include the contours of the ground surface and other natural features, particularly obstructions or

One of the two lighting towers used for mounting floodlighting projectors and searchlights at the Plymouth pageant.

vantage points at which the projectors can be mounted. The location and size of the lighting towers should be decided and drawn in on the scale plans. With the help of a protractor, and by means of beam angle and beam intensity data on the projectors (information which can be obtained from manufacturers' catalogs), it is possible to select the proper type of projectors and to lay out the unit areas to be covered by each. These unit areas should, of course, overlap enough so that no unlighted space is left between them. For the most effective results, the average angle at which the projector beams strike the acting area should be in the neighborhood of thirty degrees. Where it is desired to "spotlight" a portion of the acting area, it is usually necessary to use a searchlight of medium size, or a high-powered carbon-arc spotlight. Small floodlighting units can be used, connected with regular stage cable, for locally lighting any portion of the setting. Such lighting units can usually be concealed by natural or artificial shrubbery. All equipment used for lighting outdoor productions should be of weatherproof construction. Although necessary activities in the acting area preliminary to each scene can usually be carried out under cover of darkness, it is sometimes advantageous to provide a "glare curtain", or a "steam

The temporary switchboard erected for controlling the lighting of the Plymouth pageant.

curtain." A "glare curtain" consists simply of directing at the spectators the light from lamps in reflectors at the front edge of the acting area, which causes the spectators to be unable to see into the acting area. A "steam curtain" is a very effective device, and consists of a steam pipe, with a row of small holes drilled in its upper side, laid at the front edge of the acting area next to a row of low-wattage lamps of various colors. During intermissions, rising clouds of steam from the pipe are very beautifully tinted by the colored lamps and thus provide a pretty and effective "curtain" between the spectators and the acting area.

For the proper control of the lighting, it must be very carefully cued and coördinated with the other elements of the production. Dimmers on the projector circuits are desirable, of course, though their practicability for outdoor productions is open to question. It is not practicable to equip projectors permanently with color media and use them only when their particular color is needed. Instead, the necessary assortment of color screens should be provided for each projector, and operators should be assigned (one operator to several projectors) to place the proper color screens on the projectors at the correct moments. If the floodlighting projectors are of the type that permit manual dimming with opaque slides, these same operators can also control the intensity of the projectors. All switching, however, should be done by the electrician at the central switchboard, who has the detailed cue sheets before him and who should be in close touch with the director of the production. It is also highly desirable that this electrician keep in telephonic communication with the individual operators at the projectors.

APPENDIXES

APPENDIX A

LIGHTING EFFECTS ON THE STAGE *

WE all know that there are numerous possibilities in the field of lighting; but I am going to say a few words about the part of it that I know best, and love best, — the lighting of the drama.

My real experience began with David Belasco about twenty-two years ago; although I had been employed in theatres years previous to this time, it was not until I came to work for David Belasco that I awoke to the realization of what light means to the stage, how valuable it is, and how much it assists the drama. Volumes could be written on this subject, but they would only serve as the expression of an idea; as text books they would contain very little of value.

When we speak of light in the commercial field, it is generally treated as a slide rule proposition; it resolves itself into a thing of mathematics — of course there are some exceptions to this, but I mean in general. There are several well known systems which have proved successful, their application being a product of well worked out formulæ. In theatre lighting we have no formula; it is replaced by a truism that can be expressed in one sentence; "Love your work." This seems easy enough as there is a certain fascination about it; but with a great many newcomers the strain of long rehearsals and lack of sleep dampens the enthusiasm they felt at first.

Stage lighting cannot be treated as a subject by itself; it is but a component part of a structure and of itself has no value. But if the play and its accessories are well conceived, proper lighting is a matter of great importance, as it practically creates the atmosphere for the scenes. To obtain the best results, the lights require intelligent handling and good electrical equipment. It is very essential to have smoothly working dimmers, and a sufficient number of them, so each lamp or unit of lamps may be controlled separately. This is the only way by which the proper balance of light can be maintained; without this balance, the lighting looks just what it is, a number of separate units throwing blotches of light, creating bad

* A paper presented by Louis Hartmann before the Illuminating Engineering Society on January 11, 1923. Reprinted by permission of the Society.

shadows and sharp contrasts. If the proper equipment is not available, it is better to light a scene with the foots and borders than to try to use paraphernalia which cannot be fully controlled. The lights when badly handled only tend to draw the attention of the audience and detract from the effect the player is trying to create. Everything on the stage can be done in so many different ways; and it is far better to do it in a simple manner than to spoil it by an elaborate attempt which cannot be carried out.

I have found it necessary to have a full electrical equipment for every play, as there is no uniformity of outfit in theatres. Even when all the equipment is carried, the effect is not always the same when the play is moved to another theatre. The change is generally caused by the footlights. They are very necessary and essential when properly installed, but in most instances they are badly planned; some are not hooded at all, while others have one row under the hood (generally the colors), and the white row is either half way under the hood or entirely outside of it.

For dramatic productions no light from the foots should strike the proscenium — much less illuminate the proscenium; and when properly installed, the audience should not be aware of their existence. The light from the foots should be so directed that it does not strike the ceiling of the setting. For this purpose I have found reflectors very efficient. There are several types which serve this purpose, and by painting parts of the reflector black I have been able to place the light about where I wanted it. In most instances I have found the small round-bulb 25-watt lamp to give sufficient light for the foots when used in a "scoopette" reflector.

For a ceiling strip, I use the same reflector and lamp, fixed in a special strip. This may be tilted at any angle, takes up very little room, and does not throw the light on the ceiling. The ceiling gets all the illumination it requires from natural reflection. All scenes to be effective require light and shade. By using merely foots and ceiling strip, the scenes are flat, there being no contrast. Baby lenses have made it possible to get this contrast in interiors. This form of lighting was worked out in the Belasco Theatre and used for the first time in Mr. Warfield's play "The Music Master." One of the scenes where this was especially effective was where Von Barwig holds up the lighted lamp to see Helen's face. I'll never forget the many times Mr. Warfield lifted up that lamp during rehearsals while we struggled to bring up the babies at the right time.

For these baby lenses I found a concentrated filament lamp put on the market for use in small stereopticons for the home. It was rated at 50 candlepower. I built a housing for it, fitted it with a 5-inch × 9-inch focus lens, and to control it I used a small dimmer having fourteen steps. We called it a baby lens, and this name has stuck to it. There are thousands of them in use to-day. Of course their candle power has been increased. We have them in hoods of different shapes using from a 1½-inch lens to a 5-inch lens and ranging from 50 watts to 1000 watts. We set them behind the drapery and up and down the sides of the scene on special frames and brackets, each one controlled by a separate dimmer operated by men who are trained for weeks in handling them. On the front of the balcony we have reflectors in special housings, also on separate dimmers. In this way we get the light from all angles, and when it is balanced by proper dimmer regulation, almost any effect may be obtained with this outfit.

I have found reflex glass a very effective medium for softening the light. I use it on both reflectors and lenses. It is superior to frosted gelatin for this purpose. Mr. Belasco managed to get some very fine results with the old arc lenses. We used to soften the light with a slide having graduated thicknesses of mica, each piece cut V-shape with the edges tapered. Still, the lamps were cumbersome and could not be placed to the best advantage.

When the tungsten lamp was put on the market Mr. Belasco told me to keep after the lamp manufacturers to get something that would prove more effective for our purpose. The American Lamp Company turned out two lamps for us which were very valuable at the time. One was a 6-volt concentrated filament lamp with two filaments. The other was a 60-volt lamp in a G 40 bulb, rated at 200 candle power. I placed four of these in a bunch light; they looked like the sun — in those days. The light had an excellent quality and the diffusion was good, the filament being long, in fact; the light was superior to the modern 1000-watt lamp so far as diffusion is concerned. In those days the Ward Leonard Electric Company made hundreds of special rheostats for us. All this entailed a greater cost than if we had used stock materials, especially in the lamps, as we had to carry a large supply or wait three to four weeks for them, which was out of the question. In the theatre you need things quickly.

In some of Mr. Belasco's plays we discarded the footlights entirely. "Peter Grimm" was lighted from overhead by strips and babies. Nine men were rehearsed for two weeks and then it took six weeks on the road before the lighting was finally perfected. "Marie Odile" also was lighted without foots. The scene of this play was laid in a convent. The effect of the light was as though it came through a large Gothic opening over the door. Foots would have ruined the atmosphere of this scene.

Whatever Mr. Belasco has tried in this line has been for the purpose of obtaining atmosphere for the play. Nothing is done in haphazard fashion; everything is the outcome of a preconceived plan. The original idea is worked on and experimented with until the best result has been obtained. The results are not always satisfactory to him, but if they do not come up to his expectations, it is the fault of a condition that cannot be remedied. You cannot always have perfection in all things on the stage, as there are numerous obstacles which present themselves. In planning a production the first details are worked out from the models, which are made to a scale of one-half inch to the foot. The artist tries to make his scenes as effective as possible, and where there are several of these scenes in a production, the working room on the stage is very cramped. This is one of the reasons why the lights cannot always be placed where they will give the best effect. The only thing to do in a case of this kind is to take the available space and experiment until you have obtained the best results you can get under the prevailing conditions. I have seen Mr. Belasco cut out an entire scene and rearrange the play when the conditions for lighting proved too unsatisfactory. Scenery is nothing but canvas and paint and appears as such when badly lighted. The reason we spend so much time with the scenery and the lights is that we realize their imperfections, regarding them as necessary evils. When they become so obtrusive as to detract from the play, we eliminate them.

The tendency to-day is to use too much light. The high wattage lamp has brought about this condition. I can remember when gas was the means of illumination in theatres, and the effect of gas light on the scenery as a whole was better and softer. It was impossible to over-illuminate a scene in those days. The contrasts were worked out in the painting. To-day we depend upon the light to accomplish this. In illuminating a stage in a large theatre it is not good to bring up the footlights so high that the expression on the player's face may be seen from the last row, a feat you could not accomplish by daylight. It is a mistaken idea to think that an actor's face must always be in a bright light. It all depends upon what he is doing. To work in semi-light is an aid to the actor at times.

Another difficulty experienced to-day lies in the color values. It is almost impossible to obtain pure color, either in the pigments used on the scenery or in the gelatins used on the lamps. The colors used on the scenery are dull and lifeless. When a color should be vibrant, it is instead flat and dirty-looking. This is caused to some extent by the fire-proofing solution, which contains ammonia, an alkali that is ruinous to certain colors. Cobalt blue, an excellent medium for a sky, looks like a dirty whitewash after it has been fire-proofed. In some instances the fabric is fire-proofed before the paint is applied but the result is about the same. The anilines used in the gelatin mediums also are poor, and it is impossible to obtain a blue without a purple or green tinge. This is often the reason why the color values are unsatisfactory. We have to take the best we can get and make the most of it. I have tried to procure glass to take the place of gelatins, but could not find sufficient uniformity, especially in the blue. The light blue was effective, but the dark blue varied in shade even when all the pieces were cut from the same sheet. Colored glass is blown in large sheets and varies in thickness, which causes this difference.

For the lighting of exteriors I have found reflectors of twelve inches and over of great value when fitted with proper spill-rings; but they are harder to handle in some cases than lenses, the light leaving the reflector with such a wide spread that it is difficult at times to kill reflections. In some cases I have made the spill-rings very long, at other times I have put long flippers on the side which could be closed in. The conditions vary as to space so that one must continually experiment. Generally they can be overcome in one way or another. To light a scene where the lights remain stationary during an entire act is simple, when compared with an act that has several changes of light.

One of the most difficult changes is to reduce gradually the illumination of an interior scene in a manner to simulate the setting of the sun and the approach of twilight. To keep these graduations perfect requires a great deal of time and patience. The lights inside and out must be on certain steps of the dimmers at a certain time; and to get the same tempo they must always be on a given point when a particular line of the dialogue is spoken. This change would be easy if the man operating it could see it, but the set is boxed in and he is working on the side where he does not see. By putting the switch-board under the stage with a hood in the apron, the man can look through — but this has proved unsatisfactory for a number of reasons. It was tried in the Century Theatre and abandoned. The Metropolitan Opera House still has this system, but the same men are operating it to-day who operated it when it was first installed.

Imagination is the theory of the theatre. People do not come to the theatre to see reality. On the stage you must exaggerate to be convincing. The public comes to the theatre to be fooled, but there is a vast difference between fooling an audience and insulting its intelligence. Use your imagination, but be logical. In other words you must make the audience see things as you want them to see them, and if your imagination is great enough you can convey any mood and make them feel it. Radical departures seldom succeed in the theatre, as the audience does not want to do any guessing. If the things you are doing appear false, you lose the attention of your public. A clever stage director guards against this. If the dialogue drags he brings in something to divert unconsciously their attention; a shift of light may change the entire mood, creating a mental change, — in short, a play on the senses. You have watched a good magician. He has everything timed, nothing is left to chance. He draws your attention to something, but all the time he is talking. After you leave the theatre you don't remember what he said, but you remember his tricks. Still, in most instances, it was the talking that made the trick possible. In drama the process is the same — except that it is reversed. You remember the play but forget the trick. Big mechanical devices are generally easy to construct and the effects they create are valuable. It is the little fine touches that are really difficult, and in the end make the greatest impression, although you are not aware of it.

I could take up your time by describing to you in detail the different forms of apparatus now in use in the theatre, but you are familiar with lenses and parabolic mirrors. The housings for them depend upon the size of the lamp you wish to use, to give them proper ventilation without having leaks of light, and to make them as compact as possible. The shapes may vary to suit different conditions. But it is the intelligence you display in handling them that really counts — something that can come to you only through experience.

Good apparatus should be simple, the simpler the better. The easier it is to handle the less time is consumed in getting results, — a great factor during rehearsals when time means so much. In big productions, scene and light rehearsals take an entire week, sometimes longer, the men working night and day. Even where the expense is of no consideration, the players become nervous through waiting, so anything that will save time is of the utmost importance.

In placing the lighting equipment, it is well to have enough apparatus to be able to put it in every conceivable place where a light could possibly be used, — having it wired and connected to the switchboard. If it is not used it can be taken down, but if used the time saved is valuable.

As I have said, there are untold possibilities in the field of lighting; and not only in the theatre but everywhere that light is used. To realize this you have but to look at the number of stores where they make use of colored light in the windows, projected either by lenses or reflectors. This is an idea borrowed from the theatre. This is one of the reasons why I believe that what is done in the theatre can have a powerful influence, by stimulating the imagination, thus creating a sense of the idealistic and applying it to the commonplace.

APPENDIX B

Theatrical Lighting *

The physical effects of light on the animal organism are well known. The blisters which come from sunburn represent only an intensification of what is going on all the time, in some degree or other. That is, we are being bombarded by fiery particles which both stimulate and destroy cell life. Not less constant and potent, though more obscure, is the effect of light upon consciousness. It acts upon the emotional nature in unmistakable ways, even upon the emotional nature of animals as evinced by the saying, "like a red rag to a bull." Of these emotional reactions we are for the most part unconscious, or we attribute them to some other cause; but anyone who has worked with light in the theatre knows how inevitably an audience reacts to light changes. Light is an agent in moving men to laughter, to terror, or to tears.

In Mr. Walter Hampden's production of "Macbeth", at the first few performances some part of the audience always laughed when the murder of Banquo took place in the forest. This may have been merely a relief from tension, but it ruined the scene and was most disconcerting to the actors. A change in the lighting of the stage so altered the psychology of the audience as to eliminate the laughter from that time on. As this scene was given at first everything could be seen clearly, though dimly. People knew what to expect, and could follow every move. For this general lighting was substituted the nearly horizontal ray of a single blue projector, like a shaft of moonlight penetrating the forest. Then one saw only the lurking shadowy forms of the assassins, the quenching of the torch of their victims, and for a vivid moment the contending bodies locked in a death grapple within the lighted area. It was over almost as soon as begun, and from a mood of expectancy, curiosity, and apprehension, the audience was led to a revealing moment of shocked surprise entirely alien to the spirit of laughter.

* Part of a paper, *Decorative and Theatrical Lighting*, presented by Claude Bragdon before the Illuminating Engineering Society on October 29, 1924. Reprinted by permission of the Society.

In another instance it was desired to encourage laughter and not to quench it. As first given the graveyard scene in Hampden's "Hamlet" was played in a pallid waning daylight with the result that the comedy of the two grave-diggers with which the scene opens failed to register with the audience. We tried the experiment of beginning the scene in a bright, warm, cheerful light, and it was surprising how much better a comedian Mr. Allen Thomas and his companions suddenly became. The light was not acting against the risibilities of the audience, but with and for them.

Because the color quality of light acts powerfully and inevitably on the emotional nature, it is an aid in the induction of the particular mood which it is desired to create in the theatre. In the last act of "Cyrano de Bergerac" the time is autumn and the mood autumnal. Accordingly, this scene was drenched with amber light; in the battle scene — and in that alone — the light turned to red with telling effect. There is an intensely moving scene in the last act of Benevente's "Field of Ermine" — a passage between a jaded and heart-hungry noblewoman and the young boy who has evoked the maternal instinct in her. A great deal of the effect of this scene was due to the light, which came solely from the fireplace, waxing and waning as a wood fire does, throwing the faces and figures into intense relief, and casting strange, gigantic shadows on the opposite wall.

I have seen many other beautiful illustrations of the enhancement of a scene by means of light, but always they were the creations of artists, sensitive to light. Mr. Simonson's park scene in "Liliom" is a case in point, the background being of leaf-tracery against a night sky with the two lovers lighted by the nearer and warmer glow of a street lamp just out of sight. Mr. Robert Edmund Jones devised a most dramatic lighting for the outdoor scene in "Launzi." It was a ferry house by a dark river, out of which the heroine had just been rescued after an attempt at suicide. The only light at the beginning of the scene was from a single-shaded lamp projecting from the wall of a house. After the rescue an automobile was awaited to take the unfortunate young woman away. One hears the chug of its engine coming nearer and nearer. Then its headlights send an increasing shaft of light across the stage. It never actually appears upon the scene, but the action takes place in this horizontal beam of light, admirable for the purpose of the drama. It would be easy to multiply examples of the power of light to create and maintain the appropriate psychological mood in the theatre.

But though all people react emotionally to light, whether they know it or not, very few are able to see light — to see it analytically, that is, as a musician hears music — distinguishing the sound of separate instruments, and hearing in the harmonies their component sounds. It is music which has educated the sense of hearing to this pitch of perfection. The sense of sight to-day, not as a serviceable faculty, but as a source of esthetic enjoyment, is only just emerged from that rudimentary state in which hearing was before the rise of the musical art — rudimentary, I mean, as a source of pleasure.

The real trouble with nine-tenths of all decorative and theatrical lighting is that the very people who devise and employ it have no clear idea of the effect which it is desirable to produce. With equipment capable of producing almost any effect, they often get only the poorest results, or else arrangements and devices which are excellent in certain places and under certain conditions are used in other places and under other conditions where the results are the opposite of good.

If one can "see" light, and can imagine the effect desired before producing it, the simplest equipment can sometimes be made to produce the desired result. At Madison, Connecticut, one summer, a group of people had a barn theatre and I was called in to light a show. All they had was the current and a few lamps — no dimmers, projectors, or even colored gelatins. But we got some bright tin cracker-boxes, put a lamp in each, dipping the ones we wanted blue with shellac and "Diamond" dyes. Then I made covers for the boxes, filled with architect's tracing linen and hinged at the bottom. A string attached to this lid, passing through a screw-eye above each box, and thence to the wings, enabled us to get a fine dimming effect in one scene simply by slowly closing the lids by pulling the strings. The scene was supposed to be laid in the Egyptian department of the Metropolitan museum, late afternoon, changing to night. The moving shadow of the lid of the box, translucent because the linen let through some of the light, looked like the slowly rising shadow of some building across the way, a perfectly natural and familiar effect of light, but one which I have never seen reproduced in the theatre before or since, it being one of those infrequent happy accidents.

What is the ideal toward which one should strive in theatrical lighting? One should know first what effects it is desired to produce before concerning oneself with how effects can be produced.

My own opinion is that for true human drama — for great plays greatly acted — the lighting should be made strictly subordinate to the work of the dramatist and of the actor, enhancing both, never competing for the interest of the spectator. The lighting should be so good that it can be forgotten, just as in living in the light of the sun we are able to forget the sun. The finest compliment I ever received for the lighting of Mr. Hampden's "Hamlet"

Photograph by Francis Bruguiere.

A scene from Act II of Walter Hampden's production of *Cyrano de Bergerac*, designed by Claude Bragdon: Ragueneau reciting his verse to the poets and the pastry cooks.

production, was given by an artist whom I sent to see the play that he might pass upon the lighting. In some embarrassment he said to me afterwards, "You know, I forgot to look at the lighting I got so interested in the play." That was as it should be. Usually it is the novice and the ignoramus who strives for startling effects in the lighting of plays. I do not mean to be understood as saying that the lighting of plays should be naturalistic — no, not even in the most realistic productions. A cyclorama as bright, or anywhere nearly as bright, as the daylight sky would make a background fatal to the actor who must appear before it. As in the art of acting

Photograph by Francis Bruguiere.

Cyrano and Roxane in Ragueneau's pastry shop: a scene from Act II of Walter Hampden's production of *Cyrano de Bergerac*, designed by Claude Bragdon.

itself, one must often depart far from nature in order to give the impression of naturalness. What the lighting should express and be true to, is the mood of the play, and its psychological values, whatever these may be. It is, therefore, of the first importance to discover these things at the start.

"Hamlet", for example, is a spiritual play — a winter's tale, a northern tragedy. Its keynote is sounded in the first scene — "'Tis bitter cold, and I am sick at heart." In color it clearly belongs to the electric rather than to the thermal division of the spectrum. We made the scenery, accordingly, in grays, blues, violets, and tans and maintained a quality of light throughout which would keep those tones pure. This was done by mixing in a few bare daylight lamps to reinforce the blues of the border, which by reason of their feebleness are usually too much overpowered by the yellows and reds.

In "Macbeth" the color scale used in the scenery and costumes to express the mood of the play was as follows: black, for the powers of evil; red, the color of blood, for murder; gold, for ambition, kingly power; orange for the flame-like love which existed between Macbeth and his wife; blue-green — "glint of steel" — for cruelty and indifference to human suffering; and brown for that quality of murkiness which permeates the play. There is perhaps no play which contains so many references to the weather as "Macbeth" and the weather is always bad. The keynote is struck in the opening lines when the witch says, "When shall we three meet again, in thunder, lightning, or in rain."

Photograph by Francis Bruguiere.

Roxane on her balcony: a scene from Act III of Walter Hampden's production of *Cyrano de Bergerac*, designed by Claude Bragdon.

In the lighting of "Macbeth" I attempted to give this sense of fog and murk; an effect achieved by means of gauze curtains, keeping the top and sides of the stage dim, and using local lighting for the most part. The apparitions of the kings appear from nothingness, pass behind a gauze curtain, their figures defined against the wan light of a dying sun, and vanish into nothingness again. As so often happens, an accident helped us to one of the most telling effects. Instead of having the curtain go down on a lighted stage at the end of every scene we blanked all the lights suddenly and the curtain descended in darkness. Now Mr. Operti, who played the first witch, is of the greyhound type, an expert jumper and dancer, and at the end of one scene one night the lights happened to flash out just at the moment when from the top of a rock he had taken a leap upward in the air. This gave the illusion that he never again descended, since he was not seen to descend, giving point to Banquo's lines, "The air hath bubbles as the water hath." Thereafter the leap was the cue for putting out the lights.

Rostand's play, "Cyrano de Bergerac", though it is founded upon the life of an actual man, and introduces historic characters, is nevertheless sheer romance and fantasy. Poetry, gallantry, wit, courage, love, moonlight, beauty — they are all in this play. It is the kind of a story anyone might tell himself while day-dreaming, the sort of thing one would like to have happen to himself. The lighting therefore should be as "glamorous" as possible, not hard and bright and literal, clipping the wings of the imagination, but soft and glowing. To achieve this end we painted the scenery all very dark, a purple violet, and kept the light off it as much as possible, also the light was kept off of the sides and top of the stage, to eliminate in some degree the illusion of a picture frame. Wherever a stairway or a stage or a balcony was required it appeared, but when it was no longer wanted, it retreated into the background, as it were. The lighting for this production was done almost entirely with "soft-edge" spotlights, equipped with hinged shields by means of which the light was directed upon the actors and off of the scenery, producing the effect described.

I believe, with Mr. Bassett Jones, that the lighting should favor the actor in every possible way, for he is necessarily the center of attention and the immediate and direct interpreter of the play. Mr. Jones recommends keeping the same quality of light on the face of the actor, while varying the quantity. I have found, as he has found, that a combination of blue and amber * which exactly neutralize one another is a most satisfactory acting light. The lighting for the scenery and cyclorama may be whatever one pleases, and here color may be introduced *ad libitum*.

Footlights, which are a survival of the days of candles and lamps, should be used not at all, or sparingly — they are the worst possible light, on account of their nearness and their location. They should be employed only so far as is necessary to "kill" the dark shadow in the socket of the eye caused by overhead lighting. Side lighting is excellent, but the source of light is usually too near. Lighting from the auditorium overcomes many difficulties. In "Cyrano", top, side, and front lighting were all used, separately or together, bathing the acting area in soft, warm light, "tapering off", so to speak, toward the top and sides of the stage, to eliminate the hard rectangle of the proscenium as much as possible.

* The specific gelatin color media used by Mr. Bragdon to achieve this combination are: blue, Number D-22 dark, and amber, Number D-10, of the Pevear Color Specialty Company.

APPENDIX C

Selected Bibliography

Up to the present, separate works devoted exclusively to stage lighting are rare, and seem to be confined to the following:

Bühnenbeleuchtung, by Alfred von Engel. Leipzig: Hachmeister und Thal. This German work is highly technical in its treatment of the subject and, as is to be expected, its theatre nomenclature differs widely from that current in America. It is of interest principally to highly trained technical workers in the theatre.

Stage Lighting for 'Little' Theatres, by C. Harold Ridge. Cambridge, England: W. Heffer and Sons, Ltd. This work touches rather briefly, also with its own distinctive terminology, upon a few of the lighting problems likely to be encountered by amateur producing groups in England.

Glossary of Stage Lighting, by Stanley R. McCandless. New York: Theatre Arts, Inc. Brief descriptions and definitions of apparatus and terms.

Stage Lighting, Bulletin LD146A, by A. L. Powell and Theodore Fuchs. Harrison, N. J.: Edison Lamp Works of General Electric Company. A comparatively short though comprehensive non-technical discussion, with interesting illustrations.

Many works dealing with the various general phases of theatre activity contain material on stage lighting. Some of these are:

Modern Theatres, by Irving Pichel. New York: Harcourt, Brace and Company. The best practical treatise on the elements of modern theatre design, with two excellent chapters on lighting.

The Theatre of To-day, by Hiram Kelly Moderwell. New York: Dodd, Mead and Company. A general survey of the new factors and tendencies in the theatre — the "best-seller" in its field.

Play Production in America, by Arthur Edwin Krows. New York: Henry Holt and Company. A comprehensive, non-technical picture of the many phases of "commercial theatre" activity.

The Art Theatre, by Sheldon Cheney. New York: Alfred Knopf. The recent "art theatre movement" in Europe and America discussed by one of America's foremost art critics.

Stage Decoration, by Sheldon Cheney. New York: John Day and Company. A concise review of the development of stage decoration and stage forms. Many excellent pictures of stage settings.

The Theatre of Tomorrow, by Kenneth Macgowan. New York: Boni and Liveright. A thoughtful and suggestive discussion of the more advanced of the contemporary work in the theatre.

Continental Stagecraft, by Kenneth Macgowan and Robert Edmond Jones. New York: Harcourt, Brace and Company. A valuable record of the best Continental work, by one of the most distinguished American critics and producers in collaboration with one of the most distinguished American stage designers.

Towards a New Theatre, by Edward Gordon Craig. New York: E. P. Dutton and Company. Forty designs for stage scenes, which well illustrate the active and important rôle played by light as an integral constituent of the stage setting.

Die Musik und die Inscenierung, by Adolph Appia. Munich: Bruckmann. An exposition of a new theory of play production; including one of the earliest discussions of the newer uses of light in the theatre.

Interesting historical references may be found in the following works:

History of Theatrical Art in Ancient and Modern Times, by Karl Mantzius. Philadelphia: J. B. Lippincott Company. An authoritative treatise in six volumes; considered the standard work in its field.

The Development of the Theatre, by Allardyce Nicoll. New York: Harcourt, Brace and Company. A scholarly review of the stage up to the present period of its development.

Theatre Lighting — Past and Present. Mount Vernon, N. Y.: Ward Leonard Electric Company. An interesting summary of stage-lighting history, well illustrated.

History of Electric Light, Publication 2717, by Henry Schroeder. Washington: Smithsonian Institution. A detailed discussion covering the development of electric-lighting equipment and practice.

Comprehensive discussions of light and of color are contained in the following volumes, each of which has a separate chapter devoted to stage lighting:

Light and Shade and Their Applications, by M. Luckiesh. New York: D. Van Nostrand and Company.

Color and Its Applications, by M. Luckiesh. New York: D. Van Nostrand and Company.

Because of the almost infinite number of articles on stage lighting that have been published from time to time in various periodicals, no attempt has been made to list them here. However, an excellent index of stage-lighting articles published prior to 1927 is contained in:

The Development of Scenic Art and Stage Machinery: a list of references, by William Burt Gamble. New York: New York Public Library. Particularly rich in references to material of historical value.

References to published articles on stage lighting can be found in the monthly issues of:

Transactions of the Illuminating Engineering Society. New York: Illuminating Engineering Society. Each issue contains an *Illumination Index* which includes many references to current articles on stage lighting. In addition, the Society publishes yearly a classified reference index. The *Transactions* also include occasional papers on stage lighting, two of which have been reprinted in the present volume.

Articles on stage lighting seem to be restricted to no particular class of periodicals, though of course they are most likely to be found in the following:

Theatre Arts Monthly. New York: Theatre Arts, Inc.
Drama and Little Theatre Monthly. Chicago: Drama League of America.
Light. Cleveland: National Lamp Works of General Electric Company.

And, incidentally, the central clearing house and most convenient source of supply for domestic and foreign literature on stage lighting and on other phases of theatre activity is the

Drama Book Shop, 29 West 47th Street, New York.

APPENDIX D

List of Manufacturers and Dealers of Stage Lighting and Control Equipment

This list is presented for the convenience of those readers who wish to obtain definite information as to the specifications and costs of the various makes of equipment that are commercially available. As noted in the list, many of the firms issue descriptive catalogues of their products. These are available on request to the respective firms. A reference file of catalogues, when used with discretion and discernment, provides a liberal education in practical considerations and often proves a most valuable asset to the stage-lighting worker.

I. General

Under this heading are listed the firms that handle the usual complete line of stage-lighting and control equipment: such as footlights, spotlights, floodlights, striplights, dimmers, switchboards, wiring supplies, "effects", various accessories for lighting and control equipment, outdoor lighting units, lamps, cable, and color media, including lamp dips and gelatin sheets.

Universal Electric Stage Lighting Company, 321 West 50th Street, New York. Familiarly known as "Kliegl Brothers", this firm is one of the oldest and best known and is one of the most reliable in its field. It was founded by John Kliegl and the late Anton Kliegl, and is still conducted by the former. It handles a very wide variety of equipment and issues an excellent catalogue.

Display Stage Lighting Company, 410 West 47th Street, New York. One of the best known of the newer firms, an expression of the personality of its principal founder, William E. Price. It handles a complete line of equipment, including the "Baby Hercules" and "Aluminide" apparatus, and issues a very good catalogue.

New York Calcium Light Company, 449 West 53rd Street, New York. Perhaps the oldest existing firm — pioneers, though "progressive pioneers" — in the field, dating back to the days of gas lighting and the limelight. It is still in charge of the two "gas boys" — as stage-lighting operators were termed in the early days — William Murray and Fred S. Murray.

Duwico, 313 West 47th Street, New York. A comparatively new though enterprising firm, under the direction of 'Gus' Durkin and Harold Williams, two well known figures in metropolitan stage lighting activity.

Brenkert Light Projection Company, 7348 St. Aubin Avenue, Detroit. Although formerly specializing in high-powered projection equipment, this firm now includes among its products a complete line of newly-designed backstage apparatus. It issues a very good catalogue.

National Theatre Supply Company, 624 South Michigan Avenue, Chicago. This organization represents a recent amalgamation of numerous smaller firms, and has branches in many cities throughout the country.

Major Equipment Company, 4603 Fullerton Avenue, Chicago. Catalogue.

Hub Electric Company, 2219 West Grand Avenue, Chicago. Catalogue.

Chicago Stage Lighting Company, 55 West Wacker Drive, Chicago. Catalogue.

C. J. Holzmueller, 1108 Howard Street, San Francisco. Catalogue.

Capitol Stage Lighting Company, 626 Tenth Avenue, New York. Catalogue.

Charles I. Newton, 244 West 14th Street, New York.

Frederick A. Bohling, 503 West 43rd Street, New York.

Columbia Stage Lighting Company, 349 West 47th Street, New York.

Electrical Products Corporation, 1134 Venice Boulevard, Los Angeles.

Kansas City Scenic Company, 1000 East 24th Street, Kansas City.

A. E. Jackson, 54 Alberta Street, Toronto.

Cincinnati Stage Lighting Company, Cincinnati.

Pevear Color Specialty Company, 71 Brimmer Street, Boston. Under the direction of Munroe Pevear, this firm has developed a line of stage-lighting equipment that, in view of the scientific optical principles embodied in its design and the uniformly high standard of construction, may truly be said to be unique. This firm issues no catalogue and, as its equipment is not of the conventional type, prefers to make recommendations for its use only after a thorough, detailed study of the conditions and requirements of each individual case. Some of their achievements are "soft-edge" spotlights, tormentor and teaser lens units, cyclorama color mixing units, rotating borderlights, Wellesley and Pilgrim projector units, as well as combination direct and indirect footlight units.

II. Reflectors

Under this heading are listed firms that manufacture reflectors and reflector equipment that find use in the service of stage lighting.

Curtis Lighting, 1119 West Jackson Boulevard, Chicago. "X-Ray" mirrored-glass reflectors, and footlights and borderlights containing them; and outdoor floodlighting projectors. Catalogue.

Frink Corporation, 369 Lexington Avenue, New York. "Silverlite" silvered-metal reflectors. Catalogue.

Ivanhoe Division of the Miller Company, Cleveland. Spun aluminum reflectors especially for stage-lighting equipment, and footlights and borderlights containing them; and porcelain-enameled steel reflectors. Catalogue.

Reflector and Illuminating Company, 1407 West Jackson Boulevard, Chicago. "Sterling" mirrored-glass reflectors. Catalogue.

Pittsburgh Reflector Company, Third Street and Ross Street, Pittsburgh. "Permaflector" mirrored-glass reflectors. Catalogue.

Benjamin Electric Manufacturing Company, 120 South Sangamon Street, Chicago. Porcelain-enameled steel reflectors; also wiring devices. Catalogue.

Wheeler Reflector Company, 275 Congress Street, Boston. Porcelain-enameled steel reflectors. Catalogue.

General Electric Company, Schenectady, N. Y. Outdoor floodlighting projectors. Catalogue.

Westinghouse Electric and Manufacturing Company, East Pittsburgh, Pa. Outdoor floodlighting projectors. Catalogue.

Crouse-Hinds Company, Syracuse, N. Y. Outdoor floodlighting projectors. Catalogue.

Cahill Brothers, 517 West 45th Street, New York. Outdoor floodlights. Descriptive leaflet.

III. Lamps

Under this heading are listed the principal manufacturers of incandescent lamps for general and stage-lighting use. The products of the companies listed are uniform in all respects. These three organizations have excellent facilities, as noted, that are gratuitously available to all persons who are interested in stage lighting and in all other phases of lighting work. Each firm issues a uniform "Manufacturer's Schedules" — the equivalent of a catalogue — which gives detailed information concerning the various standard lamps available.

Edison Lamp Works of General Electric Company, Harrison, N. J. This organization is a direct outgrowth of Thomas A. Edison's original incandescent lamp factory. It maintains an engineering department that is available for advisory service in connection with matters relating to lighting problems. It maintains an extensive exhibit of lighting equipment of all types, including a special section devoted to stage lighting, at the Edison Lighting Institute, where interesting demonstrations of all phases of lighting practice are conducted for visitors. The Edison Lighting Institute is at Harrison, N. J., a few minutes distant from downtown New York. A visit to it is recommended to all persons interested in lighting matters. A series of more than fifty

Lighting Data Bulletins is published by this organization. Of this series, the following will perhaps prove of greatest interest to readers of this volume:

LD114–C Theory and Characteristics of Mazda Lamps
LD123–B Reflectors for Incandescent Lamps
LD145–A The Lighting of Theatres and Auditoriums
LD146–A Stage Lighting
LD155 Illumination Terms

These bulletins are available upon request to the Engineering Department.

National Lamp Works of General Electric Company, Cleveland, Ohio. This organization is an outgrowth of an association of Edison's original competitors. It maintains an engineering department for advisory service on lighting matters, and at Nela Park, its very attractive headquarters in the suburbs of Cleveland, it also maintains, in conjunction with its Lighting Research Laboratory, a comprehensive demonstrational lighting exhibit that is well worth a visit. Of the series of bulletins issued by this organization,

7–D Fundamentals of Illumination,

available on request, will prove of interest to readers of this volume. This organization also publishes the monthly magazine *Light*.

Westinghouse Lamp Company, Bloomfield, N. J. This company also maintains an engineering department and occasionally issues literature on lighting subjects.

IV. Color Media

Under this heading are listed firms that specialize in color media for use with stage-lighting equipment. As noted, some issue sample books of color media, which may be obtained upon request.

Charles Townsend, 276 Pearl Street, New York. This firm is perhaps the oldest in its field. Its assortment of colored gelatin sheets is a very extensive one. Approximate qualitative color-analyses of these appear on page 411. The sheets measure 19″ × 21″. Sample book.

Laco-Philips Company, 131 Hudson Street, New York. "Laco" glass color caps and colored glass sheets. Catalogue.

Corning Glass Works, Corning, N. Y. Colored glass sheets *in a wide range of colors*. Descriptive booklet giving spectral analyses.

Transolene Company, 410 Sullivan Street, Chicago. Colored transolene sheets, especially resistant to fading, climatic conditions, and rough usage. The sheets measure 19″ × 22″. Sample book.

Gelatine Products Company, 27 Sixth Avenue, Brooklyn, N. Y. Colored gelatin sheets. Sample book.

Egyptian Lacquer Company, 90 West Street, New York. Colored lamp dips.

Crown Color and Chemical Company, 33 West 17th Street, New York. Colored lamp dips.

McGill Manufacturing Company, Valparaiso, Ind. Colored lamp dips.

Zeller Lacquer Manufacturing Company, 20 East 49th Street, New York. Colored lamp dips.

Roscoe Laboratories, 131 Third Place, Brooklyn, N. Y. Colored lamp dips and colored gelatin sheets.

Alexander Strobl, 101 West 41st Street, New York. Phosphorescent and fluorescent materials in various forms and colors; ultra-violet filters. Sample card.

Chameleon Company, 136 Liberty Street, New York. This firm designs colored lighting effects for stage use, and supplies the necessary special color media, dyes, and pigments.

Pevear Color Specialty Company, 71 Brimmer Street, Boston. This firm handles and makes colored gelatin sheets of special color purity. Their sets of light primary colors are especially adapted to use with the graded-mixture method of color control. Gelatin sheets of the light primary colors are available in two sets: one set for use with lamps up to 200 watts in size, bearing the numbers, red — D-5; green — D-15; and blue — D-24; and the other set for use with lamps up to 1000 watts in size, bearing the numbers, red — D-4; green — D-17; and blue — D-26. The sheets measure 20″ × 25″. Sample book. They also make lamp dip and special dyed gelatin light-filters, which are mounted on glass. The "amber A" lamp dip, for type C lamps, is of their manufacture.

V. Cable and Wire

Under this heading are listed manufacturers of stage cable, borderlight cable, and various types of wire for switchboard and wiring circuits.

Simplex Wire and Cable Company, 63 Sidney Street, Boston.

Rome Wire Company, Rome, N. Y.

General Electric Company, Bridgeport, Conn.

Crescent Insulated Wire and Cable Company, Trenton, N. J.

John A. Roebling's Sons Company, Trenton, N. J.

United States Rubber Company, 1790 Broadway, New York.

VI. Dimmers

Under this heading are listed the manufacturers of stage dimmers.

Ward Leonard Electric Company, 38 South Street, Mt. Vernon, N. Y. "Vitrohm" dimmers of all types; and "Controlite" dimmers, with automatic disconnect flipper switches. Catalogues.

Cutler-Hammer Manufacturing Company, 1209 St. Paul Avenue, Milwaukee, Wis. "Simplicity" dimmers of all types, including the double-faced type. Catalogue.

National Electric Controller Company, 5315 Ravenswood Avenue, Chicago. Catalogue.

VII. Switchboards

Under this heading are listed manufacturers of stage switchboards, of the various types noted.

Trumbull Electric Manufacturing Company, Plainville, Conn. Direct-control "Controlite" switchboards; remote-control switchboards; "Circle-T" switches; and rotor-movement "R. M." switches. Catalogue.

Bull-Dog Electric Products Company, 6710 Jos. Campau Avenue, Detroit. Direct-control "Bull Dog" switchboards; "Bull Dog" interlocking reverse-bar-connected switches. Catalogue.

Hub Electric Company, 2219 West Grand Avenue, Chicago. Double control-circuit remote-control switchboards. Catalogue.

Frank Adam Electric Company, 3650 Windsor Place, St. Louis. Remote-control "Major System" switchboards. Catalogue.

Westinghouse Electric and Manufacturing Company, East Pittsburgh, Pa. Direct-control and remote-control switchboards. Catalogue.

Electrical Products Corporation, 1134 Venice Boulevard, Los Angeles.

Cleveland Switchboard Company, 2925 East 79th Street, Cleveland.

Powerlite Switchboard Company, 4149 East 79th Street, Cleveland.

Superior Switchboard and Devices Company, 420 Schroyer Street, Canton, Ohio.

Metropolitan Electric Manufacturing Company, Long Island City, N. Y. Catalogue.

Empire Switchboard Company, 801 Fourth Avenue, Brooklyn, N. Y.

Penn Electrical and Manufacturing Company, 35 Water Street, Irwin, Pa.

Pevear Color Specialty Company, 71 Brimmer Street, Boston. Interlocking wall-type and portable switchboards embodying the multiple dimmer unit.

VIII. European Companies

Under this heading are included a few of the outstanding manufacturers of stage-lighting and control equipment in Europe. A study of their descriptive literature is sure to prove of more than passing interest to the reader. Even though foreign equipment is not available in this country, stage-lighting workers here should be reasonably familiar with its characteristics.

Allgemeine Elektricitäts Gesellschaft, Friedrich Karl-Ufer 4, Berlin, N. W. 40. This firm issues an excellent descriptive booklet, "Die Elektrizität im Theater", available on request.

Schwabe und Company, Köpenicker Strasse 116, Berlin, S. O. 16. This firm issues an interesting descriptive booklet, "Moderne Bühnen-Beleuchtung", available on request.

General Electric Company, Magnet House, Kingsway, London, W. C. 2. This firm issues an attractive booklet, SL-2398 — Modern Stage Lighting, which describes the Schwabe equipment which is being introduced in England. This booklet is available on request.

APPENDIX E

Miscellaneous Notes for Amateur Workers

I. Makeshifts

Although the use of makeshift lighting and control equipment should, in the main, be discouraged, there are occasions when there is no alternative to its use — when conditions, financial or otherwise, decree that makeshifts must be pressed into service, and that simple, even crude devices, quickly made of readily obtainable materials, be used as substitutes for the desirable standard equipment. In such cases, the following notes, which should be considered only as being *supplemental* to the detailed suggestions for more substantial "home-built" equipment already presented in this volume, may perhaps prove of some use.

Footlights of a temporary nature can be made simply by mounting a row of sockets along short lengths of wooden boards, and providing such devices with suitable shields that will keep the light out of the spectators' eyes. Similar units can also be used as *striplights* in various positions, and, inverted, as *borderlights*. Particularly good makeshift borderlights can be devised by mounting, on the narrow under-edge of a well-suspended length of "two by four" lumber, a row of sockets that can be equipped with shadeholders and show-window reflectors that have been borrowed, for a performance or two, from a sympathetic local merchant. *Olivettes* that will serve temporarily can be made by mounting several sockets either in a wooden soap-box that has been lined with thin asbestos paper and drilled with a number of holes to provide air circulation for ventilation; or in a large white-enameled dish-pan, or in a sheet-iron roasting pan that has been painted white inside. Cheap aluminum saucepans can also be used as reflectors for various pieces of lighting apparatus. An electric heater — the type with the parabolic copper reflector — with its heating element replaced by a clear incandescent lamp, gives a rich amber flood with a bright center, which is often a very desirable and useful combination. Even the usual type of bridge lamp, when equipped with an asbestos-paper shade and with a "Benjamin" 3 or 4-way plug cluster socket, makes a serviceable bunchlight. *Spotlights* can be crudely approximated in effect by mounting a socket within a three or four-foot length of stovepipe, at one end, and using an ordinary incandescent lamp (that is, a special spotlight lamp is not necessary). With a 200-watt lamp, such a device gives a fairly satisfactory beam of light, and, if the inside of the stovepipe be coated with aluminum paint, produces a "spot" with a soft outline. Several stovepipe spotlights can be tied together and used as a unit if a more powerful beam of light is desired. If the socket mounting be made movable, this spotlight can even be "focussed." If a stereopticon is available, it can be made to serve as a spotlight. Ordinary small electric flashlights, when used with ingenuity, can serve the amateur in a variety of effective ways.

For simple productions, a serviceable substitute for a *switchboard* can be made by mounting, on a wide wooden board, a number of plugging receptacles (of the type ordinarily used for residential wiring), or sockets equipped with screw attachment-plug bodies, and connecting the receptacles or sockets, as the case may be, preferably through plug fuse cut-outs, to the electrical supply mains, which themselves should be properly protected by fuses. The flexible cables from the various units of lighting equipment should be equipped with corresponding male attachment-plug connectors. They may then be plugged into the "switchboard" receptacles when needed. Inserting a plug into a receptacle will close the particular circuit and light the lamps on it; removing it sharply will open the circuit and extinguish them. Although switches on the circuits provide greater convenience, the ordinary type of snap switches, such as are used for residential wiring, should not be employed, as they are far too noisy in operation for a small stage. Available dimmers can be permanently wired into the "switchboard" circuits, or a dimmer insertion system, as described on page 391, can be used.

Dimmers of the "water-barrel" type are easily made, but should be used only when it is impossible to secure other dimmers. For a "water-barrel" dimmer, a five-gallon earthenware crock, or a similar non-metallic vessel, should be used as the container. A smooth flat iron plate (an inch or two less in diameter than the crock) to which is firmly fastened (preferably by soldering or bolting) one of the two dimmer "leads" — a length of insulated flexible wire — should be laid in the bottom of the crock. To a second iron plate, to which is fastened the other flexible dimmer "lead", should be attached a length of heavy fishing-line. A wooden framework should be constructed to rest firmly upon the top edge of the crock, and should have a winch-like arrangement (a ratchet fishing-reel serves particularly well) upon which the fishing-line attached to the movable iron plate can be wound, and hence by which the latter can be conveniently and smoothly raised and lowered. The crock should then be filled with water to a point not less than two inches from the top. Sufficient common salt, or washing soda (the exact amount can be determined only by trial), should be added to the water so that the solution provides just the right amount of resistance for dimming the desired lamp load to "black out" when the movable iron plate is at the upper limit of its traverse. The greater the lamp load, the stronger the solution must be. If the lamps flicker when the dimmer plates are at the "bright" position — the movable one resting upon the stationary one — a few thin, narrow strips of rubber (which can be cut from an old inner tube) should be laid upon the stationary iron plate. These will prevent the plates from coming in direct contact with each other and, although the lamps will not burn at quite their full brightness, will provide a steady light at the "bright" position of the dimmer. "Water-barrel" dimmers of the size just described should not be used to dim lamp loads in excess of 1000 watts.

Amateur producing groups often use stages in churches, schools, clubs, and similar buildings. Sometimes several fixed lighting outlets have been provided on such a stage, and these are usually arranged in several circuits that are controlled from a panelboard in close proximity to the stage. If this is the case, and if it is desired to use the existing light outlets, either as they are or as plugging outlets for portable equipment, any available dimmers can easily be inserted in the stage circuits by the following simple method: If *cartridge fuses* are used on the panelboard, several "dead", or "blown," fuses of the same size should be procured (enough such discarded fuses can usually be found lying in the panelboard itself) and a flexible lead, long enough to reach to the dimmer, should be soldered to each end-ferrule. Only one of the two good fuses on each stage circuit should be replaced with a "dead" fuse so equipped, and the pair of leads connected to a dimmer, which is then in series with the circuit. If *plug fuses* are used, it is a very simple matter to replace one good fuse with a screw attachment-plug body, and equip the dimmer leads with a corresponding male attachment-plug connector, by means of which the dimmer can be plugged into the stage circuit. If single fusing is used on the panelboard, an additional fuse should be placed in series with the dimmer — a circuit should never be left entirely without fuse protection. Dimmers can also be placed in the auditorium circuits in the same manner, but unless the work is carried out with extreme care, it had better not be attempted. Some accident to the temporary dimmer wiring may extinguish all the auditorium lights, and the possibilities of panic presented by merely an auditorium suddenly darkened without apparent cause, cannot be overestimated. In fact, a very high regard for safety should characterize all amateur stage-lighting work, however temporary and makeshift it may be. Particularly should the amateur worker be certain, before he connects his equipment on a stage with which he is not familiar, that the electrical supply mains which he will use are of sufficient capacity to carry the total load that his equipment will require.

As regards makeshift *color media:* Vacuum incandescent lamps can be dipped in a quickly concocted mixture of white shellac and aniline dyes. Temporary color-frames of the larger sizes can be simply made of thin strips of wood and wide-mesh thin wire screening; smaller ones can be made of cardboard and paper fasteners. If a stereopticon is being used, sheet gelatin can be mounted between two lantern-slide cover-glasses, or a cover-glass can be colored with transparent dyes such as are ordinarily used for tinting lantern slides. For some lighting equipment, thin silk can often be successfully used as a color media. Obtaining colored light by selective reflection from colored paper or cloth, or even from color-painted surfaces, is a process that amateurs should not overlook — it produces beautiful effects that are often unobtainable by any other method.

II. References to Stage-Lighting Notes for Amateurs

Suggestions regarding makeshift lighting devices, as well as random notes that might prove directly applicable to some specific individual problem and that might prove generally useful to the amateur worker in stage lighting, may be gleaned from the following books, most of which deal with amateur play production in general, but all of which contain some material bearing on amateur stage lighting. These books contain widely varying amounts of lighting information of varying degrees of usefulness, and the material is presented in various ways, and from many different points of view.

Acting and Play Production. Harry Lee Andrews and Bruce Wierick.
Community Drama. Playground and Recreation Association.
Community Drama and Pageantry. J. R. Crawford and M. P. Beagle.
Costumes and Scenery for Amateurs. Constance D'Arcy Mackay.
Costuming a Play. Elizabeth J. Grimball and Rhea Wells.
Drama in Religious Service. Martha Candler.

Dramatics for School and Community. Claude Merton Wise.
How to Produce Amateur Plays. Barrett H. Clark.
Little Theatre Organization and Management. Alexander Dean.
Practical Stage Directing for Amateurs. Emerson Taylor.
Producing in Little Theatres. Clarence Stratton.
Shakespeare for Community Players. Roy Mitchell.
Stage Costuming. Agnes Brooks Young.
Technique in Dramatic Art. Halliam Bosworth.
Technique in Pageantry. Linwood Taft.
The Art of Producing Pageants. Esther W. Bates.
The Book of Play Production. Milton Smith.
The Community Theatre. Louise Burleigh.
The Community Playhouse. C. J. de Goveia.
The Process of Play Production. Allan Crafton and Jessica Royer.
The School Theatre. Roy Mitchell.

The following booklets contain useful information regarding amateur stage-lighting work, at the pages indicated.

The Billboard Little Theatre Handbook — pp. 19, 30, 36, and 47. Obtainable on request from Little Theatre Editor, The Billboard, 1560 Broadway, New York.

Play Production for the Country Theatre, by A. M. Drummond — p. 54. Obtainable at a nominal charge from Director of Extension Service, Cornell University, Ithaca, N. Y.

Stage Lighting, LD 146 A — p. 39. Obtainable on request from Engineering Department, Edison Lamp Works, Harrison, N. J.

Articles of special interest to the amateur stage-lighting worker appear from time to time in the following magazines:

Drama and Little Theatre Monthly. Drama League of America.
Theatre and School. Drama Teachers' Association of California.
Players' Magazine. National Collegiate Players.

The following organizations have service memberships which include the privilege of consultation and advice regarding amateur play production matters, including stage lighting:

Drama League of America, 59 East Van Buren Street, Chicago. Sue Ann Wilson, consultant.

Playground and Recreation Association of America, 315 Fourth Avenue, New York. Mabel F. Hobbs, consultant.

III. Sources of Material

Under this heading are listed firms dealing in materials required for constructing the home-built amateur equipment described in this volume, and also sources of various other material that might be required by the amateur stage lighting worker in the course of his activities. This list is intended for use as a supplement to the list in Appendix D.

The following firms manufacture wiring devices such as are used in the construction of lighting equipment and switchboards.

Trumbull Electric Manufacturing Company, Plainville, Conn. Knife switches of all types; rotor movement "R. M." switches. Catalogue.

General Electric Company, Bridgeport, Conn. General line of wiring devices, wire, and cable. Catalogue.

Harvey Hubbell, Bridgeport, Conn. General line of wiring devices. Catalogue.

Arrow Electric Company, Hartford, Conn. General line of wiring devices, including the "Arro-grip" cable grip useful for flexible cable leads of plugging-boxes at instrument locations. Catalogue.

Bryant Electric Company, Bridgeport, Conn. General line of wiring devices. Catalogue.

Graybar Electric Company, Lexington Avenue and 43rd Street, New York. General line of electrical material — very complete. Numerous branches throughout the country. Catalogue.

Sundh Electric Company, 209 Parkhurst Street, Newark, N. J. Magnet switches especially suitable for use on remote-control switchboards. Catalogue.

Special materials for use on home-built dimmers and switchboards may be obtained from

Johns-Manville, Madison Avenue and 41st Street, New York. Ebony asbestos wood for use as front face on switchboards; transite asbestos wood for mounting resistance windings on dimmers; and numerous other products that have applications in stage work. Descriptive leaflets.

Resistance wire for constructing home-built dimmers may be obtained from

Driver-Harris Company, Harrison, N. J. This firm has agreed to supply its "Advance" resistance wire (data table on page 377) in small quantities to amateurs wishing to experiment with home-built dimmer construction, at the following prices per pound of wire:

Size	Cost	Size	Cost	Size	Cost	Size	Cost	Size	Cost
#11	$1.36	#16	$1.51	#21	$1.75	#26	$2.10	#31	$2.90
12	1.39	17	1.55	22	1.80	27	2.25	32	3.10
13	1.42	18	1.60	23	1.85	28	2.40	33	3.30
14	1.45	19	1.65	24	1.90	29	2.55	34	3.70
15	1.48	20	1.70	25	2.00	30	2.70	35	4.50

It requests, however, that the following conditions be noted: No order totalling less than five dollars can be filled. Not less than a pound of any size of wire can be supplied. A spooling charge of twenty-five cents per pound of wire should be added to the cost of the wire. Remittance, including cost of wire, spooling charges, and sufficient allowance for parcel-post charges, should accompany the order. The order should specify "Advance" wire, designating sizes by number and quantities by pounds. These requirements are necessary in order to minimize the inconvenience and expense of handling very small orders in a large manufacturing organization.

Laboratory rheostats, mentioned in connection with the "color booth" described on page 131, may be obtained from

James G. Biddle, 1211 Arch Street, Philadelphia. Catalogue.

Assortments of eighteen colored papers, known as the standard Zimmermann colors, which are invaluable for use with any experiments in color that the interested amateur worker may care to conduct, may be obtained from

Emil Zimmermann, Wasserturmstrasse 33, Leipzig, O. 27. Catalogue.

And color media of high spectral purity, that are also essential in connection with color experiments, may be obtained from

Eastman Kodak Company, Rochester, N. Y. Descriptive booklet, "Wratten Light Filters", giving spectral analyses of standard filters, available at nominal cost.

Hard gelatin in flaked or ground form, for use by the experimentally inclined amateur as raw material in making his own colored gelatin sheets, may be obtained from

Charles Townsend, 276 Pearl Street, New York. Gelatin of grade #9102 is suitable. Incidentally, this firm has agreed to supply its regular colored gelatin sheets (approximate qualitative spectral analyses on page 411) at a cost of fifteen cents each, the only conditions being that twenty sheets constitute the minimum order and that remittance, including parcel post charges, accompany the order. There is no packing charge. If one hundred or more sheets (which may be of assorted colors) are ordered at one time, they are available at ten cents each. Colored gelatin sheets should be ordered by number. Selection can be made from a sample book, which is available on request.

French varnish, useful as a basis for lamp dips, as well as spirit-soluble dyes for coloring them, may be obtained from

William Zinsser, 48 Vesey Street, New York.

Water-soluble and spirit-soluble dyes, used respectively for making colored gelatin sheets and colored lamp dips, may be obtained from

E. I. DuPont de Nemours and Company, 7 Thomas Street, New York.
Its line of "Luxol" colors is especially suitable for lamp dips.
National Aniline and Chemical Company, 40 Rector Street, New York.
Newport Chemical Works, Passaic, N. J.

Various types of metallic foil, plain and colored, which can be used as color media acting by selective reflection, may be obtained from

Lehmaier, Schwarz and Company, 521 West 25th Street, New York.

Copies of the National Electrical Code may be obtained, free of charge, from

National Board of Fire Underwriters, 95 John Street, New York.

Pressed glass in various designs, for use in connection with home-built "effect" apparatus, may be obtained from

Leo Popper and Son, 142 Franklin Street, New York.

Stage rigging and counterweight systems for suspending border-lights, cycloramas, cyclorama lighting equipment, and light-bridges; as well as general gridiron and fly-loft equipment and general stage hardware, may be obtained from

J. R. Clancy, Syracuse, N. Y. Catalogue.
Peter Clark, 534 West 30th Street, New York.
James H. Channon Manufacturing Company, 223 West Erie Street, Chicago. Catalogue.

Miniature stage lighting and control equipment for use with model stages may be obtained from

George L. Hall, West Emerson Street, Melrose, Mass.

IV. List of Tools

This brief list of tools, with which it might be desirable to outfit the lighting workshop of an amateur group that possesses its own theatre, and which are more or less necessary in constructing the home-built equipment discussed in detail in this volume, is presented more as a simple reminder list than as a specific recommendation.

For wood work: small claw hammer; chisels; saws — crosscut, rip, and keyhole; brace and bits, including expansion bit and extension bit;

"Yankee" automatic wood drill; "Yankee" automatic screwdriver; try-squares — right-angled and adjustable; nail set; workbench with wood vise.

For electrical work: screwdrivers — several small and medium sizes; sharp jackknife; several pairs of pliers, including side-cutting, diagonal-cutting, and long-nosed types; small alcohol blowtorch; ribbon solder; soldering-flux paste; friction tape; rubber tape.

For simple sheet-metal work: metal shears; punches; dividers; scriber; heavy soldering iron, preferably electric; bar solder; acid flux.

For iron work: ball-pean hammer; hack saw; cold chisels; "Yankee" breast drill, with assortment of drills; taps, in machine-screw threads of various sizes, with corresponding tap drills; tap wrench; monkey wrench; center-punch; assortment of files; machinist's vise.

For pipe work (as on battens, cyclorama hangers, and electrical conduit): stocks; dies — $\frac{1}{2}''$, $\frac{3}{4}''$, and 1″; bending hickey; Stillson wrenches; reamer; pipe vise.

Stock materials: nails; wood screws; machine screws and nuts; stove bolts; rivets: — all in a sufficient assortment of types and sizes.

INDEXES

INDEX OF SUBJECT MATTER

INDEX OF NAMES OF PERSONS, PLAYS, AND THEATRES

INDEX OF NAMES